Lecture Notes in Physics

Edited by H. Araki, Kyoto, J. Ehlers, München, K. Hepp, Zürich
R. Kippenhahn, München, H.A. Weidenmüller, Heidelberg,
J. Wess, Karlsruhe and J. Zittartz, Köln

Managing Editor: W. Beiglböck

262

Stochastic Processes in Classical and Quantum Systems

Proceedings of the 1st Ascona-Como International Conference, Held in Ascona, Ticino (Switzerland), June 24–29, 1985

Edited by S. Albeverio, G. Casati and D. Merlini

Springer-Verlag

Berlin Heidelberg New York London Paris Tokyo

Editors

S. Albeverio
Fakultät für Mathematik, Ruhr-Universität
D-4630 Bochum, FRG
and
Research Centre Bielefeld-Bochum Stochastics
Volkswagenstiftung, D-4800 Bielefeld, FRG

G. Casati
Dipartimento di Fisica, Università di Milano
Milano, Italy
and
A. Volta Center for Scientific Culture
Como, Italy

D. Merlini
SCSC, Bellinzona, Switzerland
and
Dipartimento di Fisica, Università di Milano
Milano, Italy

ISBN 3-540-17166-5 Springer-Verlag Berlin Heidelberg New York
ISBN 0-387-17166-5 Springer-Verlag New York Berlin Heidelberg

Library of Congress Cataloging-in-Publication Data. Stochastic processes in classical and quantum systems. (Lecture notes in physics; 262) 1. Stochastic processes–Congresses. 2. Quantum theory–Congresses. 3. Statistical mechanics–Congresses. I. Albeverio, Sergio. II. Casati, Giulio, 1942-. III. Merlini, D., 1942-. IV. Series.
QC174.17.S76S76 1986 530.1'33 86-26078
ISBN 0-387-17166-5 (U.S.)

Printed in Germany

Printing: Druckhaus Beltz, Hemsbach/Bergstr. Binding: J. Schäffer OHG, Grünstadt
2153/3140-543210

acquaforte
EA III

La sirenetta stocastica

Solveig Albeverio-Manzoni
1986

PREFACE AND ACKNOWLEDGEMENTS

The theory of stochastic processes has developed rapidly in recent years. An important part of this development has taken place in connection with the study of problems from physics, in particular quantum theory and statistical mechanics. In fact, the theory of stochastic processes appears more and more as the appropriate general framework for discussing physical systems with infinitely many degrees of freedom, describable as interacting "particles". Thus the study of the motion of a fluid or of a solid, ordered or disordered, belongs naturally in the field of applications of the theory of stochastic processes. The investigation of equilibrium and limit behaviour (asymptotics in space and/or time) of such systems has greatly influenced and has been greatly influenced by developments in the theory of stochastic processes (e.g. theory of specification of Gibbsian fields, study of small and large deviations ...). The position of quantum theory versus probability theory is a peculiar one. Of course, probability is inherent to quantum theory because of its statistical interpretation. But in quantum theory in recent years the use of stochastic processes beyond this has been very widespread and productive, basically in two forms: via "imaginary time quantum theory", in which the time evolution is given by Markovian semigroups, and via Nelson-Guerra's stochastic formulation of quantum theory. Expectations with respect to processes governed by Markovian semigroups can be reduced in the case of not too bad potentials via the Feynman-Kac formula to expectations with respect to the Brownian motion process. In more general cases one has to handle expectations with respect to diffusion processes with possibly singular drifts, processes which have been studied intensively in recent years, in particular in connection with stochastic analysis (Girsanov formulae, stochastic differential equations, or, more generally, stochastic calculus associated with Dirichlet or energy forms). These methods can be looked upon as suitable mathematical techniques for handling problems concerning quantum mechanical expectations (like existence and various kinds of asymptotics, including the study of the classical limit). Also the formulation of quantum theory through stochastic mechanics can be viewed in these terms (and this has been exploited in various ways e.g. in Jona-Lasinio-Martinelli-Scoppola's study of tunnelling effects). However, beyond this instrumental use, a basic foundational issue is at play, namely whether the stochastic processes associated with stochastic mechanical particles themselves have a more fundamental meaning, going beyond the usual quantum mechanical interpretational formalism. Several of the talks at this Meeting, and especially the one by Ed Nelson, give new insights into this open and fascinating problem. The basic issue can also be looked upon as the question whether it is possible to create classical models of stochastic mechanical behaviour. This also gives an incentive to take a new look at classical systems. Such systems have intrinsic interesting connections with stochastic theory also from other points of view. In fact, in recent years chaotic phenomena arising in classical deterministic systems (particle systems, classical fields) have been investigated and both methodically and conceptually the ensuing description brings such systems much closer than ever thought to stochastic systems. Finally let us mention that diffusion processes of the type of those of stochastic mechanics have also been fruitfully applied to the study of classical systems involving a large number of small particles in a field of force (providing a framework explaining "confinement" or "trapping" phenomena). These are some of the basic issues discussed at the Ascona Meeting. The reader may judge for himself how vigorous this field of interconnections is. In our opinion the Meeting has given a great impetus to a whole body of investigations of basic properties and interrelations between classical, quantum and stochastic dynamical systems.

The Proceedings contain the lectures and seminars held at the Meeting. During that week one afternoon was dedicated to two main lectures on topics of more general interest, as a service to the cultural community of Ticino. These lectures were given by Prof. Dr. K. Hepp and Prof. Dr. E. Nelson (in respectively French and Italian). They are included here by the courtesy of the authors, under the heading "Special Lectures". Our special thanks go to Ed and Klaus for their generosity in agreeing to give these lectures. We also thank all lecturers and participants for making the Meeting such a great event.

The realization of the present Meeting was made possible by the support of several persons and institutions. Before mentioning them, let us make a small digression to explain the somewhat unusual conditions in which the Conference took place. Ascona is a town in the Italian speaking part of Switzerland. This part, as opposed to the French and German counterparts, has, for complex historical reasons, no university structure of any kind. In recent years a small number of scientists from this part of the world with years of research experience abroad have returned to Ticino, finding jobs either in High Schools or in small laboratories, and remaining determined to maintain research activities and contacts with universities in Switzerland, Italy and elsewhere. The presence of this group greatly encouraged attempts to create the Meeting. Owing to the absence of university or institutes supporting the initiative "in loco", the organization of the Meeting had to overcome several practical problems and we are particularly grateful to all persons and institutes who helped us.

First of all we would like to express our gratitude to Prof. Dr. G. Losa (Istituto Cantonale di Patologia, Locarno; Lausanne and Turin Universities), who in his capacity of President of the Società Ticinese di Scienze Naturali, and above all as a friend, has actively encouraged our initiative and has given us steady support with great personal engagement.

We gratefully acknowledge financial support from the Swiss Society of Natural Sciences, complemented by the Dipartimento della Pubblica Educazione del Canton

Ticino (also through its Commissione Culturale, in conjunction with the Fondo Nazionale Svizzero) and the following Institutions:

Banca di Credito Commerciale e Mobiliare, S.A., Muralto/Lugano;
Banca della Svizzera, Italiana, Lugano;
Brown Boveri, Baden;
Municipio di Ascona;
Municipio di Locarno;
Società Bancaria Ticinese, Lugano;
Società Elettrica Sopracenerina, Locarno;
Schindler, S.A., Locarno.

The Research Centre "Bielefeld-Bochum Stochastics" (BiBoS) of the Volkswagenstiftung should be especially thanked for giving a decisive impetus, by encouraging and financially supporting the participation in the Conference of its members and guests as well as sharing the costs and coordinating invitations of several lecturers.

The Centro di Cultura Scientifica A. Volta (Como) and the Collegio Papio (Ascona) provided respectively the main secretarial organization and the technical assistance for the Meeting. We would also like to thank the following persons for their support of our initiative: Prof. Dr. E. Simona (Dipartimento della Publica Educazione del Canton Ticino, Bellinzona), Prof. Dr. Ph. Blanchard and Prof. Dr. L. Streit (Department of Physics, University of Bielefeld and BiBoS Research Centre Stochastics, Volkswagenstiftung), Dr. E. Capra (Banca della Svizzera Italiana, Lugano), Dir. On. L. Generali (Lugano), Prof. Dr. A. Luban-Plozza (Centro Balint, Ascona).

Special thanks go to the secretaries of the Como Institute, in particular to Manuela, and to the secretaries at Bielefeld and Bochum, Mrs. Jahns, Mrs. Jegerlehner, Mrs. Mischke and Mrs. Richter. To Solvejg, both for her poster announcing the Conference and her etching published here, we offer "un grazie con tutto il cuore".

Finally, let us express our active hope that this Meeting be just the first in a long series.

S. Albeverio, G. Casati, D. Merlini
Bielefeld, Bochum, Milano

August 1986

CONTENTS

LECTURES, SEMINARS, SHORT COMMUNICATIONS:

The following lectures given at the Meeting will appear elsewhere:

G. CASATI. Quantum Chaos

D. CASTRIGIANO. Quantum Oscillator in a Non-Selfinteracting Radiation Field: Exact Calculation of the Partition Function

J. FRÖHLICH. Random Surface Phenomena in Statistical Mechanics and Particle Theory

V. GORINI. Gravitational Lenses

RANDOM FIELDS WITH VALUES IN LIE GROUPS AND HIGGS FIELDS

by

Sergio Albeverio[*,#], Raphael Høegh-Krohn[**]. Helge Holden[**,##]

[*] Fakultät für Mathematik, Ruhr-Universität
D-4630 Bochum 1 (W-Germany)

[#] Bielefeld-Bochum Research Centre Stochastic Processes
(BiBoS), Volkswagenstiftung

[**] Matematisk Institutt, Universitetet i Oslo, Blindern, Oslo
(Norway)

[##] Courant Institute of Mathematical Sciences,
New York (USA)

A B S T R A C T

We review recent work based on extending the known relations between Markov processes and Markov semigroups to the case where time is replaced by hypersurfaces of codimension 1 and the state space is a group. Relations with gauge fields, Higgs fields and relativistic fields are also discussed.

1. Introduction

The study of commutative and non commutative stochastic differential equations for processes with values in groups is well developed, and has found applications in particular in the investigation of the gauge groups of mappings of $\mathbb{R}$ or S^1 into Lie groups, see e.g. [1], and references therein. Problems of the theory of representations of groups of mappings and non commutative distribution theory, see e.g. [2], as well as problems of the theory of gauge fields suggest the creation of a theory of commutative and non commutative stochastic partial differential equations. E.g. a pure Yang-Mills Euclidean measure gives a white noise type distribution to a curvature 2-form and the corresponding connection 1-form has to be obtained then by "non commutative stochastic integration". In a series of papers [3] we have already given parts of such a theory, see also [4], [15] for other approaches and problems. In this lecture we give a short survey of aspects of our approach, stressing in particular the opportunity to study so called stochastic group-valued measures as basic quantities related to generalized Markov semigroups, in a similar way as Markov processes are related to Markov semigroups. Markov cosurfaces arise as objects which correspond to Markov processes in the case of one-dimensional time, and we stress their relations with stochastic group-valued measures. A Lévy-Khinchine type formula is derived for the latter und recent results by Kaufmann [5] on continuity properties (non commutative higher dimensional time analoga of Prokhorov-Kolmogorov criteria) of Markov cosurfaces are mentioned. Remarks on lattice Gibbsian models, gauge and Higgs fields, relativistic quantum fields and gauge-group representations are also given.

2. Generalized Markov semigroups on groups, and stochastic group-valued measures

Let $(M,\mathcal{B})$ be a measurable space and let G be a locally compact group. A stochastic G-valued (multiplicative) measure η on $(M,\mathcal{B})$ is a process η indexed by $\mathcal{B}$ with state space G so that $\eta(A)$ for any $A \in \mathcal{B}$ is a random variable on some probability space $(\Omega,\mathcal{A},P)$, with $\eta(\emptyset) = e$, and, for disjoint A,B, $\eta(A) \perp \eta(B)$ (where $\perp$ means independence), as well as $\eta(A \cup B) = \eta(A)\cdot\eta(B)$, where equality is in law and the product is in G. Moreover we assume that the law of $\eta(A)$ has an invariant density with respect to the Haar measure on G i.e. $P_{\eta(A)}(h_1h_2) = P_{\eta(A)}(h_2h_1)$, $h_i \in G$, and has some suitable continuity properties (cfr. [3], d,e, [5]).

Remark 1. This is obviously an extension to "times in M" of the concept of stochastic measure (random measure) associated with processes with independent stationary increments (i.e. of infinitely divisible type)([8], [9]).

As in the case of "one-dimensional time" we introduce associated (convolution) semigroups of probability measures, which we call generalized Markov semigroups: such a semigroup is a family of probability measures P on G indexed by $\mathcal{B}$, with the (generalized) semigroup law" $p_{A\cup B} = p_A * p_B$ whenever $A,B \in \mathcal{B}$ are disjoint (with * meaning convolution). Moreover we assume p_A inner invariant on G i.e. $p_A(h_1h_2) = p_A(h_2h_1)$, $h_i \in G$ and with suitable continuity properties. In the "one dimensional time case" there is a well known one-to-one correspondence between η and p (Kolmogorov construction of Markov processes from Markov semigroups and definition of Markov semigroups as transition semigroups to Markov processes). An extension of this correspondence to our case is given by the following:

Theorem 2 ([3] d), e)): There is a 1-1 correspondence between multiplicative measures and generalized Markov semigroups p, given by $p_A = P_{\eta(A)}$.

Example 3. Let μ_t, $t \in \mathbb{R}_+ \equiv [0,\infty)$ be a 1-parameter invariant convolution semigroup of probability measures (Markov semigroup) on G. Let $(M,\mathcal{B},\sigma)$ be a σ-finite positive measure space. Define $p_A \equiv \mu_{\sigma(A)}$ for any $A \in \mathcal{B}$, with the convention $\mu_{+\infty} \equiv 1$. Then p is a generalized Markov semigroup on G. For $M = \mathbb{R}_+$, σ Lebesgue measure, we see that $p_{[t_1,t_2)} = \mu_{t_2-t_1}$. In this case, with notation as in the theorem $P_{\eta([0,t))} = p_{[0,t)} = \mu_t$. If in particular μ_t is the heat kernel on G, then for any $\alpha \in \mathbb{R}$:

$$E(\exp(i\alpha\eta([0,t)))) = \int \exp(i\alpha x)\mu_t(x)dx = \exp\left(-\frac{\alpha^2}{2}t\right),$$

hence $\eta([0,t))$ is the evaluation of white noise stochastic measure at $[0,t)$.

Our η's and p's can be completely classified, similarly as in the case of "one dimensional time" for processes with independent stationary increments, at least in the case where G is a Lie group. For this the first thing to observe is that a classification is possible when G is replaced by its Lie algebra g. In this case the stochastic measure takes values in a finite dimensional vector space and by its properties it is simply an infinitely divisible random measure (random field) on g, classified by a formula of the Levy-Khinchine type. Let us call ξ such a g-valued stochastic measure on $(M,\mathcal{B})$. If G is connected and $M = \mathbb{R}_+$ and B are the Borel sets of $\mathbb{R}_+$, then we get a stochastic (multiplicative) measure η on G by "integrating" ξ (multiplicative integration, in the sense of Ito and Mc Kean): $\eta([0,t))^{-1}d\eta([0,t)) = d\xi([0,t))$. When $(M,\mathcal{B})$ is a standard Borel space we use a σ-isomorphism $\varphi: (M,\mathcal{B}) \to (\mathbb{R}_+, \mathcal{B}(\mathbb{R}_+))$ to obtain by integration from $d\xi(\varphi^{-1}[0,t))$ the stochastic measure $\eta(\varphi^{-1}[0,t))$, see [3], b), c). In this way then we get a classification of stochastic multiplicative measures on Lie groups. Concretely, they are given in terms of stochastic measures on the Lie algebra of G with known Fourier transforms, given in terms of Levy-measures , by "multiplicative stochastic integration" (similarly as for one-dimensional time: stochastic measures on Lie groups by integration from those associated with independent stationary processes on the Lie algebra).
In the next section we shall bring in contact our stochastic measures (and associated generalized Markov semigroups) with objects defined in a completely different manner, namely "Markov cosurfaces". First however we need the concept of "Markov cosurfaces".

3. Group-valued Markov cosurfaces and gauge fields.

Let M be a connected oriented Riemannian manifold of dimension d. We shall need to distinguish between $d > 2$ and $d = 2$, since for $d = 2$ we shall allow the group G to be non abelian, not so for $d > 2$. Let H_M as be a family of oriented d-1-dimensional hypersurfaces on M, more precisely: i) for $d > 2$, H_M consists of all oriented, piecewise smooth, connected and closed (d-1)-dimensional hypersurfaces in M without self-intersections; ii) for d=2, H_M is the set of all piecewise smooth curves S on M with given initial (S_-) and final points (S_+); iii) for d=1, H_M is just the point set M. We shall now define, following [3] a)-c), [5] a composition for elements in H_M. For this we shall define recurvively spaces H_M^n. Let $H_M^1 \equiv H_M$ and:

i) for $d > 2$: H_M^n, $n \geq 2$ is defined recursively as the set of all elements S of the form $S = S_1 \circ S_2$ with $S_1 \in H_M^{n-1}$, $S_2 \in H_M$, where the composition $S_1 \circ S_2$ is defined iff $S_1 \cap S_2$ is (d-2)-dimensional and we have $S_1 \cap S_2 \subset \partial S_1 \cap \partial S_2$. The orientations induced by S_1 and S_2 on $\partial S_1 \cap \partial S_2$ are opposite to each other. Furthermore $M - (S_1 \cup S_2)$ should consist of only finitely many simply connected components. On such a domain the composition $S_1 \circ S_2$ is defined as the point set $S_1 \cup S_2$, with the orientation generated by S_1 and S_2. Then the composition is extended to $\Sigma_M \equiv \bigcup_{n \in \mathbb{N}} H_M^n$.

ii) for d = 2: define as above H_M^n, $n \geq 2$ recursively as the set of all $S = S_1 \circ S_2$, $S_1 \in H_M^{n-1}$, $S_2 \in H_M$, with S_1 having endpoint coinciding with the initial point of S_2, $S_1 \cap S_2$ a finite subset of M and $M-(S_1 \cup S_2)$ consisting of only a finite number of components. $S_1 \circ S_2$ is then defined as the point set $S_1 \cup S_2$ with orientation generated by S_1, S_2 and initial resp. final points $(S_1)_-$ resp. $(S_2)_+$ and a given rule for going along the path. Then we set as above $\Sigma_M = \bigcup_{n \in \mathbb{N}} H_M^n$; iii) for d=1 we define simply $H_M \equiv \Sigma_M$.

We shall now define the concept of a <u>cosurface</u> C on Σ_M as a map associating to S on Σ_M a value in a group G, supposed to be abelian for $d > 2$, with

a) $C(S^{-1}) = (C(S))^{-1} \quad \forall S \in \Sigma_M$; b) $C(S_1 \circ S_2) = C(S_1) \cdot C(S_2) \quad \forall S_1, S_2 \in \Sigma_M$,

where for any $S \in \Sigma_M$, S^{-1} is defined as the element of Σ_M which coincides as a point set with S and has orientation opposite to the one of S. h^{-1} denotes the inverse of h in G. We shall denote by $\Gamma_{M,G}$ the set of all cosurfaces on Σ_M, with a natural measurable structure s.t. all maps $\tau_s : \Gamma_{M,G} \to G$ for $S \in \Sigma_M$ with $\tau_s(C) \equiv C(S)$ are measurable. If C is a measurable map from a probability space $(\Omega, \mathcal{A}, P)$ into $\Gamma_{M,C}$ then we call C a <u>stochastic cosurface</u> on Σ_M. Thus $C(\omega, S) \in G$, $\omega \in \Omega$, $S \in \Sigma_M$.

<u>Remark 4:</u> For $M = \mathbb{R}$ a stochastic cosurface is simply a G-valued stochastic process indexed by $\mathbb{R}$. (Perhaps in this respect a notation $X(S)(\omega)$ would be more suggestive than $C(S)(\omega)$: however we chose C, since this is the initial of "cosurface"). The above concepts were introduced in [3] a), c), [5].

Similarly as in the case of Markov processes, we are interested in specific probability distributions for stochastic cosurfaces, namely those which are determined by generalized Markov-semigroups. We shall namely see that, similarly as for "one dimensional time", there is a 1-1 correspondence between Markov cosurfaces (to be defined below) and (generalized) Markov semigroups. For this however we have first to define the Markov property for stochastic cosurfaces. This involves the concept of a complex on M, understood as an ordered n-tuple $K \equiv \{S_1,\ldots,S_n\}$, $S_i \in \Sigma_M$, $i=1,\ldots,n$, with $S_i \neq S_j$, $i \neq j$ (for d = 1, K is simply an n-tuple of points on M). If C is a cosurface i.e. $C \in \Sigma_M$ then we define $C(K) = (C(S_1),\ldots,C(S_n)) \equiv \bigotimes_{i=1}^{n} C(S_i)$. In this way C is extended to the set K_M of all complexes on M. For each $K \in K_M$ we have $C((K)) \in G_{s_1} \times \ldots \times G_{s_n}$, with G_{s_i} a copy of G. We call a complex K as above regular if, in the case $d \neq 2$, $S_i \cap S_j \subset \partial S_i \cap \partial S_j$ $\forall$ $i \neq j$, and in the case d = 2 if $S_i \cap S_j$ is either contained in the unions of ∂S_i, ∂S_j or is an initial or final point of S_i or S_j (any complex is regular if d = 1). For any subset $\Lambda \subset M$ we consider the σ-algebra $\Sigma(\Lambda)$ generated by all stochastic cosurfaces C(S) with $S \in \Sigma_M$, $S \subset \Lambda$ i.e. $\Sigma(\Lambda) = \sigma\{\{C \in \Gamma_{M,G} \mid C(S) \in B_G\} \mid S \subset \Lambda, S \in \Sigma_M, B_G \in \mathcal{B}_G\}$. We say that a regular complex $K = \{S_1 \ldots S_n\}$ splits M, through S_j, $S_{j+1},\ldots,S_\ell$, $j < \ell$, when $M - \bigcup_{i=j}^{\ell} S_i$ consists of 2 components $M^{\pm}$ with $S_1,\ldots,S_{j-1} \subset M^{+}$, $S_{\ell+1},\ldots, S_n \in M^{-}$. In this case we set $K^{+} = (S_1 \ldots S_\ell)$, $K^{-} = (S_j \ldots S_n)$. We say that the cosurface $(\Omega, \mathcal{A}, P; C(S), S \in \Sigma_M)$ has the Markov property (it is a Markov cosurface) when for all bounded measurable real-valued $f^{\pm}$ on $\bigtimes_{s \in K^{\pm}} G_s$ we have $E(f^{+}(C(K^{+}))f^{-}(C(K^{-})) \mid \Sigma(\bigcup_{i=j}^{\ell} S_i)) =$

$$= E(f^{+}(C(K^{+})) \mid \Sigma(\bigcup_{i=j}^{\ell} S_j))\, E(f^{-}(C(K^{-}) \mid \Sigma(\bigcup_{i=j}^{\ell} S_i)).$$

Remark 5: These concepts have been introduced in [3]a),b),c), [5]. For "one dimensional time", $M = \mathbb{R}$, this corresponds to the (global, simple i.e. weak) Markov property of G-valued processes. For $M = \mathbb{R}^2$ this implies, in particular, taking $S_2 = \{(x_1,x_2) \in \mathbb{R}^2 \mid x_2 = 0\}$ that stochastic cosurfaces associated with curves in Σ_M contained in the upper half-plane and those associated with curves in Σ_M contained in the lower half-plane are independent, given the knowledge of all stochastic cosurfaces associated with elements of Σ_M on the $x_2 = 0$ axis.

We shall now indicate how to define a general class of Markov cosurfaces and show that this class is in correspondence with generalized Markov semigroups (for details see [3]c), [5]). Let $K = (S_1,\ldots,S_n)$ be a regular complex. We call K saturated if $\bigcup_{i=1}^{n} S_i$ is connected and there is a decomposition $D_K = \{A_1,\ldots,A_m\}$ of finitely many connected, closed subsets A_i of M s.t. 1) $M = \bigcup_{i=1}^{m} A_i$; 2) for d = 2, the interior $\mathring{A}_i$ of A_i is simply connected, for $d \neq 2$ A_i is simply connected; 3) for all $i \neq j$, $i,j = 1,\ldots,n$ and $A_i \cap A_j \neq \emptyset$ one has either $A_i \cap A_j$ is (d-2)-dimensional or $A_i \cap A_j \subset \partial A_j \cap \partial A_j$ and $A_i \cap A_j$ is a piecewise smooth connected (d-1-)-dimensional hypersurface, which can be written as the union of some of the $S_j \in K$ i.e. $\exists j_1,\ldots,\exists j_r$ s.t. $A_i \cap A_j = \bigcup_{k=1}^{r} S_{j_k}$; 4) $\bigcup_{\substack{i,j=1 \\ i \neq j}}^{m} (A_i \cap A_j) = \bigcup_{i=1}^{n} S_i$.

To construct Markov cosurfaces, we shall need in addition, as in the case of Markov processes, a "start measure". Let for d = 1 G be a locally compact polish group, for d = 2 a compact group, for d > 2 a compact abelian group and let λ be the Haar measure on G, normalized to 1 for $d \geq 2$. We shall introduce a projective system of probability measures on $(G^K, K \in \mathcal{K}_M)$. For this we need an ordering: $K, K' \in \mathcal{K}_M$ are in the relation $K < K'$ when $K = K'$ or $\forall S \in K \exists\ S_1,\ldots,S_m \in K'$, K' saturated regular complex s.t. $S = S_1 \circ \ldots \circ S_m$. $<$ is then a partial order in $\mathcal{K}_M$.

We shall define a family $P_M \subset \mathcal{K}_M$ of complexes as follows:

a) for d = 1, P_M = all ordered subsets of M; b) for $d \geq 2$ P_M is a suitable set of complexes s.t.

i) $\forall K, K' \in P_M \exists K'' \in P_M$ with K'' regular saturated and $K < K''$, $K' < K''$;

ii) $\forall K \in \mathcal{K}_M$, $K < K'$ for some $K' \in P_M$ implies $K \in P_M$.

Define, for all $d \geq 1$, $\Sigma_{P_M} \equiv \{S \in \Sigma_M \mid \exists K \in P_M,\ S \in K\}$ (note that $\Sigma_{P_M} = \Sigma_M$ for d = 1).

Let Q_t be a convolution semigroup of probability measures on G with densities i.e. $Q_t(dx) = q_t(x)\,dx\ \forall t > 0$, $q_t(x) \geq 0\ \forall x \in G$, $q_o(dx) = \delta_e(x)$, $q_t q_s = q_{t+s}$, $Q_t \to \delta_e$ weakly as $t \downarrow 0$. If G is not commutative we require $q_t(xy) = q_t(yx)$, $\forall\, x,y \in G\ \ \forall\, t \geq 0$ i.e. Q_t is inner invariant. We extend the definition of Q_t to $t = +\infty$ by setting $Q_{+\infty} \equiv 1$. We call Q_t, $t \in \mathbb{R}_+ \cup \{+\infty\}$ an <u>invariant Markov semigroup on G</u>.

Let $K = \{S_1,\ldots,S_n\} \in P_M$ be a regular saturated complex, with $D \equiv \{A_1,\ldots,A_m\}$. For $d \geq 2$ set $\varphi(S_j)$ equal S_j (resp. S_j^{-1}) if $\partial S_j \subset \partial A$ and $S_j, \partial A$ have the same (resp. opposite) orientations, $A \in \{A_1,\ldots,A_m\}$.

Define then $\phi_A(C(K)) = \prod_{S_j \subset \partial A} C(\varphi(S_j))$ (G being abelian the product is well defined).

For d = 2, $A \in \{A_1,\ldots,A_m\}$ choose $S_{j_\ell} \subset \partial A$ s.t. the final point of S_{j_ℓ} is the initial point of $S_{j_{\ell+1}}$, $\ell = 0,\ldots, L-2$, if L is such that ∂A is the union of S_{j_ℓ}, $\ell = 0,\ldots, L-1$. We also assume the S_{j_ℓ} are such that $\varphi(S_{j_o}) \circ \ldots \circ \varphi(S_{j_{L-1}})$ is in Σ_M and has no self-interactions. In this case we set $\phi_A(C(K)) = C(\varphi(S_{j_o})) \ldots C(\varphi(S_{j_{L-1}}))$. Then define for all $d \geq 2$:

$\mu_K^Q(C(K)) = q_{|A_1|}(\phi_{A_1}(C(K))) \ldots q_{|A_n|}(\phi_{A_n}(C(K)))$, with $|A|$ the volume measure on M of A.

<u>Remark 6</u> a) Using the inner invariance of q_t we see that the definition is actually independent of the order of the product in the definition of $\phi_A(C(K))$ also in the non

abelian case. b) A corresponding definition can be given for d=1 i.e. $M = S^1$ or $\mathbb{R}$. In the case Q_t the heat semigroup on G, μ_K^Q are then the finite dimensional marginals of the Wiener measure in the points of the complex K.

The definition of μ_K^Q can be easily extended to all of P_M (hence K not necessarily regular saturated). In fact let $K = \{S_1,\dots,S_m\}$ arbitrary in P_M. By the definition of P_M there exists a regular saturated complex $\tilde{K}$ s.t. $K < \tilde{K}$, $\tilde{K} \in P_M$. Let $\tilde{K} = \{S_1,\dots,S_n\}$, $n \geq m$. Let $\gamma(K,\tilde{K}) \equiv \{S \in \tilde{K} | \tilde{S} \cap \bigcup_{i=1} S_i\}$ consists of only components of dimension $\leq d-2$. Set $d\mu_K^Q(C(K)) \equiv \int_G \dots \int_G d\mu_{\tilde{K}}^Q (C(\tilde{K})) \prod_{S \in \gamma(K,\tilde{K})} dC(S)$. One verifies that μ_K^Q is independent of the choice of $\tilde{K}$, see [5]. Assuming that G is compact, so that Haar measure is finite, hence normalizable to a probability measure, we can verify that $(\mu_K^Q, K \in P_M)$ forms a projective system of probability measures and we arrive at the following:

<u>Theorem 7.</u> Let M be an oriented, connected, Riemannian manifold of dimension d. Let G be a compact group with countable base, for d = 2, and in addition abelian for $d \geq 3$. Let $(\mu_K^Q, K \in P_M)$ be the projective system of probability measures defined by the Markovian semigroup Q_t of probability measures on G and the normalized Haar measure on G. Then there exists a unique projective limit $(\Omega, \mathcal{A}, P)$ to $(\mu_K^Q, K \in P_M)$. The coordinate process C(K) $(\cdot)$ is a stochastic cosurface on Σ_{P_M} and satisfies $P(C(K) \in A) = \mu_K^Q(A)$ $\forall K \in P_M$, $\forall A \in \mathcal{B}(G^K)$. This cosurface has the Markov property.

<u>Proof:</u> G is a polish group by the assumptions, hence we can apply a version of Kolmogorov's theorem, cfr. e.g. [6]. The verification of the Markov property is also easy, from the definitions: see [3], c), [5].

<u>Remark 8.</u> The Markov cosurface G of Theor. 1 depends on the orientation σ and the volume measure $|\cdot|$ on M. The next theorem yields an important invariance property of the constructed Markov cosurface (similar to the translation invariance of processes with independent increments in $\mathbb{R}^d$).

<u>Theorem 9.</u> Let φ be an orientation preserving global diffeomorphism of M which leaves invariant the volume measure on M. If φ maps P_M into P_M, then the Markov cosurface C of Theor. 7 is invariant under φ in the sense that $\mu_K^Q = \mu_{\varphi(K)}^Q$, $\forall K \in P_M$.
The proof is given in [3], c), [5].

<u>Remark 10.</u> 1) A partial converse can be given, see [3], c).
2) A change of the orientation is equivalent with replacing $Q_t(x)$ by $\tilde{Q}_t(x) \equiv Q_t(x^{-1})$. In particular if Q_t is reflection symmetric i.e. $Q_t(x^{-1}) = Q_t(x)$, then C does not depend on the orientation.

A. Kaufmann has given recently an extension of Kolmogorov-Prokhorov criterium for continuity of stochastic processes to the case of cosurfaces. For the statement of this result we shall need a couple of definitions.

Let d resp. d_G be some metric on Σ_{P_M} resp. G. A family $\mathcal{F} \subset \Sigma_{P_M}$ is said to be 1-parametric if there exists a subset $I \subset \mathbb{R}$ open, connected, containing the origin and there exists a bijection $\gamma: I \to \mathcal{F}$, $\gamma(t) \equiv S_t$ such that

1) $\forall K \in \mathbb{R}_+ \ \exists \sigma_K > 0$ s.t. $d_G(\gamma(t),\gamma(s)) \geq |t-s| \ \forall t \in I \cap (-K,+K)$, $s \in I$, with $d_\Sigma(\gamma(t),\gamma(s)) < \sigma_K$;

2) $\exists R \geq 1$ s.t. $d_G(\gamma(t),\gamma(s)) \leq R\,|t-s| \ \forall s,t \in I$.

Remark 11. As discussed in [5], the condition $d_\Sigma(\gamma(t),\gamma(s)) \geq |t-s|$ is actually equivalent to the same condition with the right hand side replaced by $r|t-s|$ for some $r > 0$. Here is then Kaufmann's continuity result:

Theorem 12. Let G be a Lie group, abelian if $d > 2$, polish with respect to a metric d_G. Let $(\Omega,\mathcal{A},P;C)$ be a stochastic cosurface with values in G. Let $\mathcal{F}$ be a 1-parametric family in Σ_{P_M}. A sufficient condition for the continuity of $(C(S_t),\ S_t \in \mathcal{F})$ (after, if necessary, a modification on a zero measure set) is the existence of numbers $a > 0$, $b > 1$, $c > 0$, $\delta > 0$ s.t. $\forall s,t \in I$ with $d_\Sigma(S_s,S_t) < \delta$:

$E(d_G(C(S_s),C(S_t))^a) \leq c[d(S_s,S_t)]^b$.

Proof. This is a non commutative analogue of Kolmogorov-Prokhorov-theorem as discussed in [7]. It is proven by an adaptation of the proof in [7] of corresponding results for stochastic processes. In the course of the proof other sufficient conditions analogues of Lemma 63.5 resp. Theor. 63.6 of [7] are given. For details we refer to [5]. □

The idea now is to exploit possible continuity properties in t of Q_t and the construction of the Markov cosurface to verify the above criterium and to obtain examples of continuous Markov cosurfaces. We shall first discuss the abelian case. [5] contains the following result:

Theorem 13. Let G be the n-dimensional torus T^n with Lebesgue measure as Haar measure. Define the metric T^n by $d_G(x,y) = \min\{|x-y+\nu| \ ; \ \nu \in \{-1,0,1\}^n\}$ (which generates the usual topology on T^n). Assume dim M = 2. Let $\mathcal{F} = \{S_t = \gamma(t), t \in I\}$ be a 1-parametric family in Σ_{P_M}, with γ as above. Assume S_t are closed curves and let A_t be a closed finite subset of M lying to the left of S_t with respect to the orientation in M. Assume $A_s \subset A_t \ \forall s < t$ and (S_s,S_t) is a regular complex with $(S_t)_- = (S_t)_+$ independent of t. Moreover we assume

a) $s < t \ \exists L_1,\dots,L_m \in \Sigma_{P_M}$, $m \in \mathbb{N}$ s.t. $K \equiv (S_s,S_t,L_1,\dots,L_m)$ is a saturated regular complex. K splits M into simply connected regions which consist of $A_s, A_t - A_s$ and else of regions with infinite volume.

b) Let d_Σ be a metric on Σ_{P_M} s.t. $d_\Sigma(S_s,S_t) \geq |(A_s-A_t) \cup (A_t-A_s)| \ \forall s,t \in I$.

c) Let q_t, $t \geq 0$ be the density function of a Markov convolution semigroup Q_t of probability measures on $\mathbb{R}^n$ of diffusion type (i.e. with local generator). Then $Q_t(x) \equiv \sum_{\nu \in \mathbb{Z}^n} q_t(x+\nu)$, $t>0$, $Q_o(x) \equiv \delta_o(x)$, $x \in [0,1)^n$, is a Markov semigroup on T^n and for the Markov cosurface given in terms of Q_t and the Haar measure on T^n by Theorem 7, we have that the condition of the above continuity theorem is satisfied, hence $C(S_t)$ is continuous for all $S_t \in \mathcal{F}$.

Remark 14. [5] also contains the construction of a metric d_Σ verifying b) starting from a Riemannian metric on M.

Let us now consider the case where M is a 2-dimensional manifold but G is no longer abelian. G being compact there is a left and right invariant Riemannian metric d_G on G s.t. the length of the geodesic (exp (tX)), h,t $\in$ [a,b] for X in the Lie algebra of G and $h \in G$ is precisely (b-a) $\|X\|$, with $\| \ \|$ the norm coming from a scalar product on g. Let $\mathcal{F} \equiv \{S_t, t \in I\}$ be a 1-parameter family as in Theorems 12, 13. Let ν_t be a Markov convolution semigroup on g with generator L_g of diffusion type on g. If ν_t has a "polynomial approximation property" (in the sense of [5], which uses results of [9]) then the corresponding semigroup Q_t on G is a Markov semigroup on G. We assume that it has a density with respect the Haar measure d k on G, $k \in G$. Then we have from [5]:

Theorem 15. The stochastic Markov cosurface $(\Omega, \mathcal{A}, \mu^Q; C)$ constructed from Q is continuous (and satisfies the criteria for continuity discussed above).

We close this section on stochastic cosurfaces with some remarks.

Remark A (Markov cosurfaces and lattice models)

Is it possible to construct Markov cosurfaces of the above type $(\Omega, \mathcal{A}, \mu^Q; C)$ as continuous limits from lattice models of the "Gibbsian type" given by an Euclidean lattice action involving stochastic variables associated with d-1-dimensional faces? This is discussed in [3] a), b), c), g) , [10]. Let us consider such a lattice model. The basic space (instead of $M = \mathbb{R}^d$) is $L_\varepsilon = \varepsilon \mathbb{Z}^d$ for some $\varepsilon > 0$. For any invariant function U on the compact group G (e.g. a character) and positive number ("coupling constant") $\beta > 0$, one defines a Gibbs interaction in a bounded subset Λ of L_ε, as the probability measure

$$\mu_\varepsilon^\Lambda = Z_{\Lambda,\varepsilon}^{-1} \exp\,[-\beta \sum_{\gamma \subset \Lambda} U\,(C(\partial\gamma))] \prod_{\gamma \subset \Lambda} dC(\partial\gamma),$$

with γ an elementary cell of L_ε, $\partial\gamma$ the boundary of γ, $C(\partial\gamma)$ a variable associated with $\partial\gamma$, with values in G, dk for $k \in G$ the Haar measure on G. $Z_{\Lambda,\varepsilon}$ is a normalization constant. The thermodynamic limit $\Lambda \uparrow L_\varepsilon$, which exist e.g. in the sense of projective limits of probability measures, defines a "Gibbs lattice cosurface" (μ_ε, C), with C the "coordinate process" and μ_ε such that its finite dimensional marginals, depending on the values of C on finitely many $\partial\gamma$ in Λ, are given by μ_ε^Λ. In the cases G = U(1), SU(2), $\mathbb{Z}^2$ the continuum limit of μ_ε for $\varepsilon \downarrow 0$ has also been shown to exist, for appropriate U and by a suitable choice of $\beta(\varepsilon)$ (diverging as $\varepsilon \downarrow 0$) and to coincide with the above discussed Markov cosurfaces $(\Omega, \mathcal{A}, \mu^Q; C)$ associated with $\mathbb{R}^d$, for suitable Q (depending on U). E.g. for d = 2, U the Wilson action we have Q s.t. Q_t is the heat semigroup on G ([3] c), [10]).

Remark B: (Markov cosurfaces and gauge fields)

For d = 2 a stochastic cosurface C is, by definition, a G-valued (multiplicative) stochastic curve integral on G. If S is a simple oriented loop enclosing a region A then $\eta(A) \equiv C(S)$ is a stochastic G-valued measure. If g is the Lie algebra of a Lie group G, then g-valued curve integrals C on g are in 1-1 correspondence with G-valued (multiplicative) curve integrals on G by $C \to \chi_C$, where $\chi_C(S)=\int_0^1 C(\tilde{S}(s))^{-1} dC(\tilde{S}(s))$, with $\tilde{S}(s)$ the curve S: $\{S(s),\ s \in [0,1]\}$ described until S(s) (i.e. $\tilde{S}(s)(t) \equiv S(st)$, $0 \le t, s \le 1$). If $\chi(S) = \int_S a$ for some g-valued 1-form on M, then the corresponding C_χ obtained from $d\chi(\tilde{S}(s)) = C_\chi(\tilde{S}(s))^{-1}\ dC_\chi(\tilde{S}(s))$ is the holonomy operator given by a. Our general construction of global Markov homogeneous stochastic cosurfaces (Theorem 7) yields then C (and hence χ, a, and corresponding stochastic curvature forms; see [3] e), f) h)), a is a stochastic realization of gauge fields, hence our models of stochastic cosurfaces yields models of gauge fields in the continuum (in 2-dimensional space time), with the correct properties of Markovicity and symmetry (stronger than the Osterwalder-Schrader positivity) and homogeneity. By the remark A these gauge fields are also continuum limits of lattice gauge fields.

Remark C (Relativistic models associated with Markov cosurfaces)

In the case $M = \mathbb{R}^d$, from the (global) Markov property and the symmetry property (if $Q_t(h) = Q_t(h^{-1})\ \forall\ h \in G$) of the Markov-cosurfaces we constructed one obtains "by analytic continuation in time" models of relativistic invariant quantum fields associated with d-1 hypersurfaces (in particular hyperplanes and loops). For the special case d = 2, G = U(1), SU(2), $\mathbb{Z}^2$, Q_t the heat semigroup on G, these quantum fields are a realization of relativistic fields associated with Wilson loops of pure Yang-Mills fields. The postulates discussed in the literature [11] are satisfied [3] a).

Remark D. Markov cosurfaces and Higgs fields

One can use Markov cosurfaces to construct models of Higgs fields in the continuum for space-time dimension 2. This is discussed in [3] f), h), to which we refer for details. We define a lattice Higgs interaction in $\mathbb{Z}^2$ with compact gauge group G as the limit as $\Lambda \uparrow \mathbb{Z}^2$, Λ bounded, of a probability measure of the form

$$\mu_\Lambda = Z_\Lambda^{-1} \exp\Big(-\frac{\lambda}{2} \sum_{x\in\Lambda} \big(8 + \frac{\mu^2}{\lambda}\big)|\varphi(x)|^2\Big) \exp\Big(-\frac{\lambda}{2} \sum_{x,y\in\Lambda} \langle\varphi(x), \rho(C(xy))\varphi(y)\rangle\Big) \prod_x d\varphi(x)$$

with $\langle\ ,\ \rangle$ resp. $|\cdot|$ product resp. norm in a finite dimensional unitary representation space V of the compact Lie group G, carrying the representation ρ, φ a V-valued random field over $\mathbb{Z}^2$, C a Markov cosurface (evaluated at the oriented link xy), λ, μ

positive constants. Replacing the lattice $\mathbb{Z}^2$ by $\varepsilon\,\mathbb{Z}^2$, with a suitable choice of $\lambda(\varepsilon)$, $\mu(\varepsilon)$, yields finally continuum limit Higgs models as $\varepsilon \downarrow 0$. As discussed above, in the cases $G = U(1)$, $SU(2)$, $\mathbb{Z}^2,\ldots,Q_t$ the heat semigroup, the Markov cosurface (constructed in Theor. 7) is a realization of the continuum limit of the usual Yang-Mills fields, and in this case our Higgs fields coincide with the Higgs fields as discussed in the physical literature. We shall now discuss the mathematical construction of the continuum limit $\varepsilon \downarrow 0$, keeping C (and P) fixed.
Let $\mu_\Lambda^C(\varphi)$ be the corresponding conditional measure. We are interested in computing

$$G_C(x_1,\ldots,x_n) \equiv \int \prod_{i=1}^{n} \langle\varphi(x_i),\rho(C(x_i x_{i+1}))\varphi(x_{i+1})\rangle \; d\mu_\Lambda^C(\varphi).$$

The computation for $n \geq 1$ is similar to the one of $\int d\mu_\Lambda^C(\varphi)$ and we shall only sketch briefly this latter one. After a change of variables this reduces to

$\int \exp(-\langle\varphi,(1-M(C))\varphi\rangle) \prod_{x\in\Lambda} d\varphi(x) \equiv \Phi(C)$, with $M(C)$ the matrix in V given by $(M(C)\varphi)(x) \equiv K \sum_{y\in\Lambda} (C(xy))\varphi(y)$, the sum being over the nearest neighbors y of x in Λ and K being a constant. We have $\mathrm{tr}\, M(C)^n = \tilde{K}^n \sum_{x\in\Lambda} E(\mathrm{tr}(\rho(C(b)) \mid b_- = b_+ = x,\ |b| = n)$, where $\tilde{K}$ is a constant and the expectation is with respect to a random walk b in Λ, with n jumps, starting (b-) and ending (b+) at x. We then obtain, with Z the value of $\Phi(C)$ with $C(xy)$ replaced everywhere by the unit in G, $Z^{-1}\,\Phi(C) =$

$$= \exp\Big(-\frac{1}{2}\sum_{n=0}^{\infty} \frac{K^n}{n} \sum_{x\in\Lambda} E(\mathrm{tr}(1-\rho(C(b)))\mid b_- = b_+ = x,\ |b| = n\Big).$$

This representation then yields bounds independent of a and C and "diamagnetic inequalities" (see [3], f), h) and for previous work with different methods [11] and references therein). The quantities G_C can be obtained in a similar way by expressions involving in addition to the above random walk loops also "random walk bridges". The continuum limit is obtained by replacing the random walk loop by a brownian motion loop b running in Λ in time t, replacing the sum over times by an integral over time. For G a discrete group the convergence can be controlled, see [3] h) obtaining then $Z^{-1}\Phi(C)$ in the continuum limit in terms of

$\exp\big[\int_\Lambda dx \int_0^t dt\, t^{-1} \exp(-\beta t) E(\mathrm{tr}(1-\rho(C(b)) \mid b(0) = b(t) = x)\big]$, with $\beta > 0$ a suitable constant. Then by these methods the Higgs model with discrete gauge group can be expressed in terms of Brownian motions and Markov cosurfaces. Extensions of these results to continuous groups and coupling with matter fields are being presently studied.

Remark E (Markov cosurfaces and the representation of current groups)

In [1] and [12] a unitary representation of groups of mappings from a manifold M in a Lie group G, so called "energy representation", is discussed and shown to be irreducible for $\dim M \geq 3$, reducible for $d \equiv \dim M = 1$, both the irreducible and reducible cases being possible for $d = 2$, depending on the lengths of root vectors. For $d = 1$ these representations are entirely characterized in terms of Brownian motion on G (left translation on the process). The question whether the above Markov cosurfaces are related to the energy representation also for $d \geq 2$ should be elucidated, see [13], [14]. In conclusion we might say that the non commutative stochastic calculus associated with Markov cosurfaces contains a wealth of nice mathematical problems and of directions of further developments, also in connection with the problem of construction of models of quantum fields.

Acknowledgements We thank Prof. Dr. Z. Haba, Prof. Dr. W. Kirsch, M. Koeck and especially A. Kaufmann for useful discussions. The partial financial support by the Research Centre BiBoS and by NAVF (Norway) is gratefully acknowledged. We thank Mrs. Mischke and Richter for skilful typing.

References

[1] a) S. Albeverio, R. Høegh-Krohn, D. Testard, Factoriality of representations of the group of paths of SU(n), J. Funct. Anal. 57, 49-55 (1984)

b) D. Testard, Representations of the group of equivariant loops in SU(N), BiBoS Preprint, to appear in Proc. BiBoS II Symp., Lect. Notes Maths., Springer (1986)

c) J. Marion, Dirichlet forms defined by Riemannian flags and applications, these Proceedings

d) J. Marion, On the coadjoint representation of $\mathcal{D}(\mathbb{R},G)$; organization of orbits, energy representations and Brownian functionals, Marseille Preprint (1986)

[2] S. Albeverio, R. Høegh-Krohn, J. Marion, D. Testard, Non commutative distributions, book in preparation

[3] a) S. Albeverio, R. Høegh-Krohn, H. Holden, Markov cosurfaces and gauge fields, Acta Phys. Austr., Suppl. XXVI, 211-231 (1984)

b) S. Albeverio, R. Høegh-Krohn, H. Holden, Markov processes on infinite dimensional spaces, Markov fields and Markov cosurfaces, pp. 11-40, in L. Arnold, P. Kotelenez, Edts., Stochastic space-time models and limit theorems, D. Reidel, Dordrecht (1985)

c) S. Albeverio, R. Høegh-Krohn, H. Holden, Some Markov fields and quantum fields through groups valued cosurfaces, manuscript; S. Albeverio, R. Høegh-Krohn, H. Holden, A. Kaufmann, in preparation

d) S. Albeverio, R. Høegh-Krohn, H. Holden, Stochastic multiplicative measures, generalized Markov semigroups and group-valued stochastic processes and fields, to appear in J. Funct. Anal. (1986)

e) S. Albeverio, R. Høegh-Krohn, H. Holden, Stochastic Lie group-valued measures and their relations to stochastic curve integrals, gauge fields and Markov cosurfaces, pp. 1-24 in S. Albeverio, Ph. Blanchard, L. Streit, Edts., Stochastic processes - Mathematics and Physics, Proc. BiBoS I, Lect. Notes Maths. 1158, Springer (1985)

f) S. Albeverio, R. Høegh-Krohn, Brownian motion, Markov cosurfaces, Higgs fields, BiBoS Preprint, to appear in Proc. Como Conf. "Fundamental Problems of Quantum Theory", Ed. A. Frigerio, V. Gorini, Plenum (1986)

g) S. Albeverio, J.E. Fenstad, R. Høegh-Krohn, T. Lindstrøm, Nonstandard methods in stochastic analysis and mathematical physics, Academic Press (1986)

[4] Z. Haba, Stochastic equations for some Euclidean fields, these Proceedings

[5] A. Kaufmann, Stetigkeit von Gruppenwertigen stochastischen Koflächen, Diplomarbeit, Bochum (1986)

[6] M.M. Rao, Foundations of Stochastic Analysis, Academic Press, New York (1981)

[7] H. Bauer, Wahrscheinlichkeitstheorie und Grundzüge der Maßtheorie, DeGruyter, Berlin (1974)

[8] a) C. Berg, G. Forst, Potential theory on locally compact abelian groups, Springer, Berlin (1975)

b) Ph. Feinsilver, Processes with independent increments on a Lie group, Trans. Am. Math. Soc. 242, 73-121 (1978)

c) H. Heyer, Probability measures on locally compact groups, Springer, Berlin (1977)

[9] W. Hazod, Stetige Faltungsgruppen von Wahrscheinlichkeitsmaßen und erzeugende Distributionen, Lect. Notes Maths., Springer, Berlin

[10] M. Koeck, Formulierung der Grundlagen einer 2-dimensionalen Gittereichtheorie reiner Yang-Mills-Felder als stochastische Cofläche mit Werten in einer kompakten Lie-Gruppe und Diskussion des Kontinuumslimes als schwache Konvergenz von Gibbs-Randmaßen, Diplomarbeit, Bochum (1986)

[11] E. Seiler, Gauge theories as a problem of constructive quantum field theory and statistical mechanics, Lect. Notes Phys. 159, Springer, Berlin (1982)

[12] S. Albeverio, R. Høegh-Krohn, Diffusion fields, quantum fields and fields with values in groups, in Adv. Prob., Stochastic Analysis and Applications, Ed. M. Pinsky, Dekker, New York (1984)

[13] S. Albeverio, R. Høegh-Krohn, Stochastic partial differential equation in two dimensions and the non linear σ-model, in preparation

[14] J. Marion, in preparation

[15] S. Albeverio, R. Høegh-Krohn, Euclidean Markov fields and relativistic quantum fields from stochastic partial differential equations in four dimensions, BiBoS-Preprint, March '86 (to appear in Phys. Letts. B)

STOCHASTIC PROCESSES AND CONTINUAL MEASUREMENTS IN QUANTUM MECHANICS

Alberto Barchielli

Dipartimento di Fisica dell'Università di Milano.
Istituto Nazionale di Fisica Nucleare, Sezione di Milano.
Via Celoria, 16 - 20133 Milano - Italy.

1. Continual measurements in quantum mechanics and operation valued stochastic processes.

In the last twenty years a very flexible formulation of quantum mechanics (QM) has been developed, starting from a suitable generalization of the notion of observable and of the Von Neumann reduction postulate /1,2/. A central point in this formulation is the notion of instrument /2,3/ which contains both the probabilities for the measured quantity and the way the state of the system changes under measurement.

Let $\mathcal{h}$ be a Hilbert space. Denote by $B(\mathcal{h})$ the algebra of bounded operators on $\mathcal{h}$, by $T(\mathcal{h})$ the space of trace-class operators on $\mathcal{h}$ and by $\mathcal{L}(T(\mathcal{h}))$ ($\mathcal{L}(B(\mathcal{h}))$) the space of bounded operators on $T(\mathcal{h})$ ($B(\mathcal{h})$). By $I\in B(\mathcal{h})$ we denote the identity operator on $\mathcal{h}$ and we introduce the notation

$$\langle Y,\rho\rangle := \operatorname{Tr}(Y\rho)\,,\quad Y\in B(\mathcal{h}),\ \rho\in T(\mathcal{h})\,. \tag{1.1}$$

Def.1.1. A completely positive (CP) instrument or operation valued measure $\mathcal{F}(\cdot)$ in $\mathcal{h}$ with value space (Ω,Σ) (where (Ω,Σ) is a Borel space) is a CP, normalized, σ-additive map $\mathcal{F}:\Sigma\to\mathcal{L}(T(\mathcal{h}))$, i.e.

i) if $\mathcal{I}_m$ is the identity operator on $T(\mathbb{C}^m)$, then

$$\big(\mathcal{F}(N)\otimes\mathcal{I}_m\big)\rho\geq 0\,,\quad \forall N\in\Sigma\,,$$

for any integer m and any positive ρ, $\rho\in T(\mathcal{h}\otimes\mathbb{C}^m)$;

ii) $\langle I,\mathcal{F}(\Omega)\rho\rangle = \langle I,\rho\rangle\,,\quad \forall\rho\in T(\mathcal{h})$;

iii) $\sum_i \langle Y,\mathcal{F}(N_i)\rho\rangle = \langle Y,\mathcal{F}(\bigcup_i N_i)\rho\rangle,\ \forall Y\in B(\mathcal{h}),\ \forall\rho\in T(\mathcal{h})$,

for any sequence of sets $\{N_i\}$ such that $N_i\cap N_j=\emptyset$, $i\neq j$.

Remark 1.1. Property ii) gives σ-additivity in the weak sense; however, by the positivity of $\mathcal{J}(\cdot)$, weak and strong σ-additivity are equivalent /2,3/.

Usually in QM only instantaneous measurements are considered, but there is nothing in the definition of instrument which does not allow to consider measurements which last some time. Continual measurements too will be represented by instruments; what we have to do is to choose a suitable Borel space and to require some compatibility condition between measurements referring to different time intervals.

A suitable framework for treating continually measured quantities is given by the theory of generalized stochastic processes (GSP's) /4/. Let $\mathcal{D}$ be the nuclear space of the n-component, real C^∞-functions h(t) on $\mathbb{R}$ with compact support and denote by $\mathcal{D}_{(t_1,t_2)}$ its subspace of the functions with support contained in (t_1,t_2). Let $\mathcal{D}'$ be the topological dual space of $\mathcal{D}$; for $x\in\mathcal{D}'$ and $h\in\mathcal{D}$, we denote by $\langle x|h\rangle$ the distribution x applied to the test function h. The subsets of $\mathcal{D}'$ of the form $\{x\in\mathcal{D}': (\langle x|h_1\rangle, \ldots, \langle x|h_s\rangle)\in B\}$, where B is a Borel subset of $\mathbb{R}^s$, are called cylinder sets. We equipe $\mathcal{D}'$ with the family of σ-algebras $\{\Sigma_{(t_1,t_2)},\ t_1,t_2\in\mathbb{R},\ t_1<t_2\}$, where $\Sigma_{(t_1,t_2)}$ is the σ-algebra generated by the cylinder sets defined by test functions belonging to $\mathcal{D}_{(t_1,t_2)}$. The space $\mathcal{D}'$ is interpreted as the set of the a priori possible trajectories for n real valued continually measured quantities; $x\in N$, $N\in\Sigma_{(t_1,t_2)}$, represents a possible outcome of a measurement in the time interval (t_1,t_2). Now, we formalize the idea of continual measurement in QM by the following notion of operation valued stochastic process (OVSP) /5/.

Def.1.2. An OVSP in $\mathcal{h}$ is a family of CP instruments in $\mathcal{L}\{\mathcal{J}(t_2,t_1;\cdot),\ t_1<t_2\}$, with value space $(\mathcal{D}',\Sigma_{(t_1,t_2)})$, such that, for $t_1<t_2<t_3$, $\forall N\in\Sigma_{(t_1,t_2)}, \forall M\in\Sigma_{(t_2,t_3)}$,

$$\mathcal{J}(t_3,t_2;M)\mathcal{J}(t_2,t_1;N)=\mathcal{J}(t_3,t_1;N\cap M). \tag{1.2}$$

Then, if the system is prepared in a state ρ (=statistical operator), probabilities are given by

$$P(x\in N|\rho,t_1)=\langle I,\mathcal{J}(t_2,t_1;N)\rho\rangle,\quad N\in\Sigma_{(t_1,t_2)}, \tag{1.3}$$

Moreover, after the measurement, the state conditioned upon the result $x\in N$ is given by

$$\rho_N=\mathcal{J}(t_2,t_1;N)\rho/\langle I,\mathcal{J}(t_2,t_1;N)\rho\rangle. \tag{1.4}$$

Equation (1.3) defines the probability measure of a GSP /5,6/.

Now, let us set

$$\mathcal{U}(t_2,t_1) := \mathcal{F}(t_2,t_1;\mathcal{D}') \; ; \tag{1.5}$$

then, by properties i) and ii) of Def.1.1, the operator $\mathcal{U}(t_2,t_1) \in \mathcal{L}(T(\mathcal{H}))$ is CP and trace preserving; moreover, by eq. (1.2), we have

$$\mathcal{U}(t_3,t_2)\,\mathcal{U}(t_2,t_1) = \mathcal{U}(t_3,t_1) \, , \quad t_1 < t_2 < t_3 \, . \tag{1.6}$$

The family of operators $\{\mathcal{U}(t_2,t_1),\ t_1,t_2 \in \mathbb{R},\ t_1<t_2\}$ gives the dynamics of the system under continual measurement /5/; apart from trivial cases, it must be dissipative.

2. The characteristic operator.

For any GSP one can introduce the notion of characteristic functional (the "functional" Fourier transform of the probability measure) and the GSP is uniquely determined by its characteristic functional (Minlos theorem; see ref.4). For an OVSP the analogous notion of characteristic operator can be introduced and the OVSP is uniquely determined by its characteristic operator. This result is stated, at a heuristic level, in ref.5; the main point of the present paper is to give a rigorous proof for this result.

Let $B \in \mathcal{B}$ ($\mathcal{B}$: Borel sets in $\mathbb{R}^s$) and set, for $\varphi_i \in \mathcal{D}_{(t_1,t_2)}$, i=1,...,s,

$$\mathcal{P}_{(t_1,t_2;\varphi_1,\dots,\varphi_s)}(B) := \mathcal{F}\big(t_2,t_1;\{x\in\mathcal{D}' : (\langle x|\varphi_1\rangle,\dots,\langle x|\varphi_s\rangle)\in B\}\big) . \tag{2.1}$$

Then $\mathcal{P}_{(\dots)}(\cdot)$ is a CP instrument with value space $(\mathbb{R}^s, \mathcal{B})$.

Theor.2.1. The strong integral

$$\int_{\mathcal{D}'} f(\langle x|\varphi_1\rangle,\dots,\langle x,\varphi_s\rangle)\,\mathcal{F}(t_2,t_1;dx) =$$

$$= \int_{\mathbb{R}^s} f(y_1,\dots,y_s)\,\mathcal{P}_{(t_1,t_2;\varphi_1,\dots,\varphi_s)}(d_s y) \tag{2.2}$$

exists for any bounded, continuous, complex function $f(y_1,\dots,y_s)$ on $\mathbb{R}^s$ and any choice of the test functions $\varphi_1,\dots,\varphi_s \in \mathcal{D}_{(t_1,t_2)}$. Equation (2.2) defines a bounded operator in $T(\mathcal{H})$; moreover, if $f \geq 0$, this operator is CP.

Proof. By Theor.4.1.2 of ref.2, the integral on the right hand side of

(2.2) exists in strong sense and defines a bounded operator in $T(\mathcal{h})$; moreover, $f \geq 0$ implies the positivity of this operator. By applying the same theorem to $\mathcal{P}_{(\ldots)}(\cdot) \otimes \mathcal{I}_m$, which is positive by property i) of Def.1.1, we have that for $f \geq 0$ eq.(2.2) defines a CP map. ■

Def.2.1. We call characteristic operator of the OVSP $\mathcal{F}(\ldots)$ the family $\{\mathcal{G}(t_2,t_1;\varphi), \varphi \in \mathcal{D}_{(t_1,t_2)}, t_1,t_2 \in \mathbb{R}, t_1<t_2\}$ of bounded operators in $T(\mathcal{h})$ defined by the strong integral

$$\mathcal{G}(t_2,t_1;\varphi) := \int_{\mathcal{D}'} e^{i\langle x|\varphi\rangle} \mathcal{F}(t_2,t_1;dx). \tag{2.3}$$

Theor.2.2. The family of bounded operators in $T(\mathcal{h})$ $\{\mathcal{G}(t_2,t_1;\varphi), \varphi \in \mathcal{D}_{(t_1,t_2)}, t_1,t_2 \in \mathbb{R}, t_1<t_2\}$ is the characteristic operator of an OVSP if and only if the following properties hold:

i) $\mathcal{G}(t_2,t_1;0)$ is trace preserving, i.e.

$$\langle I, \mathcal{G}(t_2,t_1;0)\rho\rangle = \langle I,\rho\rangle, \ \forall \rho \in T(\mathcal{h}); \tag{2.4}$$

ii) as a function from $\mathcal{D}_{(t_1,t_2)}$ into $\mathcal{L}(T(\mathcal{h}))$, $\mathcal{G}(t_2,t_1;\varphi)$ is strongly continuous;

iii) $\mathcal{G}(\ldots)$ is completely positive definite, which means that the operator in $T(\mathcal{h})$

$$\sum_{i,j=1}^{m} \alpha_i \mathcal{G}(t_2,t_1;\varphi_i-\varphi_j)\alpha_j^*$$

is CP for any choice of the integer m, of the complex numbers α_i and of the test functions $\varphi_i \in \mathcal{D}_{(t_1,t_2)}$;

iv) the following composition law holds: for any $\varphi_1 \in \mathcal{D}_{(t_1,t_2)}$, $\varphi_2 \in \mathcal{D}_{(t_2,t_3)}$, $t_1<t_2<t_3$,

$$\mathcal{G}(t_3,t_2;\varphi_2)\mathcal{G}(t_2,t_1;\varphi_1) = \mathcal{G}(t_3,t_1;\varphi_1+\varphi_2). \tag{2.5}$$

Proof. Let $\mathcal{F}(\ldots)$ be an OVSP.

1) For f=1 the integral (2.2) gives $\mathcal{F}(t_2,t_1;\mathcal{D}')$ which is trace-preserving by property ii) of Def.1.1.

2) Put $|X| = (X^+X)^{1/2}$ (positive square root). For any $\rho \in T(\mathcal{h})$ we have /7/

$$\|\rho\|_1 := \mathrm{Tr}(|\rho|) = \sup_{\substack{Y\in B(\mathcal{h}) \\ \|Y\|=1}} |\langle Y,\rho\rangle|, \tag{2.6a}$$

$$\|\rho\|_1 = \langle I,\rho\rangle, \ \text{if} \ \rho \geq 0, \tag{2.6b}$$

$$|\langle Y,\rho\rangle| \leq \|Y\|\,\|\rho\|_1,\ \forall Y\in B(h),\ \forall\rho\in T(h). \tag{2.6c}$$

Moreover, for any $X\in B(h)$ or $T(h)$ put

$$X_1=\frac{1}{4}\left(|X+X^+|+X+X^+\right),\ X_2=\frac{1}{4}\left(|X+X^+|-X-X^+\right),$$
$$X_3=\frac{1}{4}\left[|i(X^+-X)|+i(X^+-X)\right],\ X_4=\frac{1}{4}\left[|i(X^+-X)|-i(X^+-X)\right]. \tag{2.7}$$

Then

$$X_i\geq 0\quad i=1,\ldots,4,\ X=X_1-X_2+i(X_3-X_4),$$
$$\|X\|\leq\sum_{i=1}^{4}\|X_i\|\leq 4\|X\|,\ X\in B(h). \tag{2.8}$$

Now, for any sequence $\{\varphi_i\}$ converging to φ in $\mathcal{D}_{(t_1,t_2)}$, we have, by the positivity of $\mathcal{F}(\ldots)$,

$$\|[\mathcal{G}(t_2,t_1;\varphi_i)-\mathcal{G}(t_2,t_1;\varphi)]\rho\|_1\leq$$
$$\leq\sup_{\substack{Y\in B(h)\\ \|Y\|=1}}\sum_{k,j=1}^{4}|\langle Y_k,[\mathcal{G}(t_2,t_1;\varphi_i)-\mathcal{G}(t_2,t_1;\varphi)]\rho_j\rangle|\leq$$
$$\leq\sup_{\substack{Y\in B(h)\\ \|Y\|=1}}\sum_{k,j=1}^{4}\int_{\mathcal{D}'}\left|e^{i\langle x|\varphi_i\rangle}-e^{i\langle x|\varphi\rangle}\right|\langle Y_k,\mathcal{F}(t_2,t_1;dx)\rho_j\rangle\leq$$
$$\leq\sup_{\substack{Y\in B(h)\\ \|Y\|=1}}\sum_{k,j=1}^{4}\|Y_k\|\int_{\mathcal{D}'}\left|e^{i\langle x|\varphi_i\rangle}-e^{i\langle x|\varphi\rangle}\right|\langle I,\mathcal{F}(t_2,t_1;dx)\rho_j\rangle\leq$$
$$\leq 4\sum_{j=1}^{4}\int_{\mathcal{D}'}\left|e^{i\langle x|\varphi_i\rangle}-e^{i\langle x|\varphi\rangle}\right|\langle I,\mathcal{F}(t_2,t_1;dx)\rho_j\rangle. \tag{2.9}$$

$\mu_j(N)=\langle I,\mathcal{F}(t_2,t_1;N)\rho_j\rangle/\langle I,\rho_j\rangle$ is the probability measure of a GSP with values in $\mathcal{D}'_{(t_1,t_2)}$; then, by theorems 1 and 2 at pgs.348-350 of ref.4, this measure satisfies the continuity condition at pg.309 of ref.4. Thus, the last member of eq.(2.9) goes to zero and $\mathcal{G}(\ldots)$ is strongly continuous in φ (see also the footnotes at pgs.57 and 350 of ref.4).

3) Using definitions (2.1) and (2.3), we can write

$$\sum_{i,j=1}^{m}\alpha_i\,\mathcal{G}(t_2,t_1;\varphi_i-\varphi_j)\alpha_j^*=\int_{\mathbb{R}^m}\left|\sum_{i=1}^{m}\alpha_i e^{iy_i}\right|^2 P_{(t_1,t_2;\varphi_1,\ldots,\varphi_m)}(d_m y);$$

then property iii) follows from Theor.2.1.

4) The composition law (2.5) can be proved by a changement of integration variables in the double integral defining $\mathcal{G}(t_3,t_2;\varphi_2)\mathcal{G}(t_2,t_1;\varphi_1)$ and by using eq.(1.2).

Now, let $\mathcal{G}(\ldots)$ satisfy property i)-iv). For any $Y\geq 0$, $Y\in B(\mathcal{h})$, $\rho\geq 0$, $\rho\in T(\mathcal{h})$ such that $\langle Y, \mathcal{G}(t_2,t_1;0)\rho\rangle\neq 0$, define

$$L_{Y,\rho}(\varphi)=\langle Y,\mathcal{G}(t_2,t_1;\varphi)\rho\rangle/\langle Y,\mathcal{G}(t_2,t_1;0)\rho\rangle. \tag{2.10}$$

$L_{Y,\rho}(\varphi)$ is a positive definite continuous functional in $\mathcal{D}_{(t_1,t_2)}$ with $L_{Y,\rho}(0)=1$. By Theor.2 at pg.350 of ref.4 there exists a unique probability measure $\mu_{Y,\rho}(N)$ on $(\mathcal{D}',\Sigma_{(t_1,t_2)})$ such that

$$L_{Y,\rho}(\varphi)=\int_{\mathcal{D}'} e^{i\langle x|\varphi\rangle}\mu_{Y,\rho}(dx). \tag{2.11}$$

Then we set

$$F_{Y,\rho}(N)=\langle Y,\mathcal{G}(t_2,t_1;0)\rho\rangle\mu_{Y,\rho}(N),$$

so that eqs.(2.10) and (2.11) become

$$\langle Y,\mathcal{G}(t_2,t_1;\varphi)\rho\rangle=\int_{\mathcal{D}'} e^{i\langle x|\varphi\rangle}F_{Y,\rho}(dx), \tag{2.12}$$

where $F_{Y,\rho}(N)$ is a finite, positive, σ-additive measure on $\Sigma_{(t_1,t_2)}$. Now, it is easy to show that by property iii)

$$\langle Y,\mathcal{G}(t_2,t_1;0)\rho\rangle=0\Rightarrow\langle Y,\mathcal{G}(t_2,t_1;\varphi)\rho\rangle=0,\ \forall\varphi\in\mathcal{D}_{(t_1,t_2)}. \tag{2.13}$$

Therefore eq.(2.12) holds for any positive Y and ρ; when the left hand side of eq.(2.12) vanishes, one has $F_{Y,\rho}(\cdot)=0$. We have also

$$\sup_{\substack{Y\geq 0\\ \|Y\|=1}} F_{Y,\rho}(N)\leq\sup_{\substack{Y\geq 0\\ \|Y\|=1}} F_{Y,\rho}(\mathcal{D}')=\sup_{\substack{Y\geq 0\\ \|Y\|=1}}\langle Y,\mathcal{G}(t_2,t_1;0)\rho\rangle\leq$$

$$\leq\sup_{\substack{Y\geq 0\\ \|Y\|=1}}\|Y\|\,\|\mathcal{G}(t_2,t_1;0)\rho\|_1\leq\|\mathcal{G}(t_2,t_1;0)\|_{\mathcal{L}(T(\mathcal{h}))}\|\rho\|_1.$$

As the left hand side of (2.12) is linear in Y, we can extend by linearity $F_{\cdot,\rho}(N)$ to a positive bounded linear functional on $B(\mathcal{h})$. Now, $F_{\cdot,\rho}(\mathcal{D}')=$ $=\langle\cdot,\mathcal{G}(t_2,t_1;0)\rho\rangle$ and, therefore, it is a positive normal functional on $B(\mathcal{h})$ ($\mathcal{G}(\ldots)\rho\in T(\mathcal{h})$). But, for any $Y\geq 0$, $F_{Y,\rho}(N)\leq F_{Y,\rho}(\mathcal{D}')$ and, therefore, also $F_{\cdot,\rho}(N)$ is normal and can be identified with an element of $T(\mathcal{h})$

(ref.8, pgs.50-51). By linearity, $F_{\cdot,\rho}(N)$ can be extended to all $\rho \in T(\mathcal{h})$; in this way we define an operator $\mathcal{F}(\ldots) \in \mathcal{L}(T(\mathcal{h}))$.

Therefore, $\forall\, Y \in B(\mathcal{h})$, $\forall \rho \in T(\mathcal{h})$, we have

$$\langle Y, \mathcal{G}(t_2,t_1;\varphi)\rho\rangle = \int_{\mathcal{D}'} e^{i\langle x|\varphi\rangle} \langle Y, \mathcal{F}(t_2,t_1;dx)\,\rho\rangle,$$

where $\mathcal{F}(\ldots) \in \mathcal{L}(T(\mathcal{h}))$ is a positive operator valued measure with value space $(\mathcal{D}', \Sigma_{(t_1,t_2)})$; normalization follows from property i). Starting from the operator $\mathcal{G}(\ldots) \otimes \mathcal{I}_m \in \mathcal{L}(T(\mathcal{h} \otimes \mathbb{C}^m))$, that enjoies the same properties as $\mathcal{G}(\ldots)$, one constructs in the same way the positive operator valued measure $\mathcal{F}^{(m)}(\ldots)$. Then it is easy to show that

$$\int_{\mathcal{D}'} e^{i\langle x|\varphi\rangle} \mathcal{F}^{(m)}(t_2,t_1;dx) = \int_{\mathcal{D}'} e^{i\langle x|\varphi\rangle} \mathcal{F}(t_2,t_1;dx) \otimes \mathcal{I}_m$$

which implies (by the uniqueness of the measure determined by a characteristic functional) that $\mathcal{F}^{(m)}(\ldots) = \mathcal{F}(\ldots) \otimes \mathcal{I}_m$; therefore, $\mathcal{F}(t_2,t_1;N)$ is CP. Finally, starting from

$$\mathcal{G}\Big(t_3,t_2;\sum_{r=1}^{s} k_r h_r\Big)\mathcal{G}\Big(t_2,t_1;\sum_{m=1}^{\tilde{m}} \lambda_m g_m\Big) =$$

$$= \mathcal{G}\Big(t_3,t_1;\sum_{r=1}^{s} k_r h_r + \sum_{m=1}^{\tilde{m}} \lambda_m g_m\Big),\quad h_r \in \mathcal{D}_{[t_1,t_2)},\ g_m \in \mathcal{D}_{[t_2,t_3)},\ k_r,\lambda_m \in \mathbb{R},$$

one can show that eq.(1.2) holds when N and M are cylinder sets. Now in ref.4, pg.313, it is shown how to construct a general set starting from cylinder sets. Using that construction and the σ-additivity of the three measures in eq.(1.2), one obtains that this equation holds for general sets N and M. ■

Remark 2.1. In the reconstruction of the OVSP only the weak continuity of $\mathcal{G}(\ldots)$ in φ has been used, so that for a characteristic operator weak and strong continuity turn out to be equivalent.

3. Construction of a class of OVSP's.

In ref.3 it is proved that for any CP instrument $\mathcal{F}(N)$ in $\mathcal{h}$ there exists an Hilbert space $\mathcal{H}$, a state σ in $T(\mathcal{H})$, a projection valued measure $E(N) \in B(\mathcal{H})$ and a unitary operator U on $\mathcal{h} \otimes \mathcal{H}$ such that

$$\langle Y, \mathcal{J}(N)\rho \rangle = \mathrm{Tr}_{h\otimes\mathcal{H}}\left[(Y\otimes E(N))U(\rho\otimes\sigma)U^{+}\right]. \tag{3.1}$$

We call $\{\mathcal{H}, \sigma, E(\cdot), U\}$ a (projection valued) dilation of the CP instrument $\mathcal{J}(\cdot)$.

Consider now two CP instruments $\mathcal{J}_1$ and $\mathcal{J}_2$; up to technicalities the composition $\mathcal{J}_2 \circ \mathcal{J}_1$ defines a new instrument (ref.2, theor.4.2.2). Let $\{\mathcal{H}_i, \sigma_i, E_i(\cdot), U_i\}$ be a dilation of $\mathcal{J}_i$, i = 1,2; then, from eq.(3.1) we have

$$\langle Y, \mathcal{J}_2(N_2)\mathcal{J}_1(N_1)\rho \rangle = \mathrm{Tr}_{h\otimes\mathcal{H}_1\otimes\mathcal{H}_2}\left[(Y\otimes E_1(N_1)\otimes E_2(N_2))U_2U_1(\rho\otimes\sigma_1\otimes\sigma_2)U_1^{+}U_2^{+}\right]; \tag{3.2}$$

where $U_1 \equiv U_1\otimes I_2$, $U_2 \equiv U_2\otimes I_1$. Therefore, a dilation of $\mathcal{J}_2 \circ \mathcal{J}_1$ is given by $\{\mathcal{H}_1\otimes\mathcal{H}_2, \sigma_1\otimes\sigma_2, E_1\otimes E_2, U_2U_1\}$.

Let now $\{\mathcal{H}_{t_1}^{t_2}, \sigma_{t_1}^{t_2}, E_{t_1}^{t_2}, U(t_2,t_1)\}$ ($E_{t_1}^{t_2}$= projection valued measure on $\Sigma_{(t_1,t_2)}$) be a dilation of an OVSP $\mathcal{J}(t_2,t_1;\cdot)$. By eqs.(1.2) and (3.2), we are brought to require the following compatibility conditions among dilations referring to different time intervals ($t_1<t_2<t_3$):

$$\mathcal{H}_{t_1}^{t_2}\otimes\mathcal{H}_{t_2}^{t_3} = \mathcal{H}_{t_1}^{t_3}, \quad \sigma_{t_1}^{t_2}\otimes\sigma_{t_2}^{t_3} = \sigma_{t_1}^{t_3} \tag{3.3a}$$

$$E_{t_1}^{t_2}(N)\otimes E_{t_2}^{t_3}(M) = E_{t_1}^{t_3}(N\cap M), \; N\in\Sigma_{(t_1,t_2)}, \; M\in\Sigma_{(t_2,t_3)} \;, \tag{3.3b}$$

$$U(t_3,t_2)\,U(t_2,t_1) = U(t_3,t_1). \tag{3.3c}$$

Now, as in the case of operation valued measures, it is useful to work with the Fourier transform of the projection valued measures $E_{t_1}^{t_2}(\cdot)$. Therefore, we introduce the strong integral

$$V_{t_1}^{t_2}(\varphi) = \int_{\mathcal{D}'} e^{i\langle x|\varphi\rangle} E_{t_1}^{t_2}(dx), \quad \varphi\in\mathcal{D}_{(t_1,t_2)}. \tag{3.4}$$

$V_{t_1}^{t_2}(\cdot)$ is a strongly continuous unitary representation of $\mathcal{D}_{(t_1,t_2)}$ (considered as an Abelian group); moreover, we have

$$V_{t_1}^{t_2}(\varphi_1)\otimes V_{t_2}^{t_3}(\varphi_2) = V_{t_1}^{t_3}(\varphi_1+\varphi_2), \; \varphi_1\in\mathcal{D}_{(t_1,t_2)}, \; \varphi_2\in\mathcal{D}_{(t_2,t_3)}. \tag{3.5}$$

The unitary operators $V_{t_1}^{t_2}(\varphi)$ are linked to the characteristic operator of the OVSP by

$$\langle Y, \mathcal{G}(t_2,t_1;\varphi)\rho \rangle = \mathrm{Tr}_{h\otimes\mathcal{H}_{t_1}^{t_2}}\left[(Y\otimes V_{t_1}^{t_2}(\varphi))U(t_2,t_1)(\rho\otimes\sigma_{t_1}^{t_2})U(t_2,t_1)^{+}\right]. \tag{3.6}$$

These considerations suggest a way for constructing OVSP's starting from suitable unitary representations of $\mathcal{D}$ in a continuous tensor product structure /9/. Moreover, the operators $V_{t_1}^{t_2}(\varphi)$ and the dynamics $U(t_2,t_1)$ with the properties we need can be obtained by using the quantum stochastic calculus of Hudson and Parthasarathy /10,11/. This way of constructing the characteristic operator of an OVSP has been followed in ref. 12. Here we give only the results.

Theor.3.1. Consider the operator $\mathcal{G}(t,t_0;\varphi)\in\mathcal{L}(T(\mathcal{h})),\ \varphi\in\mathcal{D}$, defined by the differential equation

$$\text{s-}\frac{\partial}{\partial t}\mathcal{G}(t,t_0;\varphi)=\mathcal{K}(\varphi(t))\mathcal{G}(t,t_0;\varphi), \tag{3.7}$$

$$\mathcal{G}(t_0,t_0;\varphi)=1, \tag{3.8}$$

with

$$\begin{aligned}\mathcal{K}(\varphi)\rho = {}& -i[H,\rho]-\frac{1}{2}\sum_j\langle u,P_ju\rangle\left(R_j^\dagger R_j\rho+\rho R_j^\dagger R_j\right)-\\ &-\left(\frac{1}{2}\|\delta(\varphi)\|^2+i\lambda(\varphi)\right)\rho+\sum_j\Big(\langle\delta(-\varphi),P_ju\rangle R_j\rho+\\ &+\langle P_ju,\delta(\varphi)\rangle\rho R_j^\dagger\Big)+\sum_{i,j}\langle P_iu,W_\varphi P_ju\rangle R_j\rho R_i^\dagger,\end{aligned} \tag{3.9}$$

where u is a vector in an auxiliary Hilbert space $\mathcal{k}$, the P_j's are orthogonal projections in $\mathcal{k}$ such that $\sum_j P_j=1$, $H,R_j\in B(\mathcal{h})$, $H=H^\dagger$, $\sum_j\langle u,P_j u\rangle R_j^\dagger R_j$ converges strongly in $B(\mathcal{h})$, $\varphi\to W_\varphi$ is a unitary Borel representation of the group $\mathbb{R}^m$ in $\mathcal{k}$, $\delta:\mathbb{R}^m\to\mathcal{k}$ is a Borel function satisfying

$$W_g\delta(h)=\delta(g+h)-\delta(g),\quad \forall g,h\in\mathbb{R}^m, \tag{3.10}$$

and $\lambda:\mathbb{R}^m\to\mathbb{R}$ is a Borel function such that

$$\operatorname{Im}\langle\delta(h),\delta(-g)\rangle=\lambda(g+h)-\lambda(g)-\lambda(h). \tag{3.11}$$

Then, $\{\mathcal{G}(t_2,t_1;\varphi),\ \varphi\in\mathcal{D}_{(t_1,t_2)},\ t_1,t_2\in\mathbb{R},\ t_1<t_2\}$ satisfies properties i)-iv) of Theor.2.2; therefore, it is the characteristic operator of an OVSP.

The proof is essentially given in refs.12 and 13. When the set of indices $\{j\}$ is countable the results of ref.11 must be used. Particular choices of W_φ and $\delta(\varphi)$ are given in ref.12 and the meaning of the OVSP's obtained in this way is analized.

Remark 3.1. The necessity of the boundness of the operators H and R_j in Theor. 3.1 is due to the present stage of development of quantum stochastic calculus. With other techniques examples of OVSP's involving unbounded operators can be constructed /6/.

References

1. K. Kraus, States, Effects, and Operations, Lecture Notes in Physics **190** (Springer, Berlin, 1983).
2. E.B. Davies, Quantum Theory of Open Systems (Academic, London, 1976).
3. M. Ozawa, J. Math. Phys. **25**, 79 (1984).
4. I.M. Gel'fand and N.Ya. Vilenkin, Generalized Functions, vol.4, Applications of Harmonic Analysis (Academic, New York and London, 1964).
5. A. Barchielli, L. Lanz and G.M. Prosperi, Found. Phys. **13**, 779 (1983).
6. G. Lupieri, J. Math. Phys. **24**, 2329 (1983).
7. R. Schatten, Norm ideals of completely continuous operators (Springer, Berlin, 1960).
8. J. Dixmier, Les algèbres d'opérateurs dans l'espace Hilbertien (algèbres de Von Neumann) (Gauthier-Villars, Paris, 1969).
9. A. Frigerio, Covariant Markov dilations of quantum dynamical semigroups, to appear in Publ. RIMS Kyoto Univ..
10. R.L. Hudson and K.R. Parthasarathy, Commun. Math. Phys.**93**, 301 (1984).
11. R.L. Hudson and R.K. Parthasarathy, Acta Appl. Math. **2**, 353 (1984).
12. A. Barchielli and G. Lupieri, Quantum stochastic calculus, operation valued stochastic processes, and continual measurements in quantum mechanics, to appear in J. Math. Phys..
13. K.R. Parthasarathy, One parameter semigroups of completely positive maps on groups arising from quantum stochastic differential equations, preprint, Indian Statistical Institute, New Delhy.

STABILITY and CHAOTIC BEHAVIOR of QUANTUM ROTATORS °

J. BELLISSARD †

Centre de Physique Théorique §
CNRS-Luminy, Case 907
F-13288, MARSEILLE CEDEX 09 (FRANCE)

1)- INTRODUCTION AND MODELS:

The problem of stability for quantum systems have drawn the attention of the physicists since the late seventies [1]. One reason was that much progress was made during the seventies in understanding the transition to chaotic behavior for classical systems [2], raising the question whether the scenari found in this latter case could be used to describe the corresponding quantum systems. Another reason is that occurrence of chaotic behavior is considered as necessary to justify the foundations of quantum statistical mechanics. There was also a more practical one, namely the multiphotonic ionization experiment of J.E. Bayfield and P. Koch, in 1974 [3] which is still now not completely understood yet. More precisely, a beam of hydrogen atoms prepared in a state of high principal quantum number (typically $n \approx 66$) is sent through a microwave cavity. At the end, one measures the ionization rate. The frequencies used in the successive experiments [3,4], are very small (typically about 40%) compare to the resonant frequencies for a single electron excitation from the value n to n+1, and even much smaller (typically about 1%) compare to the photon frequency for excitation to the continuum. The surprising fact is that whereas at small field amplitude the ionization rate is almost equal to zero, one observes a jump above a critical field where the ionization rate saturates to one. We get a non linear effect sensitive to the <u>intensity</u> rather than to the <u>frequency</u> of the external microwave field!

All the usual methods of atomic physics failed to explain the result until, following a suggestion of Lamb, J.G. Leopold and I.C. Percival showed in 1978 [5], using a numerical simulation, that the experimental results were reproduced rather accurately from a purely classical approach. In 1982, R. Jensen [6] suggested that the increase of the quantum ionization rate was due to the disappearance of the KAM tori in the corresponding classical

° Lecture given at the Conference "Stochastic Processes in Classical and Quantum Systems", Ascona, June 1985

† Université de Provence, Marseille

§ Laboratoire Propre, Centre National de la Recherche Scientifique hamiltonian system, which usually produces a transition to some kind of chaotic behavior, and allows the system to wander in the phase space up to infinity. Using the technics developed during the seventies for systems with two degrees of freedom, he gave a way of computing theoretically the value of the critical field. Very recently [7], this kind of classical calculation was compared in great detail to the latest experimental results and from now on one can say that the classical approach even in the chaotic region is quite successful.

However, this raised the question of understanding why the classical approximation is so accurate, since the semi classical theory is not understood yet in the chaotic region. Several numerical simulations [8] were recently performed in order to compare the results obtained from the classical model to the quantum one. Among them, let us mention the work of G. Casati, B.V. Chirikov and D.L. Shepelyansky [8a] who exhibited three regions in the set of field amplitude : at small or high field, classical and quantum models exhibits essentially the same behavior, whereas there is an intermediate region where the quantum model is stable and the classical one is not. Comparing the previous analysis to the experimental situation, it has been possible to show that the experimental domain investigated never crosses the intermediate region [7]. Even though this not an explanation of the mechanism producing the effect, it suggests that a semi-classical approach is certainly a good approximation even in the chaotic region and it is a subject to look at in the next future from a more rigorous point of view.

What we want to show in this lecture is perhaps less ambitious : we intend to describe in a purely quantum way the notion of chaotic behavior, and to give a simple class of models exhibiting a transition from stable to chaotic behavior. Our point of view is that a spectral analysis of the quasi energy operator permits to separate the two regimes. More precisely we shall concentrate on the study of a quantum kicked rotator, described by the following time dependent hamiltonian :

(1) $$H(t) = -\alpha\partial^2/\partial x^2 + V(x,t)$$

acting on the space $L^2(\mathbf{T})$ of square integrable 2π-periodic functions on $\mathbb{R}$, where V is a smooth 2π-periodic function of x. In order to be concrete, we shall distinguish the following examples :

<u>The pulsed Rotator</u> (PR) [9] :

V is smooth and 2π-periodic with respect to x and t

<u>The Kicked Rotator</u> (KR) [10] : $V(x,t) = k\cos(x)\sum_{n\in\mathbf{Z}}\delta(t-2\pi n)$

<u>The Modulated Kicked Rotator</u> (MKR) [11] :

$$V(x,t) = k\,(1-\varepsilon+\varepsilon.\cos(\beta t))\cos(x)\sum_{n\in\mathbf{Z}}\delta(t-2\pi n)$$

The Randomly Kicked Rotator (RKR) [11] : $V(x,t) = k\cos(x)\sum_{n\in\mathbf{Z}}\delta(t-t_n)$ where $s_n = t_{n+1}-t_n$ are identically distributed random variables with a smooth density (we shall assume that there is $\varepsilon>0$ such that $s_n \geq \varepsilon$ almost surely).

2)- FLOQUET'S THEORY :

The study of the time behavior of a typical solution of the Schrödinger equation governed by a time dependent hamiltonian can be done in an equivalent way via a stationary hamiltonian involving additional degrees of freedom. This way of looking at non autonomous systems is usual in classical mechanics, and it had been applied in quantum mechanics by J.S. Howland [13] for the first time. Later on K. Yajima [14] made it into an efficient tool of functional analysis.

In order to take into account all the examples described previously we consider the following situation : we suppose that there is a compact space M together with a $\mathbf{R}$-flow g on M. Let P be a g-invariant ergodic probability measure on M. We assume that the hamiltonian is acting on a Hilbert space $\mathcal{H}$ and given by :

(2) $$H(t) = H(g_{-t}\xi) \qquad\qquad H(\xi) = H_0 + V(\xi)$$

where H_0 is self adjoint, and V is a strongly continuous bounded operator valued function on M.

Let us show some examples. If M is the one dimensional torus $\mathbf{T}$, and $g(t)\xi = \xi+t \pmod{2\pi}$, V is simply a 2π-periodic function of the time. We fall in the category of the pulsed or the kicked rotator. If now $M = \mathbf{T}^\nu$ and $g(t)\xi = \xi+t\omega$ where ω is some vector in $\mathbf{R}^\nu$ with rationally independent coordinates, the potential V is quasi periodic in time. This is the case for the modulated kicked rotator (here $\nu=2$), if one assumes that the Dirac function in the kicks can be smoothed out. The case of the randomly kicked rotator may be described as follows : let us assume that the density of the s's has a compact support J in $[\varepsilon,\infty)$. Let N be the infinite product space $J^{\mathbf{Z}}$ endowed with the discrete flow τ given by the two-sided shift. N is a compact space. Let f be the function on N defined by $f(\underline{s}) = s_0$ if $\underline{s} = (s_n)_{n\in\mathbf{Z}}$. Then we built the continuous flow g as the "flow under the function f" , namely M is the quotient of $N\times\mathbf{R}$ under the equivalence relation $(\underline{s},t) \approx (\tau^{-1}\underline{s},t+f(\underline{s}))$ and g(t) is the quotient of the map $(\underline{s},t') \to (\underline{s},t'+t)$ under this relation. If ρ is the common distribution of the s's, let $\underline{P}$ be the product measure $\otimes_{n\in\mathbf{Z}}\,\rho(ds_n)$. It is a τ invariant ergodic probability measure on N. Moreover, the measure $\underline{P}\otimes dt$ on $N\times\mathbf{R}$ defines, by taking the quotient and after normalization, a unique probability measure on M which turns out to be g invariant and ergodic. Then, for the RKR, V is formally given by $V(\xi) = \underline{\delta}(\xi)$ where $\xi = \text{class}(\underline{s},t)$ and $\underline{\delta}$ is the Dirac measure on the set of classes of $(\underline{s},0)$ ($\underline{s}\in N$).

It is not difficult, using an interaction picture and a Dyson expansion, to check that if V is strongly continuous, the solutions of the Schrödinger equation :

$$(3) \qquad i\partial\varphi/\partial t = H(g_{-t}\xi)\,\varphi$$

have the form :

$$(4) \qquad \varphi(t) = U_\xi(t,t')\,\varphi(t')$$

where the U's are unitary operators fulfilling the following conditions :

(5) (i) $U_\xi(t,t') = U_\xi(t,t'')\,U_\xi(t'',t')$ any t,t',t''

(ii) $U_\xi(t,t') = U_\xi(t',t)^*$ $U_\xi(t,t) = \mathbf{1}$

(iii) $U_\xi(t+a,t'+a) = U_{g_a\xi}(t,t')$

Moreover if $(z-H_0)^{-1}[H_0,V(\xi)]$ is bounded and strongly continuous with respect to ξ, we get (cf. [14] for an indication of the proof) :

(6) (iv) $(\xi,t,t') \in M\times\mathbb{R}\times\mathbb{R} \to U_\xi(t,t')$ is strongly continuous

(v) if $\varphi \in D(H_0)$ then $U_\xi(t,t')\varphi$ is differentiable with respect to t or t', it belongs to $D(H_0)$ and fulfills

$$i\partial/\partial t\, U_\xi(t,t')\varphi = H(g_{-t}\xi)\,U_\xi(t,t')\varphi \qquad -i\partial/\partial t'\, U_\xi(t,t')\varphi = U_\xi(t,t')\,H(g_{-t'}\xi)\varphi$$

Thanks to (5-iii) we define the <u>Floquet operator</u> as :

$$(7) \qquad U(\xi;t) = U_\xi(0,-t)$$

Now following K. Yajima, we introduce the Hilbert space $\mathcal{K} = L^2(M,P)\otimes\mathcal{H}$ together with the operator W(t) defined as :

$$(8) \qquad \Psi \in \mathcal{K} \qquad W(t)\Psi(\xi) = U(\xi;t)\,\Psi(g_{-t}\xi)$$

Then we get immediately the following result:

<u>Theorem 1</u> (cf. [14]) : $t \to W(t)$ is a one parameter strongly continuous group of unitary operators. There exists a selfadjoint operator K on $\mathcal{K}$ such that $\exp(itK) = W(t)$. K is called the <u>quasi energy</u> operator. ◇

It is not difficult to see that K is formally defined by :

$$K\Psi(\xi) = i\,d\Psi(g_{-t}\xi)/dt\,\big|_{t=0} + H(\xi)\,\Psi(\xi) \tag{9}$$

In other words, K coincides with the operator $i\partial/\partial t + H(g_{-t}\xi)$ with boundary conditions defined by the flow g on M.

The kicked version of the previous formalism can be described in much the same way. Let us remark however that the operator $V(\xi)$ becomes singular in this case. It can be written as a measure concentrated on a transversal T of the flow : a transversal T is a closed subset of M such that the set of t's in $\mathbb{R}$ for which $g_{-t}\xi \in T$ is a discrete ordered sequence $(t_n)_{n\in\mathbb{Z}}$ for each ξ in M. One can always smooth out such a measure by introducing an approximation of the Dirac measure $\delta(t)$ on $\mathbb{R}$, and defining $V^{\rho}(\xi) = \int dt\,\rho(t)\,V(g_{-t}\xi)$. As ρ converges to δ, the corresponding Floquet operator $U^{\rho}(\xi;t_n+0)$ converges strongly to :

$$\lim_{\rho\to\delta} U^{\rho}(g_{-0^+}\xi;t_n+0) = \prod_{j=0}^{n-1} e^{iH_0(t_{j+1}-t_j)}\, e^{iV_j(\xi)} = U(\xi;n) \tag{10}$$

$$\text{with} \quad V_j(\xi) = \int_{t_j-0}^{t_j+0} dt\, V(g_{-t}\xi)$$

In this case we just replace the continuous flow g on M by the corresponding $\mathbb{Z}$-flow on T defined by the first return map (the "Poincaré map"). With this convention everything can be done in much the same way.

3)- TIME BEHAVIOR AND QUASI ENERGY SPECTRUM :

We now intend to relate the asymptotics of the time evolution to the spectral properties of the quasi energy operator. Let φ be a vector in $\mathcal{H}$, then the solution of the Schrödinger equation coinciding with φ at time zero is given by :

$$(11) \qquad \varphi_\xi(t) = U_\xi(t,0)\varphi = U(g_t\xi,t)\varphi \quad .$$

It follows that if $\Psi \in \mathcal{K}$ and $f \in L^2(M,P)$ we get :

$$(12) \qquad \int P(d\xi)\, f(\xi) \,\langle \Psi(g_t\xi) \mid \varphi_\xi(t)\rangle_{\mathcal{H}} \;=\; \langle \Psi \mid W(t)\, f\otimes\varphi \rangle_{\mathcal{K}}$$

Therefore W(t) describes the averaged evolution of a typical vector. The "kinetic energy" is an observable the time evolution of which has been investigated numerically or theoretically :

$$(13) \qquad \mathcal{E}_\varphi(\xi;t) \;=\langle \varphi_\xi(t) \mid H_0\, \varphi_\xi(t)\rangle_{\mathcal{H}}$$

Let us mention the first result which applies to the periodic case (in what follows 1 denotes the function on M which is constant and equal to one) :

Theorem 2 (cf. [9]) : (i) Let us assume that $M = \mathbf{T}$ and g_t is the translation by t in $\mathbf{T}$. Let H_0 be positive unbounded with compact resolvent. If $1\otimes\varphi$ belongs to the continuous subspace of K, one has :

$$(14) \qquad \limsup_{t\to\infty} \int_0^{2\pi} d\xi\; \mathcal{E}_\varphi(\xi;t) \;=\; \infty$$

(ii) Let M be arbitrary. Let us assume that all the eigenvectors of K belong to the domain of $\mathbf{1}\otimes H_0$. Let φ be in $\mathcal{H}$ such that : (α) $1\otimes\varphi$ belongs to the pure-point subspace of K, (β) the coordinates of $1\otimes\varphi$ on the basis of eigenvectors of K are absolutely summable. Then the mean value of the kinetic energy :

$$(15) \qquad \langle\mathcal{E}_\varphi\rangle(t) = \int_M P(d\xi)\; \mathcal{E}_\varphi(\xi;t)$$

is an almost periodic function of the time.

◊

From this result one is justified to identify a stable motion with the appearance of a point spectrum for K. Conversely, if K has some continuous spectrum, the kinetic energy is likely to diverge. Let us remark however that the previous results are partial for they do not give a complete characterization of stability in term of point spectrum. In much the same way, the existence of an unstable motion is not characterized in term of spectral properties of the quasi energy operator in full generality. Nevertheless the previous results suggest that we may adopt the following criterion :

Criterion : in the case of quantum rotator, we shall say that the motion is stable if any φ in $\mathcal{H} = L^2(\mathbf{T})$ is such that $1\otimes\varphi$ belongs to the pure point subspace of K. We shall say that there is some chaotic motion if there is φ in $L^2(\mathbf{T})$ such that $1\otimes\varphi$ belongs to the continuous subspace of K.

The next result concerns the connection between the time behavior of the correlation functions and the spectrum of K :

Theorem 3 : Let M be arbitrary and let φ belong to $\mathcal{H}$. The correlation is defined as :

(16) $$S_\varphi(t) = \int_M P(d\xi) \langle \varphi | U_\xi(t,0)\varphi \rangle$$

(i) If $1\otimes\varphi$ belongs to the absolutely continuous subspace of K, the correlation converges to zero as $t\to\infty$.

(ii) If $1\otimes\varphi$ belongs to the continuous subspace of K, the correlation converges to zero as $t\to\infty$ in Cesaro mean.

(iii) If $1\otimes\varphi$ belongs to the pure-point subspace of K, the correlation is almost periodic in time.

◇

The key point in this result is the following identity :

(17) $$S_\varphi(t) = \int_M P(d\xi) \langle \varphi | U_\xi(t,0)\varphi \rangle = \langle 1\otimes\varphi | W(t)\, 1\otimes\varphi \rangle$$

In general the correlation splits into the sum of three terms corresponding to the absolutely continuous, the singular continuous and the pure point components of φ.

4)- QUANTUM ROTATOR : RIGOROUS RESULTS -

Let us return now on the quantum rotator problem. The first results concerns the effect of resonances. For indeed the unperturbed hamiltonian (1) (i.e. when $V = 0$) has a discrete spectrum, made of the eigenvalues $E_n = \alpha n^2$ ($n \in \mathbf{Z}$). When turning on a potential periodic in time with period commensurate to α, there is a resonance between the quantum eigenvalues and the classical period. This actually produces an instability :

Theorem 4 [10] : Let us consider the model KR with $\alpha = p/q$ a rational number. Then the quasi energy spectrum is absolutely continuous and in addition the kinetic energy satisfies :

$$(18) \qquad \langle \mathcal{E}_\varphi \rangle(t) = \eta_q t^2 + O(1) \qquad \text{as } t \to \infty$$

◇

As usual in classical mechanics, instabilities remain in the vicinity of a resonance. The next theorem expresses the same kind of result for the kicked rotator.

Theorem 5 (Casati-Guarneri [15]) : Let us consider the model KR. There is a rapidly decreasing sequence $\{\eta(q); q \in \mathbf{N}\}$ such that if α is approximated by a sequence p_n/q_n of rational fulfilling :

$$(19) \qquad |\alpha - p_n/q_n| \leq \eta(q_n) \qquad \text{all } n \in \mathbf{N}$$

then

(i) the quasi energy operator has a purely continuous spectrum
(ii) the kinetic energy is unbounded in time.

◇

The third result concerning the occurrence of instabilities was given by I. Guarneri, who created the Randomly Kicked Rotator model.

Theorem 6 (Guarneri [12]) : The quasi energy operator of the model RKR has a purely continuous spectrum.

◇

The previous results express the occurrence of instabilities under certain conditions. However at small coupling one expects the motion to be stable. This was actually observed numerically by several groups [16,17] (cf. fig.1). It is necessary to investigate this problem. The result below concerns such a property. However, as in classical mechanics it is far more difficult to prove since it requires all the machinery of the Kolmogorov-Arnold-Moser algorithm (cf. for instance [2]). Up to now the only available proof of it requires to consider the pulsed rotator model instead, for the smoothness of the potential in time plays an essential role.

<u>Theorem 7</u> (Bellissard [9]): Let us consider the model PR. We assume that the potential $V(x,t)$ is 2π-periodic in x and t, and analytic in a strip B of the form :

$$B = \{ (x,t) \in \mathbb{C}^2 \; ; |\mathrm{Im}(x)| < R, |\mathrm{Im}(t)| < R \}$$

Given $\varepsilon > 0$, there is a closed subset Ω of the interval $[1,\infty)$ with Lebesgue measure less than or equal to ε, and there is $\mu(\varepsilon) > 0$ such that if :

(i) $\alpha \in \Omega$

(ii) $\sup_{(x,t)\in B} |V(x,t)| < \mu(\varepsilon)$

one has :

(1) The quasi energy operator K has a pure point spectrum.

(2) The eigenvalues of K are given by $\omega_{m,n} = m + \alpha n^2 + g_V(\alpha;n)$ with $(m,n) \in \mathbb{Z}^2$ and :

$$\sup_{\alpha\in\Omega, n\in\mathbb{Z}} | g_V(\alpha;n) | = O(\mu(\varepsilon)) \text{ as } \varepsilon \to 0$$

(3) The corresponding eigenfunctions $\varphi_{m,n}$ are close to the eigenfunctions $e_{m,n}(x,t) = \exp\{i(mt+nx)\}$ of the unperturbed operator in the following sense :

$$| \langle \varphi_{m,n} | e_{m',n'} \rangle | \le O(\mu(\varepsilon))\, e^{-r_\infty(|m-m'| + ||n|-|n'||)} \qquad \text{for } m \neq m' \text{ or } n \neq \pm n'$$

(4) The kinetic energy is almost periodic in time.

◇

5)- CHAOTIC BEHAVIOR : NUMERICAL RESULTS -

Since it is quite hard to exhibit an exhaustive list of rigorous results concerning the problem of instability, it is useful to consider numerical works on the subject in order to have a more precise view of the subject. Let us mention the analysis of S. Fishman, D. Grempel and R. Prange (the Maryland group) [16], of B. Dorizzi, B. Grammaticos and Y. Pomeau [17] and of D.L. Shepelyansky [11]. In the present lecture we shall report on a numerical study of M. Samuelidès, R. Fleckinger, L. Touzillier, and J. Bellissard [18] which summarizes and extends the previous numerical results.

The first works investigated the time behavior of the kinetic energy of the kicked rotator. It was soon realized that at small coupling it is an almost periodic function of the time (cf. fig.1) whereas at large coupling its time behavior exhibits most of the features of the classical chaotic behavior (cf. fig. 2). However it was argued by the Maryland group [19] that there is a critical time τ depending upon the coupling constant, such that the classical and the quantum evolution are undiscernible on a scale of times of the order of τ, whereas at longer time the quantum evolution for the kicked rotator exhibits a stable motion. This was confirmed [16c] by the numerical calculation of the coordinates of the wave function after long time which shows that they are actually exponentially localized in the momentum space (represented by the Fourier components). However, the Maryland group did not consider very high values of the coupling constant and we could not exclude the possibility of a transition at higher coupling as it was argued in [9]. Later on D.L. Shepelyansky [11] reconsidered the problem using a more powerful computer. Looking also at the kinetic energy, he concluded that in the model KR it always saturates, after a time scale which increases with the coupling constant. However, he proposed to consider also the model MKR, in which he discovered that a transition to some chaotic behavior seems to occur : at high enough coupling, there is no saturation of the energy.

In [18] we have used another test to distinguish between the two kinds of behavior. We have analyzed the quasi energy spectrum through the Fourier transform in time of the correlation function. Since the models KR and MKR are kicked, the time is discrete, and the quasi energy spectrum lies on a one dimensional torus. More precisely, starting from an initial state φ in $L^2(\mathbf{T}) \approx l^2(\mathbf{Z})$ we compute the correlation :

$$(20) \qquad S_\varphi(t) = \int_M P(d\xi)\, \langle \varphi | U_\xi(t,0)\, \varphi \rangle = \int_{\mathbf{T}} \mu_\varphi(d\omega)\, e^{it\omega} \qquad t \in \mathbf{Z}$$

Thanks to the Floquet theory, μ_φ is a probability measure, which can be numerically computed by mean of a fast Fourier transform (FFT). The calculation of $U_\xi(t,0)$ can be done recursively in time by using the formula (10) of section 2. It is given by a finite product of operators of the form $e^{ik(1+\varepsilon\cos(\beta n+\xi))\cos(x)}$ which is a multiplication operator in the x-space and of the form $e^{-i\alpha\partial^2/\partial x^2}$ which is a multiplication operator in the Fourier space. Therefore, as was proposed by the Maryland group [16c], we get a repeated sequence of operations "multiplication by $e^{ik(1+\varepsilon\cos(\beta n))\cos(x)}$ - FFT - multiplication by $e^{-i\alpha\partial^2/\partial x^2}$ -FFT". Then we must average over the random variable ξ. We used mainly the Gauss method of integration.

We observe indeed a qualitative difference between the models KR and MKR at large coupling from the spectral point of view. Whereas for the KR model (i.e. for $\varepsilon=0$) we do not see any evidence for a continuous component in the spectrum even for k as large as 30 (cf. fig.3), it is clear that for the MKR model a continuous component appears (cf. fig.4).

This set of results suggests that a transition from a point spectrum to some continuous spectrum occurs for the quasi energy operator of the modulated kicked rotator, whereas the kicked rotator exhibits a stable motion for any coupling, namely, the spectrum of the quasi energy should be pure point. It is now necessary to go beyond this qualitative results and to investigate more precisely :

1- how appears the transition if any ?

2- are there some critical exponents describing the relative weight of the continuous part of the spectrum near the transition ?

3- what is the dependence of the critical coupling in the parameters ε, α, β ?

On the other hand it is also necessary to improve the mathematical methods in order to get proofs of the qualitative facts :

4- can one extend the theorem 7 for kicked rotators ?

5- can one understand more rigorously the classical approximation at short time ?

6- can one find systematic methods to investigate the continuous spectrum at high coupling ?

***

REFERENCES

[1] (a)G.CASATI,J.FORD Eds., Stochastic Behavior in Classical and Quantum Hamiltonian Systems, Springer, Berlin, Heidelberg, New York, Lectures Notes in Physics, 93 (1979).
(b)Chaotic Behavior in Quantum Systems, G.CASATI Ed., Plenum Press, New York, 1985.

[2] A.J.LICHTENBERG, M.A.LIEBERMANN, Regular and Stochastic Motion, Springer Verlag, Berlin, Heidelberg, New York, (1983).

[3] J.E.BAYFIELD, P.M.KOCH, Multiphotonic Ionization of Highly Excited Hydrogen Atoms, Phys.Rev. Lett. 33 (1974) 258.

[4] P.KOCH, Interaction of Intense Microwaves with Rydberg Atoms, J. de Phys. Colloques C2, 43 187-210, (1982)

[5] J.G.LEOPOLD, I.C.PERCIVAL a) Microwave Ionization and Excitation of Rydberg Atoms, Phys.Rev. Lett., 41 (1978) 944.
b) Ionization of Highly Excited Atoms by Electric Fields III: Microwave Ionization and Excitation, J. Phys., B12 (1979) 709-721.

[6] R.JENSEN, a) Stochastic Ionization of Surface State Electrons, Phys.Rev. Lett., 49 (1982) 1365.
b) Stochastic Ionization of Surface State Electrons: Classical Theory, Phys.Rev., A30 (1984) 386.

[7] K.A.H.Van LEEUWEN, G.V.OPPEN, S.RENWICK, J.B. BOWLIN, P.M.KOCH, R.V.JENSEN, O.RATH, D. RICHARDS, J. LEOPOLD, Microwave ionization of Hydrogen Atoms: Experiments versus Classical Dynamics, To appear in Phys.Rev. Letter, 1985.

[8] a) G.CASATI, B.V.CHIRIKOV, D.L.SHEPELYANSKY, Quantum Limitations for Chaotic Excitation of the Hydrogen Atom in a Monochromatic Field, Phys.Rev.Lett., 53 (1984) 2525-2528.
b) A.K.DHAR, P.M.ISRAELEV, M.A.NAGARAJAN, Behavior of Hydrogen Atoms under the Influence of Periodic Times Dependent Electric Fields, Preprint 83-162, Novossibirsk, (1985)

[9] J. BELLISSARD, Stability and Instability in Quantum Mechanics, in "Trends in the Eighties" Ph. Blanchard ed., Singapore, (1985).

[10] a) G.CASATI, B.V.CHIRIKOV, F.M.ISRAELEV, J. FORD, in ref. [1a]
b) F.M.IZRAELEV, D.L.SHEPELYANSKI, Quantum Resonances for a Rotator in a Non Linear Periodic Field, Theor.Mat.Fiz., 43 (1980) 553-560 (english translation).
c) B.V.CHIRIKOV, F.M.ISRAELEV, D.L.SHEPELYANSKY, Soviet Scientific Review, C2, (1981).

[11] D.L.SHEPELYANSKY, Some Statistical Properties of Simple Classically Stochastic Quantum Systems, Physica, 8D, (1983) 208-222.

[12] I.GUARNERI, Energy growth in a Randomly Kicked Quantum Rotator, Lett.Nuovo Cim., 40, (1984) 171-175.

[13] J.S.HOWLAND, a) Stationary Scattering Theory for the Time Dependent Hamiltonians, Math. Ann., 207 (1974) 315-335.
b) Scattering Theory for Hamiltonians Periodic in Time, Indiana Univ. Math.J., 28 (1979) 471-494.

[14] K.YAJIMA, a) Scattering Theory for Schrödinger Equations with Potential Periodic in Time, J.Math. Soc. Japan, 29, (1977) 729-743.
b) Resonances for the AC-Stark Effect, Comm.Math.Phys., 87, 331-352 (1982).

[15] G.CASATI, J.GUARNERI, Non Recurrent Behavior in Quantum Dynamics, Comm.Math.Phys., 95, (1984), 121-127.

[16] S.FISHMAN, D.R.GREMPEL, R.E.PRANGE, a) Chaos, Quantum Recurrences and Anderson Localization, Phys. Rev. Lett., 49, (1982) 509-512.
b) "Chaotic Behavior in Quantum Systems", G.CASATI ed., Plenum Press, New York, (1984). (ref. 1b)
c) Quantum Dynamics of a non Integrable System, Phys.Rev., A29 (1984) 1639-1647.

[17] B.DORIZZI, B.GRAMMATICOS, Y.POMEAU, The Periodically Kicked Rotator: Recurrence and/or Energy Growth, J. of Stat.Phys., 37, (1984) 93-108.

[18] M.SAMUELIDES, R.FLECKINGER, L.TOUZILLIER, J. BELLISSARD, The Rise of Chaotic Behavior in Quantum Systems and Spectral Transition, Preprint Marseille CPT-85/P.1789 (June 1985).

[19] S.FISHMAN, D.R.GREMPEL, R.E.PRANGE, Finite Planck's Constant Scaling at Stochastic Transition of Dynamical System, Preprint Univ. of Maryland (1984).

***

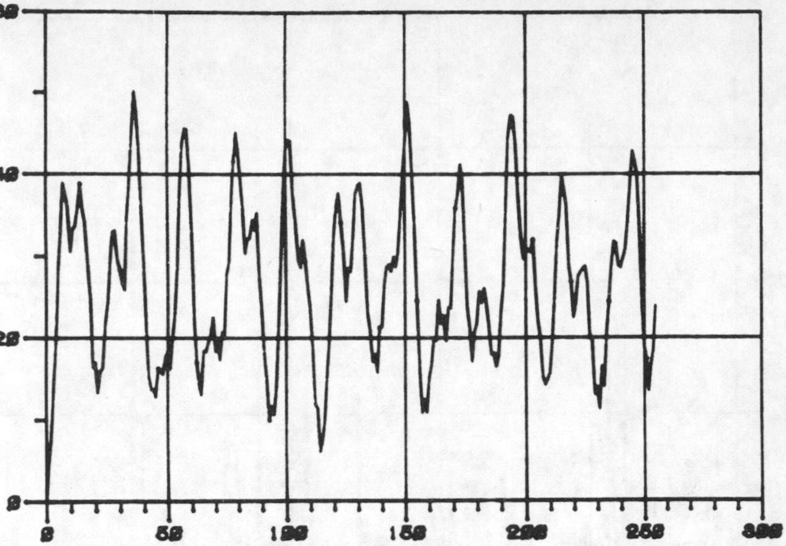

Figure 1 : Almost periodic oscillations of the kinetic energy of the model KR at small coupling ($\alpha=\pi, k=3, \varepsilon=0$)

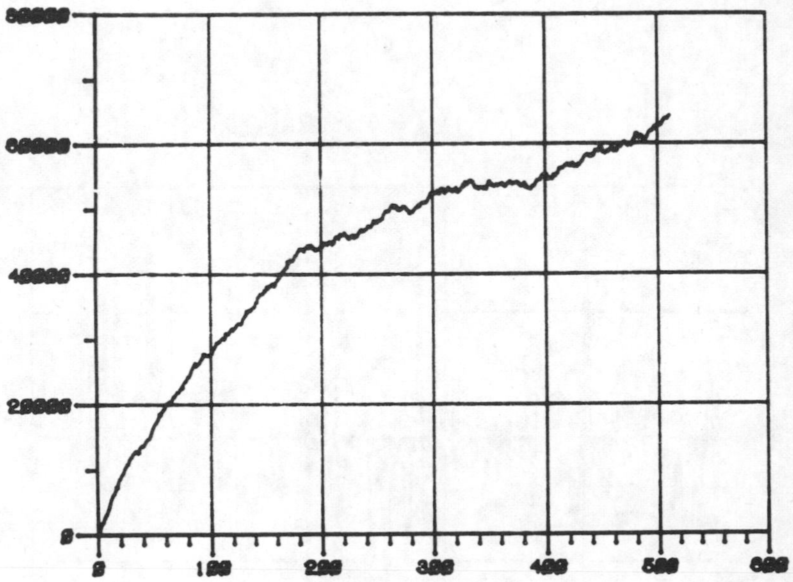

Figure 2 : Slow and irregular growth of the kinetic energy of the KR at large coupling ($\alpha=\pi, k=30, \varepsilon=0$). At short time it reflects the classical chaotic behavior.

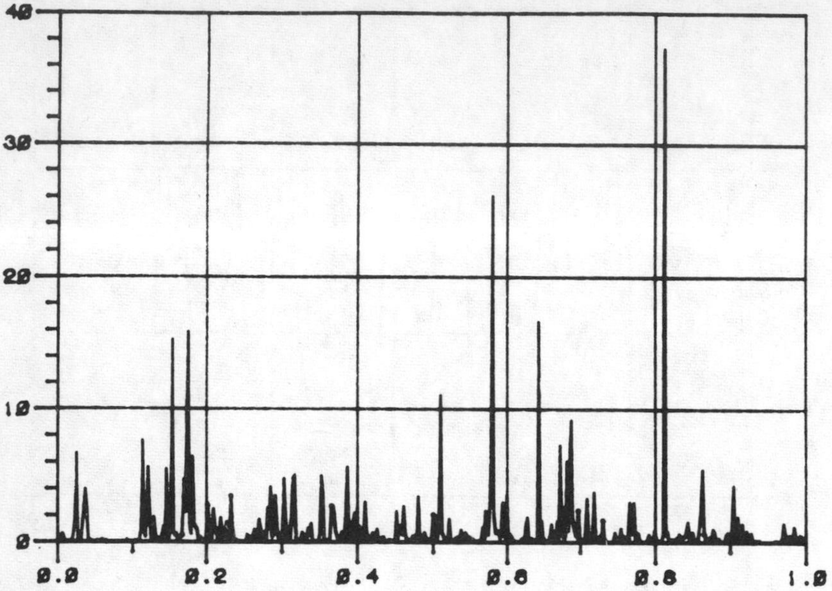

Figure 3 : Spectrum of the quasi energy operator of KR at large coupling ($\alpha = \pi$, $k = 30$, $\varepsilon = 0$). One does not see any evidence of a continuous component.

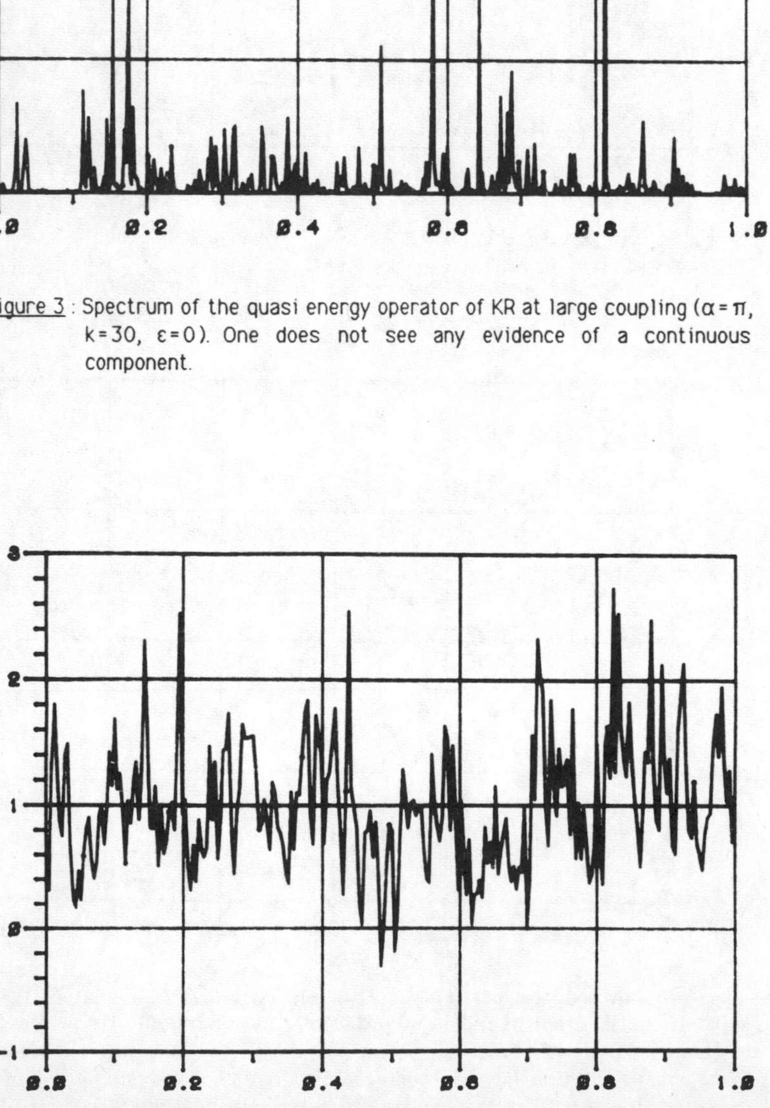

Figure 4 : Spectrum of the quasi energy operator of the MKR at large coupling ($\alpha = \sqrt{2}$, $\beta =$, $k = 20$, $\varepsilon = 1$). A continuous component appears clearly.

REGULAR AND CHAOTIC MOTIONS NEAR RESONANCES IN QUASI-INTEGRABLE HAMILTONIAN SYSTEMS

by

GIANCARLO BENETTIN

Dipartimento di Fisica dell'Università di Padova
Via Marzolo 8 - PADOVA (Italia)

1. KAM theorem and Nekhoroshev theorem.

Let us consider a nearly-integrable Hamiltonian system, i.e. a system which in action-angle canonical coordinates (p,q), with $p = (p_1,\ldots,p_n) \in \mathcal{V} \subset \mathbf{R}^n$ and $q = (q_1,\ldots,q_n) \in \mathbf{T}^n$ (where $\mathcal{V}$ is an open ball contained in $\mathbf{R}^n$, and $\mathbf{T}^n$ is the n-dimensional torus) has the Hamiltonian of the form

$$H(p,q,\varepsilon) = h(p) + \varepsilon f(p,q) . \tag{1.1}$$

The equations of motion are

$$\dot{p} = -\varepsilon \frac{\partial f}{\partial q} \; ; \qquad \dot{q} = \omega(p) + \varepsilon \frac{\partial f}{\partial p} \; , \tag{1.2}$$

with $\omega = (\omega_1,\ldots,\omega_n) = \left(\frac{\partial h}{\partial p_1},\ldots,\frac{\partial h}{\partial p_n}\right)$. For $\varepsilon = 0$ the system is integrable, and one has the trivial solution

$$p(t) = p(0) \; ; \qquad q(t) = q(0) + \omega\big(p(0)\big)t . \tag{1.3}$$

The phase space $\mathcal{W} = \mathcal{V} \times \mathbf{T}^n$ is foliated into n-dimensional invariant tori $\{p\} \times \mathbf{T}^n$, $p \in \mathcal{V}$. For $n = 2$, a family of such invariant tori, embedded in a three-dimensional space which can be thought to be a constant energy surface, is drawn in fig. 1. If we assume $\det\left(\frac{\partial^2 h}{\partial p \partial p}\right) \neq 0$ in $\mathcal{V}$, then each torus is well characterized by its angular velocity ω.

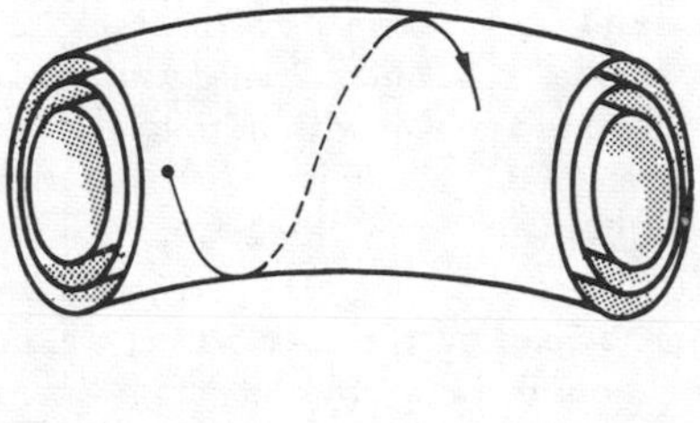

Fig. 1
A family of two-dimensional invariant tori.

For $\varepsilon \neq 0$, no matter how small, deep topological modifications to the above picture are expected; this is indeed the essential content of the celebrated Poincaré theorem on the non-existence of integrals of motion in neanly-integrable Hamiltonian systems [1] (for a discussion on the relevance of Poincaré theorem in classical perturbation theory, see ref.[2]). However, according to the celebrated KAM theorem [3–5], for small ε these modifications are confined to a set of small measure (although open and dense in $\mathcal{W}$). A recent formulation of KAM theorem [6,7] is the following:

Proposition 1 (KAM) : *Consider a Hamiltonian dynamical system, with Hamiltonian of the form (1.1), and assume:*

i) $H(p,q,\varepsilon)$ *is analytic in a neighborhood of* $\mathcal{W}$*;*

ii) $\det\left(\frac{\partial^2 h}{\partial p \partial p}\right) \geq d > 0;$

iii) ε *is smaller than a critical value* ε_0 *(depending on* n, d, *as well as on some general properties of* H*).*

Then one can find a canonical change of coordinates $(p,q) = \mathcal{C}_\varepsilon(p',q')$, *of class* C^∞ *in* $\mathcal{W}$, *and a subset* $\mathcal{V}' \subset \mathcal{V}$, *such that in the new variables the equations of motion take the form*

$$\dot{p}' = 0 \; ; \qquad \dot{q}' = \omega'(p') \tag{1.4}$$

whenever $p' \in \mathcal{V}'_\varepsilon$.

The canonical transformation is ε*-close to the identity, while* $\mathcal{V}\backslash\mathcal{V}'_\varepsilon$ *has measure small with* ε.

Thus, in spite of the perturbation, most of the phase space is still decomposed into invariant tori, which (in the new coordinates) have the form $\{p'\} \times \mathbf{T}^n$, $p' \in \mathcal{V}'_\varepsilon$. Unfortunately, the set $\mathcal{V}'_\varepsilon$, as constructed in the proof of the theorem, is topologically "strange", as its complement in $\mathcal{V}$ is open and dense.

It is then clear how fig. 1 most be modificated: while must tori are simply perturbed, taking (in the old variables) the form $\mathcal{C}_\varepsilon(\{p'\} \times \mathbf{T}^n)$, there appear now a dense set of thin "gaps" between tori. As is well known, the tori which survive after the perturbation are those which are characterized by strongly non-resonant ω, precisely ω satisfying the diophantine condition

$$|\omega \cdot k| \geq \lambda |k|^{-n} \qquad \forall k \in \mathbf{Z}^n, \quad k \neq 0 \,, \tag{1.5}$$

with $|k| = |k_1| + \ldots + |k_n|$, and λ small with ε.

Let us consider the special case $n = 2$. The set of angular velocities satisfying (1.5) is obtained by eliminating, from the frequency space (ω_1, ω_2), all the lines with rational slope ω_2/ω_1, together with a thin "corridor" around them. Corridors are dense, and for each of them we have a gap between tori.

Whenever the initial datum belongs to an invariant torus, then p' is constant, and correspondingly $p(t)$ performs small regular oscillations. For $n = 2$, and initial datum outside tori, $p(t)$ is nevertheless bounded (although possibly irregular), as an orbit with initial datum in a given gap cannot escape it. Indeed, for $n = 2$, each two-dimensional torus divides the three-dimensional energy surface where it is embedded into two disjoint parts.

For $n \geq 3$, the situation significantly changes: the above topological obstruction is no more present, so that the complement of the set of invariant tori not only is open and dense, but is also connected; p(t), for initial datum outside tori, is now bounded only by the energy conservation, and a dense orbit may exist on any constant energy surface. This phenomenon, which is compatible with KAM theorem, is called "Arnold diffusion". It certainly takes place in some dynamical systems, as we now from simple examples [8]; however, according to a theorem by Nekhoroshev [9], it is certainly a very slow phenomenon, in the sense that the difference $p(t) - p(0)$ turns out to be bounded by a power of ε, for times larger than any negative power of ε. This statement is made more precise by the following

Proposition 2 (Nekhoroshev theorem): *Consider a Hamiltonian dynamical system, with Hamiltonian of the form (1.1), and assume:*

i) $H(p,q,\varepsilon)$ *is analytic in a neighborhood of* $\mathcal{W}$*;*

ii) $\left(\dfrac{\partial^2 h}{\partial p \partial p}\right)$ *is there positive defined;*

iii) ε *is smaller than a convenient critical value* ε_0.

Then for any orbit (with any initial datum in $\mathcal{W}$*), one has*

$$|p_j(t) - p_j(0)| < A\varepsilon^a \ , \qquad j = 1, \ldots, n \ , \tag{1.6}$$

for

$$|t| < Be^{c\left(\frac{1}{\varepsilon}\right)^b} \ , \tag{1.7}$$

with suitable positive constants A, B, a, b, c.

In Nekhoroshev original paper, assumption ii) is replaced by a more general geometric condition on $h(p)$, called "steepness". Assumption ii) is instead used in the simplified proof contained in ref.[10], as well as in ref.[11,12]. In ref.[11,12] it is also shown that assumption ii) can be replaced by the assumption that the unperturbed system represents a set of free harmonic oscillators, with diophantine frequencies.

A typical unperturbed system where assumption ii) is satisfied, is a set of free rotators, say

$$h(p) = \sum_{j=1}^{n} \frac{p_j^2}{2I_j} \ , \tag{1.8}$$

$I_1, \ldots, I_n$ being positive inertia moments.

In the following, we shall shortly refer to quantities proportional to $\exp \pm c \left(\frac{1}{\varepsilon}\right)^b$ as to quantities of order $\varepsilon^{\mp\infty}$.

2. On the proof of Nekhoroshev theorem.

In order to deeply understand the dynamics of our system near resonances, where the motion is possibly non trivial, it is convenient to shortly examine the basic ideas entering the proof of Proposition 2.

a) First of all, one separates from the perturbation $f(p,q)$ in (1.1) the "ultraviolet part":

$$f^{>K}(p,q) = \sum_{\substack{k \in \mathbf{Z}^n \\ |k| > K}} f_k(p) e^{ik\cdot q} \ , \tag{2.1}$$

using a cut-off $K = \varepsilon^{-b}$. To our purpose $f^{>K}(p,q)$ can be neglected: indeed, f being analytic, its Fourier coefficients decrease exponentially with $|k|$, so that $f^{>K}$, with $K = \varepsilon^{-b}$, is of order $\varepsilon^{+\infty}$, and thus irrelevant up to times of order $\varepsilon^{-\infty}$. Such operation is essential, because now one is left with a perturbation $f^{\leq K} = f - f^{>K}$ having a finite number of Fourier components, and consequently one only needs to take care of a finite number of resonances.

b) The second step is a decomposition of the action space $\mathcal{V}$, according to the resonance properties of $\omega(p)$ with all integer vectors k with $|k| \leq K$. To this purpose, consider all integer subspaces $\mathcal{M}$ of $\mathbf{Z}^n$, of any dimension r, $0 \leq r \leq n$, which can be generated by an integer basis $\{k_1, \ldots, k_r\}$, with $|k_j| \leq K$, $j \leq r$; such a basis will be called a K-basis. To each $\mathcal{M}$ one associates a "resonant surface":

$$\Sigma_{\mathcal{M}} = \{p \in \mathcal{V};\ \omega(p) \cdot k = 0 \ \forall k \in \mathcal{M}\} \ , \tag{2.2}$$

and around it a "resonant zone" of thickness λ_r:

$$\mathcal{Z}_{\mathcal{M}} = \{p \in \mathcal{V};\ |\omega(p)\cdot k_j| < \lambda_r,\ j = 1,\dots,r, \\ \text{for at least one } K\text{-basis } \{k_1,\dots,k_r\} \text{ of } \mathcal{M}\}\ , \tag{2.3}$$

$\lambda_1,\dots,\lambda_n$ being a conveniently chosen sequence, with $\lambda_r \to 0$ for $\varepsilon \to 0$, and $\lambda_r > \lambda_{r-1}$. Finally, $\mathcal{V}$ is decomposed into resonant regions, or "blocks", defined by

$$\mathcal{B}_{\mathcal{M}} = \mathcal{Z}_{\mathcal{M}} \setminus \bigcup_{\substack{\mathcal{M}' \\ \dim\mathcal{M}' > \dim\mathcal{M}}} \mathcal{Z}_{\mathcal{M}'}\ . \tag{2.4}$$

Thus in $\mathcal{Z}_{\mathcal{M}}$, $\dim\mathcal{M} = r$, one has at least r independent resonances within λ_r, while in $\mathcal{B}_{\mathcal{M}}$ one has exactly r resonances within λ_r, further resonances being excluded even within $\lambda_{r+1} > \lambda_r$ (see fig. 3).

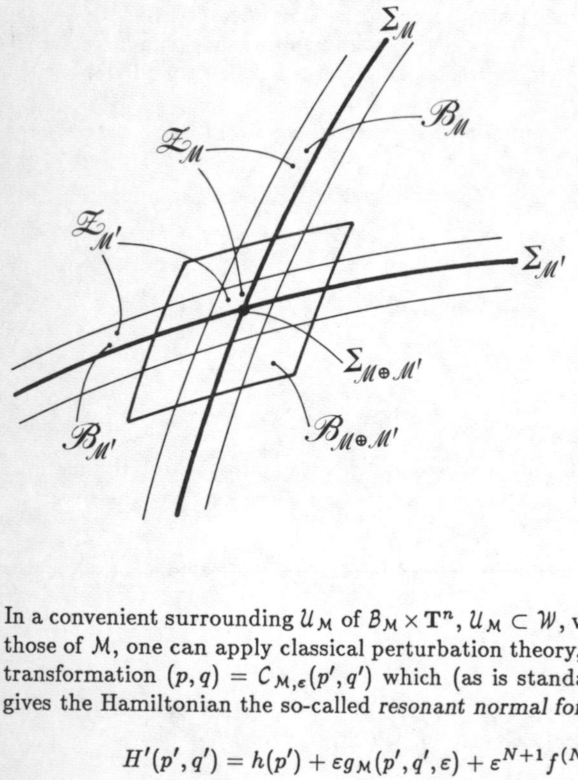

Fig. 2
Illustrating the decomposition of $\mathcal{V}$ into "Blocks".

c) In a convenient surrounding $\mathcal{U}_{\mathcal{M}}$ of $\mathcal{B}_{\mathcal{M}} \times \mathbf{T}^n$, $\mathcal{U}_{\mathcal{M}} \subset \mathcal{W}$, where all resonances are excluded but those of $\mathcal{M}$, one can apply classical perturbation theory, introducing an "adapted" canonical transformation $(p,q) = \mathcal{C}_{\mathcal{M},\varepsilon}(p',q')$ which (as is standard in classical perturbation theory) gives the Hamiltonian the so-called *resonant normal form up to order* N:

$$H'(p',q') = h(p') + \varepsilon g_{\mathcal{M}}(p',q',\varepsilon) + \varepsilon^{N+1} f^{(N+1)}(p',q',\varepsilon) + \mathcal{O}(\varepsilon^{+\infty})\ , \tag{2.6}$$

$g_{\mathcal{M}}$ being restricted by

$$g_{\mathcal{M}}(p',q',\varepsilon) = \sum_{k\in\mathcal{M}} g_k(p',\varepsilon) e^{ik\cdot q}\ . \tag{2.7}$$

Moreover, as it is non trivial (and non standard in classical perturbation theory) one proves that N can be consistently chosen to be a negative power of ε, so that, with our symbolic notation, we can write

$$H'(p',q',\varepsilon) = h(p') + \varepsilon g_{\mathcal{M}}(p',q',\varepsilon) + \mathcal{O}(\varepsilon^{+\infty})\ , \tag{2.8}$$

and disregard the last term. From this expression one immediately obtains a first constraint on the behavior of the actions: indeed, $\dot{p}'$ turns out to be linear combination of vectors of $\mathcal{M}$, and consequently $p'(t)$ is confined to a r-dimensional plain $\Pi_{\mathcal{M}}$ parallel to $\mathcal{M}$ (see fig. 3). In virtue of assumption ii), $\Pi_{\mathcal{M}}$ is easily seen to be transversal to the resonant surface $\Sigma_{\mathcal{M}}$.

d) It remains to be proven that a further mechanism of confinement keeps $p'(t)$ sufficiently close to the initial datum $p'(0)$ (for consistency with step c, one also needs that $p'(t)$ does not leave $\mathcal{U}_{\mathcal{M}}$). Such confinement [11,12] is simply provided by the conservation of energy: indeed, it follows from assumption ii) that $h(p')$, restricted to $\Pi_{\mathcal{M}}$, has a minimum in the point of intersection p^* of $\Pi_{\mathcal{M}}$ and $\Sigma_{\mathcal{M}}$, and consequently ($g_{\mathcal{M}}$ being bounded) $p'(t)$ cannot escape a convenient surrounding of p^*, of semidiameter approximately given by $\mathrm{dist}(p'(0), p^*)$. More complicated (but essentially equivalent) mechanisms of confinement can be found in ref.[9,10].

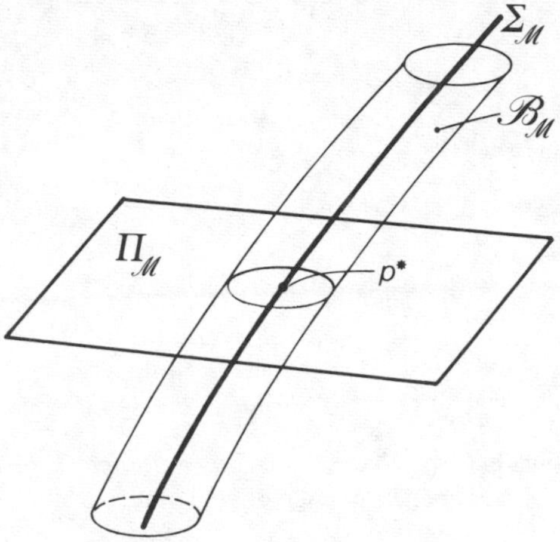

Fig. 3
Illustrating the mechanism of confinement in the action space.

As a comment to this scheme of proof, let us stress that everything is, conceptually, very simple: there are of course a lot of technical details, and some parameters must be chosen carefully, in order everything be consistent; but it is sufficient to reflect a moment, to recognize that, so to speak, Nekhoroshev theorem "must" exist.

For the precise expression of A, B, a, b, c, ε_0, as well as for other details, see ref.[12]. Unfortunately, as is typical in most theorems of classical perturbation theory, some of the above constants are very bad; in particular, their n-dependence is terrible. Much better results however can be obtained in special cases [13].

3. The dynamics inside resonances.

As we have seen, the motion of our system inside a resonance of order r (i.e., a resonance with a r-dimensional $\mathcal{M} \subset \mathbf{Z}^n$) is essentially r-dimensional. This fact is better stressed by introducing "more adapted" canonical coordinates, according to the following two steps:

a) One firstly performs a linear canonical transformation $p' = J^{-1}\tilde{p}$, $q' = J^T\tilde{q}$, with $\tilde{p} = (S, F) = (S_1, \ldots, S_r, F_1, \ldots, F_{n-r})$, $\tilde{q} = (\sigma, \varphi) = (\sigma_1, \ldots, \sigma_r, \varphi_1, \ldots, \varphi_{n-r})$; J is an integer matrix, with determinant one, which can be chosen in order to have $\tilde{\mathcal{M}} \equiv J\mathcal{M} = \{k \in \mathbf{Z}^n;\ k_{r+1}, \dots, k_n = 0\}$. The plane $\Pi_{\mathcal{M}}$ in fig. 3 appears then to be the plane F =constant, while the resonant surface $\Sigma_{\tilde{\mathcal{M}}} \equiv J\Sigma_{\mathcal{M}}$ is given by $\tilde{\omega}_j(\tilde{p}) = 0$, $j = 1, \dots, r$, and correspondingly, in the resonant zone $Z_{\tilde{\mathcal{M}}} \equiv JZ_{\mathcal{M}}$, the angles $\sigma_1, \dots, \sigma_r$ move slowly. As is usual in classical perturbation theory, (F, φ) and (S, σ) are called "fast" and "slow" variables respectively. After this change of variables, the Hamiltonian assumes the form

$$\tilde{H}(S, F, \sigma, \varphi, \varepsilon) = \tilde{h}(S, F) + \varepsilon\tilde{g}(S, F, \sigma, \varepsilon) + O(\varepsilon^{+\infty}) \; . \tag{3.1}$$

Notice that, coherently with the above considerations, the fast angles $\varphi_1, \dots, \varphi_{n-r}$do not appear in $\tilde{g}$, so that (as far as terms of order $\varepsilon^{+\infty}$ are disregarded) the actions $F_1, \dots, F_r$ are integrals of motions.

b) Let $S^*(F)$ be implicitely defined by $\tilde{\omega}_j(S^*(F), F) = 0$, $j = 1, \dots, r$; this means that, for any initial datum $(S_0, F_0) \in J\mathcal{B}_{\mathcal{M}}$, $(S^*(F_0), F_0)$ is the inverse image of p^* in fig. 3. Consider then this point to be the new origin in the action space, and perform a (trivial) rescaling of actions and time, according to

$$\begin{aligned} t &= \varepsilon^{-\frac{1}{2}}\hat{t} \\ F(t) &= F_0 + \varepsilon^{\frac{1}{2}}\hat{F}(\hat{t}) \\ S(t) &= S^*(F_0) + \varepsilon^{\frac{1}{2}}\hat{S}(\hat{t}) \\ \sigma(t) &= \hat{\sigma}(\hat{t}) \\ \varphi(t) &= \hat{\varphi}(\hat{t}) \end{aligned} \tag{3.2}$$

(for more details, see ref.[12]).

One has then the following

Proposition 3: *$(\hat{S}, \hat{F}, \hat{\sigma}, \hat{\varphi})$ are canonical coordinates, whose evolution, as function of the rescaled time $\hat{t}$, is given by a Hamiltonian (parametrized, as the change of coordinates, by F_0) of the form*

$$\begin{aligned} H_{F_0}(\hat{S}, \hat{F}, \hat{\sigma}, \hat{\varphi}, \varepsilon) = \varepsilon^{-\frac{1}{2}} h_{F_0}(\hat{F}) &+ \frac{1}{2} L_{F_0}(\hat{F})\hat{S} \cdot \hat{S} + V_{F_0}(\hat{\sigma}) \\ &+ \varepsilon^{\frac{1}{2}} W_{F_0}(\hat{S}, \hat{F}, \hat{\sigma}, \varepsilon) + O(\varepsilon^{+\infty}) \; , \end{aligned} \tag{3.3}$$

where the matrix L_{F_0} is symmetric and positive, while V_{F_0} turns out to be nothing but the average of the original perturbation f in Hamiltonian (1.1) on the fast angles.

For more details, see ref.[12].

Form (3.2) of the Hamiltonian allows us to identify three different time scales in the dynamics, which are well separated for small ε:

i) A "microscopic" time scale, $\hat{t} \sim \varepsilon^{\frac{1}{2}}$ $(t \sim 1)$, where only the fast angles move;

ii) A widely extended intermediate time scale $\varepsilon^{\frac{1}{2}} \ll \hat{t} \ll \varepsilon^{-\infty}$ $(1 \ll t \ll \varepsilon^{-\infty})$, where the fast actions are still "frozen", with regularly rotating fast angles, while on the same time (for no matter how small ε) the slow variables $(\hat{S}, \hat{\sigma})$ may have a non-trivial evolution. On this time scale $\hat{S}$ is bounded only by the conservation of energy, and $\hat{S}(\hat{t}) - \hat{S}(0)$ is expected to be of order 1 (correspondingly, $S(t) - S(0)$ will be of order $\varepsilon^{\frac{1}{2}}$).

iii) A "long" time scale $\hat{t} \sim \varepsilon^{-\infty}$ $(t \sim \varepsilon^{-\infty})$, where all of the degrees of freedom are non-trivially involved in the dynamics.

The most interesting time scale is the second one. On this time scale the evolution of the slow coordinates $(\hat{S}, \hat{\sigma})$ is given by an effective Hamiltonian with r degrees of freedom; the matrix L_{F_0}

being positive and symmetric, we can think that the effective Hamiltonian has the form

$$H_{\rm eff}(\hat{S},\hat{\sigma}) = \frac{1}{2}\sum_{j=1}^{r}\frac{\hat{S}_j^2}{I_j} + V_{\rm eff}(\hat{\sigma}) + O(\varepsilon^{\frac{1}{2}}) . \tag{3.4}$$

This Hamiltonian represents a chain of r strongly coupled rotators.

For $r \geq 2$ such a Hamiltonian will likely exhibit chaotic motions (an example of Hamiltonian of form (3.4) with a homoclinic point is provided in ref.[12]). We thus expect to have as a rule, inside a r-dimensional resonance, local chaotic motions involving just r degrees of freedom, while the remaining $n - r$ degrees of freedom are essentially free. Let us also notice that this implies a "freezing" of energy in the fast coordinates, for times of order $\varepsilon^{-\infty}$; as it is remarkable, such a possibility was outlined, in the early 1895, by Boltzmann [14], as a possible way to explain classicallly some phenomena, later considered to be quantum. For details and comments on this point, see Galgani's talk at this meeting, or ref.[15-17].

A good example of coexistence of local chaotic motions of some degrees of freedom, with simultaneous regular motions of the remaining degrees of freedom, is provided by a chain of weakly coupled rotators:

$$H(p,q) = \sum_{j=1}^{r}\frac{p_j^2}{2} - \varepsilon\sum_{j=1}^{n}\cos(q_j - q_{j-1}) \; ; \quad q_0 \equiv q_n . \tag{3.5}$$

Indeed, first of all the actions are here local variables in the chain; moreover, because of the short-range coupling, the resonances also have a local character (see ref.[18] for details): consequently, there is the nice possibility of observing localized chaotic motions, not propagating along the chain for a very long time, involving for example only three neighbouring rotators, the remaining ones being almost free. These motions were actually observed numerically in ref.[19].

REFERENCES

[1] H. Poincaré: *Les Méthodes Nouvelles de la Méchanique Céleste*, Vol. 3 (Gautier–Villars, Paris, 1899).

[2] G. Benettin, L. Galgani and A. Giorgilli: *Poincaré's Non-Existence Theorem and Classical Perturbation Theory in Nearly-Integrable Hamiltonian Systems*, preprint.

[3] A. N. Kolmogorov: *Dokl. Akad. Nauk. SSSR* **98**, 527 (1954); English translation in G. Casati and G. Ford (Editors): *Lecture Notes in Physics* No. 93 (Springer Verlag, Berlin, 1979).

[4] V. I. Arnold: *Usp. Mat. Nauk* **18**, 13 (1963) [*Russ. Math. Surv.* **18**, 9 (1963)]; *Usp. Mat. Nauk* **18**, 91 (1963) [*Russ. Math. Surv.* **18**, 85 (1963)].

[5] J. Moser: *Lectures on Hamiltonian Systems*, in *Mem. Am. Math. Soc.* No 81, 1 (1968).

[6] L. Chierchia and G. Gallavotti: *Nuovo Cimento B* **67**, 277 (1982).

[7] J. Poeschel: *Commun. Pure Appl. Math.* **35**, 653 (1982); *Celestial Mechanics* **28**, 133 (1982).

[8] V.I. Arnold: *Dokl. Akad. Nauk. SSSR* **156**, 9 (1964) [*Sov. Math. Dokl.* **6**, 581 (1964)].

[9] N. N. Nekhoroshev: *Usp. Mat. Nauk* **32**, (1977) [*Russ. Math. Surv.* **32**, 1 (1977)]; *Trudy Sem. Petrows.* No. 5, 5 (1979).

[10] G. Benettin, L. Galgani, A. Giorgilli: *A Proof of Nekhoroshev's Theorem for the Stability Times in Nearly Integrable Hamiltonian Systems*, to appear in *Celestial Mechanics* .

[11] G. Gallavotti: lectures given at the 1984 *Les Houches* Summer School, to be published.

[12] G. Benettin and G. Gallavotti: *Stability of Motions Near Resonances in Quasi Integrable Hamiltonian Systems*, submitted to *J. Stat. Phys.*.

[13] C. E. Wayne: *On the Elimination of Non-Resonant Harmonics and Bounds on Trajectories of a System of Weakly Coupled Rotators*, to appear in *J. Stat. Phys.*

[14] L. Boltzmann: *Nature* **51**, 413 (1985).

[15] G. Benettin, L. Galgani and A. Giorgilli: *Nature* **311**, 444 (1984).

[16] G. Benettin, L. Galgani and A. Giorgilli: *On the Persistence of Ordered Motions in Hamiltonian Systems and the Problem of Energy Partition*, preprint 1984.

[17] G. Benettin: *"Ordered and Chaotic Motions in Dynamical Systems with Many Degrees of Freedom"*, lectures given at the *International School of Physics* "E. FERMI" on *Computer Simulation of Molecular Dynamics*, Varenna (Italy) 1985.

[18] G. Benettin, L. Galgani, A. Giorgilli: *Numerical Investigation on a Chain of Weakly Coupled Rotators in the Light of Classical Perturbation Theory*, to appear in *Nuovo Cimento* **B**.

[19] G. Benettin, L. Galgani, A. Giorgilli: *Classical Perturbation Theory for a System of Weakly Coupled Rotators*, to appear in *Nuovo Cimento* **B**.

FLUCTUATIONS IN NUMBERS OF ENERGY LEVELS

by M.V.BERRY

In a recent paper (Berry 1985, hereinafter called I), I employed semiclassical techniques to obtain formulae for a particular statistic characterizing fluctuations of high-lying eigenvalues (excited energy levels) of quantal Hamiltonians. The statistic was the spectral rigidity $\Delta(L)$, defined for a set of levels $\{E_j\}$ in terms of the spectral staircase

$$\mathcal{N}(E) = \sum_{j=1} \Theta(E-E_j) \tag{1}$$

(Θ denotes the unit step function). $\Delta(L)$ is the least squares deviation of $\mathcal{N}(E)$ from a straight line over a stretch of L mean level spacings. My purpose here is to give a simplified outline of the rather difficult theoretical ideas developed in I, by applying them not to the rigidity but to a more elementary statistic, the <u>number variance</u> $\Sigma(L)$, which will now be defined.

A stretch of L mean level spacings, centred on energy E, extends from $E-L/2\langle d\rangle$ to $E+L/2\langle d\rangle$ where $\langle d\rangle$ is the mean level density

$$\langle d(E)\rangle \equiv \langle d\mathcal{N}(E)/dE\rangle. \tag{2}$$

Here and hereinafter, $\langle\ \rangle$ denotes semiclassical averaging, that is averaging over an energy range which is classically small but nevertheless large in comparison with h/T_{min} where T_{min} is the shortest classical orbit period (in the semiclassical limit $h\to 0$ this range contains many levels). The number of levels in this stretch is

$$n(L) = \mathcal{N}(E+L/2\langle d\rangle) - \mathcal{N}(E-L/2\langle d\rangle). \tag{3}$$

This fluctuates about the average value

$$\langle n(L)\rangle = L. \tag{4}$$

The number variance that we will calculate is the simplest measure of the size of the fluctuations:

$$\Sigma(L) \equiv \langle (n(L) - \langle n(L)\rangle)^2\rangle . \tag{5}$$

On the basis of general spectral theory for ensembles of matrices (Bohigas and Giannoni 1984) we expect to understand the function $\Sigma(L)$ in terms of three universality classes. The first class is the Poisson spectrum of uncorrelated levels (arising from matrices factorizable into independent blocks), for which, of course

$$\Sigma_{\text{poisson}}(L) = L \tag{6}$$

The second class is the Gaussian orthogonal ensemble (GOE) of real symmetric matrices with random elements, for which

$$\Sigma_{\text{GOE}}(L) \to \frac{2}{\pi^2}\left(\ell nL + \ell n2 + \gamma + 1 - \frac{\pi^2}{8}\right) \quad (L \gg 1) \tag{7}$$

where γ is Euler's constant 0.577... The third class is the Gaussian unitary ensemble (GUE) of complex Hermitian matrices with random elements, for which

$$\Sigma_{\text{GUE}}(L) \to \frac{1}{\pi^2}\left(\ell nL + \ell n2 + \gamma + 1\right) \quad (L \gg 1) \tag{8}$$

The aim is to derive these formulae not from random-matrix theory but from a semiclassical analysis based on the dynamics of the system (integrable or chaotic) as embodied in its classical closed orbits. The first main ingredient of the theory is the representation of the level density $d = d\mathcal{N}/dE$ as a sum over all distinct closed orbits at energy E (Gutzwiller 1978, Balian and Bloch 1972, Berry 1983, 1984):

$$d(E) = \langle d(E)\rangle + \sum_j A_j(E) \exp\{iS_j(E)/\hbar\}/\hbar^{1+\mu} \tag{9}$$

In this formula, j denotes all closed orbits, including multiple traversals (negative - i.e. retracings - as well as positive). The (real) amplitudes A_j will be discussed later, when we come to the other main ingredients of the theory. S_j is the classical action round the j'th orbit (with possible focusing corrections not important here). The exponent μ is $\frac{1}{2}(N-1)$ for classically integrable systems with N freedoms (closed orbits forming (N-1) parameter families filling tori), and zero for chaotic ones (isolated unstable closed orbits). (The discussion here will be restricted to the integrable and chaotic extremes.)

We begin by applying (9) to the number of levels n(L) defined by (3), restricting L so that the range $L/\langle d\rangle$ remains classically small. (This allows L to be very large, because $\langle d\rangle \sim h^{-N}$ and if for example we demand $L/\langle d\rangle < \mathcal{O}(h^{1/2})$ we need only $L < \mathcal{O}(h^{-(N-1/2)})$.) Then, using $\partial S_j/\partial E = T_j$ where T_j is the j'th orbit period we get

$$n(L) = \int_{E-L/2\langle d\rangle}^{E+L/2\langle d\rangle} dE'\, d(E')$$

$$= L + \sum_j A_j \exp\{iS_j/\hbar\} \int_{-L/2\langle d\rangle}^{L/2\langle d\rangle} d\varepsilon\, \exp\{i\varepsilon T_j/\hbar\}/\hbar^{\mu+1}$$

$$= L + (2/\hbar^{\mu}) \sum_j (A_j/T_j) \exp\{iS_j/\hbar\} \sin\{LT_j/2\hbar\langle d\rangle\} \qquad (10)$$

To find the variance we square and use semiclassical averaging to eliminate uncompensated action exponentials. This gives

$$\Sigma(L) = \frac{4}{\hbar^{2\mu}} \Big\langle \sum_{ij} \frac{A_j A_i}{T_j T_i} \exp\{\tfrac{i}{\hbar}(S_i - S_j)\} \sin\{\frac{LT_j}{2\hbar\langle d\rangle}\} \sin\{\frac{LT_i}{2\hbar\langle d\rangle}\}\Big\rangle \qquad (11)$$

As explained in I, it is not always permissable to invoke semiclassical averaging to eliminate the off-diagonal terms in the sum, but it is correct to replace T_i and T_j by their average $(T_i+T_j)/2$. Thus

$$\Sigma(L) = \frac{8}{h^{2\mu}} \int_0^{\infty} dT\, \phi(T) \sin^2\{LT/2\hbar\langle d\rangle\}/T^2 \qquad (12)$$

where

$$\phi(T) \equiv \Big\langle \sum_{ij}{}^{+} A_i A_j \exp\{i(S_i - S_j)/\hbar\}\, \delta\{T - (T_i+T_j)/2\}\Big\rangle \qquad (13)$$

the + on the summation denoting restriction to positive traversals $(T_j > 0)$. (In the corresponding formula for the rigidity $\Delta(L)$, $\sin^2$ in (12) is replaced by a more complicated function.)

The function $\phi(T)$ depends on the classical dynamics via the orbit action, periods and amplitudes. Provided $L \ll L_{max}$, where

$$L_{max} \equiv \hbar\langle d\rangle/T_{min} \sim h^{-(N-1)}, \qquad (14)$$

the integral in (12) depends on $\phi(T)$ for $T \gg T_{min}$, that is on <u>very long classical closed orbits.</u> (This exemplifies the general principle that spectral structure on a small energy scale ΔE depends on classical dynamics over long times $h/\Delta E$.) It is here that the second main ingredient enters the theory, in the form of classical sum rules obtained by Hannay and Ozorio de Almeida (1984) using the principle that very long orbits are uniformly distributed in phase space. Their sum rules concern the diagonal part ϕ_D of the sum (13), whose value results from two competing tendencies: The increasing density of orbits with period T (arising from the δ function factor) and their decreasing amplitudes A_j^2. They show that the result of this competition depends on classical dynamics, as follows:

$$\left.\begin{aligned}\phi_D(T) &\to \hbar^N\langle d\rangle/2\pi \quad &&\text{(integrable)}\\ &\to T/2\pi^2 &&\text{(chaotic with time-reversal symmetry)}\\ &\to T/4\pi^2 &&\text{(chaotic without time-reversal symmetry)}\end{aligned}\right\} \quad \text{(if } T\gg T_{min}) \qquad (15)$$

The factor 2 distinguishing $\phi_D(T)$ for chaotic systems with and without time-reversal symmetry has a very simple origin. With time--reversal symmetry, every closed orbit has a time-reversed counterpart with exactly the same action. These two orbits contribute coherently to the periodic orbit (9) and so their contribution to the squared function $\phi_D(T)$ is twice what it would be in the absence of this strict action degeneracy (i.e. $(A+A)^2=4A^2$ instead of the incoherent sum $A^2+A^2=2A^2$). This same factor 2 (and more generally, GOE rather than GUE statistics) will arise if the quantal Hamiltonian possesses any antiunitary symmetry, not necessarily time-reversal (Robnik and Berry 1985).

The three different T-dependences in (15) will lead to the three universality classes of variance (equations 6-8). It is necessary only to add the third main ingredient of the theory, which takes account of the fact that (13) cannot always be approximated by its diagonal part. The reason is that for very long times T, not just classically long but long in comparison with $\hbar\langle d\rangle \sim h^{-(N-1)}$, there can be pairs of distinct orbits with action differences S_i-S_j small in comparison with h, and these off-diagonal terms contribute coherently to (13). The third ingredient is a semiclassical sum rule (see I) giving $\phi(T)$ for such very long times and obtained from the condition that (9) must represent, asymptotically, a sequence of δ functions with the correct density $\langle d\rangle$. The rule is

$$\phi(T) \to \hbar^{2\mu+1}\langle d\rangle/2\pi \text{ if } T\gg h\langle d\rangle. \qquad (16)$$

It shows that the classical (diagonal) sum rule (15) adequately represents $\phi(T)$ only in the integrable case. For the two chaotic cases, (16) shows that the linear increase of $\phi_D(T)$ is eventully modified by the off-diagonal terms to give a $\phi(T)$ that saturates at a constant value.

Next it is convenient to define a scaled time

$$\tau \equiv T/2\pi\hbar\langle d\rangle, \tag{17}$$

and a scaled $\phi(T)$ by

$$K(\tau) \equiv 2\pi\phi(T)/\hbar^{2\mu+1}\langle d\rangle \tag{18}$$

Now the two sum rules (15) and (16) can be combined, to give

$$\left.\begin{array}{l} K(\tau) \simeq 1 \quad \text{(integrable)} \\ K(\tau) \simeq 2\tau \text{ if } \tau \ll 1 \text{ and } 1 \text{ if } \tau \gg 1 \text{ (chaotic with time-reversal symmetry)} \\ K(\tau) \simeq \tau \quad \text{if } \tau \ll 1 \text{ and } 1 \text{ if } \tau \gg 1 \text{ (chaotic without time-reversal symmetry)} \end{array}\right\} \quad (\text{if } \tau \gg T_{min}/2\pi\hbar\langle d\rangle) \tag{19}$$

Physically, $K(\tau)$ is the <u>spectral form factor</u>: apart from a δ function at the origin,

$$K(\tau)=\langle d\rangle^{-2}\int_{-\infty}^{\infty}dL\ \langle d(E-L/2\langle d\rangle)d(E+L/2\langle d\rangle)\rangle\exp\{2\pi iL\tau\}. \tag{20}$$

In terms of K, the <u>pair correlation</u> of the levels is

$$g(L) = 1-\frac{1}{\pi L}\int_0^{\infty} d\tau \sin\{2\pi L\tau\}K'(\tau) \tag{21}$$

For integrable systems, (19) gives $g(L)=1$, that is an uncorrelated (Poisson) level sequence, as already established by Berry and Tabor (1977).

Using (17) and (18) we obtain from (12) the number variance

$$\Sigma(L) = \frac{2}{\pi^2}\int_0^{\infty}\frac{d\tau}{\tau^2}\ K(\tau)\ \sin^2\{\tau L\tau\}. \tag{22}$$

For $L \ll L_{max}$ (equation 14), we can evaluate this integral by substituting the formulae (19), because then Σ is determined by τ-values exceeding $T_{min}/2\pi\hbar\langle d\rangle$ and so depends only on the long closed orbits.

For <u>integrable systems,</u> substituting $K=1$ gives exactly $\Sigma = L$, i.e.

(6), and this is the first (Poisson) of the three universality classes. For chaotic systems without time-reversal symmetry, splitting the integration range at $\tau = u$ where $0 \ll u \ll 1$ leads to

$$\Sigma(L) = \frac{2}{\pi^2} [\ell n L + \ell n(2\pi) + \gamma - \frac{1}{2} \int_0^\infty d\tau \ell n \frac{d}{d\tau} (K(\tau)/\tau)] \qquad (L \gg 1) \tag{23}$$

which apart from the constant term is exactly the result (7) for the second (GOE) universality class. For chaotic systems without time--reversal symmetry the same technique gives

$$\Sigma(L) = \frac{1}{\pi^2} [\ell n L + \ell n(2\pi) + \gamma - \int_0^\infty d\tau \ell n \tau \frac{d}{d\tau} (K(\tau)/\tau)] \qquad (L \gg 1) \tag{24}$$

which apart from the constant term is exactly the result (8) for the third (GUE) universality class. The constant terms in (23) and (24) depend on how $K(\tau)$ interpolates between the linear and constant τ-regimes given by the two sum rules, and cannot be obtained by any semiclassical argument known to me (the constants are of order unity and so do not contribute to the leading-order asymptotics of $\Sigma(L)$).

This completes the main task, which was to explain the semiclassical origin of the three universal classes (6-8) of number variance. But it is important to point out that universality breaks down for correlations between distant levels, that is when $L \simeq L_{max}$. Then (19) cannot be employed because short times $T \sim T_{min}$ contribute to (12) and then $\Sigma(T)$ does not depend solely on the very long orbits. For $L \gg L_{max}$, $\Sigma(L)$ saturates at the value

$$\Sigma_\infty = \frac{4}{\hbar^{2\mu}} \int_0^\infty dT \phi(T)/T^2 \tag{25}$$

For integrable systems, the diagonal sum for $\phi(T)$ gives Σ_∞ as a convergent sum over closed orbits:

$$\Sigma_\infty = \frac{4}{\hbar^{N-1}} \sum_j{}^{+} A_j^2/T_j^2 \tag{26}$$

For chaotic systems, extrapolation of the continuum results (24) gives the estimate

$$\Sigma_\infty \sim \frac{s}{\pi^2} \ell n(\hbar\langle d\rangle/T_{min}$$

where $s=2$ with time-reversal symmetry
$s=1$ without time-reversal symmetry . (27)

As discussed in I, a variety of numerical experiments support the theoretical ideas described here. In addition there have been two recent developments. Berry and Robnik (1985) have studied the change of spectral universality class when the time-reversal symmetry of particle motion in an enclosure with reflecting walls is broken by switching on a line of magnetic flux threading the enclosure ('Aharonov-Bohm quantum billiards'). And Seligman and Verbaarschot (1985) have studied spectral rigidity for motion in separable smooth potentials.

I thank Professor Oriol Bohigas for suggesting that $\Sigma(L)$ would be amenable to semiclassical analysis. No military agency supported this research.

REFERENCES

Balian,R and Bloch,C 1972 Ann.Phys.(N.Y) 69 76-160

Berry,M.V. 1983 Semiclassical Mechanics of Regular and Irregular Motion in Chaotic Behavior of Deterministic Systems (Les Houches Lectures XXXVI, eds G.Iooss, R.H.G.Helleman and R Stora (North-Holland: Amsterdam) pp171-271.

Berry,M.V., 1984 Structures in Semiclassical Spectra: a Question of Scale in The Wave-Particle Dualism (ed.S.Diner, D.Fargue, G.Lochak and F.Selleri) (D.Reidel: Dordrecht) 231-252.

Berry,M.V. 1985, Proc.Roy.Soc.Lond. A400 229-251 (ref.I of the text)

Berry,M.V. and Robnik,M 1985 J.Phys.A. In press.

Berry,M.V. and Tabor,M 1977 Proc.Roy.Soc.Lond. A356 375-394.

Bohigas,O and Giannoni,M.J. 1984 Chaotic Motion and Random-Matrix Theories in Mathematical and Computational Methods in Nuclear Physics eds J.S.Dehesa, J.M.G.Gomez and A.Polls, Lecture Notes in Physics 209 (Springer-Verlag, N.Y.) pp 1-99.

Gutzwiller, M.C. 1978 in 'Path Integrals and their Applications in Quantum, Statistical and Solid-State Physics' (eds. G.J.Papadopoulos and J.T.Devreese) Plenum,N.Y. 163-200.

Robnik,M and Berry, M.V. 1985 J.Phys.A. In press.

Seligman,T and Verbaarschot,J 1985. To be published.

A Poincaré-Birkhoff-type result in higher dimensions.

M. L. Bertotti*) and E. Zehnder**)

(*) I.S.A.S. - International School for Advanced Studies - Strada Costiera 11 - TRIESTE
Supported by Volkswagenstiftung and BiBoS

(**) Institut für Mathematik
Ruhr-Universität Bochum

Dedicated to the memory of
Charles C. Conley (1933 - 1984)

1. Introduction and result.

Every measure preserving homeomorphism of an annulus A in the plane $\mathbb{R}^2$, which twists the two boundaries in opposite directions possesses at least 2 fixed points in the interior of A.

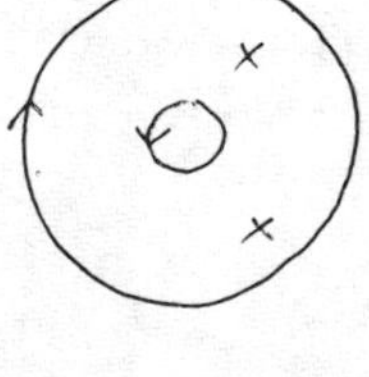

This statement, which of course is well known, was formulated by H. Poincaré in his search for periodic solutions in the restricted 3-body problem [3] and proved in (1913) by G. Birkhoff [4]. The statement is global in nature; it merely postulates some qualitative behaviour of the map at the boundary of A and none in its interior except for the measure preserving character, which of course cannot be dropped.

This is in sharp contrast to the recent investigations by J. Mather [5], S. Aubry [6] and others of measure preserving maps of the annulus A which are assumed to be monotone twist-maps. For a survey of the fascinating and intricate orbit structures of such maps which gives some insight into the crucial stability problem of Hamiltonian systems we point out J. Moser [7], [13].

It has to be said, that so far no higher dimensional analogue of the above Poincaré-Birkhoff fixed point theorem has been found. The recent global fixed point theorems [8], [9], [10] for symplectic maps on compact symplectic manifolds demonstrate however, that the phenomenon itself is not a two dimensional one.

In the following we shall describe a particular analogue for dynamical systems in higher dimensions; we consider a time dependent Hamiltonian system in $\mathbb{R}^{2n}$:

$$\dot{x} = J\nabla H(t,x), \quad (t,x) \in \mathbb{R} \times \mathbb{R}^{2n} \tag{1}$$

which we assume to be periodic in time:

$$H(t,x) = H(t+1,x). \tag{2}$$

The aim is to find forced oscillations, i.e. periodic solutions of period 1, postulating merely some qualitative behaviour of the system "at the outer boundary" i.e. the asymptotic behaviour as $|x| \to \infty$, and some qualitative behaviour "at the inner boundary" which will be the qualitative behaviour near a given forced oscillation, or near a given equilibrium point of the system. The forced oscillations correspond to the fixed points of the time 1 map of the flow of (1), which is a symplectic map of $\mathbb{R}^{2n}$. To be more precise we shall assume that the system behaves asymptotically like a linear Hamiltonian system:

$$(3) \qquad J\nabla H(t,x) = JA_\infty(t)x + o(|x|), \quad \text{as} \quad |x| \to \infty .$$

For the linear Hamiltonian system $\dot{y} = JA_\infty(t)y$ we require that it is non degenerate i.e. that it has no Floquet multiplier equal to 1. It is then described by its winding number $j_\infty \in \mathbb{Z}$, which is a Maslov-type index introduced in [11]. Under these qualitative assumptions the Hamiltonian system (1) possesses at least one forced oscillations, which we denote by x^*, $x^*(t) = x^*(t+1)$. If this periodic solution is non degenerate, it has a winding number which we denote by $j_o = j_o(x^*) \in \mathbb{Z}$, and which belongs to the linearized system along x^*. It is known that the system (1) possesses at least one additional forced oscillation provided that $j_o \neq j_\infty$, [11]. In analogy to the Poincaré-Birkhoff fixed point theorem we shall show that (1) possesses at least 2 additional forced oscillations provided $|j_o - j_\infty| \geq 2n+1$.

<u>THEOREM:</u> *Let*

$$\dot{x} = J\nabla H(t,x) \text{ and } (t,x) \in \mathbb{R} \times \mathbb{R}^{2n}, \ (n \geq 2)$$

be periodic in time t *with period* 1, *i.e.* $H(t+1,x) = H(t,x)$. *Assume* $H \in C^2$ *and* $\sup|H_{xx}(t,x)| < \infty$ *and assume the system to be asymptotically linear:*

$$J\nabla H(t,x) = JA_\infty(t)x + o(|x|), \text{ as } |x| \to \infty$$

uniformly in t, *with a continuous and symmetric* $A_\infty(t) = A_\infty(t+1)$. *Assume the linear system* $\dot{y} = JA_\infty(t)y$ *to be nondegenerate and denote its winding number by* $j_\infty \in \mathbb{Z}$.

Then (1) *possesses at least one forced oscillation* $x^*(t) = x^*(t+1)$. *Assume it is nondegenerate and denote its winding number by* $j_o \in \mathbb{Z}$. *Then there is an additional forced oscillation provided* $j_o \neq j_\infty$. *If, moreover*

(4) $$|j_\infty - j_o| > \dim M+1,$$

with $M = \mathbb{R}^{2n}$, *then there are at least 2 additional forced oscillations.*

It should be pointed out that for the 2 additional forced oscillations found no nondegeneracy conditions are required. In contrast the system (1) always possesses ≥ 3 forced oscillations in case $j_o \neq j_\infty$, provided one postulates a priori that all the forced oscillations are nondegenerate [11]. The proof of the theorem, which we shall sketch below is based on a Morse-theory for forced oscillations [11] and uses a recent argument we learned from V. Coti-Zelati [1].

In the special case in which one knows a priori the behaviour of the system at an equilibrium point, which can assumed to be x = o, (the "inner boundary") one concludes from the theorem the

<u>COROLLARY:</u> *Let* H *be as in the theorem and*

$$J\nabla H(t,x) = JA_\infty(t)x + o(|x|), \text{ as } |x| \to \infty$$

$$J\nabla H(t,x) = JA_o(t)x + o(|x|), \text{ as } |x| \to o$$

uniformly in t. *Assume the two linear systems* $\dot{y} = JA_\infty(t)y$ *and* $\dot{y} = JA_o(t)y$ *are nondegenerate and denote their winding numbers by* j_∞ *and* $j_o \in \mathbb{Z}$.

Then if $j_o \neq j_\infty$, *the system* (1) *possesses at least* 1 *nontrivial* (*i.e.* $x \neq o$) *forced oscillation. If*

$$|j_o - j_\infty| > \dim M + 1$$

then (1) *possesses at least* 2 *nontrivial forced oscillations.*

The statement extends a result in [11]. It is global in nature and concludes 2 forced oscillations if the two linear systems at o and at ∞ are qualitatively different from each other. This difference is measured merely by the winding number of a linear system, which is a homotopy invariant.

2. Proof of the theorem.

Recall first the old and well known variational principle in Hamiltonian systems for which the critical points are the periodic solutions: define on the loopspace $\Omega(M) = H^1(S^1,M)$, $M = \mathbb{R}^{2n}$, the functional

$$f(x) := \int_o^1 \{\frac{1}{2} \langle x, J\dot{x}\rangle + H(t,x(t))\}dt, \; x \in \Omega.$$

Its critical points are the forced oscillations we are looking for. This variational principle is degenerate in the sense that it is bounded neither from below now from above so that

Ljusternik-Schnirelman-variational techniques or Morse-theory do not apply directly. In fact the Morse indices of possible critical points of f are infinite, so that these critical points are at first sight topologically invisible.

However, it turns out that in our case all the critical points of f are contained in a finite dimensional submanifold. Due to the boundedness of the Hessian of H the problem of finding critical points of f on Ω can be reduced, by means of a global Ljapunov-Schmidt reduction procedure, to the equivalent problem of finding critical points of a related functional g on a finite dimensional submanifold $\tilde{\Omega} \subset \Omega(M)$, with $\dim \tilde{\Omega} = 2N$, [11]. In order to find critical points of g one then studies the gradient flow

(5) $$\frac{d}{ds} x = \nabla g(x), \quad x \in \tilde{\Omega} ,$$

whose equilibrium points clearly are the required critical points. From the assumption that the Hamiltonian system "at ∞" $\dot{y} = JA_{\infty}(t)y$ is nondegenerate one can deduce, [11] that the set of bounded orbits of (5) in $\tilde{\Omega}$, which we denote by S, is in fact compact. Therefore it possesses a Conley-index h(S), which is the homotopy-type of a pointed topological space, [14]. If can, moreover, be computed [11] to be a pointed sphere of dimension $N-j_{\infty}$:

(6) $$h(S) = [\dot{S}^{b}] \text{ and } b = N-j_{\infty} > o.$$

Hence the index of S is related to the winding number of the asymptotic system at ∞.

If the gradient system (5) has only finitely many critical points, say $x_1,\dots,x_k$, these critical points constitute a Morse-decomposition of S, so that we have the Morse-equation [11]:

$$(7) \qquad \sum_{j=1}^{k} p(t,h(\{x_j\})) = p(t,h(S)) + (1+t)\ Q(t),$$

where $p(t,X) = \sum_{q=o}^{\infty} \dim H_q(X)\cdot t^q$ denotes the Poincaré-polynomial of a space X, and where Q(t) is a polynomial having nonnegative integer coefficients. Since, in view of (6) we have $p(t,h(S)) = t^b$ we conclude from (7) that there is at least one critical point, say x^*. We assume now that x^* corresponds to a nondegenerate forced oscillation, which then has a winding number $j_o \in \mathbb{Z}$. The Conley-index $h(\{x^*\})$ is then related to the winding-number by [11]:

$$(8) \qquad h(\{x^*\}) = [\dot{S}^a] \text{ and } a = N - j_o > o,$$

so that $p(t,h\{x^*\}) = t^a$. After these preliminaries we come to the proof of the last statement of the Theorem.

We shall assume, by contradiction, that there are only two critical points of g, namely x^*, which we have already found, and an additional one, which we denote by y^*, and which necessarily is a degenerate critical point. In view of (6), (7) and (8) the Morse equation for S is then given by

$$(9) \qquad t^a + p(t) = t^b + (1+t)\ Q(t)$$

$$\underline{\text{with}}\ a = N - j_o\ \underline{\text{and}}\ b = N - j_\infty,$$

where $p(t) = p(t,h\{y^*\})$ is the Poincaré-polynomial of the Conley-index $h(\{y^*\}$ of the degenerate critical point y^*.

a) Assume:

(10) $$j_\infty - j_o \equiv a-b > \dim M+1,$$

and denote by λ the dimension of the maximal subspace on which the Hessian of g at the critical point y^*, i.e. $d^2g(y^*)$, is negative. We claim

(11) $$p(t) = t^\lambda p_1(t) \text{ \underline{and} degree } (p_1) \leq \dim M.$$

In fact, in any given isolated neighborhood of y^* we can replace the function g by a function having only nondegenerate critical points $y_1,\dots,y_k$ and such that the local Conley-index of the maximal invariant set still is equal to $h(\{y^*\})$. Observe that for a critical point y of g:

$$\dim(\text{kernel } d^2g(y)) \leq \dim M.$$

Indeed, the elements of the kernel are periodic solutions of a first order system of linear ordinary differential equations in M. Consequently the Morse-indices of the nondegenerate critical points y_j are given by $\mu(y_j) = \lambda + c_j$, for an integer $c_j \leq \dim M$, and the representation (11) for $p(t,h(\{y^*\})$ is proved. We next claim that $\lambda \leq b$. In fact if $\lambda > b$, then by (11) the polynomial $p(t)$ does not contain the monomial t^b and therefore the Morse-equation (9) is not satisfied. Therefore $\lambda \leq b$, but then by assmption (10)

$$\lambda + \dim M \leq b + \dim M < a-1.$$

Consequently the left hand side of the Morse-equation (9) contains neither t^{a-1} nor t^{a+1}. But in view of the term $(1+t)\,Q(t)$

one of these monomials occurs on the right hand side of (9) and we arive at a contradiction.

b) Assume now

(12) $$b-a > \dim M+1 .$$

Then $\lambda \leq a+1$. Indeed if $\lambda > a+1$ the left hand side of (9) does not contain the monomials t^{a+1} and t^{a-1} contradicting (9) and hence $\lambda \leq a+1$; and by (12)

$$\lambda + \dim M \leq a + \dim M + 1 < b,$$

so that in view of (11) the left hand side of (9) does not contain the monomial t^b, again a contradiction to the Morse equation.

Summarizing, the assumption that x^* and y^* are the only critical points, together with the assumption (4) lead to a contradiction with the Morse equation. Consequently the Morse decomposition of S possesses at least one additional critical point of g, which corresponds to the third forced oscillation claimed in the theorem. This finishes the outline of the proof.

For a more detailled proof of the theorem and for additional statements we refer to [2]. For a recent survey on related results concerning periodic solutions of Hamiltonian equations and global fixed point theorems for symplectic diffeomorphisms on compact manifolds we refer to [12].

References:

[1] V. Coti-Zelati: "Perturbations of second order Hamiltonian systems via Morse-theory", Bull. U.M.I., Analisi Functionale e Applicazioni, Serie VI, Vol. IV-C, N. 1, 1985, pp. 307-322.

[2] M.L. Bertotti: "Forced oscillations of asymptotically linear Hamiltonian systems", to appear.

[3] H. Poincaré: "Sur un théorème de Géométrie", Rend. Circolo Mat. Palermo 33 (1912), 375-407.

[4] G.D. Birkhoff: The restricted problem of three bodies, Rend. Circolo mat. Palermo 39 (1915), 265-334.

[5] J. Mather: Existence of quasi-periodic orbits for twist homeomorphisms of the annulus, Topology 21, 1982, 457-467.

[6] S. Aubry / P.Y. Le Daeron: "The discrete Frenkel-Kontorova model and its extensions I", Physica 8D, 381-422 (1983).

[7] J. Moser: "Recent Developments in the theory of Hamiltonian systems", ETH - Zürich, Forschungsinstitut für Mathematik (1985).

[8] C.C. Conley / E. Zehnder: The Birkhoff-Lewis fixed point theorem and a conjecture of V.I. Arnold, Invent. math. 73 (1983), 33-49.

[9] A. Floer: Proof of the Arnold Conjecture for surfaces and generalizations for certain Kähler-manifolds, RUB, Bochum (1984), erscheint in Indiana J. of Math.

[10] J.C. Sikorav: Points fixes d'un symplectomorphisme homologue de'identité; Announcement, Paris (1984).

[11] C.C. Conley / E. Zehnder: Morse type index theory for flows and periodic solutions for Hamiltonian equations, Comm. Pure and Appl. Math., Vol. XXXVII, (1984), 207-253.

[12] E. Zehnder: Periodische Lösungen von Hamilton'schen Systemen, Preprint 58 (1985), RUB Bochum.

[13] J. Moser: Break down of stability, ETH - Zürich, Forschungsinstitut für Mathematik (1985).

[14] C.C. Conley: Isolated invariant sets and the Morse index, CBMS Regional Conf. Series in Math. 38 (1978), AMS Providence, R.I.

STOCHASTIC JUMP PROCESSES ASSOCIATED WITH DIRAC EQUATION

Ph. BLANCHARD[1]   Ph. COMBE[2]

M. SIRUGUE[3]   M. SIRUGUE-COLLIN[4]

1 Fakultät für Physik, Universität Bielefeld and Research Center Bielefeld-Bochum - Stochastics (BIBOS) D4800 Bielefeld 1, F.R. Germany.

2 BIBOS (On leave of absence from CPT-CNRS and Université d'Aix-Marseille II, France).

3 CPT - CNRS, Centre de Luminy - Case 907 - F13288 Marseille, France.

4 CPT - CNRS and Université de Provence, Marseille, France.

Account of a Talk given at the 1st Ascona-Como International Conference : Stochastics Processes in Classical and Quantum Systems - 24-29 June 1985.

Abstract :We study the stochastic jump processes associated with the Dirac equation where the space derivatives are replaced by discrete approximations.

1 . INTRODUCTION

Recently there has been a revival of interest for the probabilistic representation of the solution of Dirac equation. See [1] for references. The problem is not only aesthetical but is connected with practical ones as for instance the estimate of energy levels of a spin one half relativistic particle in an external electromagnetic field. A more promising application would be field theory involving fermions.

As far as the first problem is concerned the situation is clear in two space time dimensions. The problem was already solved by Feynman and Hibbs [2] and by Gaveau et al. [3] in absence of external electromagnetic field, and in [1] in the general case. In three and four space time dimensions the situation is far from being satisfactory. Even in the free case it is not possible to give to the Dirac equation a probabilistic meaning as in the two space time case. However one can perform transformations on the solution e.g. Fourier transformation to recover an equation whose probabilistic meaning is clear, see eq. [4] .Another possibility which has many appealing features for explicit computation is to discretize the space derivatives by finite differences, as it was suggested and studied in [5] .

The purpose of this paper is to concentrate on this approach. Namely to give a simple probabilistic interpretation of the Dirac equation in two, three and four space time dimension with space derivative replaced by finite difference approximation. Using simple stochastic process it is possible to give a representation of the solution in term of expectation w.r.t. this process . Besides its own interest let us observe that this approach is certainly an important step in the treatment of more fundamental theories as the coupling of Fermi fields with gauge fields. Indeed for the sake of simplicity we do not discuss non abelian gauge fields but it is clear that the formalism developed here extends without difficulty to this case.

The general strategy consists after a time reversal to interpret the Dirac Hamiltonian as a Markov generator. This is not possible in general in $\mathbb{R}^d$ where d is the dimension of space. However if one enlarges in a suitable way the space, it appears as the restriction on $\mathbb{R}^d$ of a Markov generator in $\mathbb{R}^{d'}$ $d' > d$. As an example let us consider the Schrödinger equation for imaginary time :

$$\frac{\partial \psi(x,t)}{\partial t} = -\frac{1}{2}\Delta_x \psi(x,t) + V(x)\psi(x,t) \qquad x \in \mathbb{R}^d \tag{1.1}$$

with initial condition viz

$$\lim_{t\to 0} \psi(x,t) = \psi_0(x) \tag{1.2}$$

Let us consider the function

$$(1.3)\qquad \phi(x,y,t) = e^{-\frac{1}{2}t}\, e^{-y}\, \psi(x,t) \qquad y \in \mathbb{R}$$

which is solution of the equation

$$(1.4)\qquad \frac{\partial}{\partial t}\phi(x,y,t) = -\frac{1}{2}\Delta_{xy}\,\phi(x,y,t) - V(x)\frac{\partial}{\partial y}\phi(x,y,t)$$

Assuming that V is sufficiently smooth then the right hand side of equation (1.4) is the generator of a Markov diffusion process in $\mathbb{R}^{d+1}$

$$(1.5)\qquad X_t = x + W_t$$

$$(1.6)\qquad Y_t = y - \int_0^t V(x+W_\tau)\,d\tau + W'_t$$

W and W' being two standard independent Brownian motions. Taking into account the explicit value of $\phi(x,y,t)_{t=T}$ one rederives the Feynman Kac formula for the solution of equation (1.1) viz

$$(1.7)\qquad \psi(x,t) = \mathbb{E}\left\{\exp\left[-\int_0^t V(x+W_\tau)\,d\tau\right]\psi_0(x+W_t)\right\}$$

For the Dirac equation there is no diffusion process involved, only jump processes, but the general strategy is very similar.

Before going into the details of each case let us fix the notations. Dirac equation in $d+1$ space time dimensions $(d=1,2,3)$ is written as

$$(1.8)\qquad \frac{\partial\psi}{\partial t}(x,t) = -i\frac{mc^2}{\hbar}\beta\,\psi(x,t) - c\sum_{i=1}^{d}\alpha^i\frac{\partial}{\partial x^i}\psi(x,t) + \frac{iq}{\hbar}\left\{\sum_{i=1}^{d} c A_i(x,t)\,\alpha^i\psi(x,t) - V(x,t)\,\psi(x,t)\right\}$$

ψ is an n component spinor; $n=2$ for $d=1,2$ and $n=4$ for $d=3$. m is the mass of the particle, c the velocity of light, $\hbar$ the Planck's constant divided by 2π and q the charge of the particle.
$\{A_i(x,t)\}_{i=1,\dots,d}$ are the components of the vector potential whereas V is the scalar potential, β and $\{\alpha^i\}_{i=1\dots n}$ are hermitean $n\times n$ anticommuting matrices of square one.

In the spirit of [6] we want to treat the (discrete) spin variables on the same footing as the space variables. Consequently for a two component spinor whose components are in a given basis $\{\Psi_i\}_{i=1,2}$ we introduce a function $\tilde{\Psi}$ of u such that

(1.9) $$\tilde{\Psi}(u) = \frac{1}{2}(\Psi_1 + \Psi_2) + \frac{1}{2}(\Psi_1 - \Psi_2)\cos\left(\frac{\pi}{2}(1-u)\right)$$

So that $\tilde{\Psi}(u=1) = \Psi_1$, $\tilde{\Psi}(u=-1) = \Psi_2$.

On this vector space of periodic functions of u of period 4 let us define the following operators

(1.10) $$(\sigma^1 \tilde{\Psi})(u) = \tilde{\Psi}(u+2)$$

(1.11) $$(\sigma^2 \tilde{\Psi})(u) = -i\cos\left(\frac{\pi}{2}(1-u)\right)\tilde{\Psi}(u+2)$$

(1.12) $$(\sigma^3 \tilde{\Psi})(u) = \cos\left(\frac{\pi}{2}(1-u)\right)\tilde{\Psi}(u)$$

They anticommute and define a representation of the Pauli spin matrices on this vector space . Consequently for the α's and β which appear in the Dirac equation one can choose for the two space time dimension case any two of the Pauli matrices and for the three space time dimension case the three Pauli matrices. Which choice is made is not very important. Indeed it amounts to an unitary transformation which is easily described in this formalism (see below). In the four dimensional case, along the same lines as previously one introduces two variables u and v and identifying the four dimensional spinor space to a tensor product of two two-dimensional spaces one can choose for the α's and β matrices

(1.13) $$\beta = \sigma^1 \otimes 1$$

(1.14) $$\alpha^i = \sigma^3 \otimes \sigma^i$$

A typical difficulty to give to the right hand side of equation (1.8) a probabilistic meaning is that it involves terms of the form : $\partial_{x^i} f(x,u+2)$. These terms are replaced by discrete approximation viz

(1.15) $$\partial_{x_i} f(x,u+2) = \lim_{\varepsilon \downarrow 0} \varepsilon^{-1}\left(f(x_i+\varepsilon, u+2) - f(x_i, u+2)\right)$$

in such a way that the right hand side of equation (1.8) has the canonical form of a Markov generator viz

$$(1.16)\qquad (Af)(x) = \sum_{i=1}^{k} a^i(x) \frac{\partial}{\partial x_i} f(x) + \int_{\mathbb{R}^k} d\mu(y) \{ f(x + c(x,y)) - f(x) \}$$

where a and c are sufficiently smooth functions and μ is a positive bounded measure. Then according to general results (see e.g. [7]) one has the

Theorem : the solution f(x,t) $t \leq T$ of the integro-differential equation

$$(1.17)\qquad \frac{\partial f}{\partial t}(x,t) + (Af)(x,t) = 0$$

such that $\lim_{t \uparrow T} f(x,t) = f_0(x)$ has the representation :

$$(1.18)\qquad f(x,t) = \mathbb{E}\{ f_0(X_t(T)) \}$$

$X_t(s)$ $t \leq s \leq T$ being a stochastic process solution of the stochastic differential equation :

$$(1.19)\qquad X_t(s) = x + \int_t^s a(X_t(\tau))\, d\tau + \int_t^s \int_{\mathbb{R}^k} c(X_t(\tau), u)\, \nu(d\tau, du)$$

where $\nu(d\tau, du)$ is a random Poisson measure such that

$$(1.20)\qquad \nu([0,t[, [a,b]) = N_t^{[a,b]}$$

is a Poisson process with intensity $\mu([a,b])$. An important property of $N_t^{[a,b]}$ is that if $[a,b]$ and $[c,d]$ are disjoint the corresponding processes are independent.

The above mentioned difficulties are not present in the two space time dimensional case. We have used the theorem to study the 2-dimensional Dirac equation coupled to an electromagnetic field (see e.g. [1]).

Nevertheless for the sake of completeness let us derive the probabilistic representation of the two dimensional Dirac equation using another representation of the α, β matrices exhibiting the unitary transformation associated with rotation in spin space, and in this way the equivalence of the choice of the representation. Then the Dirac equation reads :

$$\frac{\partial \psi_t}{\partial t}(x,\sigma) = -\frac{mc^2}{\hbar}\sigma \psi_t(x,-\sigma) - c\sigma \frac{\partial}{\partial x}\psi_t(x,\sigma) - \frac{iq}{\hbar}\left(A^0(x) - c\sigma A'(x)\right)\psi_t(x,\sigma) \tag{1.21}$$

Observe that with respect to [1] here we choose $\beta = \sigma_2$, $\alpha = \sigma_3$. If one remarks that :

$$-\sigma = \exp\left\{ i\frac{\pi}{2}(1+\sigma)\right\} \tag{1.22}$$

enlarging the number of variables viz

$$\Phi_t(x,\sigma,\alpha) = e^{\frac{mc^2}{\hbar}(t-T) + i\alpha}\, \psi_{T-t}(x,\sigma) \tag{1.23}$$

allows to rewrite an equation for $\tilde{\Phi}$ viz

$$\begin{aligned}\frac{\partial \tilde{\Phi}_t}{\partial t}(x,u,\alpha) &+ \frac{mc^2}{\hbar}\left[\tilde{\Phi}_t\left(x, u+2, \alpha + \frac{\pi}{2}\left(1+\cos\left(\frac{\pi}{2}(1-u)\right)\right)\right)\right. \\ &\left. - \tilde{\Phi}_t(x,u,\alpha)\right] - c\cos\left(\frac{\pi}{2}(1-u)\right)\frac{\partial}{\partial x}\tilde{\Phi}_t(x,u,\alpha) \\ &- \frac{q}{\hbar}\left(A^0(x) - c\cos\left(\frac{\pi}{2}(1-u)\right)A'(x)\right)\frac{\partial}{\partial \alpha}\tilde{\Phi}_t(x,u,\alpha)\end{aligned} \tag{1.24}$$

We introduce the processes

$$X_t(s) = x - c\sigma\int_t^s (-1)^{N_\tau - N_t}\, d\tau \tag{1.25}$$

$$U_t(s) = u + 2(N_s - N_t) \tag{1.26}$$

$$\begin{aligned}A_t(s) = \alpha &- \frac{q}{\hbar}\int_t^s d\tau\left\{A^0(X_t(\tau)) - c\sigma(-1)^{(N_\tau - N_t)}A'(X_t(\tau))\right\} \\ &+ \frac{\pi}{2}(N_s - N_t) + \frac{\pi}{2}\sigma\int_t^s (-1)^{(N_\tau - N_t)}\, dN_\tau\end{aligned} \tag{1.27}$$

The stochastic integral which appears in the last expression can be simplified indeed

$$\int_0^t (-1)^{N_\tau}\, dN_\tau = \frac{1}{2}\left(1 - (-1)^{N_t}\right) \tag{1.29}$$

a formula which can be deduced by generalized Ito Calculus.
Collecting these results one can write the solution of equation (2.23) as :

(1.30) $$\psi_t(x,\sigma) = e^{\frac{mc^2}{\hbar}t}\, \mathbb{E}\Big\{ (-i)^{N_t} \cdot$$

$$\cdot \exp\Big[-\frac{iq}{\hbar}\int_0^t d\tau \big[A^0(X_0(\tau)) - \sigma(-1)^{N_\tau} c A^1(X_0(\tau))\big]\Big]$$

$$\cdot \exp\Big[-i\frac{\pi}{4}\sigma\big(1-(-1)^{N_t}\big)\Big]\, \psi_0\big(X_0(t), \sigma(-1)^{N_t}\big)\Big\}$$

It is fairly easy to recognize that the factor $\exp(-i\frac{\pi}{4}\sigma)\exp(i\frac{\pi}{4}\sigma(-1)^{N_t})$ corresponds to a conjugacy in the spin space by the unitary operator $\exp(-i\frac{\pi}{4}\sigma^3)$. However this is precisely the unitary transformation which exchanges σ^1 and σ^2. With this observation, the formula corresponding to the choice $\beta = \sigma^1$, $\alpha = \sigma^3$ reads :

(1.31) $$\psi_t(x,\sigma) = e^{\frac{mc^2}{\hbar}t}\, \mathbb{E}\Big\{ (-i)^{N_t}\, \psi_0\big(X_0(t), \sigma(-1)^{N_t}\big) \cdot$$

$$\exp\Big[-\frac{iq}{\hbar}\int_0^t d\tau \big[A^0(X_0(\tau)) - c\sigma(-1)^{N_\tau} A^1(X_0(\tau))\big]\Big]$$

which is precisely the formula given in [1] .

2 . THE TWO SPACE TIME DISCRETIZED DIRAC EQUATION

We start with a rather simple example which is interesting in itself. Namely let us consider the two dimensional Dirac equation with time independent external electromagnetic field.

(2.1) $$\frac{\partial \psi_t}{\partial t}(x,\sigma) = -\frac{i\, mc^2}{\hbar}\psi_t(x,-\sigma) - c\sigma\frac{\partial}{\partial x}\psi_t(x,\sigma) - \frac{i\,q}{\hbar}\left(A^0(x) - c\sigma A^1(x)\right)\psi_t(x,\sigma)$$

$$x \in \mathbb{R}$$

σ is a dichotomic variable $\sigma = \pm 1$ and for convenience we choosed $\beta = \sigma^1$ and $\alpha = \sigma^3$. First one reverses the time hence writing for some $T > 0$

(2.2) $$\psi_t(x,\sigma) = \varphi_{T-t}(x,\sigma)$$

Furthermore we define for $\alpha \in \mathbb{R}$

(2.3) $$\Phi(x,\sigma,\alpha,T-t) = \exp\left(-\frac{mc^2}{\hbar}t - i\alpha\right)\varphi_{T-t}(x,\sigma)$$

The corresponding function $\tilde{\Phi}$ of u satisfies after discretization :

(2.4) $$\frac{\partial \tilde{\Phi}}{\partial t}(x,u,\alpha,t) + \frac{mc^2}{\hbar}\left(\tilde{\Phi}(x,u+2,\alpha+\tfrac{\pi}{2},t) - \tilde{\Phi}(x,u,\alpha\, t)\right)$$
$$+\frac{1}{\varepsilon}\left(\tilde{\Phi}(x-\varepsilon c\cos(\tfrac{\pi}{2}(1-u)),u,\alpha,t) - \tilde{\Phi}(x,u,\alpha,t)\right)$$
$$+\frac{q}{\hbar}\left(A^0(x) - c\cos(\tfrac{\pi}{2}(1-u))A^1(x)\right)\frac{\partial}{\partial\alpha}\tilde{\Phi}(x,u,\alpha,t) = 0$$

To make contact with the general theory alluded in the previous section one introduces a function c from R^4 to R^3 such that

(2.5) $$c(x,u,\alpha,v=1) = (0,2,\tfrac{\pi}{2})$$

(2.6) $$c(x,u,\alpha,v=-1) = (-\varepsilon c\cos(\tfrac{\pi}{2}(1-u)),0,0)$$

and the corresponding measure

$$\mu = \frac{mc^2}{\hbar}\,\delta_{+1} + \frac{1}{\varepsilon}\,\delta_{-1} \tag{2.7}$$

to which corresponds two independent Poisson processes

$$dN_t^+ = \nu(dt, \{+1\}) \tag{2.8}$$

$$dN_t^- = \nu(dt, \{-1\}) \tag{2.9}$$

with intensities respectively $\frac{mc^2}{\hbar}$ and $\frac{1}{\varepsilon}$.
Applying the theorem of the last section one has to consider the process

$$X_t(s) = x - \varepsilon c \int_t^s \cos\left(\frac{\pi}{2}(1 - U_t(\tau)\right) dN_\tau^- \tag{2.10}$$

$$U_t(s) = u + 2(N_s^+ - N_t^+)$$

$$A_t(s) = \alpha + \frac{\pi}{2}(N_s^+ - N_t^+)$$

$$+ \frac{q}{\hbar}\int_t^s d\tau \left\{ A^0(X_t(\tau) - c\cos\left(\frac{\pi}{2}(1 - U_t(\tau)\right) A'(X_t(\tau)) \right\}$$

The above formula can be simplified if one remarks that N_t^+ has integer values :

$$\cos\left(\frac{\pi}{2}(1 - U_t(s))\right) = \cos\left(\frac{\pi}{2}(1 - u)\right)(-1)^{(N_s^+ - N_t^+)} \tag{2.13}$$

Then turning back to the original problem choosing t=0 and writing t for T , one has the following representation for the solution of equation (2.1) once the space derivative is replaced by its discrete approximation :

$$\psi_t^\varepsilon(x, \sigma) = \exp\left(\frac{mc^2}{\hbar}t\right) \mathbb{E}\left\{ (-i)^{N_t^+}\, \psi_0\left(X_0(t), \sigma(-1)^{N_t^+}\right) \cdot \right. \tag{2.14}$$

$$\left. \cdot \exp\left[-\frac{iq}{\hbar}\int_t^s d\tau \left[A^0(X_0(\tau)) - c\sigma(-1)^{N_\tau^+} A'(X_0(\tau))\right]\right] \right\}$$

In the previous formula N_t^+ is independent of ε whereas on the contrary N_t^- depends on it explicitly. However on the basis of the explicit representation of the solution of the Dirac equation obtained in [1] one expects that in some sense

$$\varepsilon \int_0^t (-1)^{N_\tau^+} dN_\tau^- \underset{\varepsilon \searrow 0}{\longrightarrow} \int_0^t (-1)^{N_\tau^+} d\tau$$

This can be made more precise using large deviations theory (see e.g. [9]). Similar techniques have been used by two of us in the sutdy of classical limit in [8] . Then let us consider another equivalent version of the generator in (2.4) namely :

$$\frac{\partial \tilde{\Phi}}{\partial t} + A\tilde{\Phi} = 0 \tag{2.16}$$

$$A\tilde{\Phi}(x,u,\alpha) = \int d\mu_{x,u,\alpha}(x',u',\alpha') \Big\{ \tilde{\Phi}(x+x', u+u', \alpha+\alpha') - \tilde{\Phi}(x,u,\alpha) \Big\} + \frac{q}{\hbar}\Big[A^0(x) - c\cos\big(\tfrac{\pi}{2}(1-u)\big) A'(x) \Big] \frac{\partial \tilde{\Phi}}{\partial \alpha}(x,u,\alpha) \tag{2.17}$$

where

$$\mu_{x,u,\alpha}(dx',du',d\alpha') = \frac{mc^2}{\hbar}\, \delta_0(dx')\, \delta_2(du')\, \delta_{\frac{\pi}{2}}(d\alpha') + \frac{1}{\varepsilon}\, \delta_{-\varepsilon c \cos(\frac{\pi}{2}(1-u))}(dx')\, \delta_0(du')\, \delta_0(d\alpha') \tag{2.18}$$

whose exponential moment can be easily computed

$$G_\varepsilon(x,u,\alpha,z_1,z_2,z_3) = \frac{mc^2}{\hbar}\left(e^{2z_2 + \frac{\pi}{2} z_3} - 1 \right) + \frac{1}{\varepsilon}\left(e^{-z_1 \varepsilon c \cos(\frac{\pi}{2}(1-u))} - 1 \right) + \frac{q}{\hbar} z_3 \left(A^0(x) - c\cos\big(\tfrac{\pi}{2}(1-u)\big) A'(x) \right) \tag{2.19}$$

The jump process whose exponential moment is $\frac{1}{\varepsilon}\exp\left(-z_1 \varepsilon c \cos\left(\frac{\pi}{2}(1-u)\right)\right)$ tends in the limit $\varepsilon \searrow 0$ to the sure process whose generator is $c\cos\left(\frac{\pi}{2}(1-u)\right)\frac{\partial}{\partial x}$

(see eg [9]).

Hence the total process tends to the process :

(2.20) $$X_t(s) = x - c\sigma\int_t^s (-1)^{N_\tau - N_t}\, d\tau$$

(2.21) $$U_t(s) = u + 2(N_s - N_t)$$

This process solves the Dirac equation where discretization has been removed (cf. [1]). Consequently in the limit $\varepsilon \searrow 0$ (2.14) becomes

(2.22) $$\psi(x,t) = e^{\frac{mc^2}{\hbar}t}\, \mathbb{E}\Big\{(-i)^{N_t}\, \psi_0\Big(x - c\sigma\int_0^t (-1)^{N_\tau} d\tau, (-1)^{N_t}\sigma\Big)$$
$$\exp\Big[-\frac{ig}{\hbar}\int_0^t d\tau\, \Big[A^0\Big(x - \sigma c\int_0^\tau (-1)^{N_{\tau'}} d\tau'\Big)$$
$$- \sigma(-1)^{N_\tau}\, c\, A^1\Big(x - c\sigma\int_0^\tau (-1)^{N_{\tau'}} d\tau'\Big)\Big]\Big]\Big\}$$

3 . THREE SPACE TIME DISCRETIZED DIRAC EQUATION

As mentioned in [1] there is an essential difficulty to interpret the Dirac hamiltonian in more than one space dimension as the generator of a Markov process. Indeed one cannot diagonalize simultaneously two of the α's. Hence one cannot disentangle the space derivatives from the jump in the indices. Of course this difficulty disappears as long as space derivatives are replaced by finite difference operators.

In three space time case it is convenient to treat the two components of the electromagnetic field on the same footing. Hence we choose for β the σ^3 Pauli matrix whereas we take $\alpha^1 = \sigma^1$ and $\alpha^2 = \sigma^2$. Other representations arizing from other choices can be deduced quite easily along the same line as it was done e.g. in section 2. According to these conventions the three space time Dirac equation rewrites

(3.1)
$$\frac{\partial \psi_t}{\partial t}(\underline{x},\sigma) = -\frac{imc^2}{\hbar}\sigma\,\psi_t(\underline{x},\sigma) - \frac{iq}{\hbar}A^0(\underline{x})\,\psi_t(\underline{x},\sigma)$$
$$-c\frac{\partial}{\partial x}\psi_t(\underline{x},-\sigma) + ic\sigma\frac{\partial}{\partial y}\psi_t(\underline{x},-\sigma)$$
$$+\frac{iq}{\hbar}c\left(A^1(\underline{x}) - i\sigma A^2(\underline{x})\right)\psi_t(\underline{x},-\sigma)$$

$$\underline{x}\in\mathbb{R}^2 \qquad \underline{x} = (x,y)$$

Again in the previous expression let us replace space derivatives by their discrete approximations.

(3.2)
$$\frac{\partial}{\partial t}\psi_t^\varepsilon(\underline{x},\sigma) = -i\left(\frac{mc^2}{\hbar}\sigma + \frac{q}{\hbar}A^0(\underline{x})\right)\psi_t^\varepsilon(\underline{x},\sigma)$$
$$+\frac{1}{\varepsilon}\left(\psi_t^\varepsilon(x-c\varepsilon,y,-\sigma) + i\,\psi_t^\varepsilon(x,y+c\sigma\varepsilon,-\sigma)\right)$$
$$-\left(\frac{1}{\varepsilon}(1+i) - \frac{iqc}{\hbar}\left(A^1(\underline{x}) - i\sigma A^2(\underline{x})\right)\right)\psi_t(\underline{x},-\sigma)$$

We introduce the two real functions $\Phi_i, i=1,2$ depending on ε such that :

(3.3)
$$-(1+i) + i\frac{qc}{\hbar}\varepsilon\left(A^1(\underline{x}) - i\sigma A^2(\underline{x})\right)$$
$$= \exp\left\{i\,\phi_1(\underline{x},\sigma) + \phi_2(\underline{x},\sigma)\right\}$$

Furthermore one introduces a time $T>0$ and for $t \leq T$

(3.4)
$$\phi^{\varepsilon}(x,y,\sigma,\alpha,\beta,t) =$$
$$\exp\left\{-\frac{3}{\varepsilon}(T-t) + i\alpha + \beta\right\}\psi^{\varepsilon}_{T-t}(x,y,\sigma)$$

$\tilde{\Phi}^{\varepsilon}(x,y,u,\alpha,\beta,t)$ satisfies the equation :

(3.5)
$$\frac{\partial\tilde{\Phi}^{\varepsilon}}{\partial t}(\underline{x},u,\alpha,\beta,t) + \frac{1}{\varepsilon}\left\{\tilde{\Phi}^{\varepsilon}(x-c\varepsilon,y,u+2,\alpha,\beta,t)\right.$$
$$-3\tilde{\Phi}^{\varepsilon}(\underline{x},u,\alpha,\beta,t) + \tilde{\Phi}^{\varepsilon}\left(x,y+c\varepsilon\cos\left(\tfrac{\pi}{2}(1-u)\right),u+2,\alpha+\tfrac{\pi}{2},\beta,t\right)$$
$$\left.+\tilde{\Phi}^{\varepsilon}\left(x,y,u+2,\alpha+\tilde{\phi}_1(\underline{x},u),\beta+\tilde{\Phi}_2(\underline{x},u)\,t\right)\right\}$$
$$-\left(\frac{q}{\hbar}A^0(\underline{x}) + \frac{mc^2}{\hbar}\cos\left(\tfrac{\pi}{2}(1-u)\right)\right)\frac{\partial}{\partial\alpha}\tilde{\Phi}^{\varepsilon}(\underline{x},u,\alpha,\beta,t) = 0$$

which has the standard form of a backward Kolmogorov equation.
We introduce a function c from $\mathbb{R}^6$ to $\mathbb{R}^5$ such that

(3.6)
$$c(x,y,u,\alpha,\beta,v=1) = (-c\varepsilon,0,2,0,0)$$

(3.7)
$$c(x,y,u,\alpha,\beta,v=2) = \left(0,c\varepsilon\cos\left(\tfrac{\pi}{2}(1-u)\right),2,\tfrac{\pi}{2},0\right)$$

(3.8) $$c(x, y, u, \alpha, \beta, v=3) = (0, 0, 2, \tilde{\phi}_1(\underline{x}, u), \tilde{\phi}_2(\underline{x}, u))$$

We can define the process : $s \leq t \leq T$

(3.9) $$X_t(s) = x - c\varepsilon(N^1_s - N^1_t)$$

(3.10) $$Y_t(s) = y + c\varepsilon \cos\left(\tfrac{\pi}{2}(1-u)\right) \int_t^s (-1)^{\sum_{i=1}^{3}(N^i_\tau - N^i_t)} dN^2_\tau$$

(3.11) $$U_t(s) = u + 2\sum_{i=1}^{3}(N^i_s - N^i_t)$$

(3.12) $$A_t(s) = \alpha + \frac{\pi}{2}(N^2_s - N^2_t) + \int_t^s d\tau\, \tilde{\phi}_1(\underline{X}_t(\tau), U_t(\tau))\, dN^3_\tau$$
$$- \int_t^s d\tau \left[\frac{q}{\hbar} A^0(\underline{X}_t(\tau)) + \frac{mc^2}{\hbar} \sigma (-1)^{\sum_{i=1}^{3}(N^i_\tau - N^i_t)}\right]$$

(3.13) $$B_t(s) = \beta + \int_t^s \tilde{\phi}_2(\underline{X}_t(\tau), U_t(\tau))\, dN^3_\tau$$

where the N^i's are independent Poisson processes of intensity $1/\varepsilon$.
Then the solution of equation (3.2) has the following representation for any bounded initial condition ψ_0

(3.14) $$\psi^\varepsilon_t(\underline{x}, \sigma) = e^{\frac{3t}{\varepsilon}}\, \mathbb{E}\Big\{ \psi_0\big(\underline{X}_0(t), \sigma(-1)^{\sum_{i=1}^{3} N^i_t}\big)$$
$$(i)^{N^2_t} \exp\left[i \int_0^t \phi_1\big(\underline{X}_0(\tau), \sigma(-1)^{\sum_{i=1}^{3} N^i_\tau}\big) dN^3_\tau \right.$$
$$\left. + \int_0^t \phi_2\big(\underline{X}_0(\tau), \sigma(-1)^{\sum_{i=1}^{3} N^i_\tau}\big) dN^3_\tau\right]$$
$$\exp\left[-i\int_0^t d\tau \left(\frac{q}{\hbar} A^0(\underline{X}_0(\tau)) + \frac{mc^2}{\hbar}\sigma(-1)^{\sum_{i=1}^{3} N^i_\tau}\right)\right]\Big\}$$

Again one can study the effect of rotations in spin space on this expression. That gives the expression for the solution of Dirac equation corresponding to different choices of β and α's.

Unfortunately the question of the limit $\varepsilon \searrow 0$ cannot be treated as simply as in the two space time dimensional case. We shall return to this question by the end of the next section.

4 . THE FOUR SPACE TIME DIMENSION DIRAC EQUATION

The treatment of the four space time discretized Dirac equation is fundamentally very similar to that in three space time dimensions. For this reason we shall insist on the necessary changes but not so much on the general strategy.

As mentioned before ψ is a four component spinor whose components are considered as functions of two dichotomic variables $\sigma, \tau \in \{\pm 1\}$. We choose for the α's and β the following representation

(4.1) $$(\beta\psi)(\sigma,\tau) = \psi(-\sigma,\tau)$$

(4.2) $$(\alpha^1\psi)(\sigma,\tau) = \sigma\psi(\sigma,-\tau)$$

(4.3) $$(\alpha^2\psi)(\sigma,\tau) = -i\sigma\tau\psi(\sigma,-\tau)$$

(4.4) $$(\alpha^3\psi)(\sigma,\tau) = \sigma\tau\psi(\sigma,\tau)$$

One checks quite easily that the α's and β have the right anticommutation relations and are hermiteans with respect to the natural scalar product

(4.5) $$(\psi\mid\varphi) = \sum_{\sigma,\tau\in\{\pm 1\}} \bar{\psi}(\sigma,\tau)\,\varphi(\sigma,\tau)$$

With these definitions Dirac equation reads as :

(4.6) $$\begin{aligned}\frac{\partial\psi_t}{\partial t}(\underline{x},\sigma,\tau) = &-i\frac{mc^2}{\hbar}\psi_t(\underline{x},-\sigma,\tau) - c\sigma\frac{\partial}{\partial x}\psi_t(\underline{x},\sigma,-\tau)\\ &+ic\sigma\tau\frac{\partial}{\partial y}\psi_t(\underline{x},\sigma,-\tau) - c\sigma\tau\frac{\partial}{\partial z}\psi_t(\underline{x},\sigma,\tau)\\ &+i\frac{qc}{\hbar}\sigma\left[A^1(\underline{x}) - i\tau A^3(\underline{x})\right]\psi_t(\underline{x},\sigma,-\tau)\\ &-i\frac{q}{\hbar}\left[A^0(\underline{x}) - \sigma\tau c A^3(\underline{x})\right]\psi_t(\underline{x},\sigma,\tau)\end{aligned}$$

$$\underline{x} \in \mathbb{R}^3$$

With such a choice of α's and β it is not necessary to discretize the $\frac{\partial}{\partial z}$ derivative. Of course it can be done with an independent parameter ε_3 introducing an extra independent jump process, as in the 1+1 dimensional case. However the limit $\varepsilon_3 \searrow 0$ can be controlled in a quite easy way as in the second section.

In the same spirit as above let us introduce the variables u and v such that :

(4.7) $$\sigma = \cos\left(\frac{\pi}{2}(1-u)\right)$$

(4.8) $$\tau = \cos\left(\frac{\pi}{2}(1-v)\right)$$

Again we reverse the time to transform the initial condition into a final condition $t \to T-t$ for some $T>0$ and we introduce two more variables α, β such that :

(4.9) $$\tilde{\Phi}_t(\underline{x}, u, v, \alpha, \beta) =$$

$$\exp\left\{-\left(\frac{mc^2}{\hbar} + \frac{3}{\varepsilon}\right)(T-t) + i\alpha + \beta\right\} \tilde{\Psi}_{T-t}(\underline{x}, u, v)$$

Also we define the two functions ϕ_1 and ϕ_2 such that :

(4.10) $$-(1+i) + i\frac{qc}{\hbar}\sigma\varepsilon\left(A^1(\underline{x}) - i\tau A^2(\underline{x})\right)$$

$$= \exp\left\{i\phi_1(\underline{x}, \sigma, \tau) + \phi_2(\underline{x}, \sigma, \tau)\right\}$$

Then replacing space derivatives by their discrete approximation equation (4.6) rewrites as :

(4.11) $$\frac{\partial}{\partial t}\tilde{\Phi}_t^{\varepsilon}(\underline{x},u,v,\alpha,\beta) + \frac{mc^2}{\hbar}\Big[\tilde{\Phi}_t^{\varepsilon}(\underline{x},u+2,v,\alpha-\tfrac{\pi}{2},\beta)$$

$$-\tilde{\Phi}_t^{\varepsilon}(\underline{x},u,v,\alpha,\beta)\Big] + \frac{1}{\varepsilon}\Big[\tilde{\Phi}_t^{\varepsilon}(x-c\varepsilon\cos(\tfrac{\pi}{2}(1-u)),y,z,u,v+2,\alpha,\beta)$$

$$+\tilde{\Phi}_t^{\varepsilon}(x,y+c\varepsilon\cos(\tfrac{\pi}{2}(1-u))\cos(\tfrac{\pi}{2}(1-v)),z,u,v+2,\alpha+\tfrac{\pi}{2},\beta)$$

$$+\tilde{\Phi}_t^{\varepsilon}(x,y,z,u,v+2,\alpha+\tilde{\Phi}_1(\underline{x},u,v),\beta+\tilde{\Phi}_2(\underline{x},u,v))$$

$$-3\tilde{\Phi}_t^{\varepsilon}(x,y,z,u,v,\alpha,\beta)\Big] - c\cos(\tfrac{\pi}{2}(1-u))\cos(\tfrac{\pi}{2}(1-v))\frac{\partial}{\partial z}\tilde{\Phi}_t^{\varepsilon}(\underline{x},u,v,\alpha,\beta)$$

$$-\frac{q}{\hbar}\Big(A^0(\underline{x}) - c\cos(\tfrac{\pi}{2}(1-u))\cos(\tfrac{\pi}{2}(1-v))A^3(\underline{x})\Big)\frac{\partial}{\partial\alpha}\tilde{\Phi}_t^{\varepsilon}(\underline{x},u,v,\alpha,\beta) = 0$$

Let C be a function of $\mathbb{R}^8 \to \mathbb{R}^7$ such that :

(4.12) $$C(\underline{x},u,v,\alpha,\beta,\omega=1) = (0,0,0,2,0,-\tfrac{\pi}{2},0)$$

(4.13) $$C(\underline{x},u,v,\alpha,\beta,\omega=2) = (-\varepsilon c\cos(\tfrac{\pi}{2}(1-u)),0,0,0,2,0,0)$$

(4.14) $$C(\underline{x},u,v,\alpha,\beta,\omega=3) = (0,\varepsilon c\cos(\tfrac{\pi}{2}(1-u))\cos(\tfrac{\pi}{2}(1-v)),0,0,2,\tfrac{\pi}{2},0)$$

(4.15) $$C(\underline{x},u,v,\alpha,\beta,\omega=4) = (0,0,0,0,2,\tilde{\Phi}_1(\underline{x},u,v),\tilde{\Phi}_2(\underline{x},u,v))$$

Let N_t^i, $i=1,2,3,4$ be four independent Poisson Processes such that N_t^1 has intensity $\frac{mc^2}{\hbar}$ whereas N_t^i $i=2,3,4$ have intensity $1/\varepsilon$.

Then we define the following processes for $s \leq t \leq T$

(4.16) $$X_t(s) = x - c\varepsilon\int_t^s (-1)^{(N_\tau^1 - N_t^1)}\, dN_\tau^2$$

(4.17) $$Y_t(s) = y + c\varepsilon\,\sigma\tau\int_t^s (-1)^{\sum_{i=1}^{4}(N_\tau^i - N_t^i)}\, dN_t^3$$

(4.18) $$Z_t(s) = z - c\sigma\tau \int_t^s (-1)^{\sum_{i=1}^{4}(N_\tau^i - N_t^i)}\, d\tau$$

(4.19) $$U_t(s) = u + 2(N_s^1 - N_t^1)$$

(4.20) $$V_t(s) = v + 2\sum_{i=2}^{4}(N_s^i - N_t^i)$$

(4.21) $$A_t(s) = \alpha - \frac{\pi}{2}(N_s^1 - N_t^1) + \frac{\pi}{2}(N_s^3 - N_t^3)$$
$$+ \int_t^s dN_\tau^4\, \phi_1\left(\underline{X}_t(\tau), \sigma(-1)^{(N_\tau^1 - N_t^1)}, \tau(-1)^{\sum_{i=2}^{4}(N_\tau^i - N_t^i)}\right)$$
$$- \frac{q}{\hbar}\int_t^s d\tau \left[A^0(\underline{X}_t(\tau)) - c\sigma\tau(-1)^{\sum_{i=1}^{4}(N_\tau^i - N_t^i)} A^3(\underline{X}_t(\tau))\right]$$

(4.22) $$B_t(s) = \beta + \int_t^s dN_\tau^4\, \phi_2\left(\underline{X}_t(\tau), \sigma(-1)^{(N_\tau^1 - N_t^1)}, \tau(-1)^{\sum_{i=2}^{4}(N_\tau^i - N_t^i)}\right)$$

where $\underline{X}_t(s)$ stands for $(X_t(s), Y_t(s), Z_t(s))$.
Then the solution of equation (4.11) has the following representation :

(4.23) $$\psi_t^\varepsilon(\underline{x}, \sigma, \tau) = \exp\left(\left(\frac{mc^2}{\hbar} + \frac{3}{\varepsilon}\right)t\right) \mathbb{E}\Big\{ (i)^{(N_t^3 - N_t^1)}$$
$$\exp\left[i\int_0^t dN_s^4\, \phi_1\left(\underline{X}_0(s), \sigma(-1)^{N_s^1}, \tau(-1)^{\sum_{i=2}^{4} N_s^2}\right)\right]$$
$$\exp\left[-\frac{iq}{\hbar}\int_0^t ds \left(A^0(\underline{X}_0(s)) - c\sigma\tau(-1)^{\sum_{i=1}^{4} N_s^i} A^3(\underline{X}_0(s))\right)\right]$$
$$\exp\left[\int_0^t dN_s^4\, \phi_2\left(\underline{X}_0(s), \sigma(-1)^{N_s^1}, \tau(-1)^{\sum_{i=2}^{4} N_s^i}\right)\right]$$
$$\psi_0\left(\underline{X}_0(t), \sigma(-1)^{N_t^1}, \tau(-1)^{\sum_{i=2}^{4} N_t^i}\right)\Big\}$$

Before closing the section let us turn back to the question of the limit $\varepsilon \searrow 0$. In contrast with the two space time dimensional case, the limit exists only if we impose severe restrictions to the initial conditions. We shall treat a very simple example which is not directly related with our problem but exhibits the same kind of difficulties.

Let us consider the equation

$$\frac{\partial}{\partial t} \varphi_t(x,\sigma) = \frac{\partial}{\partial x} \varphi_t(x,-\sigma) \tag{4.24}$$

and

$$\lim_{t \searrow 0} \varphi_t(x,\sigma) = \varphi_0(x,\sigma)$$

where $x \in R$, $\sigma = \pm 1$ and φ_0 is once derivable.

Let us observe that $\varphi_t(x,\sigma)$ obeys the wave equation viz

$$\left\{ \frac{\partial^2}{\partial t^2} - \frac{\partial^2}{\partial x^2} \right\} \varphi_t(x,\sigma) = 0 \tag{4.25}$$

In any case the general solution of (4.23) is of the form :

$$\begin{aligned} \varphi_t(x,\sigma) = {} & \tfrac{1}{2} \left[\varphi_0(x+t,\sigma) + \varphi_0(x+t,-\sigma) \right] \\ & + \tfrac{1}{2} \left[\varphi_0(x-t,\sigma) - \varphi_0(x-t,-\sigma) \right] \end{aligned} \tag{4.26}$$

However if equation (4.24) is replaced by

$$\frac{\partial}{\partial t} \varphi_t^{\varepsilon}(x,\sigma) = \frac{1}{\varepsilon} \left[\varphi_t^{\varepsilon}(x+\varepsilon,-\sigma) - \varphi_t^{\varepsilon}(x,-\sigma) \right] \tag{4.27}$$

its solution has the following representation :

$$\varphi_t^{\varepsilon}(x,\sigma) = e^{\frac{2t}{\varepsilon}} \mathbb{E} \left\{ (-1)^{N_t^2} \varphi_0\left(x + \varepsilon N_t^1, (-1)^{(N_t^1 + N_t^2)} \sigma\right) \right\} \tag{4.28}$$

where N_t^i $i=1,2$ are independent Poisson processes of intensity $\frac{1}{\varepsilon}$.

We can decompose φ_t into two parts using

$$\varphi_0(x,\sigma) = \varphi_{0+}(x) + \sigma \varphi_{0-}(x)$$

For the σ independent part of φ_t viz generated by φ_{0+} one can control easily the limit $\varepsilon \searrow 0$. However for the σ dependent part one has :

(4.29) $$\varphi^{\varepsilon}_{t-}(x) = e^{\frac{2t}{\varepsilon}} \mathbb{E}\left\{(-1)^{N'_t} \varphi_{0-}(x + \varepsilon N'_t)\right\}$$

which has no obvious limit in the general case, but as expected

$$\varphi^{\varepsilon}_{t-}(x) \underset{\varepsilon \searrow 0}{\longrightarrow} \varphi_{0-}(x)$$

if φ_{0-} is the Fourier transform of a C^{∞}_{0} function for instance.

BIBLIOGRAPHY

1 Ph. BLANCHARD, Ph. COMBE, M. SIRUGUE, M. SIRUGUE-COLLIN
Probabilistic solution of the Dirac Equation.
Preprint BIBOS (Bielefeld) (1985).

2 R.P. FEYNMAN, A.P. HIBBS
Quantum Mechanics & Path Integrals.
Mc Graw-Hill, New York (1965).

3 B. GAVEAU, T. JACOBSON, M. KAC, L.S. SHULMAN
Relativistic extension of the Analogy between Quantum Mechanics and Brownian motion.
Phys. Rev. Lett. 53, 419-422 (1984).

4 Ph. BLANCHARD, Ph. COMBE, M. SIRUGUE, M. SIRUGUE-COLLIN
Path integral representation for the solution of Dirac equation in presence of an electromagnetic field.
Preprint BIBOS (Bielefeld) (1985).

5 T. JACOBSON
Spinor Chain Path Integral for the Dirac Electron.
Thesis, University of Texas, Austin (1983).

6 G.F. DE ANGELIS, G. JONA-LASINIO, M. SIRUGUE
Probabilistic solution of the Pauli type Equations.
J. Phys. A Math. Gen. 16, 2433-2444 (1983).

7 I.I. GIHMAN, A.V. SKOROHOD
The Theory of Stochastic Processes III
Springer Verlag (1979).

8 Ph. BLANCHARD, M. SIRUGUE
Large deviations from classical paths. Hamiltonian flows as classical limits of quantum flows.
Communic. in Math. Phys. 101, p. 173-185 (1985)

9 M.I. FREIDLIN, A.D. WENTZEL
Random perturbations of dynamical systems.
Springer Verlag (1984).

JUMP PROCESSES IN QUANTUM THEORIES

Ph. BLANCHARD — Theoretische Physik and BiBoS, Universität Bielefeld

Ph. COMBE[+] — BiBoS and Universität Bielefeld

M. SIRUGUE — CPT - CNRS Marseille

M. SIRUGUE-COLLIN — CPT-CNRS and Université de Provence - Marseille

Introduction

From the very beginning of quantum mechanics the similarity between the Schrödinger equation and the Heat equation [1], [2], the possibility to derive Heisenberg-like indeterminacy relations for diffusion processes [3] and the probabilistic interpretation of the wave function [4] have been an appealing feature for a description of quantum mechanics in terms of probability concepts. Despite of the probabilistic interpretation of quantum mechanics it is not a classical probability theory [5]. Nevertheless, during the past decades stochastic methods played a major role in the development of quantum theories.

Time evolution of quantum dynamical systems is governed by the Schrödinger equation which controls the time development of the wave function. Wave functions contain all the information about the state of the system. Time evolution is as well described by the Heisenberg equations which, at least formally, are similar to the usual Liouville equations of classical mechanics. However, Heisenberg equations deal with non-commutative objects and have no natural probabilistic interpretation [5].

Hence the Schrödinger approach seems and indeed has been more successful in dealing with the relationships between classical and quantum mechanics, especially through the Feynman ideas [6], [7], [8] and Nelson's stochastic mechanics [9], [10], [11].

Roughly speaking, the Feynman idea is to describe the time evolution of the wave functions as a functional integral over the set of paths, with a suitable measure which enhances the classical path as $\hbar \to 0$. A mathematical sound treatment of these has been fairly well accomplished in the configuration space in the so-called Euclidean region (see e.g. [2] for imaginary time; see, however, for real time [12]). The main tool is the Feynman-Kac formula [12] which gives a representation of the Euclidean wave functions as a Wiener integral. To define the relevant quantity in the physical region i.e. for real time a reconstruction theorem [15] was used. However, in this domain the probabilistic representation was lost. The very reasons for this fact being the central role played by the Wiener process.

By the end of the seventies, it was remarked by Maslov and Chebotarev [15], [17] that in the momentum representation time evolution of the wave function of the quantum mechanics has a very natural probabilistic representation in terms of pure jump processes. This is the starting point toward a rigorous definition of Feynman path integral formula [18],[19]. This probabilistic representation in momentum space via jump processes is closely related with the "Fresnel" integral approach in configuration space introduced by Albeverio and Høegh-Krohn [20]. Indeed, this oscillatory integral in infinitely many dimensions is defined by duality using a generalized Parseval formula but in this framework the formulation is no more probabilistic.

In this lecture we want to show that actually the use of jump processes naturally arises in a much larger class of problems and that they are not necessarily associated with a specified representation of the quantum mechanics. There is an object well-adapted to this program, the so-called Wigner function [21], which is the "quantum joint distribution" of position and momentum. The description of quantum mechanics in terms of Wigner functions looks like a phase space ensemble description of the quantum mechanics. Wigner functions contain all the information about the quantum state of the systems. For a pure state this function integrated over momentum space yields the quantum mechanical probability distribution of position, namely $|\psi(q)|^2$, and when integrated over the position space yields the corresponding probability distribution of momenta, $|\tilde{\psi}(p)|^2$, where $\tilde{\psi}$ is the Fourier transform of ψ Moreover, its Fourier transform conserves a meaning in quantum field theory.

In Section 2, we recall the basic structure and properties of this object.

In Section 3, we derive an integral representation "à la Feynman" for the time evolution of the Wigner function by a stochastic flow on the phase space.

In Section 4, we use previous representations to discuss the existence of relativistic quantum flow associated with trigonometric models of relativistic quantum field theory.

In the last section, we are interested in the classical limit of quantum mechanics time evolution. Indeed, we show that the probability for the trajectories of the underlying process to make excursion outside of a tubular neighbourhood the classical trajectory is of order $e^{-A/\hbar}$. This result is a typical example of the usefulness of probabilistic methods one applied to quantum physics.

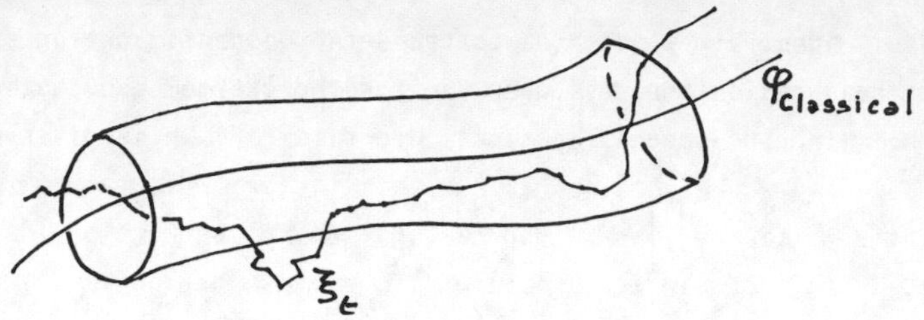

2. Wigner Functions

Let us consider a quantum system with n degrees of freedom whose classical phase space is $\mathbb{R}^{2n}$. For such a system the wave function contains all the information about state of the system. From a classical point of view it is a very singular object which roughly speaking behaves like the square root of a density. As mentioned in the introduction, there is another object, the Wigner function [21], [22] which also contains all the information about the state of the system. The advantage of this description is that it depends on variable phase spaces, hence it does not specify a given representation (position or momentum) of quantum mechanics. Moreover, we can expect a nicer behaviour in the classical limit than that of wave function.

Let $f(q,p)$ be a smooth function on the phase space $\mathbb{R}^{2n}$ and denote by $\tilde{f}(q,p)$ its symplectic Fourier transform

$$\tilde{f}(q,p) = \frac{1}{(2\pi)^n} \int_{\mathbb{R}^{2n}} f(q',p') e^{i\sigma(q,p;q',p')} dq'\, dp' \tag{2.1}$$

where σ is the canonical symplectic form on $\mathbb{R}^{2n}$

$$\sigma(q,p;q',p') = \sum_{i=1}^{n} (q_i' p_i - q_i p_i') . \tag{2.2}$$

A Wigner function W is a function on the phase space $\mathbb{R}^{2n}$ such that its symplectic Fourier transform satisfies the following properties:

$$\begin{aligned} &\text{i)} \quad q \to \tilde{W}(q,p) \quad (\text{sup } p \to \tilde{W}(q,p)) \quad \text{is continuous} \\ &\text{ii)} \quad \tilde{W}(0,0) = 1 \\ &\text{iii)} \quad \sum_{i,j=1}^{N} \lambda_i \bar{\lambda}_j \, e^{i\sigma(q_i,p_i;q_j,p_j)} \tilde{W}(q_i-q_j,\, p_i-p_j) \geq 0 \quad \text{for all } N \end{aligned} \tag{2.3}$$

for $\{\lambda_i\}_{i=1,\dots,N}$, $\lambda_i \in \mathbb{C}$, $(q_i,p_i)_{i=1,\dots,N}$, $(q_i,p_i) \in \mathbb{R}^{2n}$.

The set of Wigner functions is a convex set of bounded, continuous, real functions. In the framework of the Weyl quantization the quantum expectation of smooth observables on the phase space in the state described by W is given by

$$<f>_W = \int_{\mathbb{R}^{2n}} f(q,p)\, W(q,p) dq dp \ . \tag{2.4}$$

W is not a probability density, since as it is well-known it may assume negative values. Therefore (2.4) has not the interpretations of a statistical distribution in classical mechanics and $W(q,p)$ cannot be intepreted as the joint probability distribution of positions and momentum. However, in the classical limit it converges to a measure on phase space.

The correspondence between the ordinary description of quantum mechanics and the one given by the Wigner functions is expressed by the formula

$$W_{\hbar}(q,p) = \frac{1}{(\pi\hbar)^n} \operatorname{Tr}\left[\rho\, e^{i(\frac{2p}{\hbar} Q - \frac{2q}{\hbar} P)} M\right] \tag{2.5}$$

where Q and P are the usual position and momentum operators, ρ is the density matrix which characterizes the state of the system and M is the parity operator defined in $L_2(\mathbb{R}^n, dq)$ by

$$(Mf)(q) = f(-q) \ . \tag{2.6}$$

$\hbar$ is the Planck constant divided by 2π. For more details, see e.g. [23].

A similar object exists in Quantum Field Theory, viz. the Fourier transform of Wigner functions [24]. Let f and g be two functions in the real Schwartz space $S_R(\mathbb{R}^s)$ and define the field operators

$$B(f,g) = \pi(g) - \phi(f) \tag{2.7}$$

where ϕ and π are the usual field and momentum operators whereas $\phi(f)$ and $\pi(g)$ are the smeared out operators. For a given quantum state ω we can define the Wigner function, or, more precisely, the analogue of the Fourier transform, as the quantum expectation in the state ω of $e^{iB(f,g)}$

$$F_{\omega}(f,g) = <e^{iB(f,g)}>_{\omega} \ . \tag{2.8}$$

Moreover, the Fourier transform of Wigner functions exists for more general group structures [25], [26]. An interesting example can be given by considering as phase space the Cantor set C on $[0,1]$. C is isomorphic to the set P_{Λ} of all finite subsets of a countable set Λ. There is a natural group action on P_{Λ}. Indeed, let $\mathfrak{P}_{\Lambda}$ be the group of finite subsets of Λ, the group law being the symmetric difference, $\mathcal{P}_\Lambda$ act on P_Λ as a translation group [27]. Hence we can define a Weyl quantization procedure for functions on the Cantor set C. Using techniques similar to those developed in the next section, we can define a notion of "path integral" [18].

3. The Time Evolution of Wigner Functions

Let us consider the time evolution of a quantum system associated with the Hamiltonian operator H given by

$$H = \sum_{i=1}^{n} \left(\frac{P_i^2}{2m} + \frac{1}{2} m\omega^2 Q_i^2 + V(Q,P) \right) \tag{3.1}$$

where

$$V(Q,P) = \int_{\mathbb{R}^n} d\mu(q,p)\, e^{i \sum_{j=1}^{n} (q_j P_j - p_j Q_j)} \tag{3.2}$$

Q and P being the basic quantum position and momentum operators and μ a bounded measure on $\mathbb{R}^{2n}$ which can be written

$$d\mu(q,p) = d|\mu|(q,p)\, e^{i\varphi(q,p)} \tag{3.3}$$

where φ is a real-valued smooth function, and $|\mu|$ the absolute value of μ, i.e. the smallest positive measure such that

$$|(\mu,f)| \le (|\mu|,|f|) \; . \tag{3.6}$$

This condition can be relaxed (see e.g. [26]).

Furthermore, we require that H is a self-adjoint operator which implies that $|\mu|$ is a symmetric measure and φ and antisymmetric function

$$\int_{\mathbb{R}^{2n}} d|\mu|(q,p) f(-q,-p) = \int_{\mathbb{R}^{2n}} d|\mu|(q,p) f(q,p)$$
$$\varphi(q,p) = -\varphi(-q,-p) \; . \tag{3.5}$$

Moreover, we assume that $|\mu|$ has finite momenta up to the second order and φ is square integrable with respect to $|\mu|$.

Notice that according to the Weyl quantization prescription, the operator H corresponds to the classical Hamiltonian function

$$H(q,p) = \sum_{i=1}^{n} \left\{ \frac{p_i^2}{2m} + \frac{1}{2} m\omega^2 q_i^2 \right\} + V(q,p) \tag{3.6}$$

where

$$V(q,p) = \int_{\mathbb{R}^{2n}} d|\mu|(q',p')\cos(q'p - p'q + \varphi(q',p')) \, . \tag{3.7}$$

Let us remark that we allow for velocity dependent Hamiltonians.

It is a matter of computation to derive the integro-differential equation describing the time evolution of Wigner functions.

Proposition [22]

Let $W_{\hbar,t}$ be a Wigner function at time t, associated with the Hamiltonian operator given by (3.1) and (3.2) which is differentiable with bounded derivative, then $W_{\hbar,t}$ satisfies the equation

$$\frac{\partial W_{\hbar,t}(q,p)}{\partial t} + \sum_{i=1}^{n} \left(\frac{p_i}{m} \frac{\partial}{\partial q_i} - m\omega^2 q_i \frac{\partial}{\partial p_i} \right) W_{\hbar,t}(q,p)$$

$$- \frac{2}{\hbar} \int_{\mathbb{R}^{2n}} d|\mu|(q',p') \sin\left(\sum_{i=1}^{n} (q_i' p_i - p_i' q_i) + \varphi(q',p') \right) W_{\hbar,t}(q + \frac{\hbar}{2} q', p + \frac{\hbar}{2} p') = 0 \tag{3.8}$$

with initial boundary value

$$\lim_{t \downarrow 0} W_{\hbar,t}(q,p) = W_{\hbar}(q,p) \, .$$

This equation is a version of the Moyal equation [33]. Formally it approaches the classical Liouville equation when $\hbar$ goes to zero

$$\frac{\partial W}{\partial t} + \{W,H\} = 0 \tag{3.9}$$

where H is defined by (3.6).

The "Schrödinger-like" equation (3.8) defines a stochastic flow not directly on phase space but rather on an extended phase space, Indeed, let us remark that the integral operator in equation (3.8) looks formally like a Markov generator (of a pure jump process) except for the positivity. However, it is the trace of a true Markov generation in a $2n+1$ dimensional space.

Let F be the function from $\mathbb{R}^{2n} \times [0,T]$ to $\mathbb{C}$ and define

$$G_T(q,p,s,t) = e^{\left(4 \frac{T-t}{\hbar} \|\mu\| + i \frac{s}{\hbar}\right)} W_{\hbar,T-t}(q,p) \tag{3.10}$$

where $\|\mu\|$ is the total mass of the measure $|\mu|$. It is a linear injective embedding of bounded functions for $\mathbb{R}^{2n} \times [0,T]$ into bounded functions of $\mathbb{R}^{2n+1} \times [0,T]$. Moreover, it preserves group representation on $\mathbb{R}^k$. Then G verifies the following equation

$$\frac{\partial G_T}{\partial t}(q,p,s,t) = \sum_{i=1}^{n}\left(\frac{p_i}{m}\frac{\partial}{\partial q_i} - m\omega q_i \frac{\partial}{\partial p_i}\right) G(q,p,s,t)$$

$$+ \int_{\mathbb{R}^{2n+1}} d\pi_{qps}(q',p',s')\Big[G(q+q',\ p+p',\ s+s',t) - G(q,p,s,t)\Big] = 0 \tag{3.11}$$

with

$$\lim_{t\uparrow T} G_T(q,p,s,t) = e^{i\frac{s}{\hbar}}\, W_\hbar(q,p)$$

where π_{qps} is a positive bounded measure on $\mathbb{R}^{2n+1}$ defined as follows.

$$d\pi_{qps}(q',p',s') =$$

$$(\tfrac{2}{\hbar})^{2n+1} d|\mu|\left(\tfrac{2}{\hbar}q',\ \tfrac{2}{\hbar}p'\right)\left[\left(1-\sin\tfrac{2}{\hbar}(q'p-qp')+\varphi(\tfrac{2}{\hbar}q',\ \tfrac{2}{\hbar}p')\right)\right]\left(\delta_\hbar(s')+\delta_{-\hbar}(s')\right)$$

$$+ (\tfrac{2}{\hbar})^{2n+1} d|\mu|(\tfrac{2}{\hbar}q',\ \tfrac{2}{\hbar}p')(\delta_{\hbar/2}(s') + \delta_{-\hbar/2}(s')). \tag{3.12}$$

In Equation (3.11) we now recognize a backward Kolmogorov equation (see e.g. [26]). Therefore, the solution of (3.11) has a probabilistic representation.

<u>Proposition</u> [23], [29]

There exists a stochastic process (Q,P,S) with values in $\mathbb{R}^{2n+1}$ which satisfies the following stochastic differential equation

$$Q_t(T) = q - \frac{1}{m}\int_t^T P_T(\tau)d\tau - \int_t^T \int_{\mathbb{R}^{2n+1}} q'\ \nu_{qps}(d\tau,dq',dp',ds')$$

$$P_t(T) = p + m\omega^2 \int_t^T Q_T(\tau)d\tau - \int_t^T \int_{\mathbb{R}^{2n+1}} p'\nu_{qps}(d\tau,dq',dp',ds')$$

$$S_t(T) = s + \int_t^T \int_{\mathbb{R}^{2n+1}} s'\ \nu_{qps}(d\tau,dq',dp',ds') \tag{3.13}$$

where ν is the random Poisson measure with expectation given by

$$\mathbb{E}\,[\nu_{dps}(d\tau, A)] = \pi_{qps}\,(A)\,d\tau\ ,$$

A being a Borel set of $\mathbb{R}^{2n+1}$ while π_{qps} is defined by (3.12).

The solution of Equation (3.11) takes now the form

$$G_T(q,p,s,0) = \mathbb{E}\,[\,e^{i/\hbar\, S_0(t)}\, W_\hbar(Q_0(t),\, P_0(t))\,] \tag{3.14}$$

Moreover, taking into account Formula (3.10) we have

Proposition [23], [30], [31]

The Wigner function at time t, $W_{\hbar,t}$ has the representation

$$W_{\hbar,t}(q,p) = e^{4t/\hbar\,\|\mu\|}\,\mathbb{E}\,[e^{i/\hbar\, S_0(t)}\, W_\hbar(Q_t(0),P_t(0))] \tag{3.15}$$

For a R^{n+1}- valued process such that $(Q_0(0),B_0(0),S_0(0)) = (q,p,0)$. a.s.

Remark 1. The expectation $\mathbb{E}$ representing an integration over paths, it is clear that the previous formula is genuinely a Feynman path integral representation.

Remark 2. The method used to obtain a backward Kolmogorov equation is not unique. Each possible choice corresponds to a different measure π (see e.g. [3]). The previous choice ensures that the Markov generator (in $\mathbb{R}^{2n+1}$ space) preserves the reality of the function.

The stochastic process $(Q_0(t),P_0(t),S_0(t))$ which has been considered previously allows to define a stochastically continuous flow in phase space. Namely, let F be a bounded function on phase space and define $\alpha_t F$ by

$$(\alpha_t F)(q,p) = e^{4/\hbar\,\|\mu\| t}\,\mathbb{E}\left[e^{i/\hbar\, S_0(t)} F(Q_0(t),P_0(t)\right]. \tag{3.16}$$

This flow α_t is a semigroup of transformations of the Banach space of bounded continuous functions on $\mathbb{R}^{2n}$, furthermore

i) it preserves the reality of functions,

ii) it preserves the convex set of Wigner functions and its extremal points.

It has to be emphasized that in the previous formulae only pure jump processes appear. Let us mention a situation for which more general processes occur, namely those having also a diffusion part. Indeed, let us consider the Wigner function corresponding to the canonical state at inverse temperature β [32]

$$W_\beta(q,p) = \frac{\pi^{-n}}{\mathrm{Tr}\, e^{-\beta H}}\ \mathrm{Tr}\left[e^{-\beta H}\, e^{i\sum_{j=1}^{n} 2(q_j P_j - p_j Q_j)}\, M\right] \tag{3.17}$$

with H given by (3.1) and $\hbar = 1$.

It is more convenient to introduce the Fourier transform of quantum thermal expectation value of a smooth function f on the phase space

$$F(\beta,q,p,f) = \mathrm{Tr}\left\{e^{-\beta H}Q(f)e^{i\sum_{j=1}^{n} 2(q_jP_j-p_jQ_j)}M\right\} \tag{3.18}$$

where

$$Q(f) = \frac{1}{(2\pi)^n}\int_{\mathbb{R}^{2n}} \tilde{f}(q,p)\, e^{i\sum_{j=1}^{n}(q_jP_j-p_jQ_j)}\, dqdp. \tag{3.19}$$

Using the same method as previously, we obtain a probabilistic representation of F, namely

$$F(\beta,q,p,f) = 2^{-n}\, e^{\|\mu\|}\, \mathbb{E}\left[e^{iS_\beta} f(Q_\beta,P_\beta)\right] \tag{3.20}$$

the process $(Q_\beta,P_\beta S_\beta)$ being solution of the following stochastic differential equation

$$Q_\beta = q + \frac{1}{2\sqrt{m}}\, W_\beta + \frac{1}{2}\int_0^\beta\int_{\mathbb{R}^{2n}} q'\, \nu(d\tau,dq',dp')$$

$$P_\beta = p + \frac{\omega\sqrt{m}}{2}\, W'_\beta + \frac{1}{2}\int_0^\beta\int_{\mathbb{R}^{2n}} p'\, \nu(d\tau,dq'dp')$$

$$S_\beta = 2\int_0^\beta (P_\beta\, dQ_\beta - Q_\beta\, dP_\beta) + \int_0^\beta\int_{\mathbb{R}^{2n}} (\varphi(p',q') + \pi)\nu(d\tau,dq',dp') \tag{3.21}$$

where W, W' are independent $\mathbb{R}^n$-valued standard Wiener processes and $\nu(d\tau,A)$ is the standard Poisson measure on $\mathbb{R}^{2n}$ such that

$$\mathbb{E}\,[\nu(d\tau,A)] = d\tau\, |\mu|(A) \quad A \in \mathbb{R}^{2n}\ . \tag{3.22}$$

This representation allows a detailed control of the behaviour of the Gibbs state in the high temperature region (see [32]).

4. Local Relativistic Flow for Trigonometric Interactions in Quantum Field Theory

As described in Section 2, we are able to associate with each quantum state ω a Wigner function $F_\omega(f,g) = \langle e^{iB(f,g)}\rangle_\omega$, which is a bounded functional on $S_{\mathbb{R}}(\mathbb{R}^s) \times S_{\mathbb{R}}(\mathbb{R}^s)$, where $S_R(\mathbb{R}^s)$ is the real Schwartz space on $\mathbb{R}^s$. For the trigonometric interaction there is a natural extension of the results obtained in the previous section. In this case the interaction (Hamiltonian) is defined through the regularized potential

$$V^{\lambda,K} = \lambda \int_{\Lambda} dx \int_{0}^{\infty} d\nu(\alpha)\, \cos(\alpha\phi_K(x) + \theta)\, ,\; 0 < \theta < 2\pi \tag{4.1}$$

with ν a bounded positive measure on the real line, λ a real constant, Λ is a finite base in $\mathbb{R}^s$ (s being the space dimension) and $\phi_k(x) = (\phi * \chi_K)(x)$ is time zero regularized free field. (Viz. χ is a ultraviolet cut off function $\chi_K(x) = K^s\chi(Kx)$, $K > 0$, where χ is a positive even C^∞-function with support in the unit ball of $\mathbb{R}^s$ and such that $\int_{\mathbb{R}^s} \chi(x)dx = 1.$) A special case of a interaction of the form (4.1) is the Sine-Gordon interaction (see e.g. [33]), which corresponds to the Dirac measure $\nu = \delta_{\alpha_0}$.

Proposition [24]

For sufficiently smooth functionals on the "phase space" $S_R(\mathbb{R}^s) \times S_R(\mathbb{R}^s)$, the time translation automorphism $\alpha_t^{\Lambda,K}$, associated with the potential $V^{\Lambda,K}$, defines a stochastic flow on $S_R(\mathbb{R}^s) \times S_R(\mathbb{R}^s)$. Underlying the stochastic flow there is a random field ξ such that for $f(\sigma,x) \in C_0(0,t) \times S_R(\mathbb{R}^s)$ the characteristic functional is given by

$$\mathbb{E}\,[e^{i<f,\xi>}] = \exp\Big\{ \lambda\int_0^t d\tau \int_{\Lambda} d\tau \int d\nu(\alpha) \Big(\exp\Big[-i\alpha \int_0^t d\sigma \iint dudv\; f(\sigma,u)\, \Delta_r^m(\tau-\sigma,\, u-v)\chi_K^x(v)\Big] - 1\Big)\Big\} \tag{4.2}$$

with $\chi_K^x(u) = \chi_K(x-u)$ and Δ_r^m the usual retarded propagator with mass m where Fourier transform is $\Delta_r^m(k,t) = \frac{\sin\sqrt{k^2+m^2}}{\sqrt{k^2+m^2}} \cdot \theta(t)$, $\theta(t)$ being the Heaviside step function.

An example of smooth functionals verifying this properties is furnished by the Fourier transform of the Wigner function associated with the Fock representation of Bose quantum field theory. In this case, the "free" evolution is unitarily implemented by the strongly continuous unitary group $U_t^o = e^{iH_0t}$. For the interacting case the generator of time evolution is given by $H_0 + V^{\Lambda,K}$.

Remark. The previous proposition also holds for bounded functionals which are not necessarily Wigner functions and are therefore not associated with a state.

Actually, using the probabilistic representation of the flow $\alpha_t^{\Lambda,K}$ corresponding to trigonometric interaction, one can remove the ultraviolet cut off on a dense subset of the Banach space $\mathcal{B}$ of bounded complex functionals on

$S_{\mathbb{R}}(\mathbb{R}^s) \times S_{\mathbb{R}}(\mathbb{R}^s)$. But it is no longer possible to show that the subset has a non-void intersection with the set of states.

To be more precise, let us define the subset L of B as the union $L = L_o \cup M$ where L_o is the linear space generated by finite linear combinations of

$$\exp \frac{i}{2} \int_{\mathbb{R}^s} dx(h_1(x)k_2(x) - h_2(x)k_1(x))$$

k_1 and k_2 being tempered distributions well-defined on Δ_r^n and $\partial_t \Delta_r^m$ and M the spaces of finite linear combinations on functionals $F^f_{H_{2n}}$ defined in the following way:

Let f be a smooth bounded function on $\mathbb{R}^{2n}$ and H_{2n} be the supspace of $L^2_R(\mathbb{R}^s, dx)$ generated by $\{\phi_n\}_{m \in N}$, $\phi_n \in S_R(\mathbb{R}^s)$ then

$$F^f_{H_{2n}}(h_1,h_2) \begin{cases} f((h_1,\phi_2)(h_2,\phi_2)\dots(h_1,\phi_{2n-1})(h_2,\phi_{2n})) \\ \qquad\qquad\qquad \text{for } h_1,h_2 \in H_{2n} \\ 0 \qquad \text{otherwise} \end{cases} .$$

Now, by dominated convergence we can remove the ultraviolet cut off and prove the following

<u>Proposition</u>: On α the following limit exists

$$\lim_{K \to \infty} \alpha_t^{\Lambda,K} = \alpha_t^{\Lambda}$$

and α_t^{Λ} defines a semigroup of transformation on α_o.

Moreover, using the Kirkwood- Salzburg methods (see e.g. [31]) we can prove

<u>Proposition</u>: the limit

$$\lim_{\Lambda \uparrow \mathbb{R}^s} \alpha_t^{\Lambda} = \alpha_t^{\infty} \quad \text{exists for } t \text{ small enough.}$$

Moreover, if we replace $S_{\mathbb{R}}(\mathbb{R}^s)$ by $\mathcal{D}_{\mathbb{R}}(\mathbb{R}^s)$ the limit α_t defines a relativistic flow in the sense that

$$\alpha_t \, \alpha_s = \alpha_{t+s} \quad \text{for all } t,s \geq 0 .$$

Finally, let us remark that for any bounded $\Lambda \subset \mathbb{R}^s$ there eixsts $\lambda_o(\Lambda)$ such that for $\lambda < \lambda_o$ the limit

$$\lim_{t \to \pm\infty} \alpha_t^{\Lambda} = \alpha_{\pm}^{\Lambda}$$

exists and satisfies the usual intertwining relation with free flow (see [24]).

We summarize the results obtained for the trigonometric interaction after taking different limits in the following diagram

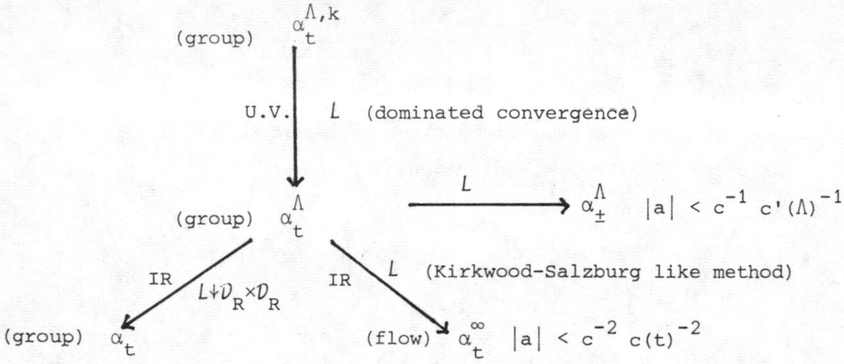

where c and c' are some positive function which tends to infinity respectively with t and $|\Lambda|$.

5. Classical Limit of Quantum Time Evolutions

This last section is devoted to the study of the behaviour as $\hbar \to 0$ of the time evolution in quantum mechanics. As mentioned in Section 3, the integro-differential equation governing the time evolution of Wigner functions converges, at least heuristically, to the Liouville equation of classical mechanics as $\hbar \to 0$. Hence we can expect that the quantum mechanical solution tends to the solution of the Liouville equation as $\hbar \to 0$. Our goal is now to derive in a rigorous way this intuitive result. More precisely, it can be proved that the trajectories of the process (3.13) defining the quantum mechanical evolution are concentrated (in probability) around the classical paths.

Before discussing the physically interesting case, let us explain the main ideas of the method on the simplest possible model. Consider the following equation

$$\left.\begin{aligned} &\frac{\partial f}{\partial t}(x,t) = \frac{1}{\hbar}\,[f(x+\hbar)t) - f(x,t)] \\ &f(x,0) = f_0(x) \end{aligned}\right\} \tag{5.1}$$

with f_0 a bounded, differentiable function.

The solution of (5.1) is obviously given by

$$f_\hbar(x,t) = e^{-\frac{t}{\hbar}} \sum_{n=0}^{\infty} \frac{1}{n!} \left(\frac{t}{\hbar}\right)^n f_0(x+n\hbar) \tag{5.2}$$

and can be rewritten immediately in a probabilistic way

$$f_{\hbar}(x,t) = E[f_o(X_t)] \tag{5.3}$$

where

$$X_t^{\hbar} = x + \hbar\, N_t^{\hbar} \tag{5.4}$$

$N_t^{\hbar}$ being the usual Poisson process with mean

$$E[N_t^{\hbar}] = \frac{t}{\hbar}\,. \tag{5.5}$$

This is just the solution we obtain if we recognize in (5.1) the backward Kolmogorov equation for Poisson process.

To compare the solution $f_{\hbar}(x,t)$ of (5.2) with the solution

$$f(x,t) = f_o(x+t) \tag{5.6}$$

of the partial differential equation

$$\left.\begin{aligned} \frac{\partial f}{\partial t}(x,t) &= \frac{\partial f(x,t)}{\partial x} \\ f(x,0) &= f_o(x) \end{aligned}\right\} \tag{5.7}$$

let us discuss the behavior of $f_{\hbar}(x,t)$ for very small values of $\hbar$. To do this, we will assume that $f_o(x)$ has a Fourier transform $\tilde{f}_o(p)$. Then (5.2) can be re-written

$$f_{\hbar}(x,t) = \frac{2}{\sqrt{2\pi}} \int_{\mathbb{R}} e^{ipx}\, e^{\frac{t}{\hbar}(e^{ip\hbar}-1)}\, \tilde{f}_o(p)dp\,. \tag{5.8}$$

For $\hbar << 1$ we obtain

$$f_{\hbar}(x,t) \approx \frac{1}{\sqrt{2\pi}} \int_{\mathbb{R}} e^{ip(x+t)}\, e^{-\frac{p^2\hbar t}{2}}\, \tilde{f}_o(p)dp \tag{5.9}$$

$$\simeq \frac{1}{\sqrt{2\pi\hbar t}} \int_{\mathbb{R}} e^{-\frac{(x+t-x')^2}{2t\hbar}}\, f_o(x)dx\,. \tag{5.10}$$

The last expression tends to the solution (5.6) when $\hbar \to 0$. Actually, the fact that the functional (5.3) has a limit does not imply that the process itself converges (in this case to the deterministic process $x+t$). To prove this and to control more precisely the convergence let us remark that

$$M_t^{\hbar} = \hbar\, N_t^{\hbar} - t \tag{5.11}$$

is a martingale with independent increments. Hence the following process

$$Q_t^{\hbar,\lambda} = \frac{e^{\lambda M_t^{\hbar}}}{\mathbb{E}\left[e^{\lambda M_t^{\hbar}}\right]} \tag{5.12}$$

with

$$\mathbb{E}\left[e^{\lambda M_t^{\hbar}}\right] = e^{\frac{t}{\hbar}[e^{\lambda\hbar} - (1+\lambda\hbar)]} \tag{5.13}$$

is also a martingale.

Now, we want to prove that the probability that the martingale $M_t^{\hbar}$ makes in a time T an excursion out of a tube of radius ε behaves as $e^{-A/\hbar}$. To do this, let us remark that

$$P\left[\sup_{t\in[0,T]} |M_t^{\hbar}| \geq \varepsilon\right] \leq P\left[\sup_{t\in[0,T]} M_t^{\hbar} \geq \varepsilon\right] + P\left[\sup_{t\in[0,T]} -M_t^{\hbar} \geq \varepsilon\right] . \tag{5.14}$$

Moreover, for any $\lambda > 0$ we have

$$P\left[\sup_{t\in[0,T]} M_t^{\hbar} \geq \varepsilon\right] \leq P\left[\sup_{t\in[0,T]} Q_t^{\hbar,\lambda} \geq e^{\lambda\varepsilon - \frac{T}{\hbar}(e^{\lambda\hbar} - (1+\lambda\hbar))}\right] \tag{5.15}$$

and

$$P\left[\sup_{t\in[0,T]} -M_t^{\hbar} \geq \varepsilon\right] \leq P\left[\sup_{t\in[0,T]} Q_t^{\hbar,-\lambda} \geq e^{\lambda\varepsilon}\, e^{-\frac{T}{\hbar}(e^{-\lambda h} - (1-\lambda h))}\right]. \tag{5.16}$$

Applying the Doob inequality (see e.g. [35]) to the right hand side of (5.14) and (5.15) and choosing $\lambda = \frac{1}{\hbar}\log(1+\frac{\varepsilon}{T})$ we obtain easily the following estimate

$$P\left[\sup_{t\in[0,T]} |M_t^{\hbar}| \geq \varepsilon\right] \leq 2\, e^{-\frac{A(\varepsilon,T)}{\hbar}} \tag{5.17}$$

with

$$A(\varepsilon,T) = \varepsilon\left[\log\left(1+\frac{\varepsilon}{T}\right) - 1\right] + T\log\left(1+\frac{\varepsilon}{T}\right) . \tag{5.18}$$

Remark that for $\varepsilon \ll T$ we have

$$A(\varepsilon,T) \approx \frac{\varepsilon^2}{2T} . \tag{5.19}$$

To investigate now the limit of the stochastic process

$$\xi_t^{\hbar}(s) = \Big(Q_t(s),\ P_t(s),\ S_t(s)\Big)$$

describing the time evolution of the Wigner function (2.5) we have to adapt to the natural filtration associated with this process and generalize the results obtained in the previous simple example. To do this, we use the Ventzel, Stroock-Varadhan approach of the large deviation theory [36], [37], [38]. The strategy of the method consists first to define the exponential momentum $G_t^{\hbar}(a,\lambda)$, $a \in \mathbb{R}^{2n+1}$, $\lambda \in \mathbb{R}^{2n+1}$, associated with the generator of the process. This exponential momentum looks like the logarithm of (5.13). In a second step we introduce the Legendre transform $G_t^{*\hbar}(a,b)$ of $G_t^{\hbar}(a,\lambda)$

$$G_t^{*\hbar}(a,b) = \sup_{\lambda} [\lambda \cdot b - G_t^{\hbar}(a,\lambda)] \tag{5.20}$$

G^* is always convex moreover, $G^{**} = G$ iff G convex.

To this Legendre transformation corresponds a choice of λ in the exponential martingale (5.13) leading to the best possible estimates in (5.15) and (5.16). In a last step we define an action functional by

$$I_{0,T}^{\hbar} = \int_0^T G_\tau^{*\hbar}(\varphi,\dot{\varphi})d\tau \tag{5.21}$$

in order to control the path $\varphi: [0,T] \to \mathbb{R}^{2n+1}$ of the underlying process, $I_{0,T}^{\hbar}$ can be ∞. Suppose now that we can find a function $g(\hbar)$ going to infinity as $\hbar \to 0$ such that on the one hand

$$\lim_{\hbar \to 0} g(\hbar)^{-1} G_t^{\hbar}(a, g(\hbar)\lambda) = G_t^1(a,\lambda) \tag{5.22}$$

and on the other hand

$$\lim_{\hbar \to 0} \nabla\left[g(\hbar)^{-1} G_t^{\hbar}(a, g(\hbar)\lambda)\right] = \nabla G_t^1(a,\lambda) \tag{5.23}$$

hold, then for any positive $\delta, \gamma, \varepsilon_o$, for $\hbar$ small enough and for $\varepsilon \le \varepsilon_o$ we have the following estimate of the probability that the paths leave a tublet around the classical trajectory

$$P\left[d_{0,T}\left(\xi^{\hbar}(t), \phi_{0,T}(\varepsilon)\right) \ge \delta\right] \le e^{-\frac{1}{\hbar}(\varepsilon-\gamma)} \tag{5.24}$$

$\phi_{0,T}$ being the tublet

$$\phi_{0,T}(\varepsilon) = \{\varphi | \varphi(0) = a, I_{0,T}^1(\varphi) \le \varepsilon\} \tag{5.25}$$

around the "classical path", i.e. the trajectory for which $I_{0,T}^1$ is extremal. In (5.24) the distance $d_{0,T}$ we use is given by

$$d_{0,T}(\varphi,\psi) = \sup_{t\in[0,T]} \|\varphi(\tau) - \psi(\tau)\| \tag{5.26}$$

$\|\cdot\|$ being the Euclidean norm in $\mathbb{R}^{2n+1}$.

Using this method to discuss the behaviour $\hbar \to 0$ of the time evolution of the Wigner function, it is possible to prove [31] that the probability that the trajectories of the process (Q,P,S) defined by (3.13) stay in a tube around the classical path is of the order $1 - e^{-c/\hbar}$. The classical path is defined as solution of the following Hamiltonian equations

$$\left.\begin{aligned} \dot{q}_t &= -\frac{\partial H(q,p)}{\partial p} \\ \dot{p}_t &= \frac{\partial H(q,p)}{\partial q} \\ \dot{S}_t &= 0 \end{aligned}\right\} \tag{5.27}$$

where H is the classical Hamiltonian.

Moreover, in the limit $\hbar \to 0$ the quantum mechanical flow

$$(\phi_{\hbar,t}F)(q,p,0) = E\Big[F(Q_o(t),\, P_o(t),\, S_o(t))\Big] \tag{5.28}$$

converges to the classical one for any sufficiently smooth function F:

$$\lim_{\hbar\to 0} (\phi_{\hbar,t}F)(q,p) = F(q_t,p_t)$$

where q_t and p_t are solutions of (5.27).

References

[1] E. Schrödinger, "Über die Umkehrung der Naturgesetze", Berlin, Sitzungsbericht 1931, 144-153

[2] E. Schrödinger, "Sur la théorie relativiste de l'électron et l'interprétation de la mécanique quantique", Annales de l'institut H. Poincaré 2, 289-295 (1932)

[3] R. Fürth, "Über einige Beziehungen zwischen klassischer Statistik und Quantenmechanik", Zeitschrift für Physik 81, 143-162 (1933)

[4] M. Born, "Zur Quantenmechanik der Stoßvorgänge", Zeitschrift für Physik 37, 863-867 (1926)

[5] S. Von Neumann, "Mathematical Foundation of Quantum Mechanics", translation by R.T. Beyer, Princeton University Press

[6] R.P. Feynman, "Space time approach to non-relativistic quantum mechanics", Rev. Mod. Phys. 20. 367-385 (1948)

[7] R.P. Feynman, A.R. Hibbs, "Quantum mechanics and path integrals", McGrawHill (1965)

[8] C. DeWitt-Morette, A. Mahcohwani, B. Nelson, "Path Integral in Non-Relativistic Quantum Mechanics", Phys. Rep. 50, 255-372 (1979) (and reference therein)

[9] E. Nelson, "Dynamical theories of Brownian Motion", Princeton University Press (1967)

[10] E. Nelson, "Quantum Fluctuation", Princeton. Princeton University Press (1985)

[11] F. Guerra, "Structural aspects of stochastic mechanics and stochastic field theory", Phys. Rep. 77, 263-312 (1981)

[12] A. Jaffe, T. Glimm, "Quantum Physics. A Functional Integral Point of View", Springer-Verlag (1981)

[13] R. Azencott, H. Doss, L'equation de Schrödinger quand $\hbar$ tend vers zero. Une approche probabiliste, in "Stochastic Aspects of Classical and Quantum Systems", Proceedings Marseille 1983, Lecture Notes in Mathematics 1109 - Springer-Verlag (1985)

[14] M. Kac, "On some connections between Probability Theory and Differential and Integral Equations", Proc. second Berkely Symp. (Univ. of California Press, Berkeley (1951)) pp. 189-215

[15] K. Osterwalder, R. Schrader, "Axioms for Euclidean Green's function I, II, Comm. Math. Phys. 31, 83-112 (1973); 42, 281-305 (1975)

[16] A.M. Chebotarev, V.P. Maslov, "Processus a sauts et leurs applications dans la mécanique quantique", in Feynman Path Integral proceedings Marseille (1978). Lecture Notes in Physics 106, Springer Verlag (1979)

[17] V.P. Maslov, A.M. Chebotarev, "Jump processes and their application to quantum mechanics", Journal of Soviet Mathematics 13 (1980) 315-357 (Engl. translation)

[18] Ph. Combe, R. Høegh-Krohn, R. Rodriguez, M. Sirugue, M. Sirugue-Collin, "Poisson Processes as Groups and Feynman Path Integrals", Commun. Math. Phys. 77, 269-288 (1980)
see also "Feynman path integral and Poisson processes with piecewise classical paths", J.M.P. 23, 405-411 (1982)

[19] J. Bertrand, G. Rideau, An intrinsic approach to the evolution of quantum observables in terms of stochastic processes on phase space. In Stochastic Aspects of Classical and Quantum Systems. Lecture Notes in Mathematics, Springer-Verlag, 1985

[20] S. Albeverio, R. Høegh-Krohn "Mathematical theory of Feynman path integrals", Lecture Notes in Math. 523 Berlin, Heidelberg, New York Springer (1976)

[21] E. Wigner, "On the quantum correction for thermodynamic equilibrium", Phys. Rev. 40, 749-759 (1932)

[22] U. Faro, "Description of States in Quantum Mechanics by density and operator techniques", Rev. Mod. Phys. 29 (1957), 74-93

[23] Ph. Combe, F. Guerra, R. Rodriguez, M. Sirugue, M. Sirugue-Collin, "Quantum dymanical time evolution as stochastic flows on phase space", Physica 124A, 561-574 (1984)

[24] S. Albeverio, Ph. Blanchard, Ph. Combe, R. Høegh-Krohn, M. Sirugue, "Local relativistic flows for quantum fields", Comm. Math. Phys. 90, 329-351 (1983)

[25] Ph. Combe, R. Rodriguez, M. Sirugue, M. Sirugue-Collin, "A Uniqueness Theorem for Anticommutative Relations and Commutation Relation of Quantum Spin Systems", Comm. Math. Phys. 63, 219-235 (1978)

[26] Ph. Combe, R. Rodriguez, M. Sirugue, M. Sirugue-Collin, A uniqueness theorem for central extensions of discrete products of cyclic groups, in "Quantum Field Algebras - Processes", ed. L. Streit, Springer-Verlag Wien (1980)

[27] Ph. Combe, R. Rodriguez, M. Sirugue, M. Sirugue-Collin, "On the quantization of spin systems and Fermi systems", J.M.P. 20, 611-161 (1979)

[28] J.E. Moyal, "Quantum Mechanics as a Stochastic Theory", Proc. Cambridge Phis. Soc. 45, 74-93 (1949)

[29] I.I. Gihman, A.V. Skorohod, "Stochastic Differential Equations", Springer Verlag (1972)
See also "The Theory of Stochastic Processes III", Springer Verlag (1979)

[30] Ph. Blanchard, Ph. Combe, M. Sirugue, M. Sirugue-Collin, Estimate of Quantum Deviations from Classical Mechanics Using Large Deviation Results , in "Quantum Probability Applications II, Heidelberg 1984", Lect. Notes in Math. 1136, Springer Verlag (1985)

[31] Ph. Blanchard, M. Sirugue, "Large deviations from classical paths". Hamiltonian flows as classical limits of quantum flows", Comm. in Math. Phys. 101, 173.185 (1985)

[32] Ph. Combe, R. Rodriguez, M. Sirugue and M. Sirugue-Collin, "High Temperature Behaviour of Quantum Mechanical Thermal Functionals", R.I.M.S. Math. Sciences, Kyoto University 19, 355-365 (1983)

[33] Ph. Combe, R. Høegh-Krohn, R. Rodriguez, M. Sirugue, M. Sirugue-Collin, "Zero mass, 2-dimensional, real time Sine-Gordon model without u.u. cut-offs", Ann. Inst. H. Poincaré 37, 115-127 (1982)

[34] D. Ruelle, "Statistical Mechanics, New York, Benjamin (1969)

[35] H.P. McKean, "Stochastic Integrals", Academic Press, New York (1969)

[36] A.D. Ventsel, "Rough limit theorem on large deviations for Markov stochastic processes I,II,III", Theory Prob. Application 21, 227-242 &1976); 21, 499-512 (1976); 24, 675-692 (1979).
See also: M.I. Friedlin, A.D. Ventsel, "Random Perturbations of Dynamical Systems", Springer-Verlag New York (1984)

[37] D.W. Stroock, Introduction to the Theory of Large Deviations: Springer-Verlag (1984)

[38] A.R.S. Varadhan, "Large Deviation and Application", Courant Institute of Mathematical Sciences, New York University

PATHWISE CONSERVATION LAW FOR STATIONARY DIFFUSION PROCESSES

Ph. Blanchard & Zheng Weian*
Theoretische Physik, Universität Bielefeld
und
Research Center Bielefeld-Bochum-Stochastics

The primary purpose of the present paper is to prove the existence of a pathwise conserved quantity for a class of stationary diffusion processes. The conservation law we obtain plays in this probabilistic framework the same role as the conservation of energy in Newtonian mechanics. Indeed for conservative classical systems the total energy remains constant, that is, is conserved as time goes on. The constancy of the energy in classical mechanics is expressed by a relation between position and momentum, namely the equation of the curve representing the system in phase space.

We focus our attention on the problem involved with the time-development of stationary diffusion process. Using this "constant of the motion", we show by elementary means that some global existence theorems can be proved. In the second half of this note we give some results related with the problem of nodes for such process.

We consider the following stochastic differential equation

$$dX_t = \nabla f(X_t)dt + dW_t \quad , \quad X_o = \eta. \tag{1}$$

where W_t is a $\mathbb{R}^d$-valued Brownian motion such that $d < W^i, W^j >_t = \nu\delta^{ij}dt$, f is a C_3-function defined on an open set $A \subset \mathbb{R}^d$ and $P[\eta \in A] = 1$.

We call the vector field $a(.): A \to \mathbb{R}^d$ defined by

$$a(x) = \nabla(\tfrac{1}{2}|\nabla f|^2 + \tfrac{\nu}{2}\Delta f)(x) \tag{2}$$

*)On leave of absence from Department of Mathematical Statistics, East-China Normal University, Shanghai, China

the <u>acceleration</u> field.

A real valued function V defined on A and for which there exists a strictly positive constant m such that

$$ma(x) = -\nabla V(x), \quad \forall x \in A \tag{3}$$

will be called <u>the forward m-potential of</u> X_t.

Let $x_o \in A$, then the stochastic differential equation (1) has at least a local solution $X_t(\omega)$, $t < \zeta(\omega)$ such that $X_o(\omega) = x_o$, where $\zeta > o$ a.s. is a stopping time, the first exit time of A, that is,

$$\zeta(\omega) = \inf\{t;\ X_t(\omega) \notin A\}. \tag{4}$$

By (3) and Ito's formula it is then easy to prove

LEMMA 1. <u>If V is a forward m-potential for the process</u> X_t, <u>then for all</u> $t < \zeta(\omega)$,

$$m[\tfrac{\nu}{2}\,\Delta f(X_t(\omega)) + \tfrac{1}{2}|\nabla f(X_t(\omega))|^2] + V(X_t(\omega)) = E(x_o) \tag{5}$$

<u>where</u> $E(.)$ <u>is some function defined on A which is constant on every open ball contained in A.</u>

REMARK. For $\nu = o$, we obtain exactly the energy conservation in classical mechanics.

The above lemma may be used to prove the existence of a global solution of the stochastic differential equation (1). Let us fix a filtration space $(\Omega, \underline{\underline{F}}, \underline{\underline{F}}_t, P)$ and suppose that $(W_t, \underline{\underline{F}}_t)$ is a Brownian motion. For a given C_2-function $\rho(x) \geqq o$, we consider the open set $A = \{x;\ \rho(x) > o\}$. Now let f(x) be a C_3-function defined on A such that the following Fokker-Planck equation holds:

$$\operatorname{div}(\rho(x)\nabla f(x)) = \frac{\nu}{2}\,\Delta\rho(x) \quad . \tag{6}$$

Let $\eta \in \underline{\underline{F}}_o$ be a random variable which has $\rho(x)$ as its probability density function. In stochastic mechanics, we considered the case where there exists some potential function $\varphi(x)$ such that (see [1])

$$V(x) = \varphi(x) - m\nu^2\,\frac{\Delta(\rho^{\frac{1}{2}}(x))}{\rho^{\frac{1}{2}}(x)}$$

is the forward m-potential of X_t.

Suppose that $\rho(x) \to o$ when $|x| \to \infty$.

THEOREM 2. Let $\inf_x \varphi(x) > -\infty$. Then $\zeta = \infty$., and the equation (1) has a global solution.

PROOF. Without losing generality, we suppose that A is connected and $E(.)$ is a constant. Otherwise, we can always decompose A into denumerable disjointed open subsets such that each subset is connected, and we treat then each subset separately.

From lemma 1, when $t < \zeta(\omega)$, we have

$$E(X_o(\omega)) = m[\frac{\nu}{2}\Delta f(X_t(\omega)) + \frac{1}{2}|\nabla f(X_t(\omega))|^2] + \varphi(X_t(\omega)) - m\nu^2|\nabla R(X_t(\omega))|^2$$
$$-m\nu^2 \Delta R(X_t(\omega))$$

where $R(x) = \frac{1}{2}\log[\rho(x)]$.

By Fokker-Planck's equation (6),

$$2\nu|\nabla R(x)|^2 + \nu\Delta R(x) = \Delta f(x) + 2\nabla R(x)\nabla f(x).$$

Thus,

$$E(X_o(\omega)) = \frac{m}{2}|\nabla f(X_t(\omega))|^2 - \frac{m\nu^2}{2}\Delta R(X_t(\omega)) + \varphi(X_t(\omega)) - m\nu\nabla R(X_t(\omega))\nabla f(X_t(\omega)),$$

that is

$$\frac{\nu}{2}\Delta R(X_t(\omega)) = \frac{1}{2\nu^2}|\nabla f(X_t(\omega))|^2 + \frac{1}{m\nu}[\varphi(X_t(\omega)) - E(X_o(\omega))] \qquad (7)$$
$$-\nabla R(X_t(\omega))\nabla f(X_t(\omega)) .$$

But from Ito's formula,

$$R(X_t)-R(X_o) = \int_o^t \nabla R(X_s)\nabla f(X_s)ds + \frac{\nu}{2}\int_o^t \Delta R(X_s)ds + \int_o^t \nabla R(X_s)dW_s \quad . \qquad (8)$$

Inserting (7) in (8), we obtain consequently

$$R(X_t)-R(X_o) = \int_o^t \nabla R(X_s)dW_s + \int_o^t [\frac{1}{2\nu}|\nabla f(X_s)|^2 + \frac{1}{m\nu}(\varphi(X_s) - E(X_o))]ds . \qquad (9)$$

Take a sequence of stopping times $S_n \uparrow\uparrow \zeta$, and denote

$$T_n(\omega) = \inf\{t;\ |\nabla R(X_t)| > n\} \wedge S_n \quad ,$$

then $T_n \uparrow\uparrow \zeta$.

Using (9), we obtain that

$$E[R(X_{T_n})-R(X_o)] = E[\int_0^{T_n}(\frac{1}{2\nu}|\nabla f(X_s)|^2 + \frac{1}{m\nu}(\varphi(X_s) - E(X_o)))ds]$$

$$\geqq \frac{-1}{m\nu} E[\int_0^{T_n} \varphi^-(X_s)ds] > -\infty, \qquad (10)$$

where φ^- is the negative part of φ. Thus we conclude that $P[\zeta < \infty] = o$.

We want now to weaken the condition that $\inf_x \varphi(x) > -\infty$, which is not necessary ones, appearing in the above theorem. Indeed we can prove

THEOREM 3. Suppose that $\rho(x) \to o$ when $|x| \to \infty$, and suppose that $\int_{\mathbb{R}^d} \varphi^-(x)\rho(x)dx < \infty$. Then, $\zeta = \infty$ a.s. and the equation (1) has a global solution which has $\rho(x)$ as its probability density function.

PROOF. We show at first that (10) holds. But in fact by lemma 2 of [2], we have (we suppose $T_n \leqq 1$ without losing generality)

$$E[\int_0^{T_n} \varphi^-(X_s)ds] \leqq \int_{\mathbb{R}^d} \varphi^-(x)\rho(x)dx . \qquad (11)$$

Thus we have (10) which implies that $\zeta = \infty$ a.s..

Now we show that $\rho(.)$ is the density function of X_t. From lemma 2 of [2], by repeating the argument used in proposition 18 of [3], we can also deduce that the probability distribution of X_t is dominated by $\rho(x)dx$. So that $\rho(.)$ is the density function.

Since the density is non-negative and of class C_2, it follows that each of its zero points is at least of degree two. Using this fact and (11), we can also treat the case where $\varphi(x) = O(d^{-2})$ where $d = d(x)$ is the distance of x from the boundary ∂A (see [4]).

ACKNOWLEDGEMENTS We are very grateful to P.A.Meyer and M.Nagasawa for helpful discussions. The support of the Stiftung Volkswagenwerk is gratefully acknowledged.

References

[1] Ph.Blanchard and Zheng Weian, "Stochastic variational principle and diffusion processes", these Proceedings.

[2] P.A.Meyer and Zheng Weian, "Sur la construction de certaines diffusions", (to appear in Séminaire de Probabilités XX, Lecture Notes in Mathematics)

[3] Zheng Weian, "Tightness results for laws of diffusion processes, application to stochastic mechanics", Ann.Inst.Henri Poincaré, Vol.21, n°2, 103-124 (1985)

[4] M.Nagasawa, "Segregation of a population in an environment", Journal of Mathematical Biology 9, 213-235 (1980)

STOCHASTIC VARIATIONAL PRINCIPLE
AND DIFFUSION PROCESSES

Ph.Blanchard & Zheng Weian*
Theoretische Physik, Universität Bielefeld
und
Research Center Bielefeld-Bochum-Stochastics

Summary

In this paper, we give a method to construct diffusion process with constant diffusion coefficient by a stochastic variational principle. The result is very similar to the classical case. We discuss also the relation between our stochastic variational principle and the stochastic mechanics.

§ 1. Some preliminary results

Given a probability space $(\Omega,\underline{\underline{F}},P)$. On a bounded interval of time $[o,T]$, we consider an increasing filtration $(\underline{\underline{F}}_t)$ which is continuous from the right and such that $\underline{\underline{F}}_o$ contains all P-negligible sets. Suppose X_t is a continuous semimartingale with values in $\mathbb{R}^d$ admitting the canonical decomposition $X_t=X_o+A_t+M_t$. We say that X belongs to $S(\underline{\underline{F}})$ if

1) X_o belongs to $L_2(\underline{\underline{F}})$;
2) M is a square-integrable $(\underline{\underline{F}}_t)$-martingale on $[o,T]$ and $M_o=o$;
3) $A_t = \int_o^t H_s\, ds$ with $E[\int_o^T |H_s|^2 ds] < \infty$.

*) On leave of absence from Department of Mathematical Statistics, East-China Normal University, Shanghai, China

It is easy to verify that $S(\underline{\underline{F}})$ is a linear space. Furthermore, we have (see Meyer and Zheng [1])

<u>LEMMA 1.1.</u> $S(\underline{\underline{F}})$ <u>is complete for the norm</u> $\| X \|_S = (E[|X_T|^2 + \int_o^T |H_s|^2 ds])^{1/2}$.

Now let (W_t) be a brownian motion with initial value W_o and let $(\underline{\underline{F}}_t)$ be a filtration containing $\sigma(W_s, \forall\, s \leqq t)$. We denote by $S_W(\underline{\underline{F}})$ the subset of $S(\underline{\underline{F}})$ such that $X \in S_W(\underline{\underline{F}})$ iff $X_o = W_o$ and its martingale part is (W_t). On $S_W(\underline{\underline{F}})$ we can define a new distance as follows. Let $X_t = \int_o^t H_s ds + W_t$ and $Y_t = \int_o^t K_s ds + W_t$, then we set

$$\| X-Y \| = (E\,[\int_o^T |H_s - K_s|^2 ds])^{1/2}. \tag{1.1}$$

On $S_W(\underline{\underline{F}})$, we have $\|X-Y\|^2 \leqq \|X-Y\|_S^2 < (T+1)\|X-Y\|^2$. So that $\|.-.\|$ and $\|.-.\|_S$ are equivalent distances on $S_W(\underline{\underline{F}})$.

<u>LEMMA 1.2.</u>i) $S_W(\underline{\underline{F}})$ <u>is an affine subset of</u> $S(\underline{\underline{F}})$

ii) $S_W(\underline{\underline{F}})$ <u>is complete for the distance</u> $\|.-.\|$.

It is a corollary to lemma 1.1.

<u>LEMMA 1.3.</u> <u>Let</u> $X \in S_W(\underline{\underline{F}})$ <u>and</u> $Y \in S_W(\underline{\underline{F}})$, <u>then</u>

$$E[\int_o^t |X_t - Y_t|^2 dt] \leqq \frac{1}{2} T^2 \|X-Y\|^2 .$$

PROOF. It follows from

$$E[\int_o^t |X_t - Y_t|^2 dt = E[\int_o^T | \int_o^t (H_s - K_s) ds|^2 dt] ,$$

and from Schwarz's inequality

$$|\int_o^t (H_s - K_s) ds|^2 \leqq t \int_o^t |H_s - K_s|^2 ds .$$

Thus we obtain

$$E[\int_o^T |X_t - Y_t|^2 dt] \leqq E[\int_o^T t dt \int_o^T |H_s - K_s|^2 ds] = \frac{1}{2} T^2 \|X-Y\|^2 .$$

We introduce now the definition of strongly convex function (see Meyer and Zheng [1]).

DEFINITION. Let $(U, |.|)$ be a normed space and let Q be a convex subset of U. We say that a convex function f defined on Q is <u>strongly convex</u> if there exists a constant $C > o$ such that we have for all pairs $a, b \in Q$ and all $\lambda \in [o,1]$,

$$(1-\lambda)f(a) + \lambda f(b) - f((1-\lambda)a+\lambda b) \geqq C\lambda(1-\lambda)||b-a||^2 . \tag{1.2}$$

Let $V(x,t)$ be a potential function. We consider the action J defined on $S_W(\underline{\underline{F}})$ in the following way: let $X_t = \int_0^t H_s ds + W_t$,

$$J(X) = E[\int_0^T (\frac{m}{2} |H_t|^2 - V(X_t,t)dt] . \tag{1.3}$$

For obtaining the strong convexity of the action (1.3), we impose that the second derivatives of $V(.,t)$ along all straight lines in $\mathbb{R}^d$ are uniformly bounded, i.e.

$$\frac{d^2}{d\lambda^2} V(x+\lambda e,t) \leqq k \tag{1.4}$$

for all $x \in \mathbb{R}^d$ and all unit vectors e. We impose also

$$|V(x,t)| \leqq C(1+|x|^2) \tag{1.5}$$

where C is some constant.

THEOREM 1.4. Under the conditions (1.4) and (1.5), for $T^2 < \frac{m}{k}$ the action J is strongly convex in $S_W(\underline{\underline{F}})$. As a consequence, there exists a unique element ξ of $S_W(\underline{\underline{F}})$ which minimizes J, i.e.

$$-\infty < J(\xi) = \inf_{X\in S_W(\underline{\underline{F}})} J(X) < \infty . \tag{1.6}$$

PROOF. Using (1.4), we deduce

$$(1-\lambda)V(X_t.t) + V(Y_t,t) - V((1-\lambda)X_t+\lambda Y_t.t) \leqq k\lambda(1-\lambda)|Y_t-X_t|^2 .$$

But from lemma 1.3,

$$E[\int_0^T |X_t-Y_t|^2dt \leqq \frac{1}{2}T^2 ||X-Y||^2 .$$

Thus we have

$$(1-\lambda)E[\int_0^T V(X_t,t)dt] + \lambda E[\int_0^T V(Y_t,t)dt] - E[\int_0^T V((1-\lambda)X_t+\lambda Y_t,t)dt] \tag{1.7}$$

$$\leqq \frac{k}{2}T^2\lambda(1-\lambda) ||Y-X||^2 .$$

On the other hand, we may write

$$(1-\lambda)|H_t|^2 + \lambda|K_t|^2 - |(1-\lambda)H_t+\lambda K_t|^2 = \lambda(1-\lambda)|H_t-K_t|^2 . \tag{1.8}$$

Then by (1.7) and (1.8) we obtain that

$$(1-\lambda)J(X) + \lambda J(Y) - J((1-\lambda)X + \lambda Y) \geqq \frac{1}{2}(m-kT^2)\,\|Y-X\|^2,$$

i.e. J is strongly convex. The condition (1.5) ensures that $-\infty < \inf_{X\in S_W(\underline{F})} J(X) < \infty$.

The existence of ξ which minimizes J and the uniqueness is a corollary to the theorem 3.1 of Meyer and Zheng [1]. It is a basic property of strongly convex functions.

§ 2. $mDD\xi_t = -\mathrm{grad}_x V(\xi_t,t)$

We are interested in the properties of the unique extremal point ξ of J. We assume now that $\mathrm{grad}_x V$ exists everywhere and

$$|V(x+\lambda r,t) - V(x,t) - \mathrm{grad}_x V(x,t)\cdot r| \leqq C\lambda^2(1+|x|^2+|r|^2) \tag{2.1}$$

$\forall x,\ r \in \mathbb{R}^d,\ \ \forall\ \lambda\in[o,1]$

where C is some constant.

THEOREM 2.1. Suppose that $V(x,t)$ satisfies the conditions (1.4), (1.5) and (2.1). Let $T^2 < \frac{m}{k}$. An element $X \in S_W(\underline{F})$ is the extremal point of J iff

$$H_s = \frac{1}{m}E\left[\int_s^T \mathrm{grad}_x V(X_u,u)du \mid \underline{F}_s\right] \tag{2.2}$$

$$= \int_o^s -\left(\frac{1}{m}\mathrm{grad}_x V(X_u,u)\right)du + E\left[\int_o^T \left(\frac{1}{m}\mathrm{grad}_x V(X_u,u)\right)du \mid \underline{F}_s\right]$$

REMARK. Using the notation of E.Nelson [1], (2.2) is just equivalent to

$$mDDX_s = -\mathrm{grad}_x V(X_s,s) \text{ and } DX_T = o \quad \text{a.s.} \tag{2.3}$$

PROOF. We give first a classical result. Let f(t) and g(t) be two integrable measurable functions, then for every $o < T < \infty$,

$$\int_o^T\left(\int_o^t f(s)ds\right)g(t)dt = \int_o^T\int_o^T I_{\{s\leqq t\}}(s,t)f(s)g(t)dsdt \tag{2.4}$$

$$= \int_o^T\left(\int_s^T g(t)dt\right)f(s)ds \quad .$$

Now let $X_t = \int_o^t H_s ds + W_t$ be the extremal point of J. If $Y_t = \int_o^t K_s ds + W_t$,

$$J(Y)-J(X) = E[\int_o^T (mH_t(K_t-H_t)-\text{grad}_x V(X_t,t)(Y_t-X_t))dt] + o(\| Y-X \|).$$

Since X is the extremal point,

$$E[\int^T (mH_t(K_t-H_t)-\text{grad}_x V(X_t,t)(Y_t-X_t))dt] = o \ . \tag{2.5}$$

That is

$$E[\int_o^T (mH_t(K_t-H_t)-\text{grad}_x V(X_t,t) \int_o^t (K_s-H_s)ds)dt] = o \ .$$

Thus by (2.4),

$$E[\int_o^T (mH_t(K_t-H_t)-(\int_t^T \text{grad}_x V(X_s,s)ds)(K_t-H_t))dt] = o \ .$$

Inserting in the above equality

$$K_t-H_t = E[mH_t- \int_t^T \text{grad}_x V(X_s,s)ds \mid \underline{\underline{F}}_t] \ ,$$

we obtain

$$mH_t = E[\int_t^T \text{grad}_x V(X_s,s)ds \mid F_t] \ . \tag{2.6}$$

Conversely, if (2.6) holds, we have also (2.5) and X is the extremal point of J.

In (2.3), $mDDX_s = -\text{grad}_x V(X_s,s)$ is just a stochastic Newtonian equation. But the condition $DX_T = o$ is too restrictive. To relax this condition, we change a little bit the action. Let $f(x) \in C^2(\mathbb{R}^d)$ such that

$$|f(x)| < C(1+|x|^2), \quad \frac{d^2}{d\lambda^2} f(x+\lambda e) \leqq k \tag{2.7}$$

for all $x \in \mathbb{R}^d$ and all unit vectors $e \in \mathbb{R}^d$, and that

$$|f(x+\lambda r)-f(x)-\text{grad}_x f(x).r| \leqq C\lambda^2(1+|x|^2 + |r|^2) \tag{2.8}$$

for all x, r $\mathbb{R}^d$, $\forall \lambda \in [o,1]$.

THEOREM 2.2. Suppose that $V(x,t)$ satisfies the conditions (1.4),(1.5) and (2.1), and that $f(x)$ satisfies the conditions (2.7) and (2.8). Let J_f be the new action defined by

$$\underline{J}_f(X) = J(X) + \tfrac{T}{2}E[f(X_b)] \ . \tag{2.9}$$

If $T^2 < \frac{m}{2k}$, the J_f is strongly convex. Moreover, an element $X \in S_W(\underline{\underline{F}})$ is the extremal point of J_f iff

$$H_s = \int_0^s -(\frac{1}{m}\mathrm{grad}_x V(X_u,u))du + E[\int_0^T (\frac{1}{m}\mathrm{grad}_x V(X_u,u))du + \frac{T}{2}\mathrm{grad}_x f(X_T) \mid \underline{\underline{F}}_s] \qquad (2.10)$$

REMARK. With the notation of E.Nelson, (2.10) can be put in the form

$$mDDX_s = -\mathrm{grad}_x V(X_s,s) \quad \text{and} \quad DX_T = \frac{T}{2}\mathrm{grad}_x f(X_1) \qquad (2.11)$$

PROOF. Since the proof is almost the same as that of theorem 2.1, we leave the details to the readers.

Now, let X be a solution of the following stochastic differential equation:

$$dX_t = b(X_t,t)dt + dW_t \quad , \qquad d < W^i, W^j >_t = \nu\delta^{ij}dt$$

and let f and V be two functions such that $\frac{T}{2}\mathrm{grad}_x f(x) = b(x,T)$ and that $-\mathrm{grad}_x V(x,t) = m(\frac{\partial}{\partial t} b(x,t) + b(x,t)\mathrm{grad}_x b(x,t) + \frac{\nu}{2}\Delta_x b(x,t))$. If the hypotheses of theorem 3.2 are satisfied, then X is the unique extremal point of the action J_f in $S_W(\underline{\underline{F}})$.

§ 3. Markov property of ξ

LEMMA 3.1. Let $F \subset G$ be two sub-σ-fields of $\underline{\underline{F}}$, and let H be an another sub-σ-field of $\underline{\underline{F}}$ such that H is independent of G. If a random variable $U \in F \vee H$ then $E[U|G] = E[U|F]$.

PROOF. It is sufficient to consider the case where $U = I_A I_B$ with $A \in H$ and $B \in F$. But it is well known that in the above case $E[U|G] = P[A]I_B \in F$.

Now let ξ be the extremal point of J_f in theorem 3.2.

LEMMA 3.2. Let $o < s < t < T$, and let $\underline{\underline{G}}_{s,t} = \sigma(\xi_s, W_u - W_s; \forall u$ such that $s \leq u \leq t)$, then $\xi_t \in \underline{\underline{G}}_{s,t}$.

PROOF. It is sufficient to consider the case where $s = o$. We can always assume that $\underline{\underline{F}}_o$ is separable and $\underline{\underline{F}}_o = \sigma(W_o, Y_o)$ where Y_o is a random variable independent of $\sigma(W_t - W_o; \forall t \leq T)$. Now we realize (according to their probabilistic distribution) W_o, Y_o, and $(W_t - W_o;\ \forall t \leq T)$ on a new filtration space $(\Omega', \underline{\underline{F}}', \underline{\underline{F}}'_t, P')$ such that $\Omega' = [0,1] \times \Omega''$, $\underline{\underline{F}}'_t = \beta([o,1] \times \underline{\underline{F}}''_t$, $F' = F'_T$ and $P' = \mu([o,t]) \times P''$ where $(\Omega'', \underline{\underline{F}}'', \underline{\underline{F}}''_t, P'')$ is the filtration space generated by (W_t). Thus the original filtration space can be considered as a sub-filtration space of $(\Omega', \underline{\underline{F}}', \underline{\underline{F}}'_t, P')$. We have thus

$$\inf_{X\in S_W(\underline{\underline{F}}'')} \underline{J}_f(X) \geqq \inf_{X\in S_W(\underline{\underline{F}})} \underline{J}_f(X) \geqq \inf_{X\in S_W(\underline{\underline{F}}')} \underline{J}_f(X) \quad . \tag{3.1}$$

It is reduced to prove that

$$\inf_{X\in S_W(F'')} \underline{J}_f(X) = \inf_{X\in S_W(\underline{\underline{F}}')} \underline{J}_f(X). \tag{3.2}$$

In fact, if (3.2) is true, from the uniqueness of the extremal point, we know that the extremal point of $\underline{J}_f$ in $S_W(\underline{\underline{F}})$ belongs to $S_W(F'')$, which proves the lemma.

Let $(A_i)_{i=1,2,\ldots}$ be a sequence of subsets of [o,1] such that $\beta([o,1]) = (A_i;\ i=1,2,\ldots)$, and let $\sigma_n = \sigma(A_1,\ldots,A_n)$. We denote $\underline{\underline{F}}_t^{(n)} = \sigma_n V \underline{\underline{F}}_t''$. To prove (3.2), it is sufficient to prove

$$\inf_{X\in S_W(\underline{\underline{F}}'')} \underline{J}_f(X) = \inf_{X\in S_W(\underline{\underline{F}}^{(n)})} \underline{J}_f(X) \quad , \quad n = 1,2,\ldots \tag{3.3}$$

(a simple application of the martingale theory!). Now the only thing we have to prove is (3.3). But in fact, if (3.3) does not hold, there will exist an extremal point ξ in $S_W(\underline{\underline{F}}^{(n)}) \setminus S_W(\underline{\underline{F}}'')$ and we can write (let $A_1^*,\ldots,A_{n'}^*$ be all the μ-atoms of σ_n)

$$\xi_t(\omega') = \sum_{i=1}^{n'} \xi_t^{(i)} I_{A_i^* \times \Omega''}(\omega') \quad , \text{ where } \xi^{(i)} \in S_W(\underline{\underline{F}}'') \quad ,$$

and there will exist i^* such that $\underline{J}_f(\xi^{(i^*)}) < \inf_{X\in S_W(\underline{\underline{F}}'')} \underline{J}_f(X)$. Since it is impossible, we obtain (3.3) and the lemma is proved.

THEOREM 3.3. Under the conditions of theorem 2.2, the extremal point of J_f is a Markov process which is the solution of the following stochastic differential equation:

$$d\xi_t = b(\xi_t,t)dt + dW_t \quad , \ \xi_0 = W_0, \tag{3.4}$$

where

$$b(\xi_t,t) = E[\int_t^b (\tfrac{1}{m}\operatorname{grad}_x V(\xi_u,u))du + \tfrac{T}{2}\operatorname{grad}_x f(\xi_T) \mid \xi_t] \ .$$

PROOF. From (2.10) it is sufficient to prove that ξ is a Markov process, i.e. $E[h(\xi_t)\mid \underline{\underline{F}}_s] = E[h(\xi_t)\mid \xi_s]$, $\forall\ h \in C_0^1\ (\mathbb{R}^d)$ and $\forall\ s < t \leqq T$. But from lemma 3.2, $\xi_t \in \sigma(\xi_s,\ W_u - W_s;\ \forall u$ such that $s \leqq u \leqq t)$. Now setting $F = \sigma(\xi_s)$, $G = \underline{\underline{F}}_s$ and $U = h(\xi_t)$ in lemma 3.1, we arrive at the conclusion.

The above theorem gives us a "stochastic mechanics method" to prove the existence of the solution of stochastic differential equation (3.4).

§ 4. Its relation with Nelson's stochastic mechanics

In Nelson's stochastic mechanics, we consider another "stochastic acceleration" defined as $\frac{1}{2}(DD_*+D_*D)X_t$. Let $\psi(x,t) = \exp(R(x,t) + iS(x,t))$ be a solution of Schrödinger's equation

$$i\hbar\frac{\partial}{\partial t}\psi(x,t) = -\frac{\hbar^2}{2m}\Delta\psi(x,t) + V(x,t)\psi(x,t) \quad .$$

We set $H(x,t) = \frac{\hbar}{m}\,\mathrm{grad}_x(R(x,t) + S(x,t))$ and $\rho(x,t) = |\psi(x,t)|^2$. Then the following Fokker-Planck's equation holds:

$$\frac{\partial}{\partial t}\rho(x,t) = \frac{\hbar}{2m}\Delta\rho(x,t) - \mathrm{div}_x[\rho(x,t)H(x,t)] \,.$$

Under some regularity conditions, there exists a diffusion process

$$dX_t = H(X_t,t)dt + dW_t \quad , \qquad d<W^i,W^j>_t = \frac{\hbar}{m}\,\delta^{ij}dt \quad ,$$

whose probability density at time t is just $\rho(x,t)$. Nelson has shown that the following stochastic Newton equation holds:

$$ma(X_t,t) = \frac{m}{2}(DD_* + D_*D)X_t = -\mathrm{grad}_x V(X_t,t), \tag{4.1}$$

where

$$a(x,t) = \mathrm{grad}_x\Big(\frac{\partial}{\partial t}\Big(\frac{\hbar}{m}\,S\Big) + \frac{\hbar^2}{2m^2}\,\Sigma_i\Big[\Big(\frac{\partial S}{\partial x_i}\Big)^2 - \Big(\frac{\partial R}{\partial x_i}\Big)^2\Big] - \frac{\hbar^2}{2m^2}\,\Delta R\Big) \quad .$$

Now if we write also DDX_t as a function of (X_t,t), we obtain

$$DDX_t = \frac{\partial}{\partial t}\,H(X_t,t) + H.\mathrm{grad}_x H(X_t,t) + \frac{\hbar}{2m}\,\Delta H(X_t,t) \quad .$$

We denote by $a'(X_t,t)$ the function of (X_t,t) on the right side of the above equality. We can easily verify that

$$a'(x,t) = \mathrm{grad}_x\Big(\frac{\partial}{\partial t}\Big[\frac{\hbar}{m}(R+S)\Big] + \frac{\hbar^2}{2m^2}\,\Sigma_i\Big[\frac{\partial(R+S)}{\partial x_i}\Big]^2 + \frac{\hbar^2}{2m^2}\,\Delta(R+S)$$

(all the calculations in this paragraph are formal!). Introducing a new function

$$V'(x,t) = \hbar\,\frac{\partial}{\partial t}\,R + \frac{\hbar^2}{m}\Sigma_i\,\frac{\partial R}{\partial x_i}\,\Big[\frac{\partial(R+S)}{\partial x_i}\Big] + \frac{\hbar^2}{2m}\,\Delta(2R+S) = \frac{\hbar^2}{m}\Big(\frac{\Delta e^R}{e^R}\Big) \;,$$

then equation (4.1) is formally equivalent to

$$mDDX_t = -\mathrm{grad}_x[V(X_t,t) - V'(X_t,t)] \ . \tag{4.2}$$

Following M.Davidson [1], we introduce operators corresponding to dynamical variables. Let H_t be the Hilbert space of real function $f : \mathbb{R}^d \to \mathbb{R}$, with scalar product

$$\langle f,g \rangle = E[f(X_t)g(X_t)] = \int_{\mathbb{R}^d} f(x)g(x)\rho(x,t)dx \ .$$

We define the operator $\dot{X}$ by

$$(\dot{X}f)(x) = \lim_{u\uparrow t, s\uparrow t} \frac{\partial}{\partial u} E[X_u f(X_t) | X_s = x] \qquad s < u < t,$$

and the operator $\ddot{X}$ by

$$(\ddot{X}f)(x) = \lim_{u\uparrow t, s\uparrow t} \frac{\partial^2}{\partial u^2} E[X_u f(X_t) | X_s = x] \qquad s < u < t,$$

We can easily verify that $\dot{X} = H + \frac{\hbar}{m}\nabla$ and (when H is a gradient), $\ddot{X} = \frac{\partial}{\partial t}H + \frac{\hbar}{2m}\Delta H + \frac{1}{2}\Delta H^2$. Reexpressing $\ddot{X}$ in terms of the potential V, the last equation can be written

$$m\ddot{X} = -\Delta V + \frac{\hbar^2}{m}\nabla\left(\frac{\Delta e^R}{e^R}\right) = -\nabla(V-V') \ .$$

It is just equality (4.2).

Acknowledgement The authors would like to thank Prof. P. A. Meyer for many useful discussions. It was him who has suggested them to prove the Markov property of the extremal process. The second author would like to thank Prof. Ph. Blanchard for his kind invitation to the workshop.

References

M.Davidson [1], Lett.Math.Phys. 3, 271 (1979);

E.Nelson [1], Dynamical theories of Brownian Motion, Princeton Univ. (1967);

P.A.Meyer & W.A.Zheng [1], "Quelques résultats de 'mécanique stochastique' ", Séminaire de Probabilités XVIII, (1984).

SPECTRAL FLUCTUATIONS, RANDOM MATRIX THEORIES AND CHAOTIC MOTION

Oriol BOHIGAS, Marie-Joya GIANNONI and Charles SCHMIT
Division de Physique Théorique*, Institut de Physique Nucléaire,
F-91406 Orsay Cedex, France

1. Introduction

A conference on Quantum Chaos was held at Como two years ago and many questions on spectral fluctuations presented there have been investigated since then [Ca-85]. Some suggested lines of inquiry are now becoming fully developed, some conjectures based on numerical experiments are being put on a firm theoretical basis and new theoretical as well as experimental progress is being made. It is the purpose of this contribution to give a brief account on some topics of this activity. The general theme will be : 'Given a system which is classically chaotic which are the manifestations in the corresponding quantum spectrum of its chaotic character ?' Emphasis will be given to works that are paving the way between the study of chaotic motion and random matrix physics.

The material of this talk is organized as follows : In Section 2 we remind how spectral fluctuations are defined and characterized, and we briefly describe the more important models of spectral fluctuations, with emphasis on random matrix theory predictions, which are compared to existing data. In Section 3 we review the present status of computer experiments and of theories that have lead to the identification of several universality classes for spectral fluctuations of quantum systems. The basis of such classification, closely inspired by random matrix theories, has its origin in the regularity properties (integrability versus chaoticity) of the corresponding classical system. The role played by symmetries is emphasized and the transition regimes between the different universality classes is discussed. In Section 4 some recent results for the hydrogen atom in a strong magnetic field and on the spectrum of the Laplacian on a surface of negative curvature, problems both of current interest in this field, are discussed. We end up with some remarks and conclusions.

2. Fluctuation measures : models and predictions [BFF-81,BG-84]

We consider the discrete spectrum $E_1, E_2, E_3, \ldots$ of a d-dimensional quantum system (an atomic nucleus, an atom, a molecule or model systems like a particle in a potential, in particular, a particle in a box) with Hamiltonian $H(\underset{\sim}{q},\underset{\sim}{p})$ and leading to the Schrödinger equation

$$(\Delta - V(\underset{\sim}{q}) + E)\Psi(\underset{\sim}{q}) = 0 \qquad (1)$$

Let N(E) be the staircase function giving the number of points on the energy axis

*Laboratoire associé au C.N.R.S.

which are below or equal to E. The question now is to separate N(E) in a smooth part $N_{av}(E)$ and the remainder will define the fluctuating part $N_{f\ell}(E)$ of N(E)

$$N(E) = N_{av}(E) + N_{f\ell}(E) \tag{2}$$

For $N_{av}(E)$ one can obtain, by taking the simple semi-classical rule that each quantum state is associated with a phase-space volume h^d

$$N_{av}(E) \simeq \frac{1}{2^d \pi^{d/2} \Gamma(d/2+1)} \int_{V(\underset{\sim}{q}) \leq E} [E - V(\underset{\sim}{q})]^{d/2} \, d\underset{\sim}{q} \tag{3}$$

For the particular case of one particle in a box in two dimensions (billiard in the classical case), one has $N_{av}(E) \simeq SE/4\pi$, where S is the area of the two-dimensional domain. If one includes corrections, which are smooth terms of lower order in E, one obtains, with Dirichlet boundary conditions

$$N_{av}(E) \simeq (1/4\pi)(SE - \mathcal{L}\sqrt{E} + K) \tag{4}$$

In Eq.(4) $\mathcal{L}$ is the length of the parameter of the boundary whose area is S ; K is a constant containing complex information on the geometrical and topological properties of the domain.

In Fig.1 are compared N(E) and $N_{av}(E)$ for some particular cases. It can be seen that $N_{av}(E)$ indeed reproduces perfectly the average behaviour of N(E), starting from the bottom of the spectrum.

Before studying fluctuations one wants to get rid of $N_{av}(E)$ in order to characterize and compare fluctuation patterns of different systems whose corresponding average behaviours are not the same. For that purpose one can "unfold" the original spectrum $\{E_i\}$ through the mapping $E \mapsto x$

$$x_i = N_{av}(E_i) \qquad i = 1,2,3,... \tag{5}$$

The effect of (5) is that the sequence $\{x_i\}$ has on the average a constant mean spacing (or a constant density) equal to unity, irrespective of the particular form of the function $N_{av}(E)$. We are now in position to study the statistical laws governing sequences $\{x_i\}$ having very different origins. By construction $x_i \simeq i-1/2$ (i=1,2,...) and the departures

$$\delta_i = x_i - (i - 1/2) \qquad i = 1,2,... \tag{6}$$

of x_i from its average value i-1/2 are the level fluctuations.

To characterize level fluctuations in a systematic way one deals with the k-level correlation functions $R_k(x_1,...,x_k)$ ($R_k(x_1,...,x_k)dx_1...dx_k$ is the probability of finding one level within each of the intervals $[x_j,x_j+dx_j]$) and measures derived from them. We shall only refer to

1/ The spacing distribution p(x) between adjacent levels.

2/ Quantities directly related to the number statistic n(L) : given an interval $[\alpha, \alpha+L]$ of length L, it counts the number of levels contained in the interval. The average

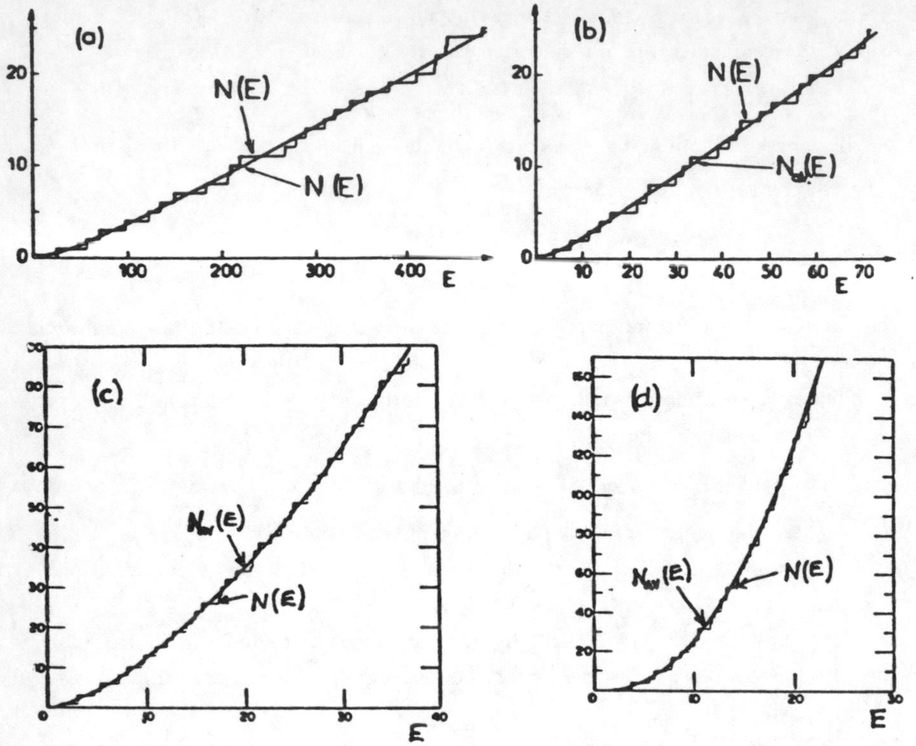

Fig.1 - Plots of N(E) and $N_{av}(E)$ for : (a) a quarter of circle and Eq.4 ; (b) a stadium (see Fig.3) and Eq.(4) ; (c) $V(\underset{\sim}{q}) = q_1^4 + q_2^4$ and Eq.(3) , d = 2 ; (d) $V(\underset{\sim}{q}) = q_1^4 + q_2^4 + q_3^4$ and Eq.(3), d = 3 ((c) and (d) taken from [HMY-81]).

value of n(L) is L (the mean spacing is unity). We shall consider higher moments or cumulants of n(L) : variance $\Sigma^2(L)$, skewness $\gamma_1(L)$ and excess $\gamma_2(L)$.

3/ The $\overline{\Delta}_3$ statistic of Dyson and Mehta. It measures, given an interval of length L, the least-square deviation of the staircase function from the best straight line fitting it. Its average value $\overline{\Delta}_3$ is related to the variance $\Sigma^2(L)$ of n(L).

In general $\Sigma^2(L)$ and $\overline{\Delta}_3(L)$ can be expressed in terms of the 2-level correlation function, whereas $\gamma_1(L)$ ($\gamma_2(L)$) depends also on the 3-level (3- and 4-level) correlation function(s) [BHP-85].

Let us consider two trivial limiting cases

1/ Take a random variable s whose probability density p(x) is exp(-x).

Construct a sequence $\{x_i\}$ as follows

$$x_1 = 1/2,\ x_{i+1} = x_i + s_i \qquad i = 1,2,3,..., \tag{7}$$

where s_i are outcomes of independent trials of the variable s. The resulting spectrum is what is called a Poisson spectrum (case of maximum randomness). One has $p(x) = e^{-x}$,

$\Sigma^2(L) = L$, $\bar{\Delta}_3(L) = L/15$.

2/ A picked fence spectrum or spectrum of the harmonic oscillator in one dimension. It is the more ordered spectrum one can imagine, with no randomness. One has $p(x)= \delta(x-1)$, $\Sigma^2(L) = 0$, $\bar{\Delta}_3(L) = 1/12$.

The 'non trivial' models of spectral fluctuations are provided by random matrix theories (RMT) [Po-65,Me-67]. In RMT one considers the Hamiltonian matrix H as an N × N stochastic matrix (the matrix elements are random variables) ; the random matrix ensemble is specified by the probability density $\mathcal{P}(H)dH$. One is interested in asymptotic results valid for large N.

General underlying space-time symmetries obeyed by the system put important restrictions on the admissible matrix ensembles. We shall refer to results of the Gaussian Orthogonal Ensemble (GOE) and the Gaussian Unitary Ensemble (GUE) which correspond to ensembles of real symmetric matrices and of hermitian matrices respectively. In general, GOE applies when time-reversal invariance is a good symmetry and GUE when it is not (see next Section for some warnings). Besides these general symmetry considerations, no other property of the system is taken into account to define the GOE or GUE.

GOE and GUE eigenvalue fluctuations are presently well known. For GOE the spacing distribution is very well approximated by

$$p(x) \simeq (\pi/2)\, x \exp(-(\pi/4)x^2) \qquad (8)$$

and for GUE by

$$p(x) \simeq (32/\pi^2)x^2 \exp(-(4/\pi)x^2) \qquad (9)$$

The spacing distributions in both cases show level repulsion, i.e. tendency to avoid level clustering or small probability of small spacings ($p(x)$ vanishes at the origin). The level repulsion is stronger for GUE than for GOE : near the origin $p(x) \sim (\pi^2/6)x$ for GOE whereas for GUE one has $p(x) \sim (\pi^2/3)x^2$. For GOE the number variance $\Sigma^2(L)$ for $L \gtrsim 1$ is given by

$$\Sigma^2(L) = (2/\pi^2)\ln L + 0.44 \qquad (10)$$

In (10) the logarithmic increase is to be compared to the linear increase with L for a Poisson spectrum. One can speak of the semicrystalline nature of the spectrum, showing long range order. The GUE spectrum is more rigid than the GOE spectrum : $\Sigma^2(L)$ is half the GOE-value plus 1/8. For large L, the average of $\Delta_3(L)$ is given for GOE by

$$\bar{\Delta}_3(L) \simeq (1/\pi^2)\ln L - 0.007 \qquad (11)$$

GUE shows also a logarithmic increase of $\bar{\Delta}_3(L)$ but with a smaller coefficient than in Eq.(11) (stronger rigidity).

How well do GOE predictions compare with experimental data ? We shall restrict to high resolution nuclear resonance data. The combined set of nuclear resonance - energy data of different nuclei- in short, the nuclear data ensemble (NDE)- has been treated as a sampling of eigenvalues of GOE matrices [HPB-82,BHP-83,BHP-85]. Results are reproduced in Fig.2. As can be seen, all the fluctuation measures considered, which include a thorough study of 2-point measures and to some extent more than 2-point measures as well as, are fully consistent with GOE predictions.

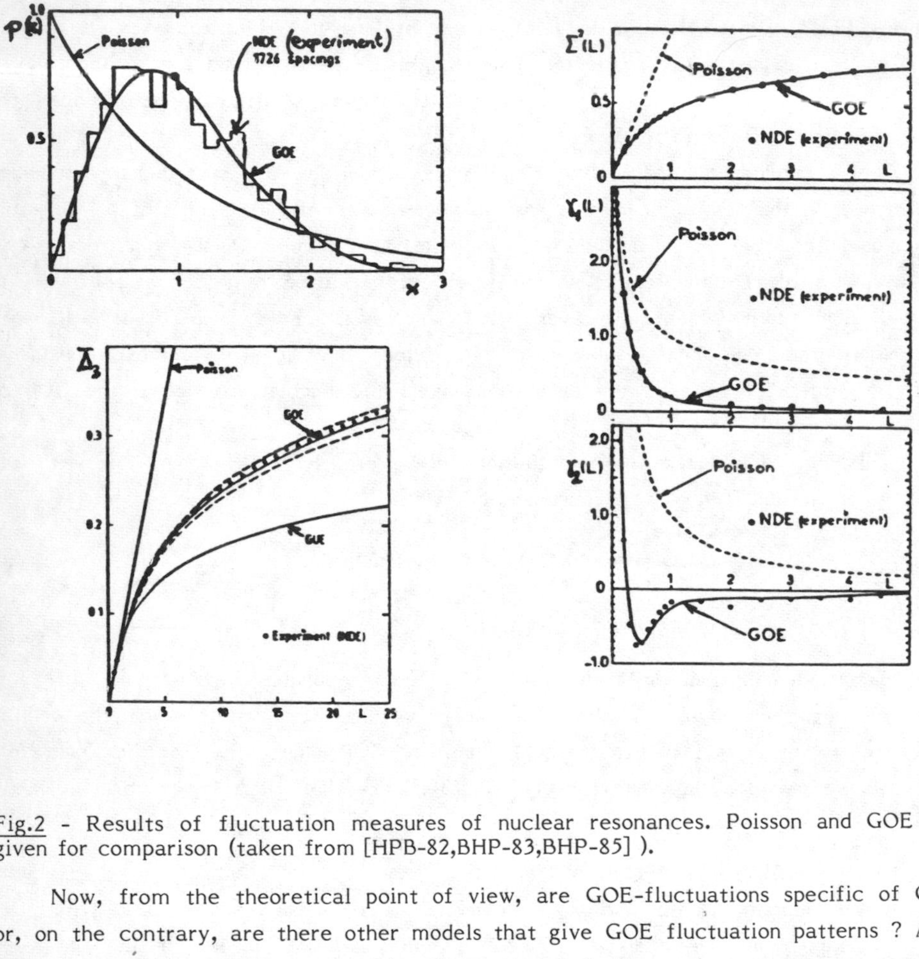

Fig.2 - Results of fluctuation measures of nuclear resonances. Poisson and GOE are given for comparison (taken from [HPB-82,BHP-83,BHP-85]).

Now, from the theoretical point of view, are GOE-fluctuations specific of GOE or, on the contrary, are there other models that give GOE fluctuation patterns ? And, from the experimental one, are the fluctuations of the nuclear resonances specific of nuclei or, on the contrary, are they also observed in other systems ? Concerning the first question, one knows that there is a whole variety of models of random matrix ensembles that give GOE-fluctuations (some results are analytical, the others are obtained from Monte Carlo calculations). Concerning the second one, some atomic spectra have also been analyzed [CG-83] and there are some pioneering studies of fluctuations of molecular spectra [HKC-83,MSP-84,LLJ-86]. And the outcome is that the fluctuations seem to be consistent with GOE predictions, although the statistical significance is much lower than for the nuclear case. We therefore see that, on the one hand, the spectra of very different systems (nuclei, some atoms and molecules), when properly scaled, seem to have identical fluctuation patterns, even though they are governed by very different force laws (short range interactions and Coulomb long range forces). On the other hand, these characteristic fluctuation patterns, although not specific of, are well reproduced by GOE, a parameter-free theory. Thus a simple picture emerges : the level fluctuation laws seem to be universal, as well from the experimental than from the theoretical point of view.

3. Spectral fluctuations and chaotic motion

To obtain some clues on the origin of the universality of level fluctuation laws and also to investigate how "complicated" a system must be in order to show RMT-fluctuations [BG-84] let us first discuss some results of numerical experiments on two-dimensional systems. The guiding lines we will try to follow are : i) the notion of simple or complicated as used in studying classical dynamical systems, namely integrable or chaoric respectively, ii) Einstein's precept "everything should be made as simple as possible, but not simpler".

Consider a particle in a box in two dimensions with boundaries as shown in Fig.3. The classical problem is a billiard problem, which is integrable with a circular boundary but fully chaotic (K- system) with Sinai's and Bunimovich's stadium boundaries. For the quantum problem we are interested in the spectrum of the Laplacian with Dirichlet boundary conditions (vanishing of the wave function on the boundary). And as explained before, we know how to separate out the average behaviour (see Eq.(4)).

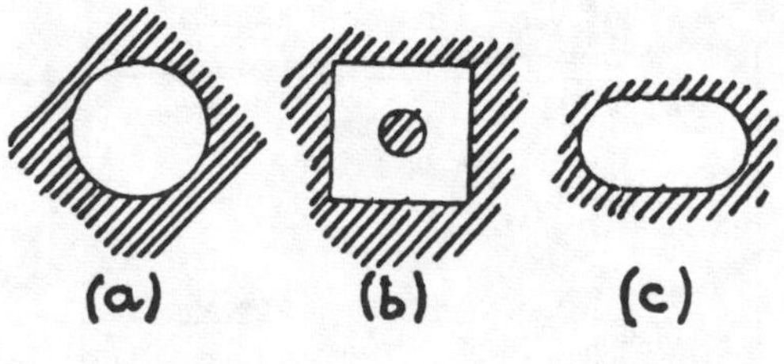

Fig.3 - Different boundaries in which a particle is enclosed :(a) circular billiard ; (b) Sinai's billiard ; (c) Bunimovich's stadium billiard.

Results of the spectral fluctuations are reproduced in Fig.4. The message seems fairly clear : The system whose classical analogue is integrable shows Poisson fluctuations whereas the systems whose classical analogues are fully chaotic show GOE fluctuation patterns.

What happens if one considers not time-reversal systems but rather time non-invariant systems ? From RMT predictions one expects to have GUE-fluctuations and it is indeed what is found as shown by Seligman and Verbaarschot [SV-85b]. These authors studied the motion of a particle in a combination of inhomogeneous magnetic and scalar force fields

$$H(\underset{\sim}{q},\underset{\sim}{p}) = \frac{1}{2}(p_1+a\, q_2^3)^2 + \frac{1}{2}(p_2 + a\, q_1^3)^2 + \\ + \alpha_1 q_1^6 + \alpha_2\, q_2^6 - \alpha_{12}(q_1 - q_2)^6 \qquad (12)$$

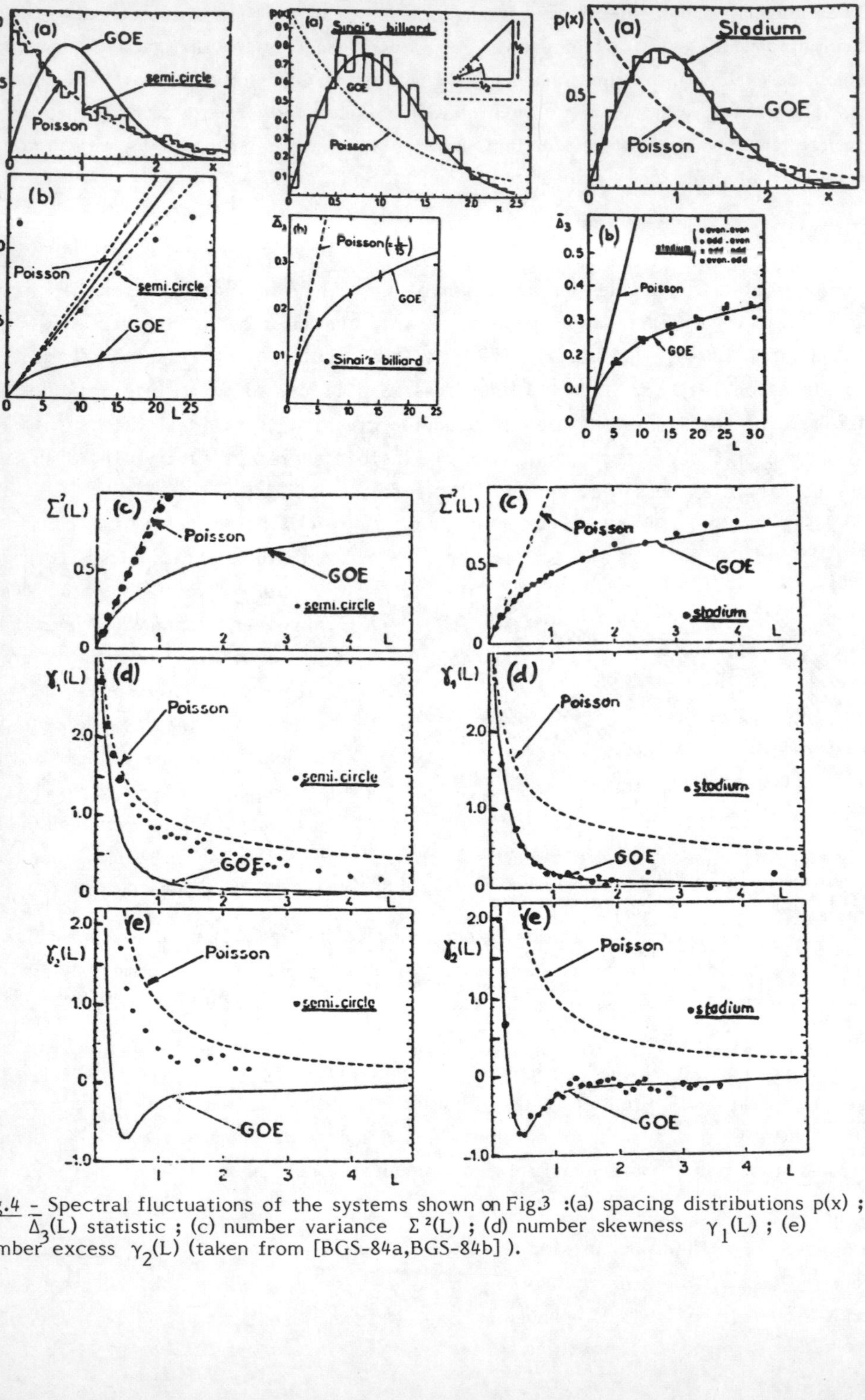

Fig.4 - Spectral fluctuations of the systems shown on Fig.3 :(a) spacing distributions p(x) ; (b) $\bar{\Delta}_3(L)$ statistic ; (c) number variance $\Sigma^2(L)$; (d) number skewness $\gamma_1(L)$; (e) number excess $\gamma_2(L)$ (taken from [BGS-84a,BGS-84b]).

By an adequate choice of the values of the parameters the classical motion is completely chaotic, and the spectral fluctuations of the quantum results are displayed in Fig.5 which, as expected, agree with GUE predictions. Berry and Robnik [BR-85] have studied the spectral fluctuations of a very interesting and subtle family of systems, which they call Aharonov-Bohm chaotic billiards. It consists of chaotic billiards with a single line of magnetic flux. The geometry of classical trajectories are unaffected by the flux, whereas the quantum mechanics -in particular the energy levels- are altered by the presence of the flux line. This system breaks time reversal invariance for the quantum particle and its spectral fluctuations are generically (i.e. except for special values of the quantum flux parameter) of the GUE type.

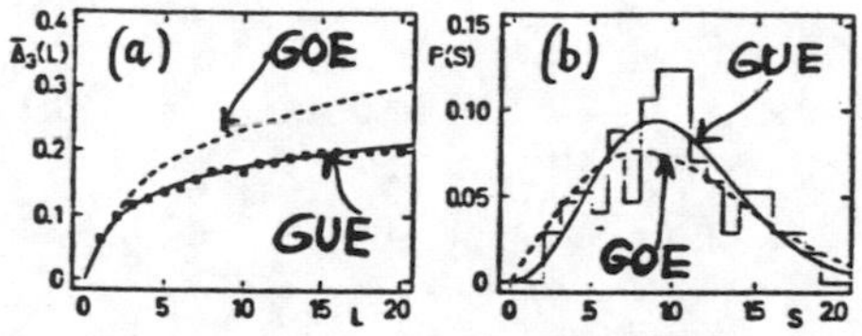

Fig.5 -Spectral fluctuations of the system governed by Eq.(12) : (a) $\bar{\Delta}_3(L)$; (b) spacing distribution p(x) (taken from [SV-85b]).

To summarize the numerical experience accumulated so far, one can say that classically integrable quantum systems show Poissonian spectral fluctuations whereas classically chaotic quantum systems show GOE(GUE) fluctuations if they are time reversal invariant (time reversal non invariant). What is important now is to understand theoretically these findings. Recently Berry [Be-85] has given a semiclassical derivation of the spectral rigidity. He employs the semiclassical techniques introduced by Gutzwiller, Balian and Bloch, which consists in an asymptotic representation of the spectral density as a sum over all the periodic orbits of the classical system. He predicts universality in the regime $1 \ll L \ll L_{max}$, with L_{max} determined by the shortest classical closed orbit ; for $L \gg L_{max}$ there is a non-universal saturation value of $\bar{\Delta}_3(L)$. In the universal regime, the long range predictions coincide with Poisson-, GOE- and GUE- predictions for classically integrable-, chaotic and time-reversal-, chaotic and time-reversal breaking- systems, in agreement with what is found numerically. It is important to notice that, in deriving the results, random matrix theory is not used and no statistical assumptions are made.

Some words concerning symmetries are in order. The random matrix predictions described in the previous section apply to levels having the same set of quantum numbers because the matrix representing the Hamiltonian is splitted into disconnected blocks, each block characterized by exact quantum numbers. If one considers a spectrum containing several sets of quantum numbers, the spectral fluctuations are obtained by an independent superposition of correlated spectra, with proper weighting factors. In order to derive the resulting fluctuations, consider more generally a spectrum obtained from the superposition of ℓ independent sequences with relative weights μ_i ($\Sigma \mu_i = 1$) and k-level cluster functions, number variance and $\bar{\Delta}_3$ statistic, $Y_{k,i}$, Σ^2_i, $\bar{\Delta}_{3,i}$ respectively. The corresponding quantities for the com bined system are [Pa-79]

$$Y_k\ (x_i,\dots,x_k) = \Sigma_i (f_i)^k Y_{k,i}(\mu_1 x_1,\dots,\mu_k,\dots,u_k x_k) \tag{13}$$

resulting in the additivity of Σ^2 and Δ_3

$$\Sigma^2(L) = \Sigma_i\ \Sigma^2{}_i(\mu_i L) \tag{14}$$

$$\overline{\Delta}_3(L) = \Sigma_i\ \overline{\Delta}_{3,i}(\mu_i L) \tag{15}$$

The spacing distribution of the combined spectrum is (see Appendix 22 of [Me-67])

$$p(x) = E(x) \left\{ \Sigma_i \mu_i^2 \frac{p_i(\mu_i x)}{E_i(\mu_i x)} + [\Sigma_i \mu_i \frac{1-F_i(\mu_i x)}{E_i(\mu_i x)}]^2 - \Sigma_i (\mu_i \frac{1-F_i(\mu_i x)}{E_i(\mu_i x)})^2 \right\} \tag{16}$$

where

$$F_i(y) = \int_o^y p_i(x)dx \quad , \quad E_i(z) = \int_z^\infty [1 - F_i(y)]dy \tag{17}$$

and

$$E(z) = \prod_i E_i(z) \tag{18}$$

For instance, for the stadium billiard, one has four different symmetry classes with equal weights $\mu_i = 1/4$, each class following GOE predictions (see Fig.4). If one considers the total spectrum without separating with respect to the symmetry classes, the results are given in Fig.6 and compared to the superposition of four independent GOE sequences with equal weights.

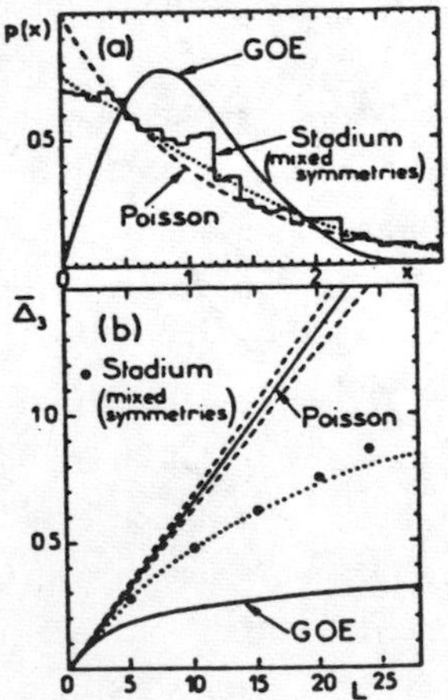

Fig.6 - Spectral fluctuations of the stadium compared to the predictions Eq.(16) and Eq.(15), dotted lines (taken from [BGS-84b]).

Robnik and Berry [RB-86] have discussed another problem of symmetries (which they call false T-violation) : there exist chaotic systems violating T but possessing an invariance under a combination of T and some other symmetry (which may be geometric -for example a reflection- but may also be of dynamical nature) such that they have GOE (and not GUE) fluctuations. Some examples are the system governed by Eq.(12) with $\alpha_{12} = 0$ (see [SV-85b]), Aharonov-Bohm billiards when the quantum flux is half integer and atoms in strong uniform magnetic fields (see next Section).

Until now we have only mentioned systems which are classically integrable or fully chaotic. But for d-dimensional generic systems the phase space is mixed : some orbits are on d-dimensinal tori and others explore (2d-1)-dimensional regions chaotically. What are the fluctuations of the corresponding quantum systems ? To investigate this question several authors have studied systems that classically show a transition between the two limiting cases of totally regular and chaotic behaviour as a parameter is varied [HKC-84,SVZ-84,IY-85,CG-86]. An example is given in Fig.7 where, in correspondence with the classical order to chaos transition one can observe the transition in the spectra from Poisson to GOE fluctuations. Based on semiclassical arguments Berry and Robnik [BR-84] suggest that the spectral fluctuations should result from independently superposing a Poisson spectrum with relative weight μ_1, given by the sum of Liouville measures of all classical regular regions, and (ℓ -1) GOE spectra with weights μ_i $i = 2,\ldots,\ell$ given by the Liouville measure of each (ℓ-1) chaotic regions. For the case of only one chaotic region (generic case for d $\geq$ 3, due to Arnold diffusion) of measure $\bar{\mu}$, Eq.(16) gives [BR-84]

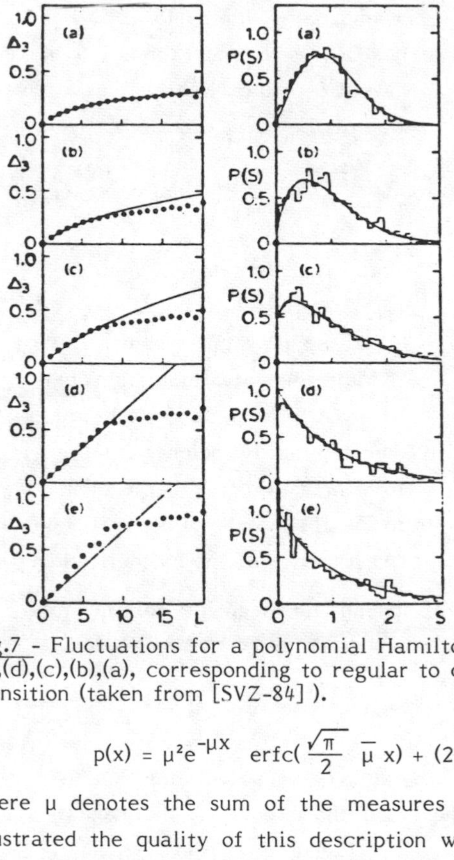

Fig.7 - Fluctuations for a polynomial Hamiltonian : (e),(d),(c),(b),(a), corresponding to regular to chaotic transition (taken from [SVZ-84]).

$$p(x) = \mu^2 e^{-\mu x} \ \mathrm{erfc}\left(\frac{\sqrt{\pi}}{2} \ \bar{\mu} x\right) + \left(2\mu\bar{\mu} + \frac{\pi}{2} \bar{\mu}^3 x\right) \exp\left(-\mu x - \frac{\pi}{4} \bar{\mu}^2 x^2\right) \tag{19}$$

where μ denotes the sum of the measures of regular regions ($\mu + \bar{\mu} = 1$). In Fig.8 is illustrated the quality of this description when applied to different systems, including some polynomial Hamiltonians [ZMK-86,MHK-84] and billiard systems [IY-85]. One compares the value of $\bar{\mu}_{c\ell}$ calculated by studying the classical motion, with the value $\bar{\mu}_{qm}$ obtained by making a best fit of the spacing distribution, obtained from the quantum spectrum, with Eq.(19). One can see that the agreement is fair (see [SV-85a, ZMK-86] for a detailed discussion).

Let us now turn to the case of a GOE to GUE transition in the fluctuations. From the random matrix theory side, this problem has been completely solved by Pandey and Mehta [PM-83], who have derived closed analytic expressions for the k-level correlation and cluster functions. In Ref.[PM-83] one considers an ensemble of $N \times N$ random matrices

$$H = H_{GOE}(v^2) + i\,\alpha\, A(v^2)\,, \qquad \alpha > 0 \tag{20}$$

where H_{GOE} is a GOE matrix (v^2 is the variance of the non diagonal matrix elements) and A is an antisymmetric matrix with matrix elements distributed normally (around zero with variance v^2) and independently. For $\alpha = 1$ one recovers the GOE and for $\alpha = 1$ the GUE. If v and α are finite the k-level correlation functions for $k > 1$ are discontinuous functions of α in the asymptotic-N limit : for $\alpha = 0$ one has GOE-results and for $\alpha \neq 0$ one has GUE-results. However, as a function of the parameter

$$\lambda = \frac{\alpha v}{D} \tag{21}$$

where D is the mean spacing, the transition is continuous.

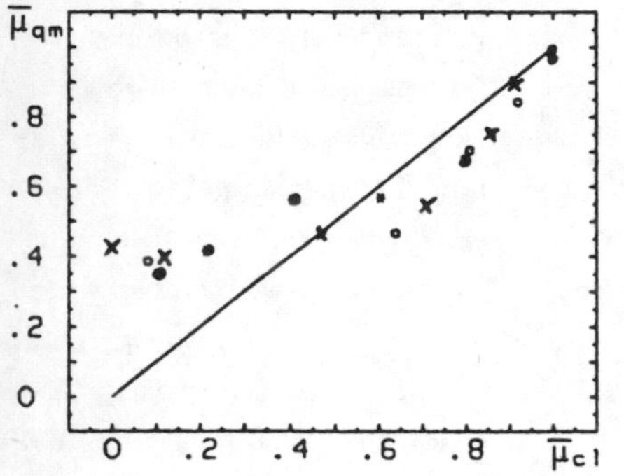

Fig.8 - Comparison of $\overline{\mu}_{c\ell}$ and $\overline{\mu}_{qm}$; see text for further explanation (taken from [ZMK-86])

Can one exhibit systems showing this intermediate fluctuations between GOE and GUE ? We have studied a billiard problem with a uniform magnetic field perpendicular to the plane of the billiard [SGB-86]. The presence of the magnetic field changes the classical trajectories from sequences of straight line segments to sequences of circular arcs. This system is obviously not invariant under time reversal. The wave function satisfies the eigenvalue equation ($E = k^2$)

$$(\vec{p} - q\vec{A})^2\, \Psi(\vec{r}) = k^2 \Psi(\vec{r}) \tag{22}$$

with Dirichlet boundary conditions. In (22) $\vec{A}$ is the vector potential which may be taken $A_x = -(B/2)y$, $A_y = (B/2)x$ and $A_z = 0$, where B is the strength of the magnetic field. With this choice Eq.(22) reads

$$\left[\, \Delta - iqB\left(x \frac{\partial}{\partial y} - y \frac{\partial}{\partial x}\right) - \left(\frac{qB}{2}\right)^2 (x^2+y^2) + k^2 \right] \Psi(x,y) = 0 \tag{23}$$

This system has the same scaling property as usual billiards, namely the spectrum depends trivially on the size of the billiard provided that the magnetic flux through the billiard is preserved (if one scales the size so that the surface S is multiplied by η , $S' = \eta S$, the spectrum is scaled by $E_n' = E_n/\eta$ provided that the magnetic field is scaled by the same factor $B' = B/\eta$). One can therefore keep constant the size of the billiard and just study the influence of the field strength. Now, if the billiard is chaotic without field, does it remain chaotic when the field is applied [RB-85, Ro-86] ? The answer will depend on the energy of the particle. Indeed, for a given billiard, the classical motion depends strongly on the Larmor radius $R = k/qB$ of the trajectory. If it is large compared to the linear dimension ℓ of the billiard, the trajectory will be close to the one in the absence of the field. One expects that in this regime ($k \gg qB\ell$) the system remains chaotic, a fact which is confirmed by the study of the Poincaré section. On the opposite, when the Larmor radius is small compared to ℓ, there exist circular trajectories which do not hit the boundary and the system is now integrable in a large domain of the phase space. And in this Landau regime ($k \ll qB\ell$) the quantum spectrum will reflect the integrability of the system. Thus for a fixed magnetic field the spectrum will be divided in three parts : A low energy part ($k \ll qB\ell$) where it is quasi-Landau, a high energy part ($k \gg qB\ell$) where it shows rigidity and an intermediate energy part ($k \simeq qB\ell$) with transition properties. We are interested in the high energy part. One can easily estimate, by using Eq.(4), that if $qBS \lesssim 2\pi$ the entire spectrum belongs to the high energy part. Attention must be payed to the symmetries :Eq.(23) is invariant under PT, where P is a symmetry with respect to the x or y axis. And if the billiard has the same symmetry axis, the spectrum will have GOE-fluctuations as mentioned before [RB-86].

We have studied an asymmetric stadium (see Fig.9) and solved Eq.(23) with Dirichlet boundary conditions, in the region $0 < qBS \lesssim 3$, where the entire spectrum is expected to show spectral rigidity. Let us discuss some results. In Fig.10 is shown the influence of the presence of the magnetic field on the fluctuation δ_n of the n-th level as a function of n (see Eq.(6)). One can note that both spectra are rigid (the fluctuations are small) and also that there are no missing levels (the fluctuations are around zero). The amplitude of the oscillations are slightly larger without than with magnetic field, as happens when going from GOE to GUE fluctuations. In Fig.11 is shown the cumulative level spacing distribution $F(y) = \int_0^y p(x)dx$. It can be seen that without field it follows closely GOE but when the magnetic field is turned on it departs from GOE towards GUE. The influence of the magnetic field is at first more important for small spacings than for large spacings and, by keeping increasing the field strength, one completes the transition to GUE fluctuations. This behaviour is very similar to the transition from GOE to GUE as a function of λ (see Eq.(21)). That the transition is faster at small than at larger scales can be seen by considering 2×2 matrices.

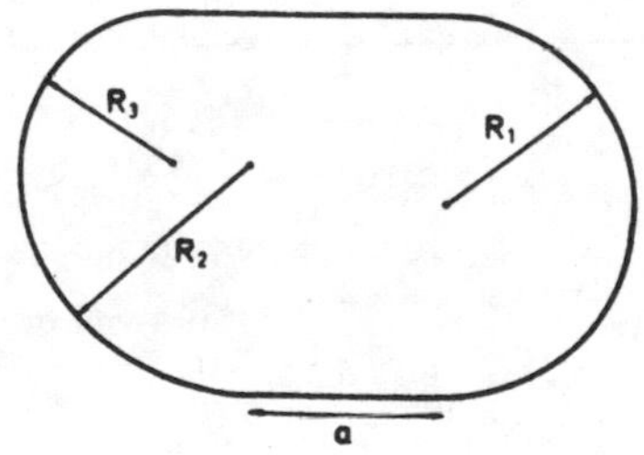

Fig.9 - Shape of the billiard :$R_1/a=1$, $R_2/a = 5/4$.

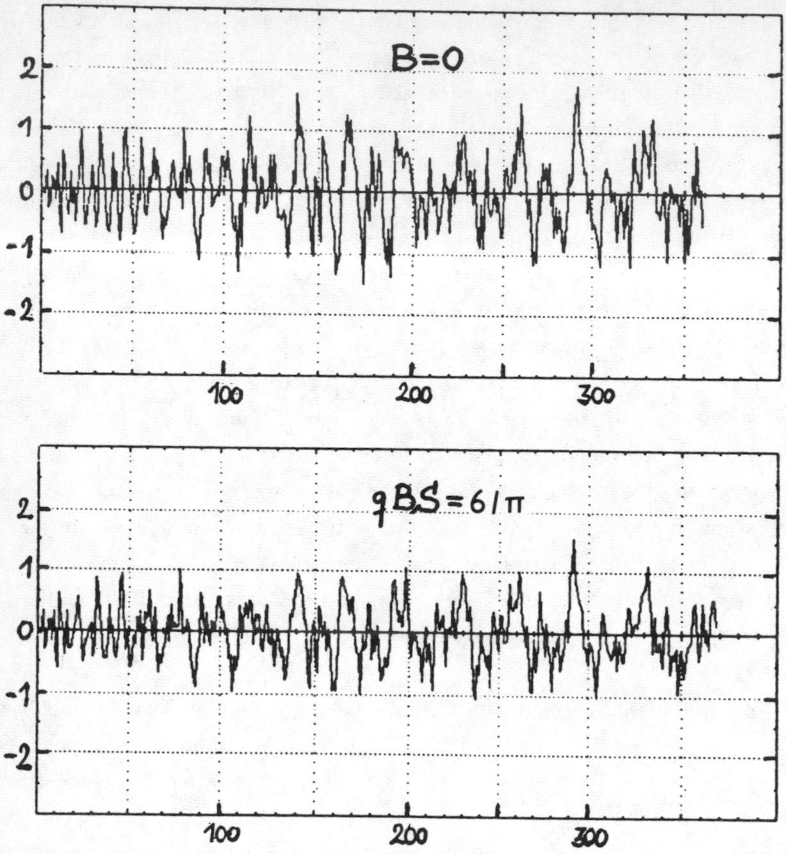

Fig.10 - Fluctuation δ_n of the n-th level plotted as a function of n for zero magnetic field and qBS = $6/\pi$ (taken from [SGB-86]).

One can easily derive the spacing distribution p(x) for this case [Fr-84]

$$p(x) = \frac{x}{4v^2\sqrt{1-\alpha^2}} \exp\left(-\frac{x^2}{8v^2}\right) \quad \mathrm{erf}\left[\left(\frac{1-\alpha^2}{8\alpha^2 v^2}\right)^{1/2} x\right] \tag{24}$$

which shows that, as soon as α is different from zero, the small x behaviour is quadratic and not linear in x (the same thing will be true in the large -N asymptotic case as a function of λ).

We have studied in detail other fluctuation measures and the results indicate that for a large enough magnetic field (qBS$\sim$ 3) the spectrum of the billiard exhibits GUE properties while for small enough values of the field it is close to GOE fluctuations. But the existence of a transition is not really well understood.

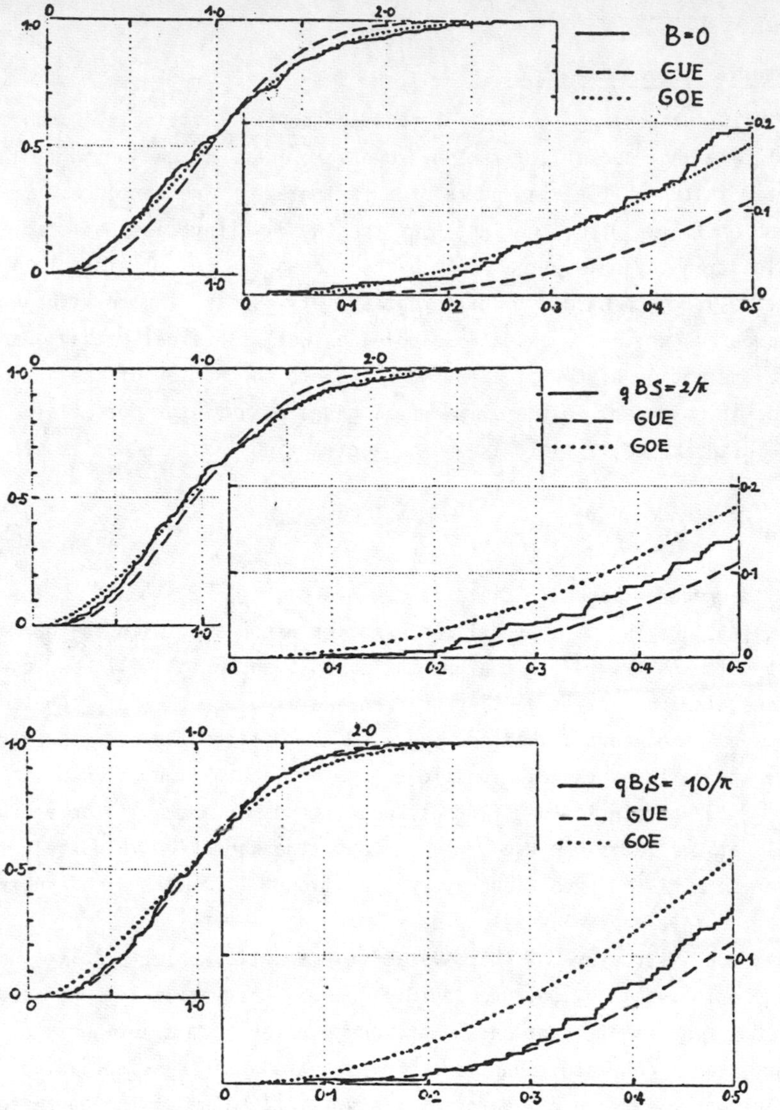

Fig.11 - Cumulative spacing distribution for qBS = 0, $2/\pi$ and $10/\pi$. The behaviour between 0 and 0.5 is enlarged on the right (taken from [SGB-86]).

4. Some recent results

Hydrogen atom in a strong magnetic field

An extremely interesting system, for its fundamental 'simplicity' and for its astrophysical relevance as well, is the hydrogen atom in a strong uniform magnetic field (see, for instance, [Ga-85] and references therein). The conceptual importance of the problem follows from the fact that the two limiting cases of zero and infinite field strength, namely the Coulomb and the Landau (oscillator like) problems respectively, which have very different symmetries, are the only three dimensional problems which are exactly soluble, as well classically than quantum mechanically. The motion of the electron submitted to the action of the Coulomb and Lorentz forces is governed, in the symmetrical gauge with vector potential $\vec{A} = (1/2)(\vec{r}\times\vec{B})$ (the magnetic field is in the z-direction), by the Hamiltonian (in a.u.)

$$H = \frac{p^2}{2} - \frac{1}{r} + \frac{\gamma}{2} L_z + \frac{\gamma^2}{8}(x^2+y^2) \tag{25}$$

In (25) γ is the reduced magnetic field strength B/B_c, $B_c = 2.35 \times 10^5$ T. The two last terms in (25) are the paramagnetic interaction associated with the normal Zeeman effect which is trivial in the present context and which will be droped from now on, and the diamagnetic interaction. L_z (and parity) are the only constants of the motion besides the energy. The importance of the diamagnetic effects are characterized by the ratio of the diamagnetic to Coulomb energy, which is proportional to $\gamma n^3 \propto \gamma|E|^{-3/2}$, where n is the principal quantum number and E is the energy. To magnify diamagnetic effects one can : i) increase the magnetic field (values of γ up to 10^{-4} can be achieved under laboratory conditions) ii) work with Rydberg atoms (one can achieve typically values of $n \simeq 50$).

The phase space structure of this system (diamagnetic Kepler problem) has been recently studied in detail by Delande and Gay [DG-86]. By increasing the value of $\gamma|E|^{3/2}$, which is the significant parameter, one evolves from a motion which is fully regular, then a connected chaotic region appears and keeps increasing until it occupies the whole surface of energy, for a critical value of the parameter. How is this behaviour reflected in the spectral fluctuations of the corresponding quantum system? One expects a transition from the Poisson to the GOE regime (as mentioned before, due to the particular spatial symmetry of the problem, although the system is not T-invariant one expects GOE-fluctuations). And this is indeed what is found by Delande and Gay when analyzing the computed spectrum. The results are illustrated in Figs.12 and 13. In Fig.12 one can see the evolution of a stretch of the spectrum. The level repulsion or avoided crossings are clearly exhibited. And results for the spacing distribution and the spectral rigidity are reproduced in Fig.13 (similar results have been obtained by Wintzen and Friedrich [WF-86]).

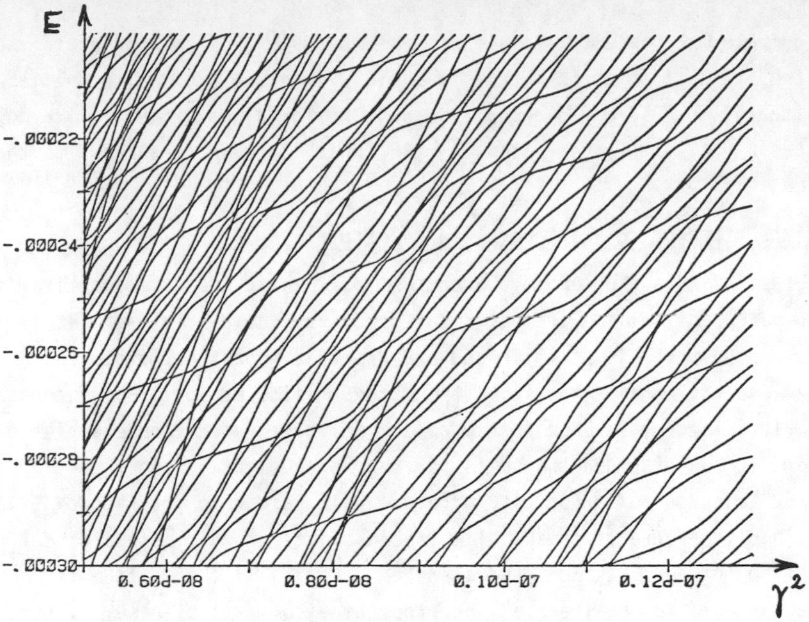

Fig.12 - Evolution of a segment of the spectrum as a function of the square of the reduced magnetic field strength γ, in the chaotic region (taken from [DG-86]).

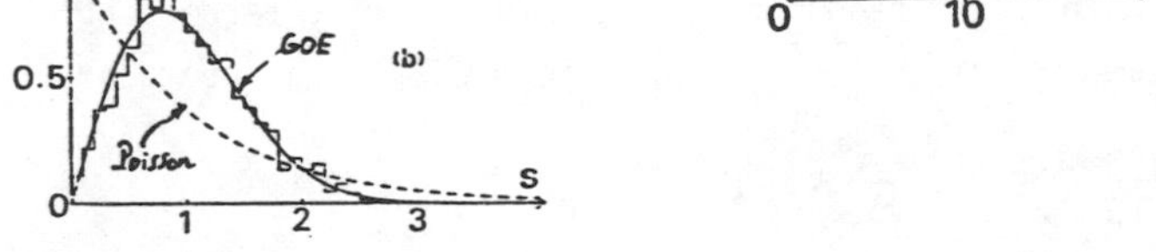

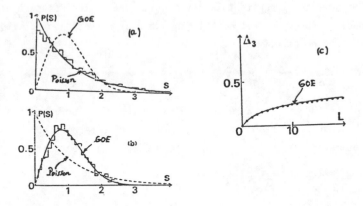

Fig.13 - (a) spacing distribution in the regular region ; (b) spacing distribution in the fully chaotic region ; (c) spectral rigidity $\bar{\Delta}_3$ in the fully chaotic region (taken from [DG-86]).

In summary, the Kepler diamagnetic problem offers a unique opportunity for studying chaotic motion : i) it is an interesting system from the point of view of symmetries (dynamical symmetries), ii) the classical as well as the quantum properties can be computed accurately ; iii) there is a transition from regular to chaotic motion when the field strength is increased ; iv) it can be studied in the laboratory. For instance, the Bielefeld group [WHW-86] performs measurements with magnetic field strengths $B \simeq 6T$ and Rydberg atoms $n \simeq 40$, which correspond already to the chaotic regime.

Billiards on a surface of constant negative curvature

The interest of this problem in the context of chaotic systems comes from the fact that, for free motion, the trajectories (geodesics) have local stability when the curvature of the space is positive and are unstable when the curvature is negative. In classical dynamical systems the geodesic flow on surfaces of constant negative curvature is one of the oldest problems and best understood examples of chaotic motion. It has provided the basis for the development of the theory of Anosov systems and the proof of ergodicity of a gas with hard core interactions. In spite of the chaotic nature of the problem, there exists in this case a direct (and exact) connection between classical and quantum mechanics if the surface is compact (Selberg trace formula) : The trace of the propagator consists of a sum of terms characterizing the lengths of closed geodesics on the surface. One of the main issues is to see if, computing closed orbits and via a Selberg trace formula determine the quantum mechanical spectrum, constitutes in principle a general method which can be applied in many other cases, chaotic as well as integrable (Gutzwiller, see [Gu-84] for a recent review).

An example of surface of constant negative curvature is the Poincaré disk model of hyperbolic space : the open unit disk in the complex plane, endowed with the metric (in polar coordinates r, ϑ)

$$ds^2 = \frac{4}{(1-r^2)^2} [dr^2 + r^2 d\vartheta^2] \tag{26}$$

(see Balazs and Voros [BV-86] for a recent review on chaos on surfaces of negative curvature). In this model the geodesics are circular curves perpendicular to the unit circle and diameters of the circle. The Laplace-Beltrami operator

$$\Delta = \frac{1}{\sqrt{g}} \frac{\partial}{\partial q_k} \sqrt{g}\, g^{kj} \frac{\partial}{\partial q_j} \tag{27}$$

where q_{kj} is the metric tensor, $g = \det(q_{kj})$, $g^{kj} = (g_{kj})^{-1}$ reads in this case

$$\Delta = \frac{(1-r^2)^2}{4} \frac{\partial^2}{\partial r^2} + \frac{1}{r}\frac{\partial}{\partial r} + \frac{1}{r^2}\frac{\partial^2}{\partial \vartheta^2} \tag{28}$$

We are now interested in the fluctuation properties of the spectrum of Δ on the triangle OLM (see Fig.14). Results are shown on fig.15a. The spacing distribution is close to the Poisson case and presumably that by going higher in energy the agreement with the Poisson distribution would improve. This result came as a surprise and does not fit with the general view discussed until now. However, the triangle OLM is not generic because it has the very special property of tiling the space. If one modifies it slightly in such a way that the resulting triangle does not tile any more, one drastically changes the fluctuation properties as shown in Fig.15b. Therefore it seems that for generic boundaries one has GOE-fluctuations, but

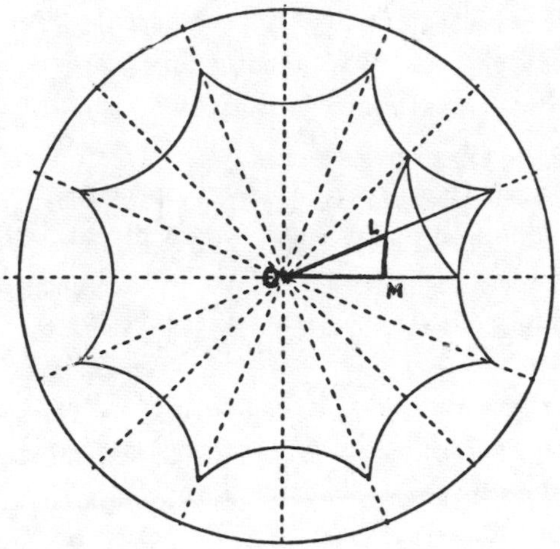

Fig.14 - From the initial problem, octogon with periodic boundary conditions, one is lead, by "desymmetrization", to consider the triangle OLM with Dirichlet boundary conditions. One has $\widehat{MOL} = \pi/8$, $\widehat{LMO} = \pi/2$, $\widehat{OLM} = \pi/3$ and the surface is $S = \pi/24$ (see [BV-86],[Sc-86]).

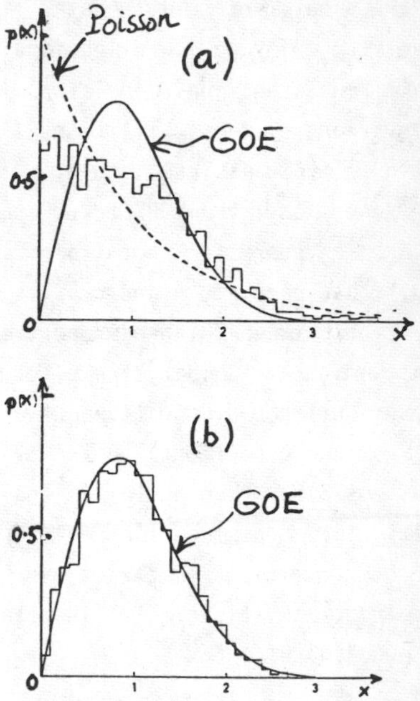

Fig.15 - Spacing distribution for the case (a) triangle OLM shown in Fig.14 ; (b) a triangle with angles $\pi/8$, $\pi/2$ and $(67/200)\pi$ with surface $S = \pi/28$. Each distribution contains 1500 spacings (taken from [Sc-86]).

that for boundaries like polygons that pave the space, even if the classical system is chaotic, one has Poisson-like fluctuations (the results in Fig.15 are shown as examples of a detailed analysis supporting these conclusions [Sc-86]). It is worth mentioning that Selberg trace formulae apply for tiling polygons but it is not known if they are still exact for cases like the one discussed here. With the possibility of performing extensive numerical results a better understanding of these problems is to be expected in the near future.

5. Remarks and conclusions

In the last two years, the gap between random matrix theories (RMT) and spectral fluctuations of classically chaotic quantum systems has been considerably filled. We know now that the fluctuations exhibited by the nuclear resonances, who gave rise to a large extent to the development of RMT, are not specific of nuclei. On the contrary, they are generic of fully chaotic (time reversal invariant) systems as demonstrated by the study of many low-dimensional model systems. It has also been possible to exhibit low-dimensional models showing : i) GUE-fluctuations for time reversal non-invariant systems, ii) transitions from Poisson —to GOE— fluctuations corresponding to the classical regular to chaotic regime transition. A transition, not fully understood, from GOE to GUE has also been found.

From a theoretical point of view, a semiclassical derivation of the spectral rigidity has been given and results agree with RMT predictions. But a more direct connection between RMT and properties of Hamiltonian systems, as well as a better understanding of 'Selberg trace formulae' are still missing. In this respect, the study of surfaces of negative curvature is promising.

From the experimental point of view, the search of the fluctuation properties of systems other than nuclei is challenging. The hydrogen atom in a strong uniform magnetic field (diamagnetic Kepler problem) deserves special mention : for its richness concerning symmetries, for its experimental feasibility, and because it can be theoretically treated in detail, it will probably become the chaotic system 'par excellence'.

Acknowledgments

We are indebted to D. Delande and J.C. Gay for discussions and for permission to present results prior to publication.

References

[Be-85] M.V. Berry, Proc. Roy. Soc. London A400 (1985) 229

[BFF-81] T.A. Brody, J. Flores, J.B. French, P.A. Mello, A. Pandey and S.S.M. Wong, Rev. Mod. Phys. 53 (1981) 385

[BG-84] O. Bohigas and M.J. Giannoni, in 'Mathematical and Computational Methods in Nuclear Physics', J.S. Dehesa et al. (eds.), Lecture Notes in Physics 209, Springer Verlag 1984, p.1

[BGS-84a] O. Bohigas, M.J. Giannoni and C. Schmit, Phys. Rev. Lett. 52 (1984) 1

[BGS-84b] O. Bohigas, M.J. Giannoni and C. Schmit, J. Physique Lett. 45 (1984) L-1015

[BHP-83] O. Bohigas, R.U. Haq and A. Pandey, in 'Nuclear Data for Science and Technology', K.H. Böckhoff (ed.), Reidel, Dordrecht, 1983, p.809

[BHP-85] O. Bohigas, R.U. Haq and A. Pandey, Phys. Rev. Lett. 54 (1985) 1645

[BR-84] M.V. Berry and M. Robnik, J. Phys. A17 (1984) 2413

[BR-85] M.V. Berry and M. Robnik, J. Phys. A19 (1985) 649

[BV-86] N.L. Balazs and A. Voros, preprint Saclay 1986

[Ca-85] G. Casati (ed.), 'Chaotic Behavior in Quantum Systems', Plenum, 1985

[CG-83] H.S. Camarda and P.D. Georgopulos, Phys. Rev. Lett. 50 (1983) 492

[CG-86] E. Caurier and B. Grammaticos, to appear in Europhys. Lett.

[DG-86] D. Delande and J.C. Gay, preprint 1986

[Fr-84] J.B. French, Lecture Notes, Rochester 1984, unpublished

[Ga-85] J.C. Gay in 'Photophysics and Photochemistry in the Vacuum Ultraviolet', S.P. McGlynn et al. (eds.), Reidel, 1985, p.631

[Gu-84] M. Gutzwiller, to appear in the Proceedings of the Americal Mathematical Society, '1984 Summer Research Conference on the Selberg Trace Formula'

[HKC-84] E. Haller, H. Köppel and L.S. Cederbaum, Phys. Rev. Lett. 52 (1984) 1665

[HMY-81] F.T. Hioe, E.W. Montroll and M. Yamawaki, in 'Perspectives in Statistical Physics', H.J. Raveché (ed.), North-Holland 1981, p.295

[HPB-82] R.U. Haq, A. Pandey and O. Bohigas, Phys. Rev. Lett. 48 (1982) 1086

[IY-85] T. Ishikawa and T. Yukawa, Phys. Rev. Lett. 54 (1985) 1617

[LLJ-86] L. Leviandier, M. Lombardi, R. Jost and J.P. Pique, Phys.Rev.Lett. A56 (1986) 2449

[Me-67] M.L. Mehta, 'Random Matrices and the Statistical Theory of Energy Levels', Academic Press, 1967

[MHK-84] H.D. Meyer, E. Haller, H. Köppel and L.S. Cederbaum, J. Phys. A17 (1984) L831

[MSP-84] S. Mukamel, J. Sue and A. Pandey, Chem. Phys. Lett. 105 (1984) 134

[Pa-79] A. Pandey, Ann. Phys. 119 (1979) 170

[PM-83] A. Pandey and M.L. Mehta, Comm. Math. Phys. 87 (1983) 449

[Po-65] C.E. Porter (ed.) 'Statistical theories of spectra : fluctuations', Academic Press, 1965

[RB-85] M. Robnik and M.V. Berry, J. Phys. A18 (1985) 1361

[RB-86] M. Robnik and M.V. Berry, J. Phys. A19 (1986) 669

[Ro-86] M. Robnik in 'Nonlinear Phenomena and Chaos', S. Sarkar (ed.), Adam Hilger, Bristol 1986

[Sc-86] C. Schmit, to be published

[SGB-86] C. Schmit, M.J. Giannoni and O. Bohigas, in 'Phase Space Approach to Nuclear Dynamics', M. Di Toro et al. (eds.), World Scientific, 1986 ; and to be published

[SV-85a] T.H. Seligman and J.J.M. Verbaaschot, J. Phys. A18 (1985) 2227

[SV-85b] T.H. Seligman and J.J.M. Verbaaschot, Phys. Lett. 108A (1985) 183

[SVZ-84] T.H. Seligman, J.J.M. Verbaaschot and M.R. Zirnbauer, Phys. Rev. Lett. 53 (1984) 215

[WF-86] D. Wintgen and H. Friedrich, preprint 1986

[WHW-86] D. Wintgen, A. Holle, G. Wiebusch, J. Main, H. Friedrich and K.H. Welge, preprint 1986

[ZMK-86] Th. Zimmermann, H.D. Meyer, H. Köppel and L.S. Cederbaum, Phys. Rev. A33 (1986)4334

THE PATHWISE DESCRIPTION OF QUANTUM SCATTERING IN STOCHASTIC MECHANICS*

Eric A. Carlen
Department of Mathematics
Massachusetts Institute of Technology
Cambridge, MA 02139, U.S.A.

Stochastic mechanics describes the behavior of quantum systems in terms of diffusions

$$t \mapsto \xi_t \tag{1}$$

in the configuration space; here we take this to be $\mathbb{R}^n$. The sample paths of these diffusions represent the actual physical trajectories of the particles which constitute the system. In this way, stochastic mechanics provides a much more detailed picture of quantum phenomena than does ordinary quantum mechanics, where it doesn't even make sense to speak of the trajectory of a particle.

As Nelson has pointed out [1][2], this is a thorny blessing. While it is very pleasant to have a paths-of-physical-particles picture of quantum phenomena, Nature simply does not always admit a particle description. By providing such an explicit particle description, stochastic mechanics lands itself in several difficulties. One can view this situation with varying degrees of approbation; perhaps stochastic mechanics as now formulated is only a particle approximation of a more complex but more physically realistic stochastic field theory. Then one would not expect stochastic mechanics to be correct in all detail where a particle description is inappropriate. But no matter how liberal one is, one must insist that these difficulties be absent in all circumstances where a particle description is appropriate. An important example is the large time regime of a scattering experiment. The naive paths-of-physical-particles picture of stochastic mechanics must be meaningful here if it is to have any meaning anywhere at all.

In this talk, I will present several results to show that the large time portions of the diffusion sample paths arising in the stochastic mechanical treatment of potential scattering contain exactly enough information to give a correct pathwise description of quantum

* This paper is an extended version of my talk, including some improvements made over the Summer.

scattering. We have shown in [3] that under rather general conditions, these diffusions possess a final momentum p_+ in the sense that

$$\lim_{t\to\infty} \frac{1}{t}\xi_t(\omega) \equiv p_+(\omega) \quad \text{exists a.s.} \tag{2}$$

and moreover, the random variable p_+ has the same distribution as does the ordinary quantum mechanical final momentum in the corresponding quantum state (see below). The new result we will discuss here is that the final momentum p_+ is all one can learn by looking at the paths only after arbitrarily late times.

More precisely, the tail σ-algebra $\mathcal{J}_+$ of our diffusion is defined by

$$\mathcal{J}_+ = \bigcap_{t>1} \sigma\{\xi_u : u \geq t\} \tag{3}$$

A random variable F is said to be tail measurable in case it is measurable with respect to $\mathcal{J}_+$. Intuitively, this means that F depends only on the tail end of the sample path ω. Clearly p_+ is tail measurable. We shall show that for at least most of our diffusions this is essentially the only example in that if F is tail measurable, then there is a Borel function f_F on $\mathbb{R}^n$ so that

$$F(\omega) = f_F(p_+(\omega)) \quad \text{a.s.} \tag{4}$$

That is, p_+ generates the tail field. This means that not only does stochastic mechanics permit a pathwise definition of the final momentum in a quantum scattering experiment, it does so without encoding any extraneous information into the large time behavior of the sample paths. There simply isn't any extraneous detail here on which one could base paradoxes of the type discussed by Nelson [2] at this conference.

We now turn to providing a more precise formulation of the stochastic mechanical treatment of quantum scattering. For more details than we will have time to provide, see [1], [3] and [4].

Consider a single particle moving in $\mathbb{R}^n$ under the influence of a continuous potential V. In stochastic mechanics, this motion is described with a diffusion process $t \mapsto \xi_t$ where

$$d\xi_t = b(\xi_t, t)\,dt + dw_t \tag{5}$$

Here, dw_t is the increment of a Brownian motion. This special choice for the noise term in our stochastic differential equation is motivated by the prejudice that «quantum fluctuations» , whatever they are, must be translation invariant and isotropic.

The drift field $b(x,t)$ is determined by the dynamics. The

dynamical law of stochastic mechanics is the Guerra-Morato variational principle [4]. This is a direct and beautiful generalization of the Lagrangean variational principle of classical mechanics to the diffusion context. Guerra and Morato prove that a diffusion is critical for their variational principle precisely when there is a solution $t \mapsto \psi_t$ of the Schroedinger equation

$$i \frac{\partial}{\partial t} \psi_t = \left(-\tfrac{1}{2}\Delta + V\right)\psi_t \tag{6}$$

for the same potential V so that the drift field $b(x,t)$ in (5) is given by $b(x,t) = u(x,t) + v(x,t)$ where

$$u(x,t) = \begin{cases} \operatorname{Re} \dfrac{\nabla\psi_t(x)}{\psi_t(x)}, & \psi_t \neq 0 \\ 0, & \psi_t = 0 \end{cases} \qquad v(x,t) = \begin{cases} \operatorname{Im} \dfrac{\nabla\psi_t(x)}{\psi_t(x)}, & \psi_t \neq 0 \\ 0, & \psi_t = 0 \end{cases} \tag{7}$$

and so that

$$\Pr\{\xi_t \in A\} = \int_A |\psi_t(x)|^2 dx \equiv \int_A \rho(x,t)\,dx \tag{8}$$

for any measurable A in $\mathbb{R}^n$. Here $\Pr$ denotes the law of the diffusion at hand. According to (8), stochastic mechanics and ordinary quantum mechanics make the same predictions for the results of experiments; however (8) says nothing about the behavior of the diffusions pathwise.

The drift field b defined in terms of ψ by the formula (7) will in general be quite singular. The worst problems arise near the zeros of ψ, and it is difficult to extract any information about these from the Schroedinger equation. Thus the first question is whether or not the would-be critical diffusions exist.

In [5], with some improvements in [6], we have shown that in case for any $T > S$, and any $f \in C^\infty(\dot{\mathbb{R}}^n)$

$$\int_S^T \int_{\mathbb{R}^n} \left(u^2(x,t) + v^2(x,t)\right)\rho(x,t)\,dx\,dt < \infty \tag{9}$$

$$\int_{\mathbb{R}^n} f(x)\rho(x,T)dx - \int_{\mathbb{R}^n} f(x)\rho(x,S)\,dx = \int_S^T \int_{\mathbb{R}^n} \left(v(x,t)\cdot\nabla f(x)\right)\rho(x,t)\,dx\,dt \tag{10}$$

then there is a unique law $\Pr$ on path space under which

$$d\xi_t = b(\xi_t,t)dt + dw_t \quad \text{and} \quad \Pr\{\xi_t \in A\} = \int_A \rho(x,t)\,dx \;\; \forall t.$$

In turn, as long as V is not too singular -- say if V is form small with respect to Δ -- then (9) and (10) follow from the finite energy condition that $\|\nabla\psi_0\|_{L^2(\mathbb{R}^n)} < \infty$. This condition, expressed in terms of the behavior of the corresponding process at time zero, is:

$$\mathbb{E}\left(u^2(\xi_0,0) + v^2(\xi_0,0)\right) = \|\nabla\psi_0\|_{L^2(\mathbb{R}^n)} < \infty \tag{11}$$

With existence of the critical diffusions now in hand, we turn to the study of their pathwise behavior in the context of potential scattering. Our program can be roughly divided into three steps.

I) For a given potential V , determine which critical diffusions $t \mapsto \xi_t$ correspond to scattering motions, and which correspond to bound motions.

II) For the scattering diffusions, show that

$$\lim_{t\to\infty} \frac{1}{t}\,\xi_t(\omega) \equiv p_+(\omega) \text{ exists a.s.}$$

III) Show that the final momentum p_+ generates the tail field $\mathcal{J}_+$. See [3] for further discussion contrasting this program and the familiar quantum scattering theory; here we simply assert that existence of the above limit is precisely what one needs to provide a pathwise description of actual quantum scattering experiments.

The first step is an easy application of the RAGE theorem [7]. We call a diffusion $t \mapsto \xi_t$ a scattering diffusion in case

$$\lim_{T\to\infty} \frac{1}{2T}\int_{-T}^{T} \Pr\{|\xi_t| \le R\}\,dt = 0 \quad \forall\, R > 0 \tag{12}$$

Since $\Pr\{|\xi_t| \le R\} = \int_{|x|\le R} |\psi_t(x)|^2 dx$ by (10), it follows that $t \mapsto \xi_t$ is a scattering diffusion critical for V precisely when the corresponding solution of the Schroedinger equation $t \mapsto \psi_t$ is a scattering solution in the sense that ψ_t is in the absolutely continuous spectral subspace of $(-\frac{1}{2}\Delta + V)$ for all t -- at least this is true for for potentials quite a bit more general than those we consider below.

For the second step, consider the process $t \mapsto \pi_t$ where $\pi_t = \frac{1}{t}\xi_t$. We wish to show that this process grinds to a halt. To do that, study the stochastic differential equation it satisfies:

$$d\pi_t = \frac{1}{t}\left(b(\xi_t,t) - \pi_t\right)dt + \frac{1}{t}dw_t \tag{13}$$

Therefore

$$\Pr\left\{\sup_{t>T} |\pi_t - \pi_T| > \varepsilon\right\} \le \Pr\left\{\int_T^\infty \frac{1}{t}|b(\xi_t,t) - \pi_t|\,dt > \varepsilon\right\} + \Pr\left\{\sup_{t>T}\left|\int_T^t \frac{1}{\tau}dw_\tau\right| > \varepsilon\right\}$$

That the second term on the right becomes arbitrarily small as T is increased is a well known fact about Brownian motion; it follows easily from Doob's martingale maximal inequalities. To control the first term on the right, one must know something about b. Since b is defined in terms of a solution of the Schroedinger equation (6), it is natural to look for L^2 estimates. And indeed by direct computation using (9) and (10),

$$\mathbb{E}\,|b(\xi_t,t)-\pi_t|^2 \leq 2\,\mathbb{E}\,|v(\xi_t,t)-\pi_t|^2 + 2\,\mathbb{E}\,|u(\xi_t,t)|^2$$

$$= 2\int\left(\left|\mathrm{Im}\frac{\nabla\psi_t}{\psi_t}-\frac{x}{t}\right|^2+\left|\mathrm{Re}\,\frac{\nabla\psi_t}{\psi_t}\right|^2\right)|\psi_t|^2\,dx$$

$$= 2\int\left|\left(\frac{1}{i}\nabla-\frac{x}{t}\right)\psi_t\right|^2 dx$$

Now suppose that last term on the right is such that

$$\int_1^\infty \frac{1}{t}\left\|\left(\frac{1}{i}\nabla-\frac{x}{t}\right)\psi_t\right\|_{L^2(\mathbb{R}^n)} dt < \infty \tag{14}$$

Then since

$$\Pr\left\{\int_T^\infty \frac{1}{t}|b(\xi_t,t)-\pi_t|\,dt>\varepsilon\right\} \leq$$

$$\frac{1}{\varepsilon}\left(\int_T^\infty \frac{1}{t}\,\mathbb{E}\,|b(\xi_t,t)-\pi_t|\,dt\right) \leq$$

$$\frac{1}{\varepsilon}\int_T^\infty \frac{1}{t}\left(\mathbb{E}\,|b(\xi_t,t)-\pi_t|^2\right)^{1/2} dt \leq$$

$$\frac{1}{\varepsilon}\int_T^\infty \frac{\sqrt{2}}{t}\left\|\left(\frac{1}{i}\nabla-\frac{x}{t}\right)\psi_t\right\|_{L^2(\mathbb{R}^n)} dt$$

we can make the first term above arbitrarily small if we take T large enough. Then a Borel-Cantelli argument shows that $\Pr\{\lim_{t\to\infty}\frac{1}{t}\xi_t \text{ exists}\} = 1$.

It remains to determine when (14) holds. Note that when $V = 0$, the solution of the Schroedinger equation is given by

$$\psi_t(x) = (2\pi i t)^{-n/2}\int_{\mathbb{R}^n} e^{-i|x-y|^2/2t}\,\psi_0(y)\,dy \tag{15}$$

Then explicit computation shows that in this case

$$\left\| \left(\frac{1}{i}\nabla - \frac{x}{t} \right) \psi_t \right\|_{L^2(\mathbb{R}^n)} = \frac{1}{t} \| x \psi_0 \|_{L^2(\mathbb{R}^n)}$$

So as long as $\|x\psi_0\|_{L^2(\mathbb{R}^n)} < \infty$, (14) holds. In fact, the quantity $\|(\frac{1}{i}\nabla - \frac{x}{t})\psi_t\|_{L^2(\mathbb{R}^n)}$ has been well studied, and piecing together existing estimates [3] one has that if V satisfies (here it is important that we are working in $\mathbb{R}^3$):

$$|V(x)| + |\nabla V(x)| \leq C(1 + |x|^2)^{-\beta} \quad \text{some } \beta > 3$$

and if there is neither a zero resonance or zero eigenfunction for $(-\frac{1}{2}\Delta + V)$, then for ψ_0 in the absolutely continuous spectral subspace of $(-\frac{1}{2}\Delta + V)$ with

$$\|(1 + |x|^2)^{3/2} \psi_0\|_{L^2(\mathbb{R}^n)} < \infty$$

there is a finite C so that

$$\left\| \left(\frac{1}{i}\nabla - \frac{x}{t} \right) e^{-i(-\frac{1}{2}\Delta + V)t} \psi_0 \right\| \leq C t^{-1/2}$$

Call such a potential admissible.

Combining our results from steps I and II we have all but the last statement in:

Theorem 1. *Let* V *be an admissible potential. Let* $t \mapsto \xi_t$ *be a critical diffusion for* V *with*

$$\lim_{T\to\infty} \frac{1}{2T} \int_{-T}^{T} \Pr\{|\xi_t| \leq R\}\, dt = 0 \qquad \forall R > 0 \tag{16}$$

and

$$\mathbb{E}\left(u^2(\xi_0, 0) + v^2(\xi_0, 0) + |\xi_0|^6 \right) < \infty . \tag{17}$$

Then $\lim_{t\to\infty} \frac{1}{t} \xi_t(\omega) \equiv p_+(\omega)$ *exist a.s.* (18)

and moreover p_+ *has the same distribution as does the final momentum in the quantum state corresponding to* $t \mapsto \xi_t$.

The last statement is an easy consequence of (18) and a simple commutation involving the wave operators, see [3].

Shucker [8] was the first to obtain a result of this type; he treated the case $V = 0$ by another method . See [3] for more references to other work.

Now recall that for $V = 0$ and $\|(\frac{1}{i}\nabla - x)\psi_0\|_{L^2(\mathbb{R}^n)} < \infty$, we had

$\| (\frac{1}{i}\nabla - \frac{x}{t}) \psi_t \|^2_{L^2(\mathbb{R}^n)} \leq \frac{C}{t^2}$ so that in this case

$$\mathbb{E}\left(\int_1^\infty |b(\xi_t,t) - \tfrac{1}{t}\xi_t|^2 dt \right) < \infty \tag{19}$$

which is a stronger statement than

$$\int_1^\infty \frac{1}{t} \mathbb{E}\, |b(\xi_t,t) - \tfrac{1}{t}\xi_t|\, dt < \infty \tag{20}$$

In fact, by Ershov's theorem [9], this implies that P_r is absolutely continuous with respect to $\widetilde{P}_r$ where $\widetilde{P}_r$ is the unique law on path space (for $t \geq 1$) under which

$$d\xi_t = \frac{1}{t}\xi_t + dw_t \quad , \quad \xi_1^{-1}(P_r) = \xi_1^{-1}(\widetilde{P}_r) \tag{21}$$

Thus another way to prove Shucker's theorem is to show that (18) holds under $\widetilde{P}_r$; P_r then inherits this property by absolute continuity.

In fact, (21) is such a simple stochastic differential equation we can say a lot more: Under $\widetilde{P}_r$, $d(\frac{1}{t}\xi_t) = \frac{1}{t}dw_t$, so

$$\xi_t = t\left(\int_1^t \frac{1}{s}\, dw_s + \xi_1 \right) \tag{22}$$

Since $\mathbb{E}\left(\int_1^\infty \frac{1}{s} dw_s\right)^2 = 1$, the martingale convergence theorem implies the existence of p_+ under this law. Moreover,

Theorem 2. *Under the law* $\widetilde{P}_r$, p_+ *exists and generates the tail field.*

The following proof of this theorem is due to Wilfred Kendall [10], to whom I express my thanks. My original proof [11] used Martin boundary techniques. While it is just as simple, and yields a bit more information, these techniques are not well known. In the interest of accessibility we sketch Kendall's argument which turns on the well known Blumenthal zero-one law, and we refer to [11] for the martin boundary discussion.

Proof. As observed above p_+ exists a.s., and by (22)

$$\xi_t = t\left(p_+ - \int_t^\infty \frac{1}{s} dw_s \right) \tag{23}$$

Now making the change of variable $\tau = 1/t$,

$$\int_t^\infty \frac{1}{s} dw_s = -\frac{1}{t} w_t + \int_t^\infty \frac{1}{s^2} w_s\, ds = -\tau w_{1/\tau} + \int_0^{1/\tau} w_{1/\sigma}\, d\sigma$$

But $\beta_\tau = \tau w_{1/\tau}$ is also a Brownian motion and so

$$\int_t^\infty \frac{1}{s} dw_s = -\beta_\tau + \int_0^{1/\tau} \frac{1}{\sigma} \beta_\sigma\, d\sigma \equiv X_\tau \tag{24}$$

Therefore $\sigma\{\xi_u : u \geq t\} = \sigma\{p_+, X_\tau : \tau \leq 1/t\}$
and so:

$$\mathcal{T}_+ = \bigcap_{t>1} \left(\sigma\{p_+\} \cup \sigma\{X_\tau : \tau \leq \tfrac{1}{t}\} \right)$$

The Blumenthal zero-one law implies $\bigcap_{t \geq 1} \sigma\{X_\tau : \tau \leq \frac{1}{t}\}$ is trivial; and though the interchange of $\cap$ and $\cup$ for σ-algebras is a subtle matter, the proof proceeds from here without difficulty (see [14]).

This means that if F is any tail measurable random variable, there is a Borel function f_F so that

$$F(\omega) = f_F(p_+(\omega)) \qquad \widetilde{P}_r \text{ a.s.} \tag{25}$$

But $P_r \ll \widetilde{P}_r$ so this also holds almost everywhere with respect to P_r.

This raises the question as to when it will be true that (19) holds; it is perhaps useful to mention that (19) is a finite entropy condition in the sense of Föllmer [12]. As observed above, it suffices to determine when

$$\int_1^\infty \left\| \left(\tfrac{1}{i}\nabla - \tfrac{X}{t} \right) \psi_t \right\|_{L^2(\mathbb{R}^n)} dt < \infty \tag{26}$$

holds for the corresponding solution of the Schroedinger equation. Perhaps this holds already under the conditions we have so far imposed on the potential and ψ_0, but the following answer can be extracted directly from Perry's work [13] on quantum scattering: If we make the additional assumptions that the potential V is dilation analytic (see [13]) and ψ_0 lies in the spectral subspace of $(-\frac{1}{2}\Delta + V)$ corresponding to (ε, ∞) for some $\varepsilon > 0$, then (26) holds. We therefore have

Theorem 3. *Assume that* V *is admissible and dilation analytic. Let* $t \mapsto \xi_t$ *be a critical diffusion for* V *with* (16) *and* (17) *satisfied, so that*

$$\lim_{t\to\infty} \frac{1}{t} \xi_t(\omega) = p_+(\omega) \quad \text{exists as.}$$

Then if for some $\varepsilon > 0$

$$P_r\{|p_+| > \varepsilon\} = 1 , \tag{27}$$

p_+ *also generates the tail field* $\mathcal{T}_+$.

Proof. Let ψ be the corresponding solution of the Schroedinger equation. Since the distribution of p_+ is the same as the distribution of the quantum mechanical final momentum in the state ψ, (27) implies ψ_0 is in the spectral subspace of $(-\frac{1}{2}\Delta + V)$ corresponding to $(\frac{1}{2}\varepsilon^2, \infty)$. Then by theorem 2.2 of [13], (26) holds so that

$$\int_1^\infty \mathbb{E}\left(|b(\xi_t,t) - \frac{1}{t}\xi_t|^2\right) dt < \infty$$

and now just as in the case $V = 0$, the result follows from Theorem 2 by absolute continuity.

The outstanding open question here is to bypass the Schroedinger equation and obtain estimates of type (19) and (20) directly from any of the equivalent dynamical laws of stochastic mechanics. Such a result might then provide a useful tool for studying the Schroedinger equation, regardless of the status of stochastic mechanics as physics. See [3] for further discussion along this line.

Bibliography

[1] Nelson, E.: Quantum Fluctuations, Princeton, Princeton University.

[2] Nelson, E.: Proceedings of this conference.

[3] Carlen, E.: Potential Scattering in Stochastic Mechanics, Ann. Insti. Henri Poincaré, Vol. 42, No. 4, 1985, pp. 407-28.

[4] Guerra, F., Morato, L.: Quantization of Dynamical Systems and Stochastic Control Theory, Phys. Rev. D., t. 27, 1983, p. 1771-86.

[5] Carlen, E.: Conservative Diffusions, Comm. Math. Phys., t. 94, 1984, p. 273-96.

[6] Carlen, E.: Existence and Sample Path Properties of the Diffusions in Nelson's Stochastic Mechanics; Proceedings of the BiBoS I conference, to appear in Springer Lecture Notes.

[7] Enss, V.: Geometric Methods in Spectral and Scattering Theory for Schrödinger Operators in Rigorous Results in Atomic and Molecular Physics, G. Velo and A. Wightman eds., New York, Plenum 1981.

[8] Shucker, D.: Stochastic Mechanics of Systems with Zero Potential, J. Func. Analysis, t. 38, 1980, pp. 146-55.

[9] Ershov, M.: On The Absolute Continuity of Measures Corresponding to Diffusion Processes, Theory of Prob. and Appl., Vol. 17, 1972, 169-74.

[10] Kendall, W.: Private Communication.

[11] Carlen, E.: Tail Fields of Some Diffusions with a Limiting Velocity, M.I.T. Preprint.

[12] Föllmer, H.: Proceedings of this conference.

[13] Perry, P.A.: Propagation of States in Dialation Analytic Potentials and Asymptotic Completeness, Comm. Math. Phys., t. 81, 1981, pp. 243-59.

[14] Weizsäcker, H.: Exchanging the Order of Taking Suprema and Countable Intersections of σ-algebras, Ann. Insti. H. Poincaré, Vol. XIX, No. 1, 1983, 91-100.

INTEGRAL REPRESENTATION OF COVARIANT OBSERVABLES

U. Cattaneo
CH-6673 Maggia (Switzerland)

1. The setting

The axiomatic approach to statistical physical theories proposed by Davies and Lewis [1] was an attempt to introduce in quantum mechanics probabilistic objects like conditional expectation, joint probability distribution, and so on. The central concept is that of an observable [1,2] in a complex Hilbert space $\mathfrak{h}$ and based on a set X equipped with a Borel structure $\mathcal{B}_X$: a mapping M of $\mathcal{B}_X$ into $\mathcal{L}(\mathfrak{h})$, the (complex) vector space of all continuous linear operators in $\mathfrak{h}$, satisfying the following conditions:

(i) M is positive, i.e., $M(\emptyset) = 0$ and $M(B) \geq 0$ for all $B \in \mathcal{B}_X$;

(ii) M is (weakly) countably additive, i.e., if $(B_n)_{n \in \mathbb{N}}$ is a sequence of mutually disjoint elements of $\mathcal{B}_X$, then

$$M(\bigcup_{n=0}^{\infty} B_n) = w\text{-}\sum_{n=0}^{\infty} M(B_n) ,$$

where " $w\text{-}\sum$ " means convergence in the weak operator topology on $\mathcal{L}(\mathfrak{h})$;

(iii) $M(X) = Id_{\mathfrak{h}}$ (normalization).

If, in addition to (i),(ii), and (iii), M satisfies

(iv) $M(B)M(B') = M(B \cap B')$ for all $B, B' \in \mathcal{B}_X$,

then M is said to be a decision (or sharp) observable.

In other words, an observable M in $\mathfrak{h}$ based on X is a normalized (weak) Borel positive-operator-valued measure (concisely: a normalized Borel POV-measure) on X acting in $\mathfrak{h}$. If M is a decision observable, then it is a normalized Borel projection-valued measure (concisely: a normalized Borel PV-measure). We tacitly assume that, when X is a topological space, then $\mathcal{B}_X$ is the Borel structure generated by its closed sets.

Let G be a topological group and let X be a topological G-space. Here, and in the following, we are tacitly understanding that every group operation considered is a left one. An observable M in $\mathfrak{h}$ based on X is said to be G-covariant with respect to a strongly continuous unitary representation U of G on $\mathfrak{h}$ if

$$U(g)M(B)U(g)^{-1} = M(g.B)$$

for all $g \in G$ and all $B \in \mathcal{B}_X$, where the dot denotes the operation of G on X. We call the ordered pair (U,M) a <u>system of G-covariance</u> in $\mathfrak{H}$ based on X. If M is a decision observable, then (U,M) is a Mackey's <u>system of imprimitivity</u> for G based on X and acting in $\mathfrak{H}$.

Two G-covariant observables, M in $\mathfrak{H}$ with respect to U and M' in $\mathfrak{H}'$ with respect to U', both based on X, are said to be <u>unitarily equivalent</u> if there exists a unitary mapping V of $\mathfrak{H}$ onto $\mathfrak{H}'$ such that

$$U'(g) = VU(g)V^{-1} \qquad \text{for all } g \in G$$

and

$$M'(B) = VM(B)V^{-1} \qquad \text{for all } B \in \mathcal{B}_X .$$

Given a locally compact group G, a closed subgroup H of G, and a nontrivial positive G-quasi-invariant measure μ on the (topological) homogeneous space G/H *), we denote by $L^2_{\mathfrak{K}}(U_o)$ a complex Hilbert space of μ-square-integrable mappings of G/H into a complex Hilbert space $\mathfrak{K}$ carrying a representation $\mathrm{Ind}_H^G U_o$ of G induced by a strongly continuous unitary representation U_o of H on $\mathfrak{K}$.

By the following result, every system of covariance can be described via a system of imprimitivity.

<u>Proposition 1.</u> [4,5] Let G be a locally compact group, let H be a closed subgroup of G, let μ be a nontrivial positive G-quasi-invariant measure on G/H, let $\mathfrak{H}$ be a complex Hilbert space, and let M be an observable in $\mathfrak{H}$ based on G/H which is G-covariant with respect to a strongly continuous unitary representation U of G on $\mathfrak{H}$. There exist a strongly continuous unitary representation $\gamma(U)$ of H on a complex Hilbert space $\mathfrak{K}$ and an isometric mapping V of $\mathfrak{H}$ into $L^2_{\mathfrak{K}}(\gamma(U))$ satisfying

$$U(g) = V^*(\mathrm{Ind}_H^G \gamma(U))(g)V \qquad \text{for all } g \in G,$$

$$M(B) = V^* P_{\mathfrak{K}}(B)V \qquad \text{for all } B \in \mathcal{B}_{G/H} ,$$

and such that the set

$$\left\{P_{\mathfrak{K}}(B)V\varphi \,\middle|\, B \in \mathcal{B}_{G/H} \text{ and } \varphi \in \mathfrak{H}\right\}$$

*) There always exists a nontrivial positive G-quasi-invariant measure μ on G/H, unique up to equivalence ([3],Chap.7,§2,Théorèmes 1 et 2), i.e., a measure μ on G/H such that $\mu_g = \alpha(g,.).\mu$ for all $g \in G$, where μ_g is defined by $\mu_g(A) = \mu(g.A)$, for all μ-integrable sets A and α is a continuous real-valued function on $G \times (G/H)$ (a continuous quasi-invariance factor

is total in $L^2_{\mathfrak{K}}(\gamma(U))$. Here $P_{\mathfrak{K}}$ is the decision observable in $L^2_{\mathfrak{K}}(\gamma(U))$ based on G/H defined by

$$P_{\mathfrak{K}}(B)[f] = [\phi_B f] \qquad (B \in \mathcal{B}_{G/H};\ [f] \in L^2_{\mathfrak{K}}(\gamma(U))),$$

where ϕ_B is the characteristic function of the set B. The mapping V is surjective if and only if M is a decision observable. The ordered triple $(L^2_{\mathfrak{K}}(\gamma(U)), \mathrm{Ind}_H^G \gamma(U), P_{\mathfrak{K}})$ is unique up to unitary equivalence. ∎

The axiomatic scheme of Davies and Lewis is realized in the case of a quantum system by taking, for instance, the real Banach space $\mathcal{T}(\mathfrak{h})_a$ of all self-adjoint trace class operators in a complex Hilbert space $\mathfrak{h}$ (with the trace norm) as the space of states. The states are then the elements of trace 1 of $\mathcal{T}(\mathfrak{h})_a^+$, the cone of all positive operators in $\mathcal{T}(\mathfrak{h})_a$, and the probability that the measurement in a state ϱ of an observable M in $\mathfrak{h}$ based on a set X yields a result in $B \in \mathcal{B}_X$ is

$$\mathrm{Prob}\{\varrho, M, B\} = \mathrm{tr}(\varrho M(B)) .$$

The usual observables are decision ones in $\mathfrak{h}$ based on $\mathbb{R}$ and they are covariant with respect to strongly continuous unitary representations of the symmetry group of the system (in particular, the Galilei or Poincaré group). However, a joint observable for position and momentum in $L^2(\mathbb{R})$ based on $\mathbb{R} \times \mathbb{R}$, which is not a decision one, can be defined ([2], 3.4, Theorem 4.1).

2. Kernel Hilbert spaces and densities

Let X be a locally compact space equipped with a measure μ, let $\mathfrak{K}$ be a complex Hilbert space, let $\mathcal{F}(X;\mathfrak{K})$ be the vector space of all mappings of X into $\mathfrak{K}$, and let $F(X;\mathfrak{K})$ be the (quotient) vector space of all μ-equivalence classes of $\mathcal{F}(X;\mathfrak{K})$, i.e., of the subsets of $\mathcal{F}(X;\mathfrak{K})$ defined, for every $f \in \mathcal{F}(X;\mathfrak{K})$, by

$$[f] = \{\hat{f} \mid \hat{f} \in \mathcal{F}(X;\mathfrak{K}) \text{ and } \hat{f}(x) = f(x) \quad \mu(x)\text{-a.e.}\}.$$

A positive kernel K on X acting in $\mathfrak{K}$ is a mapping of $X \times X$ into $\mathcal{L}(\mathfrak{K})$ such that

$$\sum_{j,k \in J} (K(x_k, x_j)\varphi_j | \varphi_k)_{\mathfrak{K}} \geq 0$$

for all finite index sets J, all $x_j, x_k \in X$, and all $\varphi_j, \varphi_k \in \mathfrak{K}$, where $(.|.)_{\mathfrak{K}}$ denotes the scalar multiplication on $\mathfrak{K}$. It is said to be μ-admissible if, for each $y,z \in X$ and each $\varphi, \psi \in \mathfrak{K}$, the equality $[K(.,y)\varphi] = [K(.,z)\psi]$ in $F(X;\mathfrak{K})$ implies the equality $K(.,y)\varphi = K(.,z)\psi$ in $\mathcal{F}(X;\mathfrak{K})$.

We have the following result [5]. Given a μ-admissible positive kernel K on X acting in $\mathfrak{K}$, there exists a unique complex Hilbert space $\mathfrak{K}_K \subseteq F(X;\mathfrak{K})$ (a <u>kernel Hilbert space</u>) satisfying the following conditions:

(1) the set $\{[K(.,x)\varphi] \mid x \in X \text{ and } \varphi \in \mathfrak{K}\}$ is total in $\mathfrak{K}_K$;

(2) for each $x \in X$, there exists a (unique) continuous linear mapping E_x of $\mathfrak{K}_K$ into $\mathfrak{K}$ (the <u>evaluation</u> at x) defined by

$$E_x[K(.,y)\varphi] = K(x,y)\varphi$$

for all $y \in X$, all $\varphi \in \mathfrak{K}$, and such that $E_x E_y^* = K(x,y)$ for all $x,y \in X$ (where E_y^* is the (continuous) adjoint of E_y).
The Hilbert space $\mathfrak{K}_K$ is the completion in $F(X;\mathfrak{K})$ of the linear span of the set $\{[K(.,x)\varphi]\}$ equipped with the positive Hermitian sesquilinear form $(.|.)_K$ defined by

$$([K(.,y)\varphi] | [K(.,x)\psi])_K = (K(x,y)\varphi|\psi)_{\mathfrak{K}} .$$

The following result establishes an equivalence between the existence of an admissible positive kernel (hence, of a kernel Hilbert space) and the existence of an integral representation of a covariant observable.

<u>Proposition 2.</u> [5] Let $G,H,\mu,\mathfrak{H},M,U,\mathfrak{K},V$ be as in Proposition 1. The following conditions are equivalent:

(i) There exists a mapping $x \longmapsto M_x$ of G/H into the set $\mathcal{L}(\mathfrak{H})^+$ of all positive continuous operators in $\mathfrak{H}$ such that

$$M(B) = \int \phi_B(x) M_x d\mu(x) \qquad \underline{\text{weakly}} \quad *)$$

for all $B \in \mathcal{B}_{G/H}$ (concisely: M admits a μ-density $x \longmapsto M_x$).

(ii) There exists a μ-admissible positive kernel K on G/H acting in $\mathfrak{K}$ such that $\mathfrak{K}_K = V\mathfrak{H}$.

(iii) For each $x \in G/H$, there exists a continuous linear mapping E_x of $V\mathfrak{H}$ into $\mathfrak{K}$ such that $E_x[f] = \sigma([f])(x)$, where σ is a linear section associated with the canonical surjection of $\mathfrak{F}(X;\mathfrak{K})$ onto $F(X;\mathfrak{K})$ (concisely: σ is a μ-<u>selection</u>). **) $\blacksquare$

---

*) We have

$$(M(B)\varphi|\psi) = \int \phi_B(x)(M_x\varphi|\psi) d\mu(x)$$

for all $\varphi, \psi \in \mathfrak{H}$, where (.|.) is the scalar multiplication on $\mathfrak{H}$.

**) $[\sigma([f])] = [f]$ for all $[f] \in V\mathfrak{H}$.

Remark 1. An immediate consequence of Proposition 2 is that, if $\mathfrak{H}$ is finite-dimensional, then the G-covariant observable M admits a μ-density [5].

Remark 2. The mappings $x \longmapsto M_x$, $x \longmapsto E_x$ are unique $\mu(x)$-a.e. and the mapping $(x,y) \longmapsto K(x,y)$ is unique $\mu(x)\mu(y)$-a.e. They are related by

$$M_x = (E_x V)^* E_x V, \qquad K(x,y) = E_x E_y^*$$

for all $x,y \in G/H$. The kernel K is a reproducing one, i.e.,

$$\int K(y,x)K(x,z)d\mu(x) = K(y,z) \qquad \underline{\text{weakly}} .$$

Remark 3. Since

$$\int M_x d\mu(x) = \int (E_x V)^* E_x V d\mu(x) = \mathrm{Id}_{\mathfrak{H}} \qquad \underline{\text{weakly}} ,$$

we say that the μ-density $x \longmapsto M_x$, as well as the mapping $x \longmapsto E_x V$ of G/H into the vector space of all continuous linear mappings of $\mathfrak{H}$ into $\mathfrak{K}$, is a (weak) μ-resolution of the identity in $\mathfrak{H}$.

3. Observables admitting densities

The following result generalizes Theorem 5.3, Chap.4 of [2].

Proposition 3. [6] Let $G,H,\mu,\mathfrak{H},U$ be as in Proposition 1. The mapping $M \longmapsto \delta(M)$ is a bijection of the set of all observables M in $\mathfrak{H}$ based on G/H which are G-covariant with respect to U and which admit a μ-density onto the set of all positive continuous linear operators $\delta(M)$ in $\mathfrak{H}$ satisfying the following conditions:

(1) $U(h)\delta(M)U(h)^{-1} = \alpha(h,x_o)\delta(M)$ for all $h \in H$, where α is a continuous quasi-invariance factor of μ and x_o is the image of the neutral element of G by the canonical surjection of G onto G/H.

(2) There exist an isometric mapping V of $\mathfrak{H}$ into $L^2_{\mathfrak{K}}(\gamma(U))$, with some $\mathfrak{K}$ and $\gamma(U)$, and a continuous linear mapping E_{x_o} of $V\mathfrak{H}$ into $\mathfrak{K}$ defined by $E_{x_o}[f] = \sigma([f])(x_o)$, where σ is a μ-selection, such that $V^*(\mathrm{Ind}_H^G\gamma(U))(g)V = U(g)$ for all $g \in G$ and $\delta(M) = (E_{x_o}V)^*E_{x_o}V$. ■

Remark 4. The existence of V in condition (2) of Proposition 3 expresses the unitary equivalence of U to a subrepresentation of a representation of G induced from H: the equivalence is established via V.

Remark 5. Condition (2) of Proposition 3 actually implies the μ-integrability of the mappings $g.x_o \longmapsto \alpha(g,x_o)^{-1}(U(g)\delta(M)U(g)^{-1}\varphi|\psi)$ for all $\varphi,\psi \in \mathfrak{h}$; the observable M is given by

$$M(B) = \int \phi_B(g.x_o)\alpha(g,x_o)^{-1}U(g)\delta(M)U(g)^{-1}d\mu(g.x_o) \qquad \underline{\text{weakly}}.$$

The μ-integrability condition is always satisfied if G is compact. If, in addition, $\mathfrak{h}$ is finite-dimensional, then every observable M in $\mathfrak{h}$ based on G/H which is G-covariant with respect to U admits a μ-density.

Remark 6. If in Proposition 3 the representation U is irreducible and the operator $\delta(M)$ is a rank one (orthogonal) projection satisfying conditions (1),(2), then the measure μ is G-invariant and U is unitarily equivalent via V to a subrepresentation of a monomial representation of G induced from H (i.e., with $\dim\mathfrak{K} = 1$). We have

$$\delta(M) = \|\varphi\|^{-2}(.|\varphi)\varphi \quad , \quad E_{x_o}V = \|\varphi\|^{-1}(.|\varphi) \quad , \quad (E_{x_o}V)^* = \|\varphi\|^{-1}\varphi ,$$

where φ is an arbitrary element of $\mathfrak{h}$ satisfying the convergence condition

$$\int U(g)\delta(M)U(g)^{-1}d\mu(g.x_o) = Id_{\mathfrak{h}} \qquad \underline{\text{weakly}} .$$

The (reproducing) kernel K of Proposition 2 is now defined by

$$K(g.x_o,g'.x_o) = \|\varphi\|^{-2}(U(g)\varphi|U(g')\varphi).$$

The mapping $g.x_o \longmapsto U(g)\delta(M)U(g)^{-1}$ of G/H into $\mathcal{L}(\mathfrak{h})^+$ is called a family of coherent projections and the mapping $g.x_o \longmapsto U(g)\varphi$ of G/H into $\mathfrak{h}$ is called a (square integrable) family of coherent states relative to U based on G/H. When G is the (three-dimensional) Heisenberg group, H is its center, $\mu = \pi^{-1}\nu$, where ν is the Lebesgue measure on $\mathbb{R}^2$, U is the Schrödinger representation of G, and φ is the ground state of the harmonic oscillator, then the convergence condition is satisfied and the coherent states are the usual Glauber coherent states.

References

[1] E.B.Davies and J.T. Lewis: Commun.Math.Phys.17, 239-260 (1970).
[2] E.B.Davies: Quantum Theory of Open Systems. London: Academic Press 1976.
[3] N. Bourbaki: Éléments de mathématiques. Livre VI: Intégration, Chaps. 7 et 8 (ASI 1306). Paris: Hermann 1963.
[4] U. Cattaneo: Comment.Math.Helv. 54, 629-641 (1979).
[5] U. Cattaneo: J.Math.Phys. 23, 659-664 (1982).
[6] U. Cattaneo: To appear.

SOME REMARKS ON THE SUBSEQUENCE PRINCIPLE

IN PROBABILITY THEORY.

S.D. Chatterji

§1.

The subsequence principle in probability theory, stated in an imprecise but suggestive form, says that given any sequence of real-valued random variables (r.v.'s) satisfying certain moment boundedness conditions, one can find a subsequence such that it and all its further subsequences will satisfy the same types of laws as do independent identically distributed (i.i.d.) r.v.'s fulfulling the same moment boundedness. In fact, the principle is applicable to sequences of real-valued measurable functions defined on arbitrary non-negative measure spaces finite, σ-finite or not. To substantiate these remarks, let us state a theorem which presents some of the known facts which vindicate the subsequence principle.

Theorem 1.

Let (Ω,Σ,μ) be an arbitrary non-negative measure space and let $f_n : \Omega \to \mathbb{R}$, $n = 1,2,\ldots$ be a sequence of measurable functions such that $\sup_n \int |f_n|^p \, d\mu < \infty$ for some $p > 0$. Then we can find a subsequence $\{f_{n_j}\}$ such that any further subsequence $\{g_k\}_{k\geq 1}$ of it will have the following properties :

(i) If $0 < p < 1$ then

$$\lim_{n\to\infty} n^{-1/p} \sum_{k=1}^{n} g_k = 0 \quad \text{a.e.}$$

(ii) If $1 \leq p < 2$ then there exists an L^p-function α such that

$$\lim_{n\to\infty} n^{-1/p} \sum_{k=1}^{n} (g_k - \alpha) = 0 \quad \text{a.e.}$$

(iii) If $p = 2$ then there exists an L^2-function α such that

$$\sum_n a_n (g_n - \alpha) \quad \text{converges} \quad \text{a.e.}$$

for any real sequence $\{a_n\}$ with $\sum_n |a_n|^2 < \infty$.

(iv) If $p = 2$ then there exist an L^2-function α and a non-negative L^1-function β such that

(a) $$\mu\left\{\beta=0;\ \frac{1}{\sqrt{n}}\ \left|\sum_{k=1}^{n}(g_k-\alpha)\right|>\varepsilon\right\}\to 0 \quad \text{as } n\to\infty \quad \text{for any } \varepsilon>0;$$

(b) $$\mu\left\{A\quad;\ \frac{1}{\sqrt{n\beta}}\sum_{k=1}^{n}(g_k-\alpha)\leqslant x\right\}\to\mu(A)\ \frac{1}{\sqrt{2\pi}}\int_{-\infty}^{x}e^{-u^2/2}\,du$$

as $n\to\infty$ for any $A\in\Sigma$, $0<\mu(A)<\infty$, $A\subset\{\beta>0\}$, $x\in\mathbb{R}$;

(c) $$\limsup_{n\to\infty}\left[\frac{\sum_{k=1}^{n}(g_k-\alpha)}{(2n\ \ell n\ \ell n\ n)^{\frac{1}{2}}}\right]=\beta^{\frac{1}{2}}\quad \text{a.s.}$$

Theorem 1 summarizes the results of several propositions proved by various authors (Gaposhkin, Komlós, Révész, Chatterji) over a number of years. The exact references to these can be looked up in the recent survey article Chatterji [1985]. It will be immediately clear from the theorem that (i) and (ii) above constitute a justification of the subsequence principle as regards the Kolmogorov-Marcinkiewicz-Zygmund strong law of large numbers for real-valued i.i.d. r.v.'s and that (iv) constitutes a similar justification in relation to the central limit theorem and the law of the iterated logarithms.

Many other results of the type contained in thm. 1 can be proven. Some of these are referred to in the article already mentioned above (Chatterji [1985]). They were originally proven by the following technique. One finds a subsequence $\{fn_j\}_{j\geqslant 1}$ such that any of its subsequences $\{g_k\}_{k\geqslant 1}$ has the structure

$$g_k = h_k + r_k$$

where $\{h_k\}_{k\geqslant 1}$ is a martingale difference sequence and $\sum_k |r_k| < \infty$ a.s. The laws satisfied by $\{g_k\}$ are then essentially those that are followed by the martingale difference sequence $\{h_k\}$. These latter are then made to obey the laws in which we are interested.

A completely different approach due to Aldous [1977] establishes large parts of the vaguely stated subsequence principle as a precise theorem. Let us state that part of Aldous' theorems which contains a statement about a.e. convergence. For simplicity, we shall restrict ourselves to probability spaces (Ω,Σ,P). Let us introduce some terminology. Let (S,d) be a Polish space (e.g. $S=\mathbb{R}$) and let $P(S)$ be the space of all probability measures on S endowed with its (Polish) topology of weak convergence. A Borel subset A of $P(S)\times S^{\infty}$ ($S^{\infty} = S\times S\times\ldots$) is called a statute (in S)

if for any $\nu \in P(S)$,

$$\nu^{\infty}(A_{\nu}) = 1$$

where $A_{\nu} = \{x \in S^{\infty} : (\nu,x) \in A\}$ and $\nu^{\infty} = \nu \otimes \nu \otimes \dots$.

Since ν^{∞} is the mathematical model of a sequence of i.i.d. S-valued r.v.'s, the concept of a statute covers a large part of what we think of as an a.s. limit property of such a sequence. If $S = \mathbb{R}$ and A is taken to be the set of all (ν,x) in $P(\mathbb{R}) \times \mathbb{R}^{\infty}$ such that either $\int_{-\infty}^{\infty} |u| \nu(du) = \infty$ (and then x is unrestricted) or $\int_{-\infty}^{\infty} |u| \nu(du) < \infty$ and $x = (x_i)$ is such that

$$\lim_n \frac{1}{n} \sum_{i=1}^{n} x_i = \int_{-\infty}^{\infty} u \, \nu(du)$$

then the Kolmogorov strong law of large numbers is exactly equivalent to the fact that A is a statute (Kolmogorov statute).

Let us say that A is a <u>limit statute</u> (in S) if A is a statute such that if $(\nu,x) \in A$ then $(\nu,y) \in A$ whenever

$$\sum_{i=1}^{\infty} d(x_i, y_i) < \infty$$

where $x = (x_i)$, $y = (y_i)$ and d is the metric in S. Clearly, the above Kolmogorov statute is a limit statute (with d = usual metric in $\mathbb{R}$).

We now state Aldous' theorem.

<u>Theorem 2.</u>

Let (Ω,Σ,P) be a probability space and S a Polish space.

Let $\{f_n\}_{n \geq 1}$ be any sequence of S-valued r.v.'s whose laws form a tight family i.e. for any $\varepsilon > 0$ there is a compact set K_{ε} in S such that

$$P\{f_n \in K_{\varepsilon}\} > 1 - \varepsilon, \qquad n \geq 1.$$

There is then a measurable map

$$\lambda : \Omega \to P(S)$$

with the following property : if A is any limit statute in S then there is a subsequence $\{f_{n_j}\}_{j \geq 1}$ such that for any of its further subsequences $\{g_k\}_{k \geq 1}$ we have the relation :

$$(\lambda(\omega),\ g(\omega)) \in A \qquad \text{a.s.}(\omega)$$

where $g(\omega) = (g_k(\omega))$. Further the map λ is such that

$$\int_\Omega |\lambda(\omega)|_p\ P(d\omega) \leq \limsup_{n\to\infty} \int_\Omega d^p(s_o, f_n(\omega))\ P(d\omega)$$

where

$$|\lambda(\omega)|_p = \int_S d^p(s_o, s)\ \lambda(\omega)(ds)$$

and s_o is some fixed point in S.

It is easy to see that if we apply the above theorem to the Kolmogorov statute (with $S = \mathbb{R}$, $s_o = 0$, d = usual distance) then we obtain Komlós theorem (proved by Komlós in 1967) i.e. case p = 1 of thm. 1(ii). Similarly, parts (i), (ii) (general case) and (iv)(c) will also follow from thm. 2 applied to appropriate statutes in $\mathbb{R}$. Of course, parts (iv)(a) and (b) are note covered by thm. 2. However, Aldous [1977] has given a formulation of the subsequence principle which contain these two also. Unfortunately, this formulation is not quite so simple to state as the one in thm. 2.

The situation as regards part (iii) of thm. 1 (due originally to Révész, 1965) is different. In its present form, thm. 2 cannot give a statement like thm. 1(iii) since the latter has to do with a non-denumerable family of statutes, one for each sequence $\{a_n\}$, $\sum_n |a_n|^2 < \infty$. Although Aldous [1977] manages to prove a much stronger theorem (viz. the series appearing in (iii), thm. 1, converges a.s. for <u>every</u> permutation of its terms), it is unfortunate that no general theorem of the type of thm. 2 exists as yet which would permit us to prove even (iii) of thm. 1. Incidentally, (iii) itself can be proved rather easily by the martingale method outlined before (cf. Chatterji [1985]).

Aldous' proof of his theorem (thm. 2) is based on the use of exchangeable sequences of r.v.'s. A sequence of r.v.s $\{\eta_n\}_{n\geq 1}$ is said to form an <u>exchangeable sequence</u> if the law of $\{\eta_{n_j},\ 1\leq j\leq k\}$, for any $k \geq 1$ and for any choice of distinct indices $n_1 \ldots n_k$, is the same as that of $\{\eta_1, \ldots, \eta_k\}$. Clearly, an i.i.d. sequence is an exchangeable sequence. On the other hand, it is also known that an exchangeable sequence is a "probabilistic mixture" of i.i.d. variables. This statement is called de Finetti's theorem (for further information concerning which the articles of Aldous [1977], Chatterji [1985] may be consulted). Thus, almost any statements valid for i.i.d. sequences have a good chance of being true for exchangeable sequences as well.

Given an arbitrary sequence of r.v.'s $\{f_n\}$ as in thm. 2, Aldous establishes the existence of a subsequence whose law is very close to that of a suitable exchangeable sequence. Unfortunately, the details of the approximation are rather technical and no simplification of Aldous' original proof has been achieved yet.

§2.

We have already pointed out above that subsequence statements like (iii) of thm. 1 are not covered by thm. 2. Other statements which involve convergence in L^p or convergence in probability are also not directly deducible from thm. 2. It would be interesting to formulate a version of thm. 2 which would allow this. This does not seem too difficult to do.

There is another class of statements valid for i.i.d. real r.v.'s which seem to be definitely wrong in our context. Take, for example, the elegant result due to Hsu and Robbins (1947, cf. Stout [1974] for a recent presentation) which says that if $\{\eta_n\}_{n\geq 1}$ is an i.i.d. sequence of real r.v.'s with 0 expectation and finite variance and $\xi_n = \eta_1 + \ldots + \eta_n$ then, for any $\varepsilon > 0$, $\sum_n P\left\{\left|\frac{1}{n}\xi_n\right| > \varepsilon\right\} < \infty$ (i.e. $\frac{1}{n}\xi_n \to 0$ completely, which implies, of course, that it converges a.s. also). It does not seem to be known whether such a statement is valid for an exchangeable sequence of r.v.'s $\{\eta_n\}$. The corresponding subsequence statement would be that if $\sup_n \int |f_n|^2 dP < \infty$ then for some subsequence $\{fn_j\}_{j\geq 1}$ and some centering function α,

$$\frac{1}{n}\sum_{k=1}^{n} (g_k - \alpha) \to 0$$

completely whenever $\{g_k\}$ is a subsequence of $\{fn_j\}$ i.e.

$$\sum_n P\left\{\frac{1}{n}\left|\sum_{k=1}^{n}(g_k-\alpha)\right| > \varepsilon\right\} < \infty$$

for all $\varepsilon > 0$. I am convinced that this is wrong and feel that a counter-example should not be too hard to obtain. In fact, it seems that a counter-example involving an exchangeable sequence $\{f_n\}$ should be possible.

For partial extensions of thm. 1 to Banach space valued sequences as well as for references to other aspects of the subsequence principle, the article Chatterji [1985] may be consulted.

References.

Aldous, D.J.

Limit theorems for subsequences of arbitrarily-dependent sequences of random variables. Z. Wahrscheinlichkeitstheorie verw. Gebiete 40 [1977] 59-82.

Chatterji, S.D.

A subsequence principle in probability theory. Jber. d. Dt. Math.-Verein 87 [1985] 91-107.

Stout, W.F.

Almost sure convergence. Academic Press, N.Y. [1974] .

Département de Mathématiques
Ecole Polytechnique Fédérale de Lausanne
1015 Lausanne (Switzerland).

A Route to Stochastic Mechanics

G.F.De Angelis

Dipartimento di Fisica,Università di Salerno

84100 Salerno, Italy.

and

INFN Sezione di Napoli.

§1. The road to stochastic mechanics is paved with good (Kolmogorov) equations.

In the present article I'll try to illustrate the power of a **general heuristic principle** for constructing stochastic mechanics **from** quantum mechanics.It consists in comparing continuity equations of quantum mechanical origin with forward Kolmogorov equations for suitably chosen classes of random processes.This guiding principle was introduced explicitly for the first time,as far as I know,in /1/ where it was applied to the construction of stochastic mechanics for a non relativistic spin 1/2 particle in a magnetic field and it proved to be useful also in other interesting cases /2,3/.Let us consider,for instance,the Schrödinger equation in configuration space $\mathbb{R}^d$:

$$i\hbar\partial_t\psi = \frac{1}{2m}(-i\hbar\nabla - \frac{e}{c}\mathbf{A})^2\psi + V\psi \qquad 1)$$

with the associated continuity equation for the probability density $\rho(t,\mathbf{x}) = |\psi(t,\mathbf{x})|^2$:

$$\partial_t\rho = -\frac{\hbar}{m}\operatorname{div}\operatorname{Im}\{\psi^*(\nabla - \frac{ie}{\hbar c}\mathbf{A})\psi\} \qquad 2)$$

Given a normalized solution $\psi(t,\mathbf{x})$ of 1),we wish to find a diffusion $\boldsymbol{\xi}_t$ in $\mathbb{R}^d$ (verifing $d\boldsymbol{\xi}_t = \mathbf{b}(t,\boldsymbol{\xi}_t)dt + \sqrt{\frac{\hbar}{m}}\,d\mathbf{W}_t$) such that,at every time t and for every region B in the space,$\text{Prob.}(\boldsymbol{\xi}_t \in B) = \int_B|\psi(t,\mathbf{x})|^2d\mathbf{x}$.

By comparing 2) with the Fokker-Planck equation for the probability density ρ of $\boldsymbol{\xi}_t$:

$$\partial_t\rho = \frac{\hbar}{2m}\Delta\rho - \operatorname{div}\mathbf{b}\rho \qquad 3)$$

we must find a vector field (drift) $\mathbf{b}(t,\mathbf{x})$ such that:

$$\mathrm{div}\{\mathbf{b}|\psi|^2 - \frac{\hbar}{m}\,\mathrm{Im}\psi^*(\nabla - \frac{ie}{\hbar c}\mathbf{A})\psi\} = \frac{\hbar}{2m}\,\Delta|\psi|^2 \qquad 4)$$

Under the additional assumption $\mathrm{rot}\,\mathbf{b} = -\frac{e}{mc}\mathbf{B}$, the only possible choice is $\mathbf{b} = \mathbf{u} + \mathbf{v} = \frac{\hbar}{m}\mathrm{grad}\ln|\psi| + \frac{\hbar}{m}\,\mathrm{Im}\psi^*(\nabla - \frac{ie}{\hbar c}\mathbf{A})\psi/|\psi|^2$ and from 1) we obtain Nelson's equations of motion /4/ for the osmotic velocity $\mathbf{u}$ and the current velocity $\mathbf{v}$:

$$\begin{aligned} \partial_t\mathbf{u} &= -\frac{\hbar}{2m}\,\mathrm{grad}\,\mathrm{div}\mathbf{v} - \mathrm{grad}\,\mathbf{u}\cdot\mathbf{v} \\ \partial_t\mathbf{v} &= -\frac{1}{m}\mathrm{grad}\,V + \frac{1}{2}\,\mathrm{grad}||\mathbf{u}||^2 - \frac{1}{2}\mathrm{grad}||\mathbf{v}||^2 + \frac{\hbar}{2m}\Delta\mathbf{u} \end{aligned} \qquad 5)$$

which can be assumed as the starting point of stochastic mechanics (in configuration space) for a Schrödinger particle.

As a further illustration of the heuristic principle I'll consider the rather elementary example of a spin 1/2 in a magnetic field,the stochastic mechanics of a Dirac particle in 1+1 space-time dimensions,moving in some arbitrary external electromagnetic field,and a stochastic description of Schrödinger particles in **momentum space**,at least for a suitable class of potentials.

I want to point out that **diffusions**,familiar in Nelson stochastic mechanics, are by no means **natural** in a general stochastic setting for quantum systems.For instance,stochastic processes associated to solutions of Dirac equation are of non diffusive type and a similar feature holds for Schrödinger particles in **momentum space** where the "good" class of processes is a class of generalized Poisson processes.From such examples we learn that the set of random processes we need in constructing **a** stochastic mechanics depends from the quantum system we consider but also,for a given quantum system,from the **complete set of commuting observables** that we choose as starting point in our stochastic description.

My hour is almost come when I to sulphurous and tormenting flames must render up myself,but I still should like to remind you,Horatio,of the case against (a too "realistic" interpretation of)stochastic mechanics that a Founder brought during this Conference /5,6/and then,because there are more things in heaven and earth than are dreamt in your philosophy,I want to stress that,before we'll be able to use some stochastic description of quantum phenomena to set up a radically new physical viewpoint of the microscopic world (angels and ministers of grace,defend us!),we must have at our disposal lots and lots of succesful examples of "classical" probabilistic description for many standard quantum theories from which we may gain,eventually,some general wisdom. At the moment,to be on the safe side,I believe that stochastic mechanics is useful in two important aspects:to physicists as source of a new way of thinking about quantum phenomena and as springs of valuable mathematical analogies/7,8,9,10,11,12,13/,to mathematicians,working in stochastic processes and stochastic differential equations,by suggesting new problems and ideas /14,15,16,17/.

Commenting on the divorce between physics and mathematics,Res Jost remarked /18/ "as usual in such affairs one of two parties has clearly got the worst of it",now I hope that,in this new marriage-tie,both partners will get the best of it.

§2. An elementary example: spin 1/2 in a magnetic field.

As an elementary example of application of the heuristic principle, I take a spin 1/2 in a magnetic field $\mathbf{B} = (B,0,0)$ (for simplicity only). By choosing the usual representation of Pauli matrices: $\sigma_1=\begin{pmatrix}0&1\\1&0\end{pmatrix}$, $\sigma_2=\begin{pmatrix}0&-i\\i&0\end{pmatrix}$, $\sigma_3=\begin{pmatrix}1&0\\0&-1\end{pmatrix}$ one gets the following"Schrödinger"equation for the wave function $\psi(t,\sigma)$ considered as a complex valued function of time t and of a dichotomic variable $\sigma \in \mathbf{Z}_2=\{-1,1\}$:

$$i\frac{d}{dt}\psi(t,\sigma) = -\frac{B}{2}\psi(t,-\sigma) \qquad 6)$$

Starting from a normalized solution $\psi(t,\sigma)$ of 6),I consider the probability distribution $\rho(t,\sigma)=|\psi(t,\sigma)|^2$ on $\mathbf{Z}_2$ and I ask if it is possible to construct a jump Markov process ξ_t on $\mathbf{Z}_2$ such that,at every time t, $\mathrm{Prob.}(\xi_t=\sigma) = |\psi(t,\sigma)|^2$. I compare the quantum mechanical continuity equation for $\rho(t,\sigma)$:

$$\frac{d}{dt}\rho(t,\sigma) = B\ \mathrm{Im}\{\psi(t,\sigma)\psi(t,-\sigma)^*\} \qquad 7)$$

with Kolmogorov forward equation for the probability distribution of ξ_t:

$$\frac{d}{dt}\rho(t,\sigma) = p(t,-\sigma)\rho(t,-\sigma) - p(t,\sigma)\rho(t,\sigma) \qquad 8)$$

(where $p(t,\sigma)$ represents the probability per unit time of a jump of ξ_t from the initial state σ to the final state $-\sigma$) and I have to solve the following problem: given the wave function $\psi(t,\sigma)$, find a **non negative** $p(t,\sigma)$ such that:

$$B\,\mathrm{Im}\{\psi(t,\sigma)\psi(t,-\sigma)^*\} = p(t,-\sigma)\rho(t,-\sigma) - p(t,\sigma)\rho(t,\sigma) \qquad 9)$$

A nice solution (see /1/ for a more comprehensive discussion) is given by:

$$p(t,\sigma) = \frac{B}{2}\left\{\frac{|\psi(t,-\sigma)|}{|\psi(t,\sigma)|} + \mathrm{Im}\,\frac{\psi(t,-\sigma)}{\psi(t,\sigma)}\right\} \qquad 10)$$

Once the jump probability per unit time is given, from Kolmogorov equation I obtain the probability of transition, from probability of transition and initial probability distribution I can construct my Markov process ξ_t. In this way I get a "classical" probabilistic description of spin 1/2 in the magnetic field $\mathbf{B} = (B,0,0)$ and it is not difficult to generalize the whole procedure for an arbitrary magnetic field $\mathbf{B}$ and for any component of the spin $\boldsymbol{\sigma}$ in order to exibit the rotational invariance of such a stochastic description (moreover one can do it for a non pure quantum state also) /1/. By defining two functions $z(t), w(t)$

$$\begin{aligned} \psi(t,\sigma) &= \exp\{R(t,\sigma) + iS(t,\sigma)\} \\ R(t,\sigma) &= \frac{1}{2}(R_0(t) - \sigma z(t)) \\ S(t,\sigma) &= \frac{1}{2}(S_0(t) - \sigma w(t)) \end{aligned} \qquad 11)$$

I get, from 6), the following set of non linear equations of motion:

$$\begin{aligned} \frac{dz}{dt} &= B \sin w \cosh z \\ \frac{dw}{dt} &= -B \cos w \sinh z \end{aligned} \qquad 12)$$

(By charting the two-dimensional unit sphere $S^2 = \{\mathbf{S} \in \mathbb{R}^3 : ||\mathbf{S}|| = 1\}$ through $S_x = \frac{\cos w}{\cosh z}$, $S_y = \frac{\sin w}{\cosh z}$, $S_z = -\tanh z$, the set 12) represents exactly the precession $\frac{d\mathbf{S}}{dt} = -\mathbf{B}\times\mathbf{S}$ **of** the unit vector $\mathbf{S} = \langle\boldsymbol{\sigma}\rangle$) I forget now quantum mechanics and I take the equations 12) as starting point by associating to each solution (z,w) of them a jump Markov process ξ_t through the formulas (automatically consistent with forward Kolmogorov equation 8)):

$$\mathrm{Prob.}(\xi_t=\sigma) = (2\cosh z(t))^{-1}\exp{-\sigma z(t)},\ \lim_{\delta\downarrow 0} \mathrm{Prob.}(\xi_{t+\delta} = -\sigma|\xi_t=\sigma)/\delta = \frac{B}{2}(1+\sigma\sin w(t))\exp\sigma z(t) = p(t,\sigma) \qquad 13)$$

Each such process mirrors some (pure) quantum state of our spin 1/2 and the more complicated case of full Pauli equation in a (non necessarily homogeneous) magnetic field $\mathbf{B}(\mathbf{x})$ can be treated along this line.

I turn now to Dirac equation in 1+1 space-time dimensions. First of all I'll show how it is possible to associate to each solution of Dirac equation a random process reproducing, at every time t, the quantum mechanical joint probability distribution of space position and speed of the particle and then how to construct "hydrodynamical" covariant equations for a set of four (gauge-invariant) fields describing kinematics and dynamics of such class of processes. A short discussion of relativistic invariance of Dirac theory in this stochastic context will be also given.

§3. Stochastic processes from solutions of Dirac equation.

By using Weyl representation of Dirac matrices and by treating Dirac spinors (in 1+1 dimensions) as complex valued functions of space-time coordinates (t,x) and of a dichotomic variable σ in $\mathbb{Z}_2$, Dirac equation, in the external electromagnetic field $A^\mu(t,x) = (A^0(t,x), A^1(t,x))$, is:

$$i\hbar\partial_t\psi(t,x,\sigma) = c(-i\hbar\partial_x - \frac{e}{c}A^1(t,x))\psi(t,x,\sigma) + Mc^2\psi(t,x,-\sigma) + eA^0(t,x)\psi(t,x,\sigma) \qquad 14)$$

I take, as probability density in $\mathbb{R}\times\mathbb{Z}_2$: $\rho(t,x,\sigma) = |\psi(t,x,\sigma)|^2$ and then from 14), the quantum mechanical continuity equation follows:

$$\partial_t\rho(t,x,\sigma) = -c\sigma\partial_x\rho(t,x,\sigma) - \frac{2Mc^2}{\hbar}\mathrm{Im}\{\psi(t,x,\sigma)^*\psi(t,x,-\sigma)\} \qquad 15)$$

According to the heuristic principle, I wish to find a **non negative** function $p(t,x,\sigma)$ in order to rewrite 15) in the new form:

$$\partial_t\rho(t,x,\sigma) = -c\sigma\partial_x\rho(t,x,\sigma) + p(t,x,-\sigma)\rho(t,x,-\sigma) - p(t,x,\sigma)\rho(t,x,\sigma) \qquad 16)$$

The last equation is exactly Kolmogorov forward equation for the class of random processes $\xi_t = \xi_0 + \sigma_0 c\int_0^t (-1)^{N_s} ds$ where ξ_0 and σ_0 are, respectively, random variable on the real line and on $\mathbb{Z}_2$ while N_s is a point (counting) process, non pure Poisson in general. The processes in the above class share a very simple interpretation: they describe a point particle moving on a line with speed of constant magnitude c and inverting its motion at random times non necessarily Poisson distributed. Of course $p(t,x,\sigma)$

represents the probability per unit time of inverting the motion when the space-time position of the particle is (t,x) and the velocity $c\sigma$. By looking at 15) and 16), we see that the problem is exactly as in the case of a spin 1/2 in a magnetic field $\mathbf{B}=(B,0,0)$ with $B = \frac{2Mc^2}{\hbar}$ (the frequency of Zitterbewegung) and the solution is:

$$p(t,x,\sigma) = \frac{Mc^2}{\hbar}\left\{\frac{|\psi(t,x,-\sigma)|}{|\psi(t,x,\sigma)|} - \mathrm{Im}\frac{\psi(t,x,-\sigma)}{\psi(t,x,\sigma)}\right\} \qquad 17)$$

From jump probability per unit time and initial probability distribution I get my random process ξ_t and, by construction, Prob.$(\xi_t \in B$ **and** $\frac{d}{dt}\xi_t = c\sigma) = \int_B |\psi(t,x,\sigma)|^2 dx$ at every time t and for every region B on the line. I conclude that Dirac equation admits a "classical" probabilistic description in terms of random processes (of **non diffusive** type) which represent random motions on a line with speed of constant magnitude and whose trajectories are zig-zag path in Minkowski space-time.

Of course, this scenario reminds us Feynman path integral representation of Dirac propagator in two space-time dimensions. I remark that a generalization of the above construction can be done also in more than 1+1 space-time dimensions but with random motions faster than light.

§4. Hydrodynamical equations and relativistic invariance.

In the following $x = (x^0,x^1) = (ct,x^1)$ will represent a point in Minkowski space-time. By defining four (gauge-invariant) fields u_μ, v_μ, z, w, through :

$$\begin{aligned}
\psi(x,\sigma) &= \exp(R(x,\sigma) + iS(x,\sigma)) \\
R(x,\sigma) &= \tfrac{1}{2}(R_0(x) - \sigma z(x)) \\
S(x,\sigma) &= \tfrac{1}{2}(S_0(x) - \sigma w(x)) \\
u_\mu(x) &= -\frac{\hbar}{2M}\partial_\mu R_0(x) \\
v_\mu(x) &= -\frac{\hbar}{2M}\partial_\mu S_0(x) + \frac{e}{Mc}A_\mu(x)
\end{aligned} \qquad 18)$$

one can reconstruct from them $\psi(x,\sigma)$ up to a phase factor and a normalization constant, moreover, from Dirac equation, I get the following set of "hydrodynamical" equations:

$$\partial_\mu u_\nu - \partial_\nu u_\mu = 0 \;, \qquad \partial_\mu v_\nu - \partial_\nu v_\mu = \frac{e}{Mc}F_{\mu\nu} \qquad 19)$$

$$\partial_0 z \pm \partial_1 z \pm \frac{2M}{\hbar}u_0 + \frac{2M}{\hbar}u_1 = -\frac{2Mc}{\hbar}\sin w \exp\pm z$$

$$\partial_0 w \pm \partial_1 w \pm \frac{2M}{\hbar}v_0 + \frac{2M}{\hbar}v_1 = \frac{2Mc}{\hbar}\cos w \exp\pm z \qquad 19')$$

which are **non linear** (as Nelson equations 5)) and contain only **gauge-invariant** quantities (as the electromagnetic tensor $F_{\mu\nu} = \partial_\mu A_\nu - \partial_\nu A_\mu$).

I forget now Dirac equation and assume the set 19),19') as starting point.From every solution (u_μ, v_μ, z, w) of field equations I construct a random process ξ_t on the real line $\mathbb{R}$ according to the recipe:

$$\rho(x,\sigma) = K\exp-\{\frac{2M}{\hbar}\int_0^x u_\mu(y)dy^\mu + \sigma z(x)\}$$

$$p(x,\sigma) = \frac{Mc}{\hbar}(1+\sigma\sin w(x))\exp\sigma z(x) \qquad 20)$$

(the constant K being fixed by normalization of ρ).The class of stochastic processes obtained in this way mirrors the set of solutions of Dirac equation.From the definition,it is easy to see that $u_\mu, v_\mu, \partial_\mu z, \partial_\mu w$ transform as (covariant) vector fields under Lorentz boosts while w is a scalar.The field equations 19),19') are **covariant** and Kolmogorov forward equation (which follows automatically from 19') and 20)) is **invariant**.The probability measure on zig-zag paths in Minkowski space-time associated to each process,transforms in the obvious way under Lorentz boosts and the "classical" probabilistic interpretation of (1+1 dimensional) Dirac theory is relativistically invariant.

§5. Schrödinger particles in momentum space.

As a final illustration of the heuristic principle,I consider a Schrödinger particle in d-dimensions subjected to a potential $V(\mathbf{x})$ which is Fourier transform of an even Borel measure $\mu(d\mathbf{p})$:

$$V(\mathbf{x}) = \int_{\mathbb{R}^d} \exp\{i\mathbf{p}\,\mathbf{x}\}\mu(d\mathbf{p}) \qquad 21)$$

for instance,in $d = 1, V(x) = g\cos x$.

Schrödinger equation in **momentum space** is ($\hbar = 1$):

$$i\partial_t\psi(t,\mathbf{p}) = \frac{||\mathbf{p}||^2}{2m}\psi(t,\mathbf{p}) + \int_{\mathbb{R}^d}\psi(t,\mathbf{p}-\mathbf{q})\mu(d\mathbf{q}) \qquad 22)$$

with the corresponding continuity equation:

$$\partial_t|\psi(t,\mathbf{p})|^2 = -2\mathrm{Im}\int_{\mathbb{R}^d}\psi(t,\mathbf{p})^*\psi(t,\mathbf{p}-\mathbf{q})\mu(d\mathbf{q}) \qquad 23)$$

(same general structure as 7) with the discrete group $\mathbf{Z}_2$ replaced by momentum space $\mathbb{R}^d$).It is convenient to recast the continuity equation in the (equivalent) "integrated" form:

$$\frac{d}{dt}\nu_t(B) = \int_{\mathbb{R}^d} \nu_t(d\mathbf{p}) \int_{\mathbb{R}^d} \mu(d\mathbf{q})(\chi_B(\mathbf{p}) - \chi_{B+\mathbf{q}}(\mathbf{p}))\operatorname{Im}\frac{\psi(t,\mathbf{p}-\mathbf{q})}{\psi(t,\mathbf{p})} \tag{24}$$

where $\nu_t(d\mathbf{p}) = |\psi(t,\mathbf{p})|^2 d\mathbf{p}$ and $\chi_B(\cdot)$ is the characteristic function of Borel subset B of momentum space $\mathbb{R}^d$.By looking at Kolmogorov forward equation of a jump Markov process ξ_t in $\mathbb{R}^d$,I have to solve the following problem:find a family of (signed) measures in momentum space $B \to p(t,\mathbf{p},B)$ such that:

i) $p(t,\mathbf{p},B) \geq 0$ **if** $\mathbf{p} \notin B$

ii) $p(t,\mathbf{p},\mathbb{R}^d) = 0$ for every $\mathbf{p}$ in $\mathbb{R}^d$

iii) $\frac{d}{dt}\nu_t(B) = \int_{\mathbb{R}^d} p(t,\mathbf{p},B)\nu_t(d\mathbf{p})$ for every Borel set B in $\mathbb{R}^d$

The last equation is exactly Kolmogorov forward equation for a jump Markov process ξ_t in $\mathbb{R}^d$ with $\nu_t(B) = \text{Prob.}(\xi_t \in B)$ and $p(t,\mathbf{p},B) =$ $= \lim_{\delta \downarrow 0}\{\text{Prob.}(\xi_{t+\delta} \in B \mid \xi_t = \mathbf{p}) - \chi_B(\mathbf{p})\}/\delta$ .Because:

$$0 = \int_{\mathbb{R}^d} |\psi(t,\mathbf{p})|^2 d\mathbf{p} \int_{\mathbb{R}^d} \mu(d\mathbf{q})(\chi_{B+\mathbf{q}}(\mathbf{p}) - \chi_B(\mathbf{p}))\frac{|\psi(t,\mathbf{p}-\mathbf{q})|}{|\psi(t,\mathbf{p})|}$$

,a convenient solution of the problem (assuming $\mu(d\mathbf{p})$ positive,for simplicity only) is:

$$p(t,\mathbf{p},B) = \int_{\mathbb{R}^d} \mu(d\mathbf{q})(\chi_{B+\mathbf{q}}(\mathbf{p}) - \chi_B(\mathbf{p}))\left\{\frac{|\psi(t,\mathbf{p}-\mathbf{q})|}{|\psi(t,\mathbf{p})|} - \operatorname{Im}\frac{\psi(t,\mathbf{p}-\mathbf{q})}{\psi(t,\mathbf{p})}\right\} \tag{25}$$

(compare with 10)).In this way,starting from a reasonable and normalized solution $\psi(t,\mathbf{p})$ of 22),I can construct a jump Markov process ξ_t in the **momentum space** $\mathbb{R}^d$,such that $\text{Prob.}(\xi_t \in B) = \int_B |\psi(t,\mathbf{p})|^2 d\mathbf{p}$ at every time t and for every Borel set B in momentum space.I conclude that also the non-relativistic quantum mechanics in **momentum space** admits a "classical" probabilistic interpretation (in terms of **jump** Markov processes), at least for potentials which are Fourier transforms of Borel measures.

Problem:what is the relation (if there is any) between the **diffusion** ξ_t^c and the **jump Markov process** ξ_t^m associated to same quantum state respectively in **configuration space** and **momentum space**?

Potentials which are Fourier transforms of Borel measures are in the class considered by Maslov,Chebotarev /19/ and Combe,Høegh-Krohn, Rodriguez,Sirugue and Sirugue-Collin /20/ in their version of Feynman path integral in momentum space.A connection between stochastic mechanics and probabilistic solution of heat equation,well known for Schrödinger equation in configuration space /21/,exists also in the case of Dirac equation (see remark at the end of /3/ and compare random processes considered in §3 with the process described in references /22,23/) and this fact suggests further investigations.

References.

1. G.F.De Angelis and G.Jona-Lasinio: "A stochastic description of a spin 1/2 particle in a magnetic field" J.Phys.A,15,2053,(1982).
2. M.Cini and M.Serva: "Stochastic theory of emission and absorption of quanta" Preprint Dipartimento di Fisica,Università di Roma "La Sapienza" and BiBoS,Bielefeld,(1985).
3. G.F. De Angelis,G.Jona-Lasinio,M.Serva and N.Zanghi: "Stochastic mechanics of a Dirac particle in two space-time dimensions" Preprint Dipartimento di Fisica,Università di Roma "La Sapienza" and BiBoS,Bielefeld,(1985).
4. E.Nelson: "Dynamical theories of brownian motion",Princeton University Press,Princeton,(1967).
5. E.Nelson:"Quantum fluctuation",Princeton University Press,Princeton,(1985).
6. E.Nelson: "Field theory and the future of stochastic mechanics" in these Proceedings.
7. S.Albeverio,R.Høegh-Krohn and L.Streit: "Energy forms,hamiltonian and distorted brownian paths",J.Math.Phys.,18,907,(1977).
8. G.Jona-Lasinio,F.Martinelli and E.Scoppola: "New approach to the semiclassical limit of quantum mechanics",Comm.Math.Phys.,80,223,(1981).
9. G.Jona-Lasinio,F.Martinelli and E.Scoppola: "The semiclassical limit of quantum mechanics:a qualitative theory via stochastic mechanics",Phys.Rep.,77,313,(1981).
10. G.Jona-Lasinio,F.Martinelli and E.Scoppola: "Decayng quantum-mechanical systems: an informal discussion within stochastic mechanics",Lett.al Nuovo Cimento,34,13,(1982).
11. F.Guerra and L.Morato: "Quantization of dynamical systems and stochastic control theory",Phys.Rev.D,27,1774,(1983).
12. E.A.Carlen: "Potential scattering in stochastic mechanics",Ann.Inst.Henri Poincarè,42,407,(1985).
13. A.Truman and J.T.Lewis: "The stochastic mechanics of the ground state of the hydrogen atom", talk given at BiBoS Symposium,Bielefeld,september 1984.
14. E.A.Carlen: "Conservative diffusions",Comm.Math.Phys.,94,293,(1984),see also F. Guerra:"Carlen processes:A new class of diffusions with singular drifs",Preprint Università di Roma "La Sapienza",(1985).
15. W.A.Zheng and P.A.Meyer: "Quelques resultats de "mécanique stochastique" ",Seminaire de Probabilités XVIII,LNM,Springer-Verlag,(1984).
16. W.A.Zheng and P.A.Meyer: "Construction de processus de Nelson reversibles",Preprint,(1984).
17. W.A.Zheng and Ph.Blanchard: "Stochastic variational principle and diffusion processes",Preprint BiBoS,Bielefeld,(1985).
18. F.Dyson: "Missed opportunities",Bull.ofAm.Math.Soc.,78,635,(1972).

19.V.P.Maslov and A.M.Chebotarev: "Processus de sauts et leurs applications dans la mécanique quantique",Lectures Notes in Physics,106,Springer-Verlag,(1979).
20.Ph.Combe,R.Høegh-Krohn,R.Rodriguez,M.Sirugue and M.Sirugue-Collin: "Poisson processes on groups and Feynman path integral",Comm.Math.Phys.,77,269,(1980).
21.S.Albeverio and R.Høegh-Krohn: "A remark on the connection between stochastic mechanics and the heat equation",J.of Math.Phys.,15,1745,(1974).
22.B.Gaveau,T.Jacobson,M.Kac and L.S.Schulman: "Relativistic extension of the analogy between quantum mechanics and brownian motion",Phys.Rev.Letters,53,419,(1984).
23.Ph.Blanchard,Ph.Combe,M.Sirugue and M.Sirugue-Collin: "Probabilistic solution of Dirac equation",Preprint BiBoS,Bielefeld,(1985).

QUANTUM FIELDS ON A GRAVITATIONAL BACKGROUND FROM RANDOM FIELDS ON RIEMANNIAN MANIFOLDS

Gian Fabrizio De Angelis

Diego de Falco

Glauco Di Genova

Dipartimento di Fisica, Università di Salerno,

I-84100 Salerno, Italy

We follow a "Euclidean" or, better, a "properly Riemannian" strategy for the construction of quantum fields on curved spacetime. Our work can best be described as a study of the proposal advanced by J.B.Hartle and S.W.Hawking in their 1976 article "Path integral derivation of black hole radiance" (1), in much the same sense as the Euclidean program for the flat case has been a successful attempt to understand, by a precise mathematical construction, K.Symanzik's Varenna Lectures (2).

We are perfectly well aware of the conceptual difficulties of a "Euclidean" approach to quantum field theory on a gravitational background, such as the lack of a general covariant analysis of the procedure of analytic continuation to "imaginary time" (3) and the related difficulty of getting information back to real time (4). On this reconstruction problem we take the attitude that, before tackling it in all its generality and difficulty, it might be worth to explore it on explicitly constructed, if possible interacting, models.

A related objection to the "properly Riemannian approach" is the observation that the well established "Euclidean" approach refers to the analytically continued vacuum expectation values of the fields, while on a curved manifold with, in general, a non stationary metric one has neither Poincaré invariance by which to characterize a vacuum state nor an energy-momentum by whose spectral properties to ensure the possibility of analytic continuation.

Work supported in part by Ministero della Pubblica Istruzione and by Istituto Nazionale di Fisica Nucleare.

On this problem one can, however, take the alternative point of view, encouraged by the axiomatic analysis of G.Sewell (5), that all that is in fact needed in the theory is a distinguished state sharing with the conventional vacuum the technical advantage of permitting a reconstruction theorem from the expectation values in it of the fields and the physical characterization as an equilibrium state, one to which the field might have settled after all the dishomogeneities, with respect to whatever symmetry the background manifold has, have been radiated away. A better, more realistic, characterization of such a state would be in terms of its stability with respect to local perturbations or of the invariance, with respect to the details of the coupling, ot its response to local probes (6). Extensive experience in statistical mechanics relates then this stability to some analiticity of the correlation functions, in the specific form of the Kubo, Martin, Schwinger condition (7). In this perspective, the work of R.Figari, R.Höegh-Krohn, C.Nappi (8) provides an example, that of the De Sitter universe,in which, once equilibrium considerations have privileged thermal states, geometric considerations single out one such state invariant under the symmetry group of the manifold.

In some sense the "properly Riemannian" approach explores the final act of this scenario, which, at least for linear fields, has the advantage of being unique.

Indeed, let, as always in what follows, M be a paracompact, complete, C^∞ properly Riemannian manifold; let Δ_M be the Laplace-Beltrami operator on M. Results of H.O. Cordes (9) show that, as an unbounded linear operator of $L^2(M)$, $-\Delta_M + m^2$ is essentially selfadjoint in $C_0^\infty(M)$. No ambiguity which might otherwise have resulted from the choice of a selfadjoint extension appears then in the definition of the covariance of the free field as $C = (-\Delta_M + m^2)^{-1}$.

Correspondingly, the free Gaussian measure is uniquely defined by the characteristic functional

$$S: f \in C_0^\infty(M) \longrightarrow S(f) = \exp-(f,Cf)/2$$

$$S(f) = \int_{D'(M)} \exp\ i(\varphi, f)\ d\mu(\varphi).$$

Technical problems one faces when dealing with fields on a manifold are:

i. the lack of explicit representations of the kernel $C(x,y)$;

ii. the lack of a useful notion of Fourier transform;

iii. (includes and explains the previous difficulties) the lack of translational invariance.

The only tool one has to overcome these difficulties is the representation (10):

$$C(x,y) = \int_0^{\infty} \exp(-tm^2)\, p(t,x,y)\, dt$$

where p is the heat kernel on M, namely the transition probability density of Brownian motion on M:

$$\partial_t p = \Delta_M p \; ; \qquad p \xrightarrow[t \searrow 0]{} \delta_M$$

For instance, one sees from this representation that there must be ultraviolet problems coming from the singular behavior of $p(t,x,y)$ as $t \searrow 0$ and $d(x,y) \searrow 0$ (d being the geodesic distance on M).

This observation is made precise by Molchanov's analysis of the small time asymptotics of the heat kernel (11):

$$p(t,x,y) \underset{t \searrow 0}{\sim} (4\pi t)^{-\nu/2}\, H(x,y) \exp - \frac{d^2(x,y)}{4t}$$

uniformly on all compact sets of MxM which do not intersect the cut locus of M (here $\nu = \dim M$ and H is the Ruse invariant).

Molchanov's asymptotics is at the root of the legitimate expectation that "interacting field theories in curved spacetime seem to be renormalizable provided they are renormalizable in flat spacetime" (12).

The theorem that follows conferms this expectation in two dimensions:

Theorem 1 (13): If dim M = 2, then for every $1 \leq q < +\infty$ and for every compact set K in M

$$\sup_{x \in M} \left\| C(x,\cdot) \right\|_{L^q(K,dV)} < +\infty \qquad \text{L.R. 1}$$

$$\left\| C^{(k)}(\cdot,\cdot) - C(\cdot,\cdot) \right\|_{L^q(KxK,dVxdV)} \leq O(k^{-2/q}) \qquad \text{L.R. 2}$$

$$\sup_{x \in K} C^{(k)}(x,x) \leq O(\log_{\gamma} k) \qquad \text{L.R. 3}$$

Here dV is the Riemannian volume element on M, γ is a parameter larger than 1 and the Gallavotti-Pauli-Villars regularization has been adopted (14):

$$C(x,y) = \sum_{r=0}^{\infty} C_r(x,y)$$

$$C_r(x,y) = \int_0^{\infty} (\exp-m^2 \gamma^{2r} t \; - \; \exp-m^2 \gamma^{2r+2} t)\, p(t,x,y)\, dt$$

$$C^{(k)}(x,y) = \sum_{r=0}^{\log_{\gamma} k - 1} C_r(x,y)$$

The local regularity (L.R.) properties 1 and 3 express the fact that the singularity of C(x,y) at coinciding points is logarithmic, a fact one could read directly from the small time, small distance behavior of the heat kernel.

More subtle is L.R. 2 (essential for Nelson's proof (15) of the removal of ultraviolet divergencies in two dimensions by Wick subtraction to go through): its proof requires indeed to estimate away the contribution of large times (via the Chapman--Kolmogorov equation, namely the Markov property of Brownian motion on M) and the contribution of large distances (via Azencott's method to propagate local estimates (16), based on the strong Markov property).

Rather than giving a formal proof of Theorem 1 and of its application to extend Nelson's theorem, we wish to conclude the discussion of the ultraviolet problem with a remark on how natural the Gallavotti-Pauli-Villars regularization looks on a non flat manifold: the metric tensor contains, for dimensional reasons, parameters with the dimensions of length

$$g(x) = G(x/L).$$

Again for dimensional reasons, the various Gallavotti modes scale as:

$$C_r(x,y \mid L) = C_0(\gamma^r x, \gamma^r y \mid \gamma^r L).$$

As, in turn, the curvature scales as L^{-2}, the higher modes reproduce the zero mode on flatter and flatter manifolds, a good a priori reason to expect that the ultraviolet problem is exactly as severe as in the flat case.

Another result we wish to quote from ref. (13) is the following theorem:

Theorem 2: Suppose that

i. $M = V_+ \cup V_- \cup \partial V$, where $V_\pm$ are smooth submanifolds of M with common boundary ∂V;

ii. there exists an isometric map θ: $M \to M$ such that $\theta V_\pm = V_\mp$ and $\theta\,\partial V = \partial V$ pointwise;

iii. having set $(\theta f)(x) = f(\theta x)$, θ commutes with Δ_M and $\underline{n}\cdot \mathrm{grad}(\theta f) = -\,\underline{n}\cdot \mathrm{grad}\, f$ on ∂V.

Then, for every $f \in C_0^\infty(M)$ with supp $f \subset V_+$, $C(\theta f,f) \geq 0$.

Again we refer to (13) for details of the proof; the idea is very simple and consists in implementing, by repeated applications of Gauss' theorem, E.Lieb's suggestion (17) that Osterwalder-Schrader positivity describes the fact that the potential energy between a given charge distribution and its "mirror" image is nonnegative.

As usual, O.S. positivity should play a major role in the control of the infinite volume limit for the interacting measure, providing exponential bounds (18). Incidentally, the fact that all two dimensional manifolds are locally conformally flat, so that in a suitable chart the Laplace-Beltrami operator is just a positive function times the ordinary Laplacian,shows that because of the ferromagnetic nearest neighbor character of the coupling imposed by the free measure, in many instances the infinite volume limit can be reached by monotone growth.

Beyond its technical relevance, we wish to point out that O.S. positivity plays a major role in the reconstruction scenario outlined at the beginning.

Let us focus our attention, from now on, on two dimensional manifolds which are surfaces of revolution, the "Euclidean" analogues of manifolds with Lorentz symmetry considered in ref.(5).

In this case a meaningful notion of reflection exists: θ = reflection about any plane through the axis of revolution.

The properly Riemannian construction leaves us with a periodic (in the imaginary proper time of an observer that sees the metric stationary), O.S. positive stochastic process, one for which the general analysis of ref.(19) ensures the possibility of uniquely reconstructing a stochastically positive K.M.S. system. In this respect one expects that for the quantum theory to be reconstructed from the random field on surface of revolution Sewell's axiom C.3 of ref (5) (to the effect that a distinguished state in the theory, restricted to a suitable algebra of observables, is an equilibrium state at some temperature) automatically holds. Otherwise stated, Theorem 2 substantiates assumption C.2 of ref. (20) by providing a whole class of models for which suitably adapted Nelson's axioms, including O.S. positivity, hold.

Remaining in the perspective that a reconstruction effort from Hartle-Hawking's properly Riemannian approach should have as its target Sewell's axioms, we wish to comment on axioms A.5, E.5, E.6 of ref.(5). These axioms can be informally restated as follows: if the Lorentzian manifold considered admits Lorentz-like boosts as isometries, time translations appear as isometries of the event horizons; Sewell requires that the given quantum field theory on the entire manifold gives rise to a conventional Wightman theory, spectral condition for the generator of time translations and therefore analyticity properties of the "Wightman functions " included, on such horizons. While it is an open technical problem, and probably one which is not solvable without further assumptions, whether this germ of analyticity on the event horizons can be exploited to reach the "Schwinger" points, it is rewarding to observe that there is at least a non trivial model for which the crucial spectral condition can be recovered by reconstruction from a properly Riemannian model.

Consider, indeed, the manifold

$$X = \left\{ (x^0 , x^1) \in \mathbb{R}^2 \ : \ (x^0)^2 - (x^1)^2 < L^2 \right\}$$

with Lorentzian metric

$$ds^2 = -\left(1 - \frac{(x^0)^2 - (x^1)^2}{L^2}\right)\left((dx^1)^2 - (dx^0)^2\right)$$

Such a spacetime is considered, for example, by Hu, O'Connor (21) as a local approximation to more general geometries.

The naive analytic continuation to imaginary values of the time coordinate, "$x^0 = ix^2$", leads to the properly Riemannian manifold $M = \mathbb{R}^2$ with metric

$$ds^2 = (1 + \|x\|^2/L^2)\left((dx^1)^2 + (dx^2)^2\right).$$

Since

$$\Delta_M = (1 + \|x\|^2/L^2)^{-1} \sum_{i=1}^{2} \frac{\partial^2}{\partial x_i^2}$$

the covariance satisfies

$$(-\Delta_x + m^2(1 + \|x\|^2/L^2))\, C(x,y) = \delta(x - y).$$

Recalling Mehler's formula for the kernel of the Hamiltonian semigroup for the harmonic oscillator (18) one finds easily:

$$C(x,y) = \exp\left(-\frac{m^2}{8n}\|x-y\|^2\right)\int_0^{\infty}\left(1+\frac{m^2}{n}t\right)^{-n}\frac{1}{4\pi t}\exp\left(-\frac{\|x-y\|^2}{4t}\right).$$

$$\cdot\left(1+\frac{m^2 t}{2n}\right)^{-1}\exp\left(-\frac{m^4 t\,\|x+y\|^2}{8n(2n+m^2 t)}\right)$$

Here $\|\cdot\|$ is the Euclidean norm and $n = mL$.

The restriction of $C(x,y)$ to $x^2 - y^2 > 0$ admits analytic continuation to all of $\mathrm{Re}(x^2 - y^2) > 0$, thus allowing one to define, as one would in the flat case $L = \infty$, the Wightman two point function as

$$W_2((x^0,x^1),(y^0,y^1)) = \lim_{\substack{(x^2-y^2)\to i(x^0-y^0)\\ \mathrm{Re}(x^2-y^2)>0}} C((x^1,x^2),(y^1,y^2))$$

The restriction Λ of W_2 to ExE where $E = \{x \in X:\ x^0+x^1 = 0\}$, by using the parametrization $x^0 = t_1$, $y^0 = t_2$, $x^1 = -t_1$, $y^1 = -t_2$, is given by

$$\Lambda(t_1-t_2) = \lim_{\varepsilon\searrow 0}\int_0^{\infty}\frac{\exp(-\varepsilon|t_1-t_2|/4\lambda)}{(1+im^2\lambda\,\mathrm{sgn}(t_1-t_2)/n)^n\,(1+im^2\lambda\,\mathrm{sgn}(t_1-t_2)/2n)\,4\pi\lambda}\,d\lambda$$

The fact that the singularities in t are in $\mathrm{Im}\, t > 0$ immediately assures that the Fourier transform $\tilde{\Lambda}(\omega)$ of $\Lambda(t)$ is zero for $\omega < 0$, which is compatible with the spectral assumption E.5, in the tentative identification

$$(\Psi, \varphi_E(t_1)\, \varphi_E(t_2)\, \Psi) = (2\pi)^{-1} \int \omega^2 \tilde{\Lambda}(\omega) \exp -i\,\omega(t_1-t_2)\, d\omega$$

Also compatible with this identification is the fact that $\tilde{\Lambda}(\omega) \geq 0$ corresponding to the physical positivity

$$(\Psi, \varphi_E(\bar{f})\, \varphi_E(f)\, \Psi) \geq 0 .$$

The reconstruction of the full Wightman-Sewell structure from the initial data

$$-\frac{\partial}{\partial t}\varphi(t,-t) = \varphi_E(t) ,$$

once completed exhibits then, according to the general analysis of ref. (5), Ψ as a thermal state on the algebra of observables localized in the wedge $X_+ = \{x^1 > |x^0|\}$.

A very clear phenomenological picture of what this means can be given by rephrasing in slightly more general terms the analysis based on the quantum Wiener-Khinchin formula given in ref. (22): a point-like detector linearly coupled to the field (this restriction is in fact removed in ref. (23)) has probability per unit time

$$p_{i\to f} = |M_{if}|^2 \int_{-\infty}^{\infty} \exp -i\frac{\omega\tau}{\hbar}\, W_2(x(\tau),x(0))\, d\tau \equiv$$

$$\equiv |M_{if}|^2\, \Pi(\omega)$$

of performing a transition from its state of energy ε_i to its state of energy ε_f. Here M_{if} is the matrix element of the interaction, $\omega = \varepsilon_f - \varepsilon_i$, and $x = x(\tau)$ is the world line of the detector parametrized by its proper time. Suppose, in particular, that the metric has the form

$$ds^2 = A((x^1)^2 - (x^0)^2)\, ((dx^1)^2 - (dx^0)^2)$$

and that the world line of the detector, in terms of proper time, is

$$x^0 = r \sinh\left(\frac{c\tau}{r\sqrt{A}}\right)$$

$$x^1 = r \cosh\left(\frac{c\tau}{r\sqrt{A}}\right)$$

so that the detector experiences a constant proper acceleration

$$a = \frac{c^2}{r\sqrt{A}} .$$

The integral defining $\Pi(\omega)$ can be easily studied from the known properties of the covariance C. It has the form

$$\Pi(\omega) = I(\omega)/(1 - \exp(\omega\frac{2\pi r\sqrt{A}}{c\hbar}))$$

because C is periodic in imaginary τ.

$I(\omega)$ (the result of encircling the singularity of C at coinciding points) has in turn, because C is symmetric in its arguments, the property

$$I(-\omega) = -I(\omega) .$$

This easily implies that:

$$p_{f \rightarrow i} = \exp((\mathcal{E}_f - \mathcal{E}_i)\frac{2\pi r \sqrt{A}}{c \hbar})\, p_{i \rightarrow f}$$

so that if the detector is to be in equilibrium with the field, the probabilities ρ_j of occupation of the various energy states must be in the ratios (23):

$$\rho_f / \rho_i = \exp(-\mathcal{E}_f / K\, T(r)) / \exp(-\mathcal{E}_i / K\, T(r))$$

with

$$T(r) = \frac{\hbar}{2\pi c K}(c^2/(\sqrt{A}\, r)) = \frac{\hbar}{2\pi c\, K} a(r) .$$

Namely, quite independently from the details of the interaction with the field, the only state of equilibrium accessible to the detector is a Gibbs state at temperature $T(r)$.

One can therefore make appeal to the operational meaning given to the concept of temperature by the zero-th law of thermodynamics to conclude that the field itself is at such a temperature.

Observe that the dependence of T on the generalized Schwarzschild distance r causes no problem to this interpretation: the relation $T(r)\, r\sqrt{A} = \text{const}$ is exactly Tolman's redshifted equilibrium temperature distribution (24) $T\sqrt{-g_{00}} = \text{const}$.

Observe, furthermore, that the temperature $T(r)$ is exactly the Unruh temperature (25) measured by an observer moving with proper acceleration $a(r)$ in the Wightman vacuum in Minkowski spacetime.

An, as yet vague, appeal to the equivalence principle, once made precise, should substantiate the point of view that Sewell's state Ψ, as reached by analytic continuation from properly Riemannian "Schwinger" functions, provides the right analogue of the vacuum state on a gravitational background.

Aknowledgements:

We are deeply indebted to Professor Geoffrey Sewell for correspondence and discussions on the physical and mathematical aspects of the reconstruction problem as presented in this paper.

References:

1. J.B. Hartle, S.W.Hawking: Phys. Rev. D13, 2188 (1976)
2. K.Symanzik: "Euclidean quantum field theory" Proceedings of the International School of physics "E.Fermi" Varenna, corso XLV, R.Jost ed., Academic press (1969)
3. F.Guerra: "Quantum field theory and probability theory. Outlook on new possible developments" Contribution to the IV Bielefeld Encounter in Mathematics and Physics, S. Albeverio, P. Blanchard eds. (1984)
4. J. Dimock: Ann. Phys. 154, 287 (1984)
5. G. Sewell: Ann. Phys. 141, 201 (1982)
6. G. Sewell: Physics Reports 57, 307 (1980)
7. R.Haag, N.M.Hugenholtz, M.Winnink: Comm. Math. Phys. 5, 215 (1967)
8. R.Figari, R.Höegh-Krohn, C.Nappi: Comm. Math. Phys. 44, 265 (1975)
9. H.O.Cordes: Math. Ann. 195, 257 (1972)
10. R.M.Wald: Comm. Math. Phys. 70, 221 (1979)
11. S.A. Molchanov: Russian Math. Survey 30, 1 (1975)
12. S.W.Hawking: Comm. Math. Phys. 80, 421 (1981)
13. G.F. De Angelis, D. de Falco, G. Di Genova: "Random fields on Riemannian manifolds. A constructive approach" to appear in Comm. Math. Phys.
14. G.Benfatto, M.Cassandro, G.Gallavotti, F.Nicolò, O.Olivieri, E.Presutti, E.Scacciatelli: Comm. Math. Phys. 71, 95 (1980)
15. E.Nelson:"Probability theory on Euclidean field theory" in "Constructive quantum field theory" G.Velo, A.S.Wightman eds., Lecture Notes in Physics vol. 25 Springer-Verlag (1973)
16. R. Azencott: Astérisque, 84-85, 131 (1981)
17. E. Lieb: Lecture Notes in Physics 80, 59 (1978)
18. J.Glimm, A.Jaffe: "Quantum Physics. A functional integral point of view " Springer-Verlag (1981)
19. A. Klein, L. Landau: J. Funct. An. 42, 368 (1981)
20. G. Sewell: Phys. Lett. 79A, 23 (1980)
21. B.L. Hu, D.J. O'Connor: Phys. Rev. D30, 743 (1984)
22. D. Sciama, P.Candelas, D.Deutsch: Advances in Physics 30, 327 (1981)
23. J.Bell, R.Huges, J.Leinaas:"The Unruh effect in extended thermometers" CERN-TH 3948/84
24. R.Tolman: "Relativity, thermodynamics and cosmology" (Oxford 1934, Clarendon-Press)
25. W.G. Unruh: Phys. Rev. D14, 870 (1976)

TIME REVERSAL AND SMOOTHING OF
INFINITE - DIMENSIONAL DIFFUSION PROCESSES

J.D. DEUSCHEL and H. FOELLMER

ETHZ, Mathematikdepartement
CH-8092 Zürich

1. Introduction

Consider an infinite-dimensional diffusion process $X_t = (X_t^i)_{i\in I}$ of the form

$$(1.1) \qquad dX_t^i = dW_t^i + b^i(X_t, t)dt \qquad (i \in I)$$

where I is some countable index set and $(W^i)_{i\in I}$ is a collection of independent Wiener processes.

In the time-homogeneous case, and under some bounds on the interaction in the drift terms, reversible equilibrium distributions of the process can be characterized as Gibbs measures whose interaction potential is determined by $(b^i)_{i\in I}$; cf., for example, [5], [9], [11].

In this note we discuss two aspects of this relation between infinite-dimensional diffusions and Gibbs measures. First, one can describe the structure of the time-reversed process $\hat{X}_t = X_{1-t}$ by an infinite-dimensional analogue of the duality equation which appears in Stochastic Mechanics. The Gibbs description of reversible equilibria then appears as a special case of the general duality equation. This result was obtained jointly with A. Wakolbinger; cf. [8]. But the relation between infinite-dimensional diffusions and Gibbs measures may also be viewed as a projection of the fact that the entire diffusion process, considered as a random field with state space $C[0,1]$, admits a Gibbsian description. The computation of the local conditional probability of this random field is an infinite-dimensional analogue of the non-linear smoothing problem considered by Bismut-Michel [1] and Pardoux [16]. In terms of these conditional probabilities, and using estimates for the Vasserstein distance on $C[0,1]$, one can then apply Dobrushin's contraction technique in order to obtain information about macroscopic properties of the entire diffusion process. This program has been carried out by the first author in [2].

Both points of view are summarized (section 2) and then illustrated by an explicit example related to the Martin boundary of an infinite-dimensional Wiener process (section 3). General results and proofs can be found in [8] resp. in [2] .

2. Infinite-dimensional diffusions and Gibbs measures

Let P be a probability measure on $C[0,1]^I$ such that the coordinate process $X_t = (X_t^i)_{i \in I}$ satisfies a stochastic differential equation of the form (1.1). Other than in the finite-dimensional case $|I| < \infty$, the time-reversed process $\hat{X}_t = X_{1-t}$ is not necessarily governed by a stochastic differential equation of the same type; see [8] for a counterexample. Some bounds on the interaction are needed, and we can formulate such bounds in terms of entropy. Suppose in fact that

$$H(P|P^i) = \int \log \frac{dP}{dP^i}\, dP < \infty \qquad (i \in I) \tag{2.1}$$

where P^i is the distribution of the modified diffusion whose i-th coordinate performs an independent Wiener process. This finite entropy condition is equivalent to a finite energy condition for the drift terms (b^i) together with a bound on how strongly a given coordinate i influences the other coordinates $k \neq i$ ("active locality"); cf. [8]. Under (2.1) one can show that for almost all $t \in (0,1)$ the distribution μ_t of X_t has smooth conditional probabilities. More precisely: the conditional probability

$$\mu_t\,(dx^i | x^j\ (j \neq i))$$

is given by a conditional density

$$\rho_t^i\,(x^i \mid x^j\ \ (j \neq i))$$

which is a.e. differentiable in x^i. Moreover, the time-reversed process is again of the form (1.1), and its drift $(\hat{b}^i)_{i \in I}$ is given by the duality equation

$$\partial_i \log \rho^i\,(x^i|x^j\ (j\neq 1)) = b^i(x,t) + \hat{b}^i(x,\ 1-t)\ ; \tag{2.2}$$

cf. [8] .

The duality equation (2.2) shows, in particular (with $b^i(x,t) = \hat{b}^i(x,1-t) = b^i(x)$ and $\mu_t \equiv \mu$), that a reversible equilibrium distribution μ has a Gibbsian description, i.e. its conditional densities are determined by $(b^i)_{i \in I}$. Thus the Gibbs structure of reversible equilibria is a special case of the duality equation which governs the time-reversal of the infinite-dimensional diffusion, just as Kolmogorov's expression of the reversible equilibrium density of a finite-dimensional diffusion in terms of its drift is a special case of the basic duality equation in Stochastic Mechanics; cf. [14] , [15].

Let us now consider the measure P on $C[0,1]^I$ as a random field with state space $C[0,1]$, and let us determine its local specification, i.e. the conditional probability distributions $P^i(\cdot|X)$ of $X^i = (X^i_t)_{o\leq t\leq 1}$ given X^k $(k\neq i)$. If the drifts (b^i) are given by a smooth gradient system with local pair interaction,

$$b^i(x,t) = \partial_i B^i (x^i,t) + \sum_{k\in N(i)} \partial_i B^{i,k} (x^i,x^k,t) ,$$

then we have

$$(2.3) \qquad P^i(dX^i|X) = \exp[\psi^i(X^i, X)]\, Z^i(X)^{-1}\, Q^i(dX^i)$$

where Q^i denotes Wiener measure, $Z^i(X)$ a normalizing factor, ψ^i **is a** smooth functional on $C[0,1] \times C[0,1]^{N^2(i)}$, and $N(i)$ some finite neighbourhood of i. Performing a Girsanov transformation with $X\in C[0,1]^{N^2(i)}$ fixed as a parameter, one can show that the conditional process satisfies a stochastic differential equation with Markovian drift

$$(2.4) \qquad b^{i,X} (x^i,t) = \partial_i G(x^i, t)$$

where $G(x^i,t)$ is the solution of a non-linear partial differential equation of the form

$$(2.5) \qquad \partial_t G + \frac{1}{2} \partial_i^2 G + \frac{1}{2} (\partial_i G)^2 = g^i$$

with boundary condition

$$G(x^i,1) = B^i(x,1) + \sum_k B^{i,k} (x^i, X^k_1,1) ;$$

cf. Theorem (II.4.9) in [2] and also [13] for the relation to a minimum action principle.

The smoothness of ψ^i implies that the conditional probabilities $P^i(\;|X)$ are continuous in $X\in C[0,1]^{N^2(i)}$, i.e. for each f in the class $L(C[0,1]^I)$ of Lipschitz continuous functions on $C[0,1]^I$, the function

$$X \longrightarrow \int f \; dP^i(\;|X)$$

is again in $L(C[0,1]^I)$. We can now apply Dobrushin's contraction technique to the system $P^i(\;|X)$ $(i\in I)$. For two probability measures Q and $\tilde{Q}$ on $C[0,1]$, let $R(Q,\tilde{Q})$ be the Vasserstein metric defined by

$$R(Q,\tilde{Q}) = \sup \{ | \int f \, d\, Q - \int f \, d\, \tilde{Q} | , \delta(f) \leq 1 \}$$

where $$\delta(f) = \sup \{ \frac{|f(X) - f(Y)|}{\| X - Y \|} , X \neq Y \; C[0,1] \}$$

is the oscillation of the function f. Using the explicit form of the Girsanov density and the mean value theorem on $C[0,1]$, we can obtain estimates for the Dobrushin's coefficients

$$C^{k,i} = \sup \{ \frac{R(P^i(\,|X), P^i(\,|Y))}{\| X^k - Y^k \|} , X^j = Y^j , j \neq k \}$$

cf. [4]. In particular, we can bound the interaction of the drifts in such a way that Dobrushin's uniqueness condition

(2.6) $$\sup_i \sum_{k \neq i} C^{k,i} < 1$$

is fulfilled. More precisely, let γ, β and N be bounds for the self-interaction $\partial_i B^i$, the pair-interaction $\partial_i B^{i,k}$ and the range $N(i)$. For all $\gamma \in \mathbb{R}^+$ one can then find a $\beta^* = \beta^*(\gamma) > 0$ such that the condition (2.6) holds if $\beta < \beta^*(\gamma)/N$.

As an application one gets conditions which guarantee the uniqueness of P, exponential decay of correlations and the central limit theorem for functions of the class $L(C[0,1]^I)$. This is carried out in chap. III 5-6 of [2]. In particular, one can derive the stochastic differential equation of the fluctuation field in the sense of Itô [10] ; cf. [3].

3. A Martin boundary example

Consider the infinite-dimensional Wiener measure $P = \prod_{i \in I} P_i$ on $C[0,1]^I$, where each P_i is a Wiener measure on $C[0,1]$.
For $z = (z^i) \in \mathbb{R}^I$, the Brownian bridge to z is given by

$$P^z = \prod_{i \in I} P_i^{z^i} ,$$

where $P_i^{z^i}$ is the distribution of a one-dimensional Brownian bridge leading from 0 at time 0 to z^i at time 1. The measures P^z $(z \in \mathbb{R}^I)$ are the extreme points in the class of all probability measures on $C[0,1]^I$ which have the same conditional probabilities with respect to the future σ-fields $\hat{\mathcal{F}}_t = \sigma(X_s ; s \geq t)$ as P, and each measure in this class has a representation

$$P^{\nu} = \int_{\mathbb{R}^I} P^z \; \nu(dz)$$

with some probability measure ϑ on $\mathbb{R}^I$. In this sense, $\mathbb{R}^I$ may be viewed as the Martin boundary of P ; cf. [6] , [7] .

A measure P^{ϑ} is the distribution of an infinite-dimensional Brownian motion conditioned to have terminal distribution ϑ at time 1. Let us now use time reversal in order to determine the stochastic differential equation of (X_t) under P^{ϑ}. Clearly, the time-reversed process satisfies the stochastic differential equation

$$d\hat{X}^i = d\hat{W}^i + \frac{-\hat{X}^i}{1-t}\, dt \qquad (i \in I)$$

with initial distribution ν. Therefore, the duality equation (2.2) implies that (X_t) satisfies the stochastic differential equation (1.1), where the drift terms

$$(3.1) \qquad b^i(x,t) = \frac{x^i}{t} - \partial_i \log \rho_t^i \, (x^i | x^j (j \neq 1))$$

are given by the conditional densities $\rho_t^i(\cdot|\cdot)$ of the distribution μ_t of X_t under P^{ϑ}.

In order to have a simple explicit example take $I = \mathbb{Z}^d$ and a centered translation invariant Gaussian measure ϑ on $\mathbb{R}^I$ with covariance $\Gamma = (\Gamma^i)_{i \in I}$, i.e., $\int x^i x^k d\vartheta = \Gamma^{k-i}$, and conditional distributions

$$(3.2) \qquad \vartheta^i(\cdot|x^j(j\neq i)) = N(\sum_{k\neq o} a^k x^{i+k}, 1).$$

Then we have $\mu_t = N(o,\Gamma(t))$ with $\Gamma(t) = t^2\Gamma + t(1-t)^I$, and the conditional distributions of μ_t are of the form

$$\mu_t^i \, (\cdot|x^j(j\neq 1)) = N\,(\sum_{k\neq o} a^k(t)x^{k+i}, t)$$

with

$$(3.3) \qquad \Gamma^k(t) - \sum_{j\neq o} a^j(t)\Gamma^{k+j}(t) = t \cdot \delta_{o,k} \; ;$$

cf. [12] . This together with (3.1) implies the stochastic differential equation

$$(3.4) \qquad dX_t^i = dW_t^i + \sum_{k\neq o} \frac{a^k(t)}{t} X_t^{k+i} \, dt \qquad (i \in I)$$

for (X_t) under P^{ν}: If $d \geq 3$ then we can choose the coefficients a^k so that $\sum a^k = 1$. In this case ν admits a trivial phase transition: each $\nu_m = \nu + m$ $(m \in \mathbb{R}^I)$ has the same conditional distributions and leads to the same stochastic differential equation (3.4). Thus, a phase transition for ν translates into non-uniqueness of the solution of (3.4).

As to the Gibbsian description of P^{ν}, we can now follow the derivation scetched in section 2, starting with the stochastic differential equation (3.4). This leads to the solution

$$G(x^i,t) = x^i \sum_k a^k X_1^{i+k}$$

of the partial differential equation (2.5), hence to the constant drift

$$b^{i,X}(x^i,t) = \sum_k a^k X_1^{i+k} \tag{3.5}$$

in the stochastic differential equation of the conditional process $P^{\nu,i}(\cdot|X)$. In this particular case, we could as well proceed directly: $P^{\nu,i}(\cdot|X)$ is simply the distribution of a Brownian motion constrained to have terminal distribution

$$\nu^i(\cdot|X_1^j \; (j \neq i)) = N(\sum_{k \neq o} a^k X_1^{i+k}, 1) ,$$

and this also implies (3.5). Note that for a Markov field ν these conditional drifts depend only on finitely many coordinates, whereas the drifts in the forward description (3.4) are not local. The Dobrushin coefficients $C^{k,i}$ of the local specification of P^{ν} reduce to $C^{k,i} = |a^{k-i}|$. In particular, a phase transition for P^{ν} is equivalent to a phase transition for ν and under the uniqueness condition $\sum_k |a^k| < 1$, we obtain exponential decay of correlations for functionals on $C[0,1]$.

Of course, the example is misleading in so far as all the difficulties have disappeared. In particular, the non-linear smoothing problem has reduced to a trivial linear problem. In the general non-linear case, the PDE (2.5) cannot be solved explicitely. But one can use the Feynman-Kac formula to obtain estimates for the Vasserstein distance on $C[0,1]$, and this allows to verify Dobrushin's uniqueness condition (2.6) under suitable assumptions on the forward drift (b^i); cf. [2].

REFERENCES

[1] J.M. Bismut, D. Michel: Diffusions Conditionnelles I, II
J. Funct. Anal. 44 (1981), 174-211, 45 (1982), 274-292.

[2] J.D. Deuschel: Lissage de Diffusions à Dimension Infinie et leurs Propriétés en tant que Mesure de Gibbs,
Dissertation, ETH Zürich, 1985.

[3] J.D. Deuschel: Représentation du Champ de Fluctuation de Diffusions Indépendantes par le Drap Brownien,
Preprint (1985)

[4] R.L. Dobrushin: Prescribing a System of Random Variables by Conditional Distributions.
Theor.Prob.Appl. 15 (1970) 458-486.

[5] H. Doss, G. Royer: Processus de Diffusions Associés aux Mesures de Gibbs,
Z. Wahrscheinlichkeitstheorie verw., Geb. 46 (1979) 125-158

[6] E.B. Dynkin: Sufficient Statistics and Extreme Points,
Ann.Probability 6(1978) 705-730.

[7] H. Föllmer: Phase Transitions and Martin Boundary, in Sém. Prob. IX, Lecture Notes in Mathematics 465, 305-318,
Springer-Verlag Berlin, Heidelberg, New York 1975.

[8] H. Föllmer, A. Wakolbinger: Time Reversal of Infinite-Dimensional Diffusions, to appear in: Stochastic Processes and their Applications (1986).

[9] J. Fritz: Stationary Measures of Stochastic Gradient Systems, Infinite Lattice Models,
Z. Wahrscheinlicheitstheorie verw. Geb. 59(1982) 479-490

[10] K. Itô: Distribution valued Processes arising from Independent Brownian Motions,
Math. Zeitschrift 182 (1983) 17-33.

[11] G. Jona-Lasinio, P.K. Mitter: On Stochastic Quantization of Field Theory,
Preprint (1985).

[12] H.R. Künsch: Thermodynamics and Statistical Analysis of Gaussian Random Fields,
Z. Wahrscheinlichkeitstheorie verw. Geb. 58 (1981) 407-421.

[13] S. Mitter: On the Analogy between Mathematical Problems of Non-Linear Filtering and Quantum Physics
Ricerche Automat. 10 (1979) 163-216

[14] M. Nagasawa: The Adjoint Process of a Diffusion with Reflecting Barrier, Kodai Math.Sem. Report 13 (1961) 235-248.

[15] E. Nelson: The Adjoint Markov Process, Duke Math. J.25 (1958) 671-690.

[16] E. Pardoux: Equations du Filtrage Non-Linéaire, de la Prédiction et du Lissage, Stochastics 6 (1982) 193-231.

ON THE MOTION OF AN IMPURITY IN AN INFINITE HARMONIC CRYSTAL.

Detlef Dürr, Vladimir Naroditsky*, Nino Zanghi

Research Center BiBoS, University of Bielefeld, FR Germany.
(*Permanently at: Department of Mathematics, San Jose State University, San Jose, U.S.A.)

INTRODUCTION.

The Model (S 1, 2, 3, 4, 5).

The nearest neighbor harmonic crystal (or lattice) is the collection of positions $\{\underline{x}_i(t)\}$, $i \in \mathbf{Z}^d$, $t \in \mathbf{R}$ of masses $\{m_i\}$, $i \in \mathbf{Z}^d$, where $\{\underline{x}_i(t)\}$, $i \in \mathbf{Z}^d$ is the solution of the infinite system of equations

$$(1) \qquad m_i \ddot{\underline{x}}_i = \kappa \Delta \underline{x}_i, \qquad i \in \mathbf{Z}^d, \qquad \kappa > 0,$$

where Δ is a discrete Laplacian on $\mathbf{Z}^d$; $\{\underline{x}_i(0)\}=\{\underline{x}_i\}$, $\{\dot{\underline{x}}_i(0)\} = \{\underline{v}_i\}$, $i \in \mathbf{Z}^d$.

Since the forces are linear, we call κ the spring constant. Obviously, $\underline{x}_i = i$, $i \in \mathbf{Z}^d$ and $\underline{v}_i = 0$, $i \in \mathbf{Z}^d$ is stationary, hence the name "harmonic crystal" (this notion should be taken *cum grano salis*, see below).

The mass $m_0 \equiv M$ is called the tagged particle (tp) and is an impurity if $M \neq m = m_i$, $i \in \mathbf{Z}^d$, $i \neq 0$.

Since the theory is linear, existence and uniqueness of solutions of (1) are not difficult to obtain, but the statistical mechanics of the harmonic crystal, i.e., the definition of stationary ensembles of the initial values $\{x_i\}$, $\{v_i\}$ is not trivial. The Gibbs measure ~ exp($-\beta$ Energy), β = inverse temperature, does not exist in d = 1,2 as a finite measure; but it exists for $d \geq 3$. The reason is roughly this: consider (1) for a finite volume $\Lambda \subset \mathbf{Z}^d$ with fixed boundaries (i.e., Dirichlet conditions for $\Delta \equiv \Delta_D$). Then the (Gaussian) Gibbs measure has variance $(\Delta_D)^{-1} \sim |\Lambda|$ in d=1, $\sim \ln|\Lambda|$ in d = 2, $\sim |\Lambda|^{-1}$ in d = 3. As $|\Lambda| \to \infty$, the variances in d = 1,2 become infinite. Considering these fluctuations, one better calls the harmonic crystall in d=1 a harmonic gas, in d=2 a harmonic fluid and only from d=3 on one may speak of a crystalline structure. That the equilibrium measure in d=1,2 is infinite is reflected also in the long time behaviour of the trajectory of the tp: it will typically wander out to infinity in d = 1,2, whereas in $d \geq 3$ it will remain in a bounded region.

We define an initial state, i.e., a distribution of initial values $\{x_i\}$, $\{v_i\}$, in which $x_0=0$ and the rest (the bath) is loosely speaking in thermal equilibrium with the velocity of the tp.

The velocities are then independent, Maxwellian with variance βm_i, and moreover the evolution of the velocities is stationary. We call this initial distribution the Palm-Gibbs measure in accordance with the Palm measure of point processes.

Since the Palm-Gibbs measure is Gaussian and the evolution is linear, we deal with Gaussian processes.

All this is subject of Part I. Much of the information given there may also be extracted (as we did) from the nice works of van Hemmen [1] and Lanford, Lebowitz [2].

The TP-Motion. (S 6, 7, 8)

We are concerned with the long time behaviour of the tp trajectory when the initial state of the system is given by the Palm-Gibbs measure. Then the tp trajectories constitute a random process on the probability space of the initial values. This is the subject of Part II.

Our motivation is to test principal ideas of nonequilibrium statistical mechanics concerning tp motion in fluids. The problems we looked at are explained below and they express some of those ideas.

To test the harmonic lattice as a heat bath is, of course, not original. The previous outstanding contributions to this, and clearly our source of inspiration, are Rubin's papers [3], [4]. Also the work of Mori and Morita should be mentioned here [5]. We shall shortly discuss previous works on this subject as it compares to our work at the end of the introduction.

We describe now heuristically the topics we considered. We tried to expose our paper such that the reader can easily read off the sharp statements (or theorems if you like) and the relevant details (without the technical ballast) in the corresponding section.

Heavy Mass Limit; Model of Brownian Motion. (S 9, 13, 14).

A classical model of Brownian motion is the motion of a very heavy particle ($M\to\infty$) in a fluid of light particles looked upon on a macroscopic scale; see, e.g., [6].

Let $m_i=m$, $i\in\mathbb{Z}$, $i\neq 0$ and $m_0=M$. By $(X(t),V(t))_{t\geq 0}$ we denote position and velocity of the tp. We wish to let $M\to\infty$ but simultaneously changing the time and space scale in such a way that the velocity process converges to a non-trivial limit, namely, to an Ornstein-Uhlenbeck process. Since the Maxwellian distribution with like magnified difference $(\eta_M,\xi_M)=M^{1/4}((X_M,V_M)-(X^*,V^*))$, where the difficulty lies in putting (X_M,V_M) and (X^*,V^*) on a common probability space, i.e., to couple the initial values such that the convergence takes place in a suitable sense. We prove that (η_M,ξ_M) converges to a Gaussian process, determined by a stochastic differential equation with drift given by the harmonic force in (X^*,V^*) and additional Wiener noise in case the system starts in the Gibbs ensemble, and additional integrated Wiener noise when the system starts with a Palm measure. We do not know whether a similar treatment in d=2 is possible.

Long Time Behaviour (S 10, 14).

The motion of the tp is unbounded in d=1,2. We wish to observe its escape to infinity on a macroscopic scale but not scaling the mass. From the above, it comes as no surprise that in d=1 the tp behaves diffusively, i.e., $X_A(t) \equiv A^{-1/2}X(At)$ (note the classical CLT type scaling) goes in law as $A\to\infty$ to a Wiener process with diffusion constant D, which, and that is surprising, does not depend on the mass of the tp (compare also with the random mass harmonic chain).

In d=2 the tp however moves only on a logarithmic scale to infinity. Here we show that $X_A(t)\equiv A^{1/2}X((1+t)^A)$ converges in distribution to a Gaussian process, which locally behaves like a Wiener process, with diffusion constant D^*. This result is shown to hold for a large but finite mass.

Einstein Relation. Smoluchowski Equation. (S11,14).

We consider the tp on the same time scale as for the long time behaviour but now it is also subjected to an external potential (acting only on the tp) $U_A(x)$ which varies on the macroscopic scale $U_A(x) \equiv U(A^{-1/2}x)$. Then the force acting on the tp is weak: $F_A=A^{-1/2}F(A^{-1/2}x)$ $(F=-\nabla U)$.

In d=1 it is shown that for quite general U, X_A converges in law to X^* given by the stochastic differential equation

$$(3) \qquad dX^*(t) = F/\gamma M \, dt + D^{1/2}\, dW(t),$$

where γ is the friction coefficient in (2). $F/\gamma M$ is, roughly speaking, the mean velocity achieved by the tp under the driving force F and the friction force $-\gamma V$. The stationary distribution of X^* is $\sim\exp(-2U/\gamma MD)$ which should equal the Gibbsian distribution $\exp(-\beta U)$. Therefore $(\gamma M)^{-1} = \frac{1}{2}\beta D$, the famous Einstein relation.

The Fokker-Planck equation corresponding to (3) is called Smoluchowski's equation [7] (see also [8]), describing in the configuration space a Brownian particle in a force field.

variance $(\beta M)^{-1}$ is stationary, we change V to $M^{1/2}V$ to keep the velocity of order one. To fix the time scale, consider the following very rough but useful idea suggested from a Central Limit Theorem type argument; write $M^{1/2}V(t) = M^{1/2}\sum_{i=1}^{t}\Delta V_i\,\Delta t_i$, by breaking time into unit intervals. The diffusion term in the Ornstein-Uhlenbeck process arises from the variance $\langle(M^{1/2}\sum_{i=1}^{t}\Delta V_i\,\Delta t_i)^2\rangle \sim Mt\langle\Delta V^2\rangle$ if the velocity increments were well mixing. By(1), $\Delta V \sim M^{-1}$, thus $\langle\Delta V^2\rangle \sim M^{-2}$ and we need to stretch time by M to obtain a variance of order one.

Indeed, in d=1 $V_M(t) \equiv M^{1/2}V(Mt)$ converges in distribution to an Ornstein-Uhlenbeck process $V^*(t)$ given by

$$dV^*(t) = -\gamma\, V^*(t)dt + \sigma\, dW(t), \tag{2}$$

where $W(t)$ is a standard Wiener process, γ is the transport coefficient, σ obeys the "fluctuation dissipation theorem" $2\gamma/\sigma^2 = \beta$.

In d≥2 this is not so. Note first that the variance $\langle(M^{1/2}\sum_{i=1}^{t}\Delta V_i\Delta t_i)^2\rangle \sim Mt^2\langle\Delta V^2\rangle$ if velocity increments are strongly depedent. Then stretching time like $M^{1/2}$ keeps the variance from exploding. Loosely speaking, this scaling corresponds to a Law of Large Numbers type theorem.

Now look at d=3. Since the Gibbs measure does exist as a finite measure, $X(t)$ and $V(t)$ defined on the Gibbsian ensemble, have stationary variances, and since $\dot{X}(t) = V(t)$, the only scaling in which $M\to\infty$, preserving the stationary values, is in fact $V_M(t) \equiv M^{1/2}V(M^{1/2}t)$, and hence $X_M(t) \equiv X(M^{1/2}t)$. Indeed, we show that in this scaling, in d=3, (X_M, V_M) converges weakly to a deterministic process (X^*, V^*) of a harmonically bound particle, with $V^*(0)$ distributed according to the Maxwellian distribution with variance β^{-1}. On the "short" time scale $M^{1/2}$ relaxation can not be seen.

d=2 is the critical dimension. The tp behaviour is intermidiate between d=1 and d=3. The correct time scale has essentially a logarithmic (enlarging) correction to $M^{1/2}$ on which V_M however converges again to the deterministic process V^* of a harmonically bound particle.

Fluctuations (S 16).

The convergence in d=3 of (X_M, V_M), $V_M = M^{1/2}V(M^{1/2}t)$ to (X^*, V^*), a deterministic process with random initial values, may be roughly seen as a Law of Large Numbers ($\sim M^{1/2}$ terms). As usual, then the next correction (or the speed of convergence) should be given by the Central Limit theorem. Hence, it is natural to study the CLT

It is remarkable that also in d=2 the Einstein relation may be proved for F a constant and D replaced by D^*.

Random Mass Chain (S 12).

We consider in d=1 the case when $\{m_i\}$, $i\in\mathbb{Z}$ is a sequence of arbitrary masses, for example $\{m_i\}$, $i\in\mathbb{Z}$ is an ergodic sequence. We prove in great generality a formula for the diffusion constant of the tp. We do not know whether this formula is known to physicists. It shows that the diffusion constant depends on the tails of the mass distribution to the left and to the right of the tp in form of ergodic means. The proof is a straightforward and therefore, beautiful application of Krein's theory of strings in connection with generalized diffusion processes [9].

Comparison With Other Works.

The heavy mass limit, apart from the fluctuations, is essentially discussed in Rubin's papers. In there is also the long time behaviour in d=1. Similar to that but restricted to the case d=1 is the work of Mori and Morita [5]. It was our aim to present this in a rigorous mathematical language.

The use of the Palm-Gibbs measure simplifies and clarifies the questions and statements.

The often cited work of Ford, Kac, Mazur [10] on the Brownian motion in a harmonic bath does not compare with the ideas basic to ours and the above mentioned works. Brownian motion in their understanding does not appear as a macroscopic description of an underlying microscopic phenomenon by virtue of scaling mass, space and time.

Final Remarks and Acknowledgements.

We tried to write a self contained review-like paper including original results. We owe a lot to many helpful discussions with H.Spohn, H.Rost, E.Presutti, P.Calderoni, S.Albeverio, C.Marchioro, J.L.Lebowitz, O.Lanford, G.Papanicolaou. In particular, the random mass harmonic chain was most fruitfully discussed with S.Kusuoka and M.Tomisaki.

Two of us (V.N. and N.Z.) thank the organizers of the project BiBoS S.Albeverio, Ph.Blanchard and L.Streit for their kind invitation and for the warm hospitality at ZiF.

List of Symbols.

A	scaling parameter (S 6)
$A = M^{-1/2}(-\kappa\Delta)M^{-1/2}$	dynamical matrix (2.4)
$\hat{A} = -\kappa M^{-1}\Delta$	(S 12)
$a_{ij}(t)$	(2.7)

$a(t) = a_{00}(t)$	(normalized) velocity autocorrelation function of the tp (§ 6)
$\tilde{a}(\tau)$	Laplace transform of $a(t)$ (§ 8)
$\mathcal{B}(\Omega)$	Borel σ-algebra of Ω (§ 4)
$b_{ij}(t)$	(2.7)
$b(t) = b_{00}(t)$	(§ 6)
$c(t)$	(6.6)
$D; D^*$	diffusion constants (10.2); (§ 14)
$E; E_0; \hat{E}$	expectation; expectation w.r.t. P_0 (§ 5); expectation w.r.t. $\hat{P}$ (§ 5)
$\{e_i\}; \{e_\alpha\}$	standard orthonormal basis in $l_2(\mathbb{Z}^d)$ (§ 2); in $\mathbb{R}^d$ (§ 1)
$g_{\lambda^2}(x,y)$	kernel of $(\lambda^2 + \hat{A})^{-1}$ (§ 12)
H_t	generalized diffusion process (§ 12)
h_+, h_-	Krein correspondences to $\mathfrak{m}_+, \mathfrak{m}_-$ (§ 12)
i, j, k	elements of $\mathbb{Z}^d$ (§ 1)
$I(\tau)$	(8.9)
$l_2(\mathbb{Z}^d); L_2([-\pi,\pi]^d)$	spaces of square summable sequences (§ 1); functions (§ 3)
$\mathbf{M} = (\delta_{ij} m_j)$	(§ 1)
$m_i; \{m_i\}$	mass of the particle at the site i of $\mathbb{Z}^d$ (§ 1); distribution of masses (§ 12)
$M = m_0$	mass of the tp (§ 6)
$\mathfrak{m}; \mathfrak{m}_+; \mathfrak{m}_-$	measures induced on $\mathbb{Z}$ by $\mathbf{M}$ (§ 12)
$m_+; m_-$	ergodic mean of $\{m_i\}$, $i \geq 0$; ergodic mean of $\{m_i\}$, $i \leq 0$ (§ 12)
$m = (m_1, \ldots, m_d)$	multiindex of nonnegative integers (§ 1)
M^*	unit of mass (§ 9, 13, 15)
$P_0; \hat{P}; P$	Palm-Gibbs measure; Gibbs measure (§ 4); P_0 or $\hat{P}$ (§ 5)
$p(t) = \{p_i(t)\}; q(t) = \{q_i(t)\}$	(2.2)
$p = \{p_i\}; q = \{q_i\}$	initial conditions (§ 2)
$s_m(\mathbb{Z}^d), s_{-m}(\mathbb{Z}^d), s(\mathbb{Z}^d), s'(\mathbb{Z}^d)$	sequence spaces (§ 1)
T_t	dynamical flow (§ 1)
$\underline{v}(t) = \{\underline{v}_i(t)\}; \underline{v} = \{\underline{v}_i\}$	velocity vector of the crystal; velocity vector at t=0 (§ 1)

$v(t)=\{v_i(t)\}$; $v=\{v_i\}$	arbitrary space component of $\underline{v}(t)$; of $\underline{v}$ (S1)
$W(t)$	standard Wiener process ($E(W(t)W(s))=\min(t,s)$) (S9)
$\underline{x}(t)=\{\underline{x}_i(t)\}$; $\underline{x}=\{\underline{x}_i\}$	position vector of the crystal; position vector at t=0 (S1)
$x(t)=\{x_i(t)\}$; $x=\{x_i\}$	arbitrary space component of $\underline{x}(t)$; of $\underline{x}$ (S1)
$(\underline{X}(t), \underline{V}(t))_{t\geq 0}$	tp process (S6)
$(X(t), V(t))_{t\geq 0}$	arbitrary space component of the tp process (S 6)
$(\hat{X}(t), \hat{V}(t))_{t\geq 0}$	tp process with $\hat{\beta}$ -distributedinitial conditions (S 15)
Y_A; Y^*	scaled process; limiting process (S 6)
$Z(t)$	position process of the tp with external force (S 11)
$\mathbb{Z}^d$	d-dimensional lattice (S1)
β	inverse temperature (= 1/kT, k Boltzmann constant) (S 4)
γ	friction coefficient (S11)
Δ	d-dimensional discrete Laplacian (S1)
ζ_0	(8.33)
(η_A, ξ_A);$(\hat{\eta}_A, \hat{\xi}_A)$	scaled fluctuation process with $P_0(\hat{\beta})$ distributed initial conditions(S16)
(η, ξ); $(\hat{\eta}, \hat{\xi})$	limit of (η_A, ξ_A); limit of $(\hat{\eta}_A, \hat{\xi}_A)$ (S 16)
$\theta = (\theta_1,\dots,\theta_d) \in [-\pi,\pi]^d$	(S 3)
κ	spring constant (S 1)
ν	mobility (S11)
$\sum_i$	denotes summation on $i\in\mathbb{Z}^d$ (S1)
σ	(S9, 16)
$\sigma(A)$	spectrum of A (S 3)
$\tau_{\pm}$	poles of $\tilde{a}(\tau)$ (S 8)
$\Psi(\theta)^2$	Fourier transform of $-\Delta$ (S 3)
ω_0	isolated mode (3.5)
$\omega_L = 2(\kappa/m)^{1/2}$	(S1, S 8)
$\omega = 2(\kappa/\zeta_0)^{1/2}$	(S8, S 13)
$\Omega = s'(\mathbb{Z}^d) \oplus s'(\mathbb{Z}^d)$	phase space (S1)
$\langle . , . \rangle$	duality between spaces; scalar product (S1)
$\doteq$	uniform approximation (S 8)
$\Rightarrow$	weak convergence (S 6)
$\cdot$	derivative with respect to time (S 1)
$f(t)=O(M^{-1})$	$f(t)$ is uniformly bounded in t by Const. M^{-1} for large t
∎	end of the proof

PART I. GLOBAL PROPERTIES OF THE INFINITE HARMONIC CRYSTAL.

S 1. The equations of motion.

The dynamics of an infinite cubic harmonic crystal is described in terms of the displacement at time t $\underline{x}_i(t)\in\mathbb{R}^d$, $i\in\mathbb{Z}^d$ of the particle at the site i from its equilibrium position and its velocity at time t $\underline{v}_i(t)\in\mathbb{R}^d$, $i\in\mathbb{Z}^d$. The equations of motion are:

$$(1.1)\qquad \begin{aligned} \dot{\underline{x}}_i(t) &= \underline{v}_i(t) \\ m_i\,\dot{\underline{v}}_i(t) &= -\sum_j \Phi_{ij}\underline{x}_j(t), \end{aligned}$$

where m_i is the mass of the particle at the site $i\in\mathbb{Z}^d$ and $\Phi = (\Phi_{ij})$, $i,j\in\mathbb{Z}^d$, the interaction matrix, is a real infinite matrix with entries Φ_{ij} being d-dimensional matrices.

From now on we shall consider the case of the nearest neighbor interactions with the spring constant κ being the same for all directions in $\mathbb{R}^d$. Then the equations of motion for each space component $x_{i,\alpha}(t)$, $v_{i,\alpha}(t)$ $(\alpha=1,\dots,d)$ of $\underline{x}_i(t)$, $\underline{v}_i(t)$ become:

$$(1.2)\qquad \begin{aligned} \dot{x}_{i,\alpha}(t) &= v_{i,\alpha}(t) \\ m_i\,\dot{v}_{i,\alpha}(t) &= \kappa\sum_j \Delta_{ij}\, x_{j,\alpha}(t). \end{aligned}$$

Throughout the paper, whenever possible, and no confusion arises, the subscript α will be omitted. $\Delta = (\Delta_{ij})$, $i,j\in\mathbb{Z}^d$ is the d-dimensional discrete Laplacian:

$$(1.3)\qquad (\Delta x)_i = \sum_j \Delta_{ij}x_j = \sum_{\alpha=1}^{d}(x_{i+e_\alpha} - 2x_i + x_{i-e_\alpha}),$$

where $(e_\alpha)_{\alpha=1}^d$ is the standard basis for $\mathbb{R}^d$.

Introducing the vectors $x(t)=\{x_i(t)\}$, and $v(t)=\{v_i(t)\}$, $i\in\mathbb{Z}^d$ and the matrix

$$(1.4)\qquad \mathbf{M} = (\delta_{ij}m_j), \qquad i,j\in\mathbb{Z}^d$$

the equations (1.2) can be rewritten as

$$(1.5)\qquad \begin{aligned} \dot{x}(t) &= v(t) \\ \mathbf{M}\,\dot{v}(t) &= \kappa\,\Delta\, x(t) \end{aligned}$$

In order to specify the initial conditions for (1.5) and prove the existence of the solution, we shall consider the following spaces:

$$s_m(\mathbb{Z}^d) = \{\xi=(\xi_i),\ i\in\mathbb{Z}^d;\ \xi_i\in\mathbb{R}\ \mid\ \|\xi\|_m^2 = \sum_i (1+i^2)^m|\xi_i|^2 < \infty\},$$

where $m=(m_1,\dots,m_d)$ is a multiindex of nonnegative integers and

$$(1+i^2)^m \equiv \prod_{\alpha=1}^{d} (1+i_\alpha^2)^{m_\alpha}.$$

In particular, for $m = 0 = (0,\ldots,0)$, $s_0(\mathbf{Z}^d) = l_2(\mathbf{Z}^d)$. Each $s_m(\mathbf{Z}^d)$ is a Banach space, and $\{s_m(\mathbf{Z}^d)\}$ forms a directed family of Banach spaces. Thus $s(\mathbf{Z}^d) = \bigcap s_m(\mathbf{Z}^d)$ becomes a topological space with the topology of a projective limit.

By the Hahn-Banach theorem, the dual spaces are:

$$s_m'(\mathbf{Z}^d) \equiv s_{-m}(\mathbf{Z}^d) = \{\xi = (\xi_i),\ i\in\mathbf{Z}^d;\ \xi_i \in R \mid \|\xi\|_{-m}{}^2 = \sum_i (1+i^2)^{-m}|\xi_i|^2 < \infty\}$$

with the duality defined by

$$\langle\xi,\eta\rangle = \sum_i \bar{\xi}_i\eta_i,\quad \xi\in s_{-m}(\mathbf{Z}^d),\ \eta\in s_m(\mathbf{Z}^d). \tag{1.6}$$

In the case $m = 0$, this relation gives the usual scalar product in $l_2(\mathbf{Z}^d)$.

$s'(\mathbf{Z}^d) = \bigcup s_{-m}(\mathbf{Z}^d)$ is a topological space with the topology of an inductive limit; it is the dual space of $s(\mathbf{Z}^d)$. $s(\mathbf{Z}^d)$ and $s'(\mathbf{Z}^d)$ are the space of sequences decaying faster than any polynomial and the space of polynomially bounded sequences respectively. Both spaces are nuclear. Thus we have the following chain of spaces:

$$s(\mathbf{Z}^d) \subset s_m(\mathbf{Z}^d) \subset l_2(\mathbf{Z}^d) \subset s_{-m}(\mathbf{Z}^d) \subset s'(\mathbf{Z}^d). \tag{1.7}$$

We may now define the Cauchy problem for the equations (1.5). Introducing the vector $\zeta(t) = (x(t), v(t))$, the equations of motion (1.5) can be formally rewritten in the form

$$\dot{\zeta}(t) = S\,\zeta(t), \tag{1.8}$$

where $S\zeta = (v,\ \kappa M^{-1}\Delta x)$.

Theorem 1.1. Let $\inf\{m_i\}>0$, $i\in\mathbf{Z}^d$. Then for any initial condition $\zeta(0)=(x, v) \in s_{-m}(\mathbf{Z}^d) \oplus s_{-m}(\mathbf{Z}^d)$, there exists a unique global solution $\zeta(t) = \exp(St)\,\zeta(0) \in s_{-m}(\mathbf{Z}^d) \oplus s_{-m}(\mathbf{Z}^d)$ of the equation (1.8).

Proof. We need only show that S is a linear bounded operator on $s_{-m}(\mathbf{Z}^d) \oplus s_{-m}(\mathbf{Z}^d)$ for each multiindex m.

Linearity of S is obvious.

For boundedness, let $\zeta = (x,v) \in s_{-m}(\mathbf{Z}^d) \oplus s_{-m}(\mathbf{Z}^d)$. We wish to show:

$$\|S\zeta\|_{-m} \le \text{Const.}(\|x\|_{-m} + \|v\|_{-m}). \tag{1.9}$$

Now, $\|S\zeta\|_{-m} = \|v\|_{-m} + \|\kappa M^{-1}\Delta x\|_{-m} =$

$$\|v\|_{-m} + \Big[\sum_i (1+i^2)^{-m} (\kappa/m_i)^2 \Big|\sum_{\alpha=1}^{d} (x_{i+e_\alpha} - 2x_i + x_{i-e_\alpha})\Big|^2\Big]^{1/2} \le$$

$$\|v\|_{-m} + \text{Const.}\Big[\sum_i (1+i^2)^{-m} \sum_{\alpha=1}^{d} (|x_{i+e_\alpha}|^2 + |x_i|^2 + |x_{i-e_\alpha}|^2)\Big]^{1/2}.$$

Note that $\sum_i (1+i^2)^{-m} |x_{i+e_\alpha}|^2 = \sum_i (1+[i-e_\alpha]^2)^{-m} |x_i|^2 =$

$$\sum_i \prod_{\substack{\beta=1\\ \beta\neq\alpha}}^{d} (1+i_\beta^2)^{-m_\beta} (1+[i_\alpha-1]^2)^{-m_\alpha} |x_i|^2 \le \text{Const.}\|x\|_{-m}^2$$

The same inequality holds for all terms, and (1.9) follows.

The proof of the uniqueness of the global solution is straightforward. ∎

Remark. Since $S'(\mathbf{Z}^d) = \cup\, S_{-m}(\mathbf{Z}^d)$, Theorem 1.1 implies that $T_t \equiv \exp(St)$ leaves $S'(\mathbf{Z}^d) \oplus S'(\mathbf{Z}^d)$ invariant. The dynamics of the system is now defined by the unique flow T_t on the space $\Omega \equiv S'(\mathbf{Z}^d) \oplus S'(\mathbf{Z}^d)$.

Assume now that there is an external force f acting on the tp. Then the equations of motion for the positions $z(t)=\{z_i(t)\}$ and the velocities $v(t)=\{v_i(t)\}$ are

$$\text{(1.10)} \qquad \begin{aligned} \dot{z}(t) &= v(t) \\ \mathbf{M}\dot{v}(t) &= \kappa\Delta z(t) + f(t) \end{aligned}$$

where $f(t) = (f_j(t)),\ j\in\mathbf{Z}^d,\ f_j(t) = \delta_{j,0} f(z_0(t))$.

The standard argument for the Lipschitz perturbation of a linear differential equation gives:

Theorem 1.2. Let f be a Lipshitz continuous real function. Then Theorem 1.1 holds for the system (1.10) (see, e.g., [11]).

S2. Canonical Transformation.

In this section we shall introduce a change of variables in Ω convenient for expressing the solution of (1.5).

Consider the canonical "isomorphic" transformation φ on Ω

$$\text{(2.1)} \qquad \varphi(x,v) = (\mathbf{M}^{1/2} x, \mathbf{M}^{1/2} v)$$

for any $(x,v) \in \Omega$. The equations of motion for

$$\text{(2.2)} \qquad (q(t),p(t)) = (\mathbf{M}^{1/2} x(t), \mathbf{M}^{1/2} v(t))$$

are

$$(2.3)\qquad \begin{aligned} \dot{q}(t) &= p(t) \\ \dot{p}(t) &= -\mathcal{A}\, q(t) \end{aligned}$$

where

$$(2.4)\qquad \mathcal{A} = \mathbf{M}^{-1/2}(-\kappa\Delta)\,\mathbf{M}^{-1/2}$$

is the so-called dynamical matrix.

It was shown in the proof of Theorem 1.1 that $-\Delta$ is a bounded linear operator in the space $S_{-m}(\mathbf{Z}^d)$ for any multiindex m. By duality, $-\Delta$ is a bounded linear operator in each $S_m(\mathbf{Z}^d)$. The assumption $\inf(m_i)>0$ guarantees that $\mathcal{A}$ is a bounded operator in the same space. The fact that $-\Delta$ is a positive self-adjoint operator in $l_2(\mathbf{Z}^d)$ and the structure of $\mathcal{A}$ imply that $\mathcal{A}$ is also a positive self-adjoint operator in $l_2(\mathbf{Z}^d)$.

Since $\mathcal{A}$ is positive, $\mathcal{A}^{1/2}$ is well-defined. If $q(0) = q \in l_2(\mathbf{Z}^d)$ and $p(0)= p \in l_2(\mathbf{Z}^d)$ then the solutions of (2.3) are:

$$(2.5)\qquad \begin{aligned} q(t) &= \cos(\mathcal{A}^{1/2}t)\, q + \mathcal{A}^{-1/2}\sin(\mathcal{A}^{1/2}t)\, p; \\ p(t) &= -\mathcal{A}^{1/2}\sin(\mathcal{A}^{1/2}t)\, q + \cos(\mathcal{A}^{1/2}t)\, p. \end{aligned}$$

$\mathcal{A}^{-1/2}\sin(\mathcal{A}^{1/2}t)$ is a formal expression for the bounded operator $\sum_{j=0}^{\infty}(-1)^j \mathcal{A}^j\, t^{2j+1}/(2j+1)!$

Since $\mathcal{A}$ is a bounded operator in each $S_{-m}(\mathbf{Z}^d)$, $\mathcal{A}^{1/2}$ can be extended to a bounded operator in the same space. Therefore, (2.5) remains valid for the initial conditions in Ω and defines the flow $T_t \circ \varphi^{-1}$ on Ω, which is the image of the flow T_t under the canonical transformation (2.1).

The components of $q(t)$ and $p(t)$ in (2.5) are given by:

$$(2.6)\qquad \begin{aligned} q_i(t) &= \sum_j a_{ij}(t) q_j + \sum_j b_{ij}(t) p_j; \\ p_i(t) &= \sum_j \dot{a}_{ij}(t) q_j + \sum_j a_{ij}(t) p_j \end{aligned}$$

where

$$(2.7)\quad b_{ij}(t)=\langle e_i, \mathcal{A}^{-1/2}\sin(\mathcal{A}^{1/2}t)\, e_j\rangle\,;\; a_{ij}(t)=\dot{b}_{ij}(t)=\langle e_i, \cos(\mathcal{A}^{1/2}t)\, e_j\rangle\,;\; \dot{a}_{ij}(t)=\langle e_i, -\mathcal{A}^{1/2}\sin(\mathcal{A}^{1/2}t)\, e_j\rangle,$$

here $\{e_i\}$, $i\in\mathbf{Z}^d$ is the standard orthonormal basis for $l_2(\mathbf{Z}^d)$. Using the projector-valued measure of $\mathcal{A}^{1/2}$, $P_{\mathcal{A}^{1/2}}(d\omega)$, one can write the spectral representation of the coefficients in (2.7). For example,

$$a_{ij}(t) = \int_{\sigma(A^{1/2})} \cos\omega t \ \langle e_i, P_{A^{1/2}}(d\omega) e_j \rangle$$

where $\sigma(A^{1/2})$ is the spectrum of $A^{1/2}$.

Since the operators $A^{-1/2}\sin(A^{1/2}t)$ and $\cos(A^{1/2}t)$ are bounded in each $S_m(\mathbf{Z}^d)$, for each i the sequences $\{a_{ij}(t)\}$, $j\in\mathbf{Z}^d$ and $\{b_{ij}(t)\}$, $j\in\mathbf{Z}^d$ are elements of the space $S_m(\mathbf{Z}^d)$ for all m's, and thus are elements of the space $s(\mathbf{Z}^d)$. Therefore, the series in (2.6) converge for $\{q_j\}$, $\{p_j\}$, $j\in\mathbf{Z}^d$ in $s'(\mathbf{Z}^d)$.

Under the transformation (2.1), the equation (1.10) becomes:

$$\text{(2.8)} \qquad \begin{aligned} \dot q(t) &= p(t) \\ \dot p(t) &= -A q(t) + F(t) \end{aligned}$$

where $F(t) = (F_k(t))$, $k\in\mathbf{Z}^d$, $F_k(t) = \delta_{k,0} m_0^{-1/2} f(m_0^{-1/2} q_0(t))$, and m_0 is the mass of the tp. (2.8) is equivalent to the following integral equation:

$$\text{(2.9)} \qquad q_i(t) = \sum_j a_{ij}(t) q_j + \sum_j b_{ij}(t) p_j + \int_0^t du \int_0^u dv\, a_{i0}(u-v) F_0(v)$$

Using (2.1) and (2.6), the solution of (1.2) can be written in the form:

$$\text{(2.10)} \qquad \begin{aligned} x_i(t) &= \sum_j m_i^{-1/2} m_j^{1/2} a_{ij}(t) x_j + \sum_j m_i^{-1/2} m_j^{1/2} b_{ij}(t) v_j \\ v_i(t) &= \sum_j m_i^{-1/2} m_j^{1/2} \dot a_{ij}(t) x_j + \sum_j m_i^{-1/2} m_j^{1/2} a_{ij}(t) v_j . \end{aligned}$$

and using (2.9), (1.10) becomes equivalent to the following integral equation:

$$\text{(2.11)} \qquad z_i(t) = x_i(t) + (m_0 m_i)^{-1/2} \int_0^t du \int_0^u dv\, a_{i0}(u-v) f(z_0(u))$$

where $x_i(t)$ is given by (2.10).

§ 3. Spectral properties of the dynamical matrix.

The Fourier transform of an element $\xi \in s(\mathbf{Z}^d)$ is defined by:

$$\text{(3.1)} \qquad (F\xi)(\theta) = \hat\xi(\theta) \equiv \sum_k \xi_k e^{ik\cdot\theta},$$

where $\theta = (\theta_1, \dots, \theta_d) \in [-\pi, \pi]^d$, $k \cdot \theta = \sum_{\alpha=1}^{d} k_\alpha \theta_\alpha$.

The transformation (3.1) defines a homeomorphism of $s(\mathbf{Z}^d)$ onto the space $\mathcal{S}([-\pi,\pi]^d)$ of infinitely differentiable periodic functions on $\mathbf{R}^d$. Given $\mathcal{S}([-\pi,\pi]^d) \subset L_2([-\pi,\pi]^d)$, $\mathcal{S}'([-\pi,\pi]^d)$ can be defined as the dual space of $\mathcal{S}([-\pi,\pi]^d)$.

Let $\xi \in s'(\mathbf{Z}^d)$. Define the Fourier transform $F\xi \equiv \hat{\xi} \in \mathcal{S}'([-\pi,\pi]^d)$ by $\langle \hat{\xi}, e^{-ik\cdot\theta} \rangle = \xi_k$, for any $k \in \mathbf{Z}^d$. Restricting the map F on the spaces $s_{-m}(\mathbf{Z}^d)$ and $s_m(\mathbf{Z}^d)$, define the spaces

$$\mathcal{S}_{-m}([-\pi,\pi]^d) \equiv F(s_{-m}(\mathbf{Z}^d)) \text{ and } \mathcal{S}_m([-\pi,\pi]^d) \equiv F(s_m(\mathbf{Z}^d)).$$

Under the Fourier transform, the chain (1.7) is isomorphically transformed into the chain

$$(3.2) \qquad \mathcal{S}([-\pi,\pi]^d) \subset \mathcal{S}_m([-\pi,\pi]^d) \subset L_2([-\pi,\pi]^d) \subset \mathcal{S}_{-m}([-\pi,\pi]^d) \subset \mathcal{S}'([-\pi,\pi]^d).$$

For $\varphi \in \mathcal{S}_m([-\pi,\pi]^d)$, the mapping F^{-1} is given by the formula:

$$(3.3) \qquad (F^{-1}\varphi)_k = (2\pi)^{-d} \int_{-\pi}^{\pi} \dots \int_{-\pi}^{\pi} \varphi(\theta)\, e^{-ik\cdot\theta}\, d\theta_1 \dots d\theta_d$$

and is extended by duality on all the elements of the chain (3.2).

In what follows, (3.1) and (3.3) will be used as formal expressions even when $\xi \in s'(\mathbf{Z}^d)$ and $\varphi \in \mathcal{S}'([-\pi,\pi]^d)$.

Note that the Fourier transform diagonalizes the operator $-\Delta$, i.e., $F(-\Delta)F^{-1}$ is the multiplication operator by the function

$$(3.4) \qquad \psi(\theta)^2 = 2\sum_{\alpha=1}^{d} (1 - \cos\theta_\alpha).$$

It follows from (3.4) that $-\Delta$ is a positive self-adjoint bounded operator with the absolutely continuous spectrum: $\sigma(-\Delta) = \sigma_{\text{abs.cont.}}(-\Delta) = [0, 4d]$.

The existence of equilibrium measures for the dynamical system and its ergodic properties depend on the spectral properties of the dynamical matrix $\mathbf{A}$ defined by (2.4) which, in their turn, depend on the distribution of masses $\{m_i\}$, $i \in \mathbf{Z}^d$. The spectrum of $\mathbf{A}$ can be easily determined when the elements of the matrix $\mathbf{M}$ defined by (1.4), are such that $m_i = m$ for all $i \neq 0$ and $m_0 = M$.

Theorem 1.3. (a) For $M > m$ the spectrum of the operator $\mathbf{A}$ is absolutely continuous: $\sigma(\mathbf{A}) = \sigma_{\text{abs.cont}}(\mathbf{A}) =$

$=[0, \omega_L{}^2 d]$ where $\omega_L = 2(\kappa/m)^{1/2}$.

(b) For $d=1$ and $0 < M < m$ the spectrum of the operator A consists of an absolutely continuous part and a single isolated eigenvalue of multiplicity one:

$\sigma(A) = \sigma_{abs.cont}(A) \cup \{\omega_0{}^2\}$ where $\sigma_{abs.cont}(A) = [0, \omega_L{}^2]$ and

$$\omega_0 = 2\sqrt{\frac{\kappa m}{2mM - M^2}} \tag{3.5}$$

(c) For $d>1$ and M sufficiently small, the operator A has the same absolutely continuous part of the spectrum as in part (a) and one isolated eigenvalue.

Proof. The operator A can be written in the form:

$$A = (-\kappa/m)\Delta + B,$$

where B is a finite rank linear operator. Since the spectrum of the operator $-\Delta$ is absolutley continuous, $\sigma(-\Delta) = \sigma_{abs.cont}(-\Delta) = [0, 4d]$, by Weyl's Lemma the esssential spectrum of A is the same as the essential spectrum of $-\Delta$. Since A is a positive operator, in addition to the continuous part it might have only single isolated eigenvalues. To determine whether it is indeed the case, we shall solve the eigenvalue equation $A\xi = \lambda\xi$ with $\xi \in l_2(Z^d)$, i.e.,

$$\kappa \sum_{\alpha=1}^{d} \left[-\frac{1}{\sqrt{m_j m_{j+e_\alpha}}} \xi_{j+e_\alpha} - \frac{1}{\sqrt{m_j m_{j-e_\alpha}}} \xi_{j-e_\alpha} + \frac{2}{m_j} \xi_j \right] = \lambda \xi_j \quad , \tag{3.6}$$

with $m_j = m$, $j \neq 0$, $m_0 = M$. In the Fourier transform, the eigenvalue equation $(FAF^{-1})\,\hat{\xi}(\theta) = \lambda\,\hat{\xi}(\theta)$ becomes

$$\begin{aligned} &\frac{\kappa}{m}\psi^2(\theta)\hat{\xi}(\theta) + \left[\frac{\kappa}{m} - \frac{\kappa}{\sqrt{mM}}\right] \sum_{\alpha=1}^{d} (\xi_{e_\alpha} + \xi_{-e_\alpha} + 2\xi_0 \cos\theta_\alpha) \\ &\quad + 2d\kappa\xi_0\left(\frac{1}{M} - \frac{1}{m}\right) = \lambda\hat{\xi}(\theta) \end{aligned} \tag{3.7}$$

Letting $j=0$ in (3.6) and substituting the obtained expression in (3.7), we find:

$$\hat{\xi}(\theta) = c(\theta)\,\xi_0 \, , \tag{3.8}$$

where $c(\theta)$ is given by

$$c(\theta) = \frac{\left[\frac{1}{m} - \frac{1}{\sqrt{mM}}\right]\left[\sqrt{mM}\left(\frac{2d}{M} - \frac{\lambda}{\kappa}\right) + 2d - \psi^2(\theta)\right] + 2d\left(\frac{1}{M} - \frac{1}{m}\right)}{\frac{\lambda}{\kappa} - \frac{1}{m}\psi^2(\theta)}$$

Clearly, (3.8) implies

$$(3.9) \qquad (2\pi)^{-d}\int_{-\pi}^{\pi}\ldots\int_{-\pi}^{\pi}c(\theta)d\theta_1\ldots d\theta_d = 1$$

for $\xi_0 \neq 0$.

The facts that A is a positive operator and $\sigma_{abs.cont}(A)=[0,4dK/m]$ imply $\lambda > 4dK/m$. If $M \geq m$, a simple estimate shows that the denominator of the integrand in (3.9) is negative and the numerator is positive, so the left-hand side of (3.9) is negative. Therefore, the eigenvalue equation has no solutions, and part (a) is proved.

For d=1 and $0 < M < m$ the equation (3.9) becomes

$$\left[\left(\frac{1}{m}-\frac{1}{\sqrt{mM}}\right)\sqrt{mM}\left(\frac{2}{M}-\frac{\lambda}{K}\right)+2\left(\frac{1}{M}-\frac{1}{m}\right)\right]\frac{1}{\sqrt{\frac{\lambda^2}{K^2}-\frac{4\lambda}{Km}}}$$

$$+\left(\frac{1}{m}-\frac{1}{\sqrt{mM}}\right)\left[m-\frac{\frac{m\lambda}{K}-2}{\sqrt{\frac{\lambda^2}{K^2}-\frac{4\lambda}{Km}}}\right] = 1.$$

and its solution is

$$\lambda \equiv \omega_0^2 = \frac{4Km}{2mM - M^2}$$

It remains to verify that the vector $\hat{\xi}(\theta)$ satisfying the equation (3.8) with $\lambda \equiv \omega_0^2$ is indeed an element of $L_2([-\pi,\pi])$. A simple computation shows that $\hat{\xi}(\theta)$ is even an element of $\mathcal{S}([-\pi,\pi])$, and part (b) is proved.

In the case $d > 1$, tedious calculations show that the equation (3.9) has a solution when M is sufficiently small and the corresponding vector $\hat{\xi}(\theta)$ is an element of $L_2([-\pi,\pi]^d)$. ∎

Remark. The spectral properties of A for an arbitrary distribution of masses with the only condition $\inf\{m_i\} > 0$ (which guarantees the existence of the dynamics) are in general not known for $d>1$. In one dimension, for a chain of periodically distributed masses the spectrum of A is absolutely contionuous [12] and for a random i.i.d. mass chain the spectrum of A is a pure point spectrum with probability one [13],[14].

S 4. Equilibrium states.

In this section equilibrium states on $\Omega = s'(Z^d)\oplus s'(Z^d)$ will be considered. Linearity of the dynamical system implies that such states are Gaussian measures on Ω.

Ω is a nuclear space. According to Minlos' Theorem, a Gaussian measure on Ω is defined by a continuous, bilinear, positive-definite form Q on $\Omega' \times \Omega'$. Q is called the covariance matrix. Note that $\Omega' = s(Z^d) \oplus s(Z^d)$.

A covariance matrix of the form $Q = Q^{(1)} \oplus Q^{(2)}$ generates a product measure P on the space $\Omega = s'(Z^d) \oplus s'(Z^d)$. For P to be the Gibbs measure of the infinite harmonic crystal at the inverse temperature $\beta > 0$, $Q^{(1)}$ and $Q^{(2)}$ should be such that

$$Q^{(1)}(e_j, e_k) = (\kappa\beta)^{-1} \langle e_j, -\Delta^{-1} e_k \rangle \tag{4.1}$$

$$Q^{(2)}(e_j, e_k) = (\beta m_j)^{-1} \delta_{jk} . \tag{4.2}$$

However, $\langle e_j, -\Delta^{-1} e_k \rangle = (2\pi)^{-d} \int_{-\pi}^{\pi} \cdots \int_{-\pi}^{\pi} e^{i(k-j)\cdot\theta} \psi(\theta)^{-2} \, d\theta_1 \ldots d\theta_d$

diverges for $d = 1,2$ and converges for $d \geq 3$.

Since for $\xi \in s(Z^d)$

$$(2\pi)^{-d} \int_{-\pi}^{\pi} \cdots \int_{-\pi}^{\pi} |\hat{\xi}(\theta)|^2 \psi(\theta)^{-2} \, d\theta_1 \ldots d\theta_d \tag{4.3}$$

is finite for $d=1,2$ only when $\hat{\xi}(0) = 0$, we define for $d=1,2$

$$Q_0^{(1)}(\xi,\xi) = (\kappa\beta)^{-1} (2\pi)^{-d} \int_{-\pi}^{\pi} \cdots \int_{-\pi}^{\pi} |\hat{\xi}(\theta) - \hat{\xi}(0)|^2 \psi(\theta)^{-2} \, d\theta_1 \ldots d\theta_d . \tag{4.4}$$

Notice that with this definition we have:

$$Q_0^{(1)}(e_j, e_k) = (\kappa\beta)^{-1} \langle e_j - e_0, -\Delta^{-1}(e_k - e_0) \rangle \tag{4.5}$$

$\langle \cdot , \cdot \rangle$ in (4.5) is understood in the sense of the duality between $e_j - e_0 \in s(Z^d)$ and $-\Delta^{-1}(e_k - e_0) \in s'(Z^d)$.

The quadratic form $Q_0^{(1)}$ defined by (4.4) extends to a positive definite continuous bilinear form on $s(Z^d) \times s(Z^d)$.

The condition $\inf\{m_j\} > 0$ guarantees that

$$Q^{(2)}(\xi,\eta) = \beta^{-1} \langle \xi, M^{-1} \eta \rangle \tag{4.6}$$

is also a positive definite continuous bilinear form on $s(Z^d) \times s(Z^d)$.

Then Q_0 given by

$$Q_0 = Q_0^{(1)} \oplus Q^{(2)} \tag{4.7}$$

defines the measure $\mathbf{P}_0$ on Ω. We call $\mathbf{P}_0$ Palm-Gibbs measure: it is the conditional "equilibrium measure" for the flow T_t given the position of the test particle at the origin. Note that for d=1, $Q_0^{(1)}(e_k,e_j) = \min(|k|, |j|)$ which is the covariance of the Wiener process at integer times.

Of course, the definition of the Palm measure is valid for d=3, but in this case we can also consider the Gibbs measure $\hat{\mathbf{P}}$ characterized by the covariance matrix $Q = Q^{(1)} \oplus Q^{(2)}$ where $Q^{(1)}$ is given by

$$Q^{(1)}(\xi,\eta) = (\kappa\beta)^{-1} \langle \xi, -\Delta^{-1}\eta \rangle \tag{4.8}$$

and $Q^{(2)}$ is given by (4.6).

§ 5. The dynamical system.

When the initial conditions (x,v) are distributed in Ω according to the measure $\mathbf{P}$ (Palm-Gibbs for d=1,2,3 or Gibbs for d≥3), the solution of the equation of motion (1.5) or (1.10) becomes a stochastic process $(x(t),v(t))$ on the probability space $(\Omega, \mathcal{B}(\Omega), \mathbf{P})$. Let $\mathbf{E}_0$ $(\hat{\mathbf{E}})$ denote the expectation with respect to $\mathbf{P}_0$ $(\hat{\mathbf{P}})$. Then for Palm-Gibbs distributed initial conditions $(\{x_i\},\{v_i\}) \in \Omega$ we have:

$$\mathbf{E}_0(x_i x_j) = (\kappa\beta)^{-1} \langle e_i - e_0, -\Delta^{-1}(e_j - e_0)\rangle \tag{5.1}$$

$$\mathbf{E}_0(v_i v_j) = (\beta m_j)^{-1} \delta_{ij}. \tag{5.2}$$

$$\mathbf{E}_0(x_i v_j) = 0 \text{ for all } i,j \in \mathbf{Z}^d. \tag{5.3}$$

For $\hat{\mathbf{E}}$ (d≥3), the right-hand side of (5.1) becomes $(\kappa\beta)^{-1} \langle e_i, -\Delta^{-1} e_j \rangle$.

The solution of (1.5) with Gibbs distributed initial conditions (d≥3) is a stationary Gaussian process $(x(t),v(t))$ on $(\Omega, \mathcal{B}(\Omega), \hat{\mathbf{P}})$.

If the initial conditions for (1.5) are distributed according to the Palm-Gibbs measure, then the process $(x(t),v(t))$ on $(\Omega, \mathcal{B}(\Omega), \mathbf{P}_0)$ is Gaussian, but the position process $x(t)$ is not anymore stationary. However, the velocity process still is. This fact turns out to be a direct consequence of the translation invariance of the system:

Theorem 1.4. Let $(x(t),v(t))$ be the solution of (1.5) with the initial conditions distributed according to the Palm-Gibbs measure. Then $v(t)$ is a stationary process.

Proof. Since the stationarity of the process $p(t) = \mathbf{M}^{-1/2}v(t)$ implies the stationarity of the process $v(t)$, it is sufficient to prove that for $i,j \in \mathbf{Z}^d$, $E_0(p_i(t)p_j(s))$ is a function of $(t-s)$. From (2.6)

$$(5.4) \qquad E_0(p_i(t)p_j(s)) = \sum_k\sum_n a_{ik}(t)a_{jn}(s)E_0(p_kp_n) + \sum_k\sum_n \dot{a}_{ik}(t)\dot{a}_{jn}(s)E_0(q_kq_n).$$

From (5.2) $E_0(p_kp_n) = (\beta)^{-1}\delta_{kn}$. (2.7) and the Parseval identity give:

$$\sum_k\sum_n a_{ik}(t)a_{jn}(s)E_0(p_kp_n) = (\beta)^{-1}\langle e_i, \cos(A^{1/2}t)\cos(A^{1/2}s)\, e_j\rangle.$$

Letting $v_j=0$ and $x_j=1$ for all $j\in\mathbf{Z}^d$ in (2.10), yield: $v_i(t) = \sum_j (m_i)^{-1/2}(m_j)^{1/2}\dot{a}_{ij}(t)$. Translation invariance implies: $v_i(t) = 0$ for all t and all $i \in \mathbf{Z}^d$, hence

$$(5.5) \qquad \sum_j \dot{a}_{ij}(t)\,(m_j)^{1/2} = 0.$$

From (5.1), $E_0(q_kq_n) = (\beta)^{-1}\langle e_k - (m_k/m_0)^{1/2}e_0, A^{-1}(e_n-(m_n/m_0)^{1/2}e_0)\rangle$.

(5.5) yields:

$$\sum_k\sum_n \dot{a}_{ik}(t)\dot{a}_{jn}(s)E_0(q_kq_n) = (\beta)^{-1}\sum_k\sum_n \dot{a}_{ik}(t)\dot{a}_{jn}(s)\langle e_k, A^{-1}(e_n-(m_n/m_0)^{1/2}e_0)\rangle$$

$$-(\beta)^{-1}\sum_n \dot{a}_{jn}(s)\langle e_0, A^{-1}(e_n-(m_n/m_0)^{1/2}e_0)\rangle \sum_k \dot{a}_{ik}(t)(m_k/m_0)^{1/2}$$

$$= (\beta)^{-1}\sum_n \dot{a}_{jn}(s)\sum_k \dot{a}_{ik}(t)\langle e_k, A^{-1}(e_n-(m_n/m_0)^{1/2}e_0)\rangle.$$

Using (2.7), the Parseval identity and (5.5) we obtain: $\sum_k\sum_n \dot{a}_{ik}(t)\dot{a}_{jn}(s)E_0(q_kq_n)$ $= (\beta)^{-1}\langle e_i, \sin(A^{1/2}t)\sin(A^{1/2}s)\, e_j\rangle$. Finally,

$$(5.6) \qquad E_0(p_i(t)p_j(s)) = (\beta)^{-1}\, a_{ij}(t-s). \qquad \blacksquare$$

It follows immediately from (5.6) that the covariance matrix of the velocity process $v(t)$ is

$$(5.7) \qquad E_0(v_i(t)v_j(s)) = (\beta)^{-1}(m_im_j)^{-1/2}a_{ij}(t-s).$$

Remark. $(\Omega, \mathrm{B}(\Omega), \mathrm{P}, T_t)$ is isomorphic to a dynamical system. For the distribution of masses considered in Theorem 1.3 with M sufficiently small, the system is not ergodic: an isoloted mode appears in the spectrum of the dynamical matrix (for $d=1$ this mode is given by (3.5)). In case $M \geq m$ the operator A has Lebesgue spectrum, and thus the flow T_t is a Bernoulli flow.

PART 2. THE TP MOTION.

S 6. The TP stochastic process.

The zero component of the stochastic process $(\underline{x}(t),\underline{v}(t))$ with initial conditions $(\underline{x}_i,\underline{v}_i)\in\Omega$ distributed according to the Palm measure $\mathbf{P}_0$,

$$(\underline{x}_0(t),\underline{v}_0(t))_{t\geq 0} \equiv (\underline{X}(t),\underline{V}(t))_{t\geq 0} \equiv(\underline{X},\underline{V})$$

is the tp process, with values in $\mathbb{R}^d$, realized on the probability space $(\Omega, \mathbf{B}(\Omega),\mathbf{P}_0)$.

Remark. Since the dynamics given by (1.2) does not couple different directions, the components of $(\underline{X}(t),\underline{V}(t))_{t\geq 0}$ are i.i.d. random variables and therefore, without loss of generality, we can consider only one space component of the tp process, $(x_0(t),v_0(t))_{t\geq 0} \equiv (X(t),V(t))_{t\geq 0} \equiv(X,V)$. In what follows all the statements will be made only for one component of $(\underline{X}(t),\underline{V}(t))_{t\geq 0}$, and the the subscript of the component will be omitted.

The path space of (X,V) is $C(0,\infty)$, the space of continuous functions on the positive real axis. By (2.10), with $\mathbf{M}$ given by $m_i=m$ for all $i\neq 0$ and $m_0 = M$,

$$X(t) = \sum_j M^{-1/2}m_j^{1/2}a_{0j}(t)x_j + \sum_j M^{-1/2}m_j^{1/2}b_{0j}(t)v_j, \tag{6.1}$$

$$V(t) = \sum_j M^{-1/2}m_j^{1/2}\dot{a}_{0j}(t)x_j + \sum_j M^{-1/2}m_j^{1/2}a_{0j}(t)v_j, \tag{6.2}$$

and, of course, under $\mathbf{P}_0$,

$$X(t) = \int_0^t V(s)\, ds \tag{6.3}$$

In S 5 we showed that $V(t)$ is stationary and from (5.7),

$$E_0(V(t)V(s)) = (\beta M)^{-1}\, a_{00}(t-s) \equiv (\beta M)^{-1}a(t-s). \tag{6.4}$$

The function $(\beta M)^{-1}a(t)$ is the velocity autocorrelation function of the tp.

By (6.3) and (6.4),

$$E_0(X(t)X(s)) = (\beta M)^{-1}[c(t) + c(s) - c(|t-s|)] \tag{6.5}$$

where

$$c(t) = \int_0^t ds \int_0^s du\, a(u) \tag{6.6}$$

and

(6.7) $\quad E_0(X(t)Y(s)) = (\beta M)^{-1}\{b(s) + \mathrm{sign}(t-s)b(|t-s|)\}$

where

(6.8) $$b(t) = \int_0^t du\, a(u)$$

We shall prove weak convergence of the processes X and Y scaled with a parameter A on compact intervals [0,T]. Henceforth,

$$Y_A \Rightarrow Y^*$$

means that the family of measures induced by Y_A on C[0,T], T < ∞, converges weakly to the measure induced by the limit process Y* on C[0,T] as A→∞.

Abusing slightly the notation, we shall call a family of processes $\{Y_A\}$: weakly convergent, tight, etc., if such is true for the induced measures on the path space.

S 7. Some remarks on weak convergence.

We shall mostly be concerned with the weak convergence of continuous Gaussian processes. In the proof of such results only the key point will be shown. The complete theorem will then follow, by observing the remarks below.

Let $\{Y_A\}$ be a family indexed by A of $\mathbb{R}$-valued centered Gaussian processes with continuous paths.

Remarks.

1. Tightness in C[0,T].

The family $\{Y_A\}$ is tight (i.e., the family of measures on C[0,T], induced by $\{Y_A\}$ is tight), if for all t,s ∈ [0,T]

(7.1) $$E((Y_A(t) - Y_A(s))^2) \le \text{Const.}|t-s|^\gamma$$

for some Const. > 0, $\gamma > 0$ and all A large enough.

Suppose that Y_A is stationary with $E(Y_A{}^2) = 1$. Then (7.1) is equivalent to

(7.2) $$2(1 - E(Y_A(t)Y_A(0))) \le \text{Const.}\, t^\gamma.$$

But

$$|1-E(Y_A(t)Y_A(0)| = \left|\int_0^t \frac{d}{ds}E(Y_A(s)Y_A(0)ds\right| \le \int_0^t \left|\frac{d}{ds}E(Y_A(s)Y_A(0)\right|ds \le \frac{\text{Const.}}{2}t$$

if

(7.3) $$\left|\frac{d}{ds}E(Y_A(s)Y_A(0)\right| \le \frac{\text{Const.}}{2}$$

Hence (7.3) implies tightness.

Let

(7.4) $$Q_A(t) = \int_0^t Y_A(s)\,ds .$$

Then $\{Q_A\}$ is tight, if $\{Y_A\}$ is tight, since the mapping $Y_A \to Q_A$ is continuous.

Suppose that Y_A is stationary and (7.4) holds. Then $\{Q_A\}$ is tight if for all $t \in [0,T]$ and some Const. > 0, $\gamma > 0$, and all A large enough

$$\left| \int_0^t ds \int_0^s du\; E(Y_A(u)Y_A(0)) \right| \le \text{Const.}\, t^{\gamma}$$

This is easy: apply (7.1) to Q_A and use (7.4).

2. Weak convergence.

Suppose $\{Y_A\}$ is tight. To prove weak convergence of Y_A to a Gaussian limit Y^* it is enough to check

(7.5) $$E(Y_A(t)Y_A(s)) \underset{A\to\infty}{\to} E(Y^*(t)\,Y^*(s)) \quad \text{pointwise.}$$

Suppose Y_A is stationary, then (7.5) is equivalent to

(7.6) $$E(Y_A(t)Y_A(0)) \underset{A\to\infty}{\to} E(Y^*(t)\,Y^*(0)) \quad \text{pointwise.}$$

Suppose (7.4) holds. Then by continuity

$$Q_A \Rightarrow Q^*, \qquad Q^* = \int_0^t Y^*(s)\,ds ,$$

if (7.5) or (7.6) holds.

Since

$$E(Q_A(t)Y_A(s)) = E\Big(\int_0^t Y_A(u)du\,Y_A(s)\Big) = \int_0^t du\; E(Y_A(u))Y_A(s)) \underset{A\to\infty}{\longrightarrow}$$

$$\int_0^t du\; E(Y^*(u))Y^*(s)) = E(Q^*(t)Y^*(s))$$

if (7.5) or (7.6) holds, we have that

$$(Q_A, Y_A) \Rightarrow (Q^*, Y^*)$$

if (7.5) or (7.6) holds.

The next section provides the necessary formulae for studying the tp-motion under various scalings. It is now quite clear that we need facts about the velocity autocorrelation function $(\beta M)^{-1}a(t)$.

S 8. The velocity autocorrelation function.

The velocity autocorrelation function of the tp process, $E(V(t)V(0)) = (\beta M)^{-1}a(t)$ can be determined by the spectral analysis of the interaction matrix $\mathcal{A}$. This approach leads directly to the Wiener - Kchinchin representation

$$(8.1) \qquad a(t) = \int_{\sigma(A^{1/2})} \cos\omega t \ \langle e_0, P_{A^{1/2}}(d\omega)e_0\rangle .$$

However, it turns out that a representation in terms of the Laplace transform is more suitable for our purposes.

In this paragraph we summarize the results obtained by Rubin [3], [4], solving the equation of motion by Laplace transform method.

For $m_i=m$, $i\neq 0$ and $m_0=M$, (1.2) can be rewritten as:

$$(8.2) \qquad m\ddot{x}_i(t) = \kappa \sum_{\alpha=1}^{d} (x_{i+e_\alpha}(t) - 2x_i(t) + x_{i-e_\alpha}(t)),$$

$$(8.3) \qquad M\ddot{x}_0(t) = \kappa \sum_{\alpha=1}^{d} (x_{e_\alpha}(t) - 2x_0(t) + x_{-e_\alpha}(t)).$$

Let $\xi(t) = F(x(t)) \in S'([-\pi,\pi]^d)$ be the Fourier transform of $x(t) = \{x_i(t)\} \in S'(\mathbb{Z}^d)$ for each t. The equation for $\xi(t)$ is

$$(8.4) \qquad m\ddot{\xi}(t) = -\kappa\psi(\theta)^2\xi(t) - (M-m)\ddot{x}_0(t),$$

where $\psi(\theta)$ is given by (3.4).

The Laplace transform is well-defined for the periodic distributions:

$$(8.5) \qquad \mathcal{L}(\xi)(\tau) \equiv \tilde{\xi}(\tau) = \int_0^\infty \xi(t)\, e^{-\tau t}\, dt.$$

Performing the Laplace transform for (8.4) yields:

$$(8.6) \qquad \tilde{\xi}(\tau) = \frac{m(\tau\xi(0) + \dot{\xi}(0)) - (M-m)[\tau^2\tilde{x}_0(\tau) - \tau x_0 - v_0]}{m\tau^2 + \kappa\psi(\theta)^2}.$$

Substituting $\xi(0) = \sum_j x_j e^{ij\cdot\theta}$ and $\dot{\xi}(0) = \sum_j v_j e^{ij\cdot\theta}$ in (8.6), recalling that $\tilde{\xi}(\tau) = \sum_k \tilde{x}_k(\tau) e^{ik\cdot\theta}$, and equating the coefficients of $e^{ik\cdot\theta}$ in both sides of (8.6) for k=0 gives:

$$(8.7) \qquad \tilde{x}(\tau) \equiv \tilde{x}_0(\tau) = \sum_j [\tilde{a}_j(\tau)x_j + \tau^{-1}\tilde{a}_j(\tau)v_j]$$

where

$$(8.8)\quad \tilde{a}_j(\tau) = \frac{m\tau I_j(\tau)}{m + (M-m)\tau^2 I_j(\tau)}, \; j\neq 0, \quad \tilde{a}(\tau) \equiv \tilde{a}_0(\tau) = \frac{M\tau I(\tau)}{m + (M-m)\tau^2 I(\tau)}$$

and

$$(8.9)\quad I_j(\tau) = (2\pi)^{-d}\int_{-\pi}^{\pi}\cdots\int_{-\pi}^{\pi} \frac{e^{ij\cdot\theta}}{\tau^2 + \frac{1}{4}\omega_L^2\psi(\theta)^2}\, d\theta_1 \ldots d\theta_d, \quad I(\tau) = I_0(\tau).$$

Comparison with (6.1) leads to:

$$(8.10)\qquad a_{0j}(t) = M^{1/2}m^{-1/2}\mathcal{L}^{-1}[\tilde{a}_j](t), \quad \text{for } j\neq 0,$$

and for j=0

$$(8.11)\qquad a(t) \equiv a_{00}(t) = \mathcal{L}^{-1}[\tilde{a}](t),$$

or explicitly, using the Laplace inversion formula,

$$(8.12)\qquad a(t) = \frac{1}{2\pi i}\int_L \tilde{a}(\tau)\, e^{\tau t}\, d\tau .$$

where L is the vertical line on the complex τ-plane to the right of all the singularities of the integrand. As we shall see, $\tilde{a}(\tau)$ analytically continued to the complex plane, contains singularities of two types: branch points and poles which determine the properties of the function $a(t)$. We shall now list these properties in all three dimensions.

d=1.

In one dimension the calculation of the integral in (8.9) for j=0 gives: $I(\tau) = \tau^{-1}(\tau^2+\omega_L{}^2)^{-1/2}$ and therefore

$$(8.13)\qquad \tilde{a}(\tau) = \frac{M}{m\sqrt{\tau^2+\omega_L^2} + (M-m)\tau}.$$

The function in (8.13) can be analytically continued to the complex τ-plane by choosing the domain $\mathbb{C} \setminus \{\tau \,|\mathrm{Re}\tau=0,\ |\mathrm{Im}\tau| \leq \omega_L\}$. This is achieved defining $(\tau^2+\omega_L{}^2)^{1/2} \equiv \exp \frac{1}{2}[\ln(\tau + i\omega_L)+\ln(\tau - i\omega_L)]$ where the ln has domain $\mathbb{C}\setminus\{\mathrm{Re}\tau=0,\ \mathrm{Im}\tau\geq 0\}$ and range $\mathbb{R} \times (-3\pi/2, \pi/2)$.

For M<m, $\tilde{a}(\tau)$ has poles at $\tau=\pm i\omega_0$ where ω_0 is given by (3.5). Deforming L into a contour containing the cut and noticing that $\omega_0 > \omega_L$, (8.12) gives:

$$(8.14)\qquad a(t) = a_{(0)}(t) + \frac{2(m-M)}{2m-M}\cos\omega_0 t ,$$

where the second term is the contribution from the poles and $a_{(0)}(t)$ is the contribution from the integral along the cut:

$$(8.15)\qquad a_{(0)}(t) = \frac{2m}{\pi(2m-M)}\int_0^{\omega_L} \frac{\sqrt{\omega_L^2-\omega^2}}{\omega_0^2-\omega^2}\cos\omega t\, d\omega .$$

For $M=m$, $\tilde{a}(\tau)$ has poles at the branch points $\pm i\omega_L$ and (8.12) gives:

$$(8.16)\qquad a(t) = \frac{2}{\pi}\int_0^{\omega_L} \frac{1}{\sqrt{\omega_L^2 - \omega^2}} \cos \omega t \, d\omega = J_0(\omega_L t).$$

Here J_0 is the Bessel's function of order zero.

For $m < M < 2m$, $\tilde{a}(\tau)$ has two poles $\tau = \pm i\omega_0$ which are inside of the contour containing the cut, since in this case $\omega_0 < \omega_L$, and (8.12) gives:

$$(8.17)\qquad a(t) = a_{(0)}(t)$$

with $a_{(0)}(t)$ given by (8.15).

For $M=2m$, there is only a pole at ∞ and (8.12) gives:

$$(8.18)\qquad a(t) = \frac{2}{\omega_L t} J_1(\omega_L t).$$

Here J_1 is the Bessel's function of order one.

For $M > 2m$, there are no poles and (8.12) gives:

$$(8.19)\qquad a(t) = \frac{2m}{\pi(M-2m)}\int_0^{\omega_L} \frac{\sqrt{\omega_L^2 - \omega^2}}{\omega_0^2 + \omega^2} \cos \omega t \, d\omega .$$

Using the integral representation of J_0, given by (8.16), (8.19) can be rewritten as

$$(8.20)\quad a(t) = -\frac{m}{M-2m} J_0(\omega_L t) + \frac{m}{\pi(M-2m)}\int_{-\omega_L}^{\omega_L} \frac{\omega_L^2 + \omega_0^2}{(\omega_0^2 + \omega^2)\sqrt{\omega_L^2 - \omega^2}} \cos \omega t \, d\omega$$

Remark. The representations for $a(t)$ given above are spectral representations of the form (8.1), where the spectrum and the spectral measure can be read of each representation. These representations give an alternative proof of Theorem 1.3 in the one-dimensional case.

The asymptotic behaviour of $a(t)$ for large t is described in the following lemma:

Lemma 8.1. 1. $a_{(0)}(t) \sim O(t^{-3/2})$; thus, for $M<m$ $a(t)$ is the sum of an absolutely integrable function on $[0,+\infty)$ and an oscillating function;

2. For $M=m$, $a(t) \sim O(t^{-1/2})$; $a(t)$ is integrable on $[0,+\infty)$ but not absolutely integrable;

3. For $M>m$, $a(t) \sim O(t^{-3/2})$ and $a(t)$ is absolutely integrable on $[0,+\infty)$.

Proof. Since each integrand in the above representations of $a(t)$ is an even function, integration can be extended to the symmetric interval $[-\omega_L, \omega_L]$. Then each integral can be viewed as a cosine-Fourier representation:

$a(t)=\int_{-\infty}^{\infty}\hat{a}(\omega)\cos\omega t\,d\omega$ where $\hat{a}(\omega)$ has singularities at the points $\pm\omega_L$. A straightforward application of Lighthill theorem [15], based on the analysis of these singularities, gives the asymptotic behaviour of such integrals. ∎

Remark. Contary to the one-dimensional case, for $d\geq 2$ the singularities of $\tilde{a}(\tau)$ can not be located exactly. However, for M sufficiently large, a uniform approximation for $a(t)$ was obtained by Rubin [3], [4], i.e., $a(t) \doteq a_*(t)$ where $\doteq$ means that $|a(t)-a_*(t)| <$ Const. $O(M^{-1})$ uniformly in t, and the constant in the last estimate depends only on d and on ω_L. $a_*(t)$ is determined only by the singularities of $\tilde{a}(\tau)$ around $\tau=0$.

d=2.

In two dimensions the calculation of the integral in (8.9) for j=0 gives [16]:

$$I(\tau) = \frac{2}{\pi(\tau^2+\omega_L^2)}\, K\left(\frac{\omega_L^2}{\tau^2+\omega_L^2}\right), \tag{8.21}$$

where $K(u)$ is the complete elliptic integral $K(u)=\int_0^1[(1-t^2)(1-u^2t^2)]^{-1/2}\,dt$. Using the relation $K(u)=\frac{1}{2}\pi\, F(\frac{1}{2},\frac{1}{2};1;u^2)$ where F is the hypergeometric function, $I(\tau)$ can be written as:

$$I(\tau) = \frac{1}{\tau^2+\omega_L^2}\, F\left(\tfrac{1}{2},\tfrac{1}{2};1;\left(\frac{\omega_L^2}{\tau^2+\omega_L^2}\right)^2\right). \tag{8.22}$$

Then the expression for $\tilde{a}(\tau)$ becomes:

$$\tilde{a}(\tau) = \frac{\tau M}{m(\tau^2+\omega_L^2)F^{-1}\left(\tfrac{1}{2},\tfrac{1}{2};1;\left(\frac{\omega_L^2}{\tau^2+\omega_L^2}\right)^2\right)+(M-m)\tau^2}. \tag{8.23}$$

The hypergeometric function $F(\frac{1}{2},\frac{1}{2};1;z)$ has singularities at $z = 1, +\infty$ (branch points) and can be analytically continued to the z-complex plane with the domain $\mathbb{C}\setminus[1,+\infty)$ and therefore $\tilde{a}(\tau)$ has branch points at $\tau=0$, $\tau=\pm i\omega_L$, $\tau=\pm\sqrt{2}\,i\omega_L$. The poles of $\tilde{a}(\tau)$, i.e., the zeros of the denominator in (8.23) can be determined only approximately. For M sufficiently large, the only possible poles are located near $\tau=0$ and can be written as $\tau_\pm = \varepsilon(M)\,\omega_L \exp[\pm i(\frac{1}{2}\pi+\delta(M))]$ where $\varepsilon(M)$ and $\delta(M)$ are such that

$$\lim_{M\to\infty} M\,\varepsilon^2(M)\,|\ln\varepsilon(M)| = \text{Const.}\,; \tag{8.24}$$

$$\lim_{M\to\infty} \delta(M)\,|\ln\varepsilon(M)| = \text{Const.} \tag{8.25}$$

Then, using the asymptotic expression for the hypergeometric function, the uniform approximation for a(t) obtained in [3] with a proper choice of a cut in the complex τ-plane is

$$(8.26)\qquad a(t) \doteq a_{(0)}(t) +$$

$$\exp(-\omega_L \varepsilon(M) t \sin\delta(M)) \frac{\cos(\omega_L \varepsilon(M) t \cos\delta(M)) - m^{-1} M \varepsilon^2(M) \pi^{-1} \cos(\omega_L \varepsilon(M) t \cos\delta(M) - \delta(M))}{1 - 2m^{-1} M \varepsilon^2(M) \pi^{-1} \cos\delta(M) + (m^{-1} M \varepsilon^2(M) \pi^{-1})^2}$$

where the second term is the contribution from the poles and $a_{(0)}(t)$ is the contribution from the integral along the cut:

$$(8.27)\qquad a_{(0)}(t) = -\frac{2M}{\pi m} \int_0^1 \frac{y e^{-\omega_L t y}}{[1 + m^{-1} M y^2 \pi^{-1} \ln(8/y^2)]^2 + 4m^{-2} M^2 y^4}\, dy .$$

The asymptotic behaviour in t of $a_{(0)}(t)$ is

$$(8.28)\qquad a_{(0)}(t) \sim M[\tfrac{1}{2}\pi m \omega_L{}^2 t^2]^{-1}.$$

The corresponding expression for c(t) defined by (6.6) is

$$(8.29)\qquad c(t) = c_{(0)}(t) -$$

$$-\frac{\exp(-\omega_L \varepsilon(M) t \sin\delta(M))}{\omega_L^2 \varepsilon^2(M)} \cdot \frac{\cos(\omega_L \varepsilon(M) t \cos\delta(M) - 2\delta(M)) - m^{-1} M \varepsilon^2(M) \pi^{-1} \cos(\omega_L \varepsilon(M) t \cos\delta(M) - 3\delta(M))}{1 - 2m^{-1} M \varepsilon^2(M) \pi^{-1} \cos\delta(M) + (m^{-1} M \varepsilon^2(M) \pi^{-1})^2}$$

where the asymptotic behaviour in t of $c_{(0)}(t)$ is

$$(8.30)\qquad c_{(0)}(t) \sim M[\pi m \omega_L{}^2]^{-1} \ln(\omega_L t).$$

d=3.

In three dimensions calculation of the integral $I(\tau)$ gives [16]:

$$(8.31)\qquad I(\tau) = \frac{2}{\omega_L^2} \cdot \frac{1}{\pi^2} \int_0^{\pi} \frac{2}{q(\theta,\tau)} K\left(\frac{2}{q(\theta,\tau)}\right) d\theta ,$$

where $q(\theta,\tau) = \dfrac{2\tau^2}{\omega_L^2} + 3 - \cos\theta$.

Then the formula for $\tilde{a}(\tau)$ becomes:

$$(8.32)\qquad \tilde{a}(\tau) = \frac{\tau M}{\tfrac{1}{2} m \pi^2 \omega_L^2 \left[\int_0^{\pi} \frac{2}{q(\theta,\tau)} K\left(\frac{2}{q(\theta,\tau)}\right) d\theta\right]^{-1} + (M-m)\tau^2} .$$

It is shown in [16] that $I(\tau)$ is analytic at $\tau = 0$, i.e., it is not a branch point contrary to the two-dimensional case, and the first two terms of the Taylor's expansion for $I(\tau)$ are

$$(8.33)\qquad I(\tau) = \omega_l{}^{-2}\{\zeta_0 - (\tfrac{1}{2}\omega_l \pi)^{-1}\tau + \ldots\}$$

where $\zeta_0 = \omega_L{}^2 I(0) = 1.019...$ and

$$(8.34)\quad I(0) = \frac{4}{\omega_L^2}(2\pi)^{-3}\int_{-\pi}^{\pi}\int_{-\pi}^{\pi}\int_{-\pi}^{\pi}\frac{d\theta_1\, d\theta_2\, d\theta_3}{\psi(\theta)^2} = \frac{4}{\omega_L^2}\langle e_0, -\Delta^{-1} e_0\rangle.$$

Since $\tilde{a}(\tau)$ is analytic in the neighborhood of $\tau=0$, the uniform approximation of $a(t)$ is determined by the poles of $\tilde{a}(\tau)$ located near $\tau=0$. The denominator in (8.32) has two zeros which can be written as $\tau_{\pm} = \omega(M)\exp[\pm i(\tfrac{1}{2}\pi + \delta(M))]$ where for M sufficiently large the uniform approximation for $\omega(M)$ and $\delta(M)$ is given by

$$(8.35)\qquad \omega(M) \doteq \omega M^{-1/2}; \qquad \delta(M) \doteq \pi^{-1}\zeta_0{}^{-3/2}(M/m)^{-1/2},$$

where $\omega = 2(\kappa/\zeta_0)^{1/2}$.

Then $a(t) = \mathrm{Res}(\tau_+) + \mathrm{Res}(\tau_-) + O(A^{-1})$ and the uniform approximation of $a(t)$ obtained by using (8.35) becomes:

$$(8.36)\quad a(t) \doteq e^{-\frac{2}{\pi}(\kappa m)^{1/2}\zeta_0^{-2}M^{-1}t}\left[\cos \omega M^{-1/2}t - (m^{1/2}\pi^{-1}\zeta_0^{-3/2})M^{-1/2}\sin \omega M^{-1/2}t\right].$$

Here the relation $\omega_L = 2(\kappa/m)^{1/2}$ has been used.

§ 9. The heavy mass limit in one dimension.

In one dimension the motion of the tp with sufficiently large mass considered on a macroscopic scale is well approximated by the Ornstein-Uhlenbeck process. The meaning of this statement is made precise in what follows.

Let $(X,V) \equiv (X(t),V(t))_{t\geq 0}$ be the tp process in one dimension. Let

$$M = AM^*$$

$$(9.1)\qquad V_A(t) = A^{1/2}V(At)$$

$$X_A(t) = A^{-1/2}X(At)$$

where M^* is a unit of mass.

Theorem 9.1. Let (X^*,V^*) be given by

$$dX^*(t) = V^*(t)dt$$

$$dV^*(t) = -\gamma V^*(t)dt + \sigma\, dW(t)$$

with $X^*(0) = 0$ and $E(V^*(0)^2) = (\beta M^*)^{-1}$; here

$$\gamma = \frac{m\omega_L}{M^*}, \qquad \sigma = \frac{1}{M^*}\sqrt{\frac{2m\omega_L}{\beta}}$$

and $W(t)$ is the standard Wiener process. Then

$$(X_A, V_A) \Rightarrow (X^*, V^*).$$

Proof. Since M^* is a unit of mass, without loss of generality we assume $M^*=1$ (M^* can be reintroduced into the final formulae by dimensional considerations).

To prove tightness, we verify (7.3) for

$$E_0(V_A(t)V_A(0)) = A\,E_0(V(At)V(0)) = A(\beta A^{-1})a(At) = \beta^{-1}a(At),$$

i.e., we have to prove: $|A\dot{a}(At)| \le$ Const. Using (8.20)

$$a(At) = -\frac{m}{A-2m} J_0(\omega_L At) + \frac{m}{\pi(A-2m)} \int_{-\omega_L}^{\omega_L} \frac{\omega_L^2 + \omega_0^2(A)}{(\omega_0^2(A)+\omega^2)\sqrt{\omega_L^2-\omega^2}} \cos\omega At\, d\omega$$

where $\omega_0^2(A) = \dfrac{\omega_L^2 m^2}{A(A-2m)}$. Therefore

$$\left|A\dot{a}(At)\right| \le \left|\frac{Am\omega_L}{A-2m} J_0(\omega_L At)\right| + \left|\frac{m}{\pi(A-2m)} \int_{-\omega_L}^{\omega_L} \frac{\omega_L^2+\omega_0^2(A)}{(\omega_0^2(A)+\omega^2)\sqrt{\omega_L^2-\omega^2}}\, \omega \sin\omega At\, d\omega\right|$$

$$\le \text{Const.} + \left|\frac{m}{\pi(A-2m)} \int_{-\omega_L}^{\omega_L} \frac{\omega_L^2+\omega_0^2(A)}{(\omega_0^2(A)+\omega^2)\sqrt{\omega_L^2-\omega^2}}\, \omega\, d\omega\right| \le \text{Const.}$$

Since $E(V^*(t)V^*(0)) = \beta^{-1} e^{-m\omega_L t}$ (with $M^*=1$) we need to prove pointwise convergence of $a(At)$ to $e^{-m\omega_L t}$. Using the Fourier representation of $e^{-m\omega_L t}$, we have:

$$\left|a(At) - e^{-m\omega_L t}\right| \le O(A^{-1}) +$$

$$\left|\frac{m}{\pi(A-2m)} \int_{-\omega_L}^{\omega_L} \frac{\omega_L^2+\omega_0^2(A)}{(\omega_0^2(A)+\omega^2)\sqrt{\omega_L^2-\omega^2}} \cos\omega At\, d\omega - \frac{m}{\pi}\int_{-\infty}^{+\infty} \frac{\omega_L}{m^2\omega_L^2+\omega^2} \cos\omega t\, d\omega\right|$$

Using the expression for $\omega_0^2(A)$ and performing the substitution $\omega \to \omega/A$ in the first integral, standard estimate shows that the term under the sign of absolute value is also of order A^{-1}.

Invoking the remarks of S 7, the complete proof of the theorem follows. ∎

S 10. Long time behaviour of tp in one dimension.

The scaled position process of the tp:

(10.1) $$X_A(t) = A^{-1/2}X(At)$$

for any value of the mass M converges to a Wiener process with the diffusion constant independent of M.

Theorem 10.1. Let W(t) be the standard Wiener process and

(10.2) $$D = \frac{2}{\beta m\omega_L} = \frac{1}{\beta\sqrt{mK}} .$$

Then

$$X_A \Rightarrow D^{1/2} W.$$

Proof. From (6.5) we have:

(10.3) $$E_0(X_A(t)X_A(s)) = (\beta M)^{-1}A^{-1}\{c(At) + c(As) - c(A|t-s|)\}.$$

It follows from the Remark 1 of S 7 that in order to prove tightness, it is sufficient to show:

(10.4) $$A^{-1}c(At) \le \text{Const. } t$$

for some Const. > 0 and A large enough.

We consider the three cases:

(i) M > m:

$$A^{-1}c(At) = A^{-1}\int_0^{At} du \int_0^u a(v)\, dv = \int_0^t du \int_0^{Au} a(v)\, dv \le \int_0^t du \int_0^{Au} |a(v)|\, dv \le t\int_0^\infty |a(v)|\, dv = \|a\|_1\, t.$$

In the last step we used the fact that for M > m, $\|a\|_1 = \int_0^\infty |a(v)|\, dv < \infty$, since $|a(t)| \sim \text{Const. } t^{-3/2}$ for large t (Lemma 8.1).

(ii) M = m. To prove (10.4), it is sufficient to prove that |c(t)| is bounded. From (8.16)

$$|c(t)| = \left|\int_0^t J_0(\omega_L u) du\right|,$$

which is bounded since it is a continuous function of t, having value zero in 0 and converging to ω_L^{-1} as $t \to \infty$.

(iii). M < m. From (8.14),

$$c(t) = \int_0^t du \int_0^u a_{(0)}(v)dv + \frac{2(m-M)}{2m-M} \cdot \frac{1-\cos\omega_0 t}{\omega_0^2} .$$

Since $a_{(0)}(t)$ is an absolutely integrable function, $A^{-1}c(At) \le \text{Const. } t + O(A^{-1})$ and (10.4) follows.

Now we check pointwise convergence. For M > m and M < m

(10.5) $$\lim_{A\to\infty} A^{-1} c(At) = t\int_0^\infty a(u)\, du = tM\,(m\omega_L)^{-1}$$

easily follows from the absolute integrability of $a(t)$ and $a_{(0)}(t)$.

For $M = m$ (10.5) also holds. Indeed, observing that

$$\frac{1}{\pi}\int_{-\infty}^{\infty}\frac{1-\cos\omega t}{\omega^2}\,d\omega = |t| = t, \qquad \text{for } t > 0,$$

we have

$$\left|\frac{1}{A}\int_{-\omega_L}^{\omega_L}\frac{1}{\sqrt{\omega_L^2-\omega^2}}\;\frac{1-\cos\omega At}{\omega^2}\,d\omega - \frac{1}{\omega_L}\int_{-\infty}^{\infty}\frac{1-\cos\omega t}{\omega^2}\,d\omega\right| \le$$

$$\frac{\text{Const.}}{A} + \left|\int_{-\omega_L A}^{\omega_L A}\frac{1-\cos\omega t}{\omega^2}\left(\frac{1}{\sqrt{\omega_L^2-A^{-2}\omega^2}} - \frac{1}{\omega_L}\right)d\omega\right| \le$$

$$\frac{\text{Const.}}{A} + \left|\int_{-\omega_L A}^{\omega_L A}\frac{1-\cos\omega t}{\omega^2}\;\frac{A^{-2}\omega^2}{\omega_L\sqrt{\omega_L^2-A^{-2}\omega^2}\,(\omega_L+\sqrt{\omega_L^2-A^{-2}\omega^2})}\,d\omega\right| \le$$

$$\frac{\text{Const.}}{A} + \left|\int_{-\omega_L}^{\omega_L}\frac{2}{A\omega_L^2}\;\frac{d\omega}{\sqrt{\omega_L^2-\omega^2}}\right| \le \frac{\text{Const.}}{A}\,.$$

Finally, from (10.3) and (10.5):

$$\lim_{A\to\infty} E_0(X_A(t)X_A(s)) = 2(\beta m\omega_L)^{-1}\min(t,s) \equiv D\min(t,s).$$

∎

S 11. Einstein relation and Smoluchowski equation.

In the last section we showed that the scaled position $A^{-1/2}X(At)$ of the tp for any finite value of the mass behaves like a Wiener process with diffusion constant D given by (10.2). Suppose now that tp is charged and subjected to a "small" electric field. Then in the diffusive scaling one expects that the tp acquires a mean velocity νf, ν denoting the mobility and f the force due to the electric field. Furthermore, one expects that the famous Einstein relation holds ([7],[17]):

(11.1) $$\nu = \tfrac{1}{2}\beta D.$$

More generally, suppose that the tp is subjected to an external potential $U_A(x) = U(A^{-1/2}x)$, $x\in\mathbb{R}$, which varies on the "macroscopic" scale. Then

$$F_A(x) = -\nabla_x U(A^{-1/2}x) = A^{-1/2}F(A^{-1/2}x)$$

is the force $f(x)$ acting on the tp.

In this situation we expect that the position process of the tp

$$Z_A(t) = A^{-1/2}Z(At)$$

in the diffusive scaling converges as $A\to\infty$ to a Smoluchowski diffusion process with drift νF and diffusion constant D [18]. Thus "small" above means $\sim A^{-1/2}$.

The Einstein relation (weak constant force) is the content of Theorem 11.1 of this paragraph and Smoluchowski equation (slowly varying potential) is described in Theorem 11.2. That we state two theorems has technical reasons (which we refer to in the proofs); the Einstein relation holds generally, whereas for Smoluchowski equation we need $M > m$.

The motion of the system, when the tp is subject to an external force f is described in Theorem 1.2. We obtain from (2.11) and (6.1) for the position of the tp (henceforth denoted by $Z(t)$):

$$(11.2) \qquad Z(t) = X(t) + M^{-1}\int_0^t du \int_0^u dv\, a(u-v)\, f(Z(v))$$

Theorem 11.1. Let $F_A(x) = A^{-1/2}F$, F a constant. Then

$$Z_A \Rightarrow Z^*, \quad Z^*(t) = \nu F t + D^{1/2} W(t)$$

with $\nu = \frac{1}{2}\beta D$ (Einstein relation), $D = 2(\beta m\omega_L)^{-1}$, where $Z(t)$ is the solution of (11.2) with $f \equiv F_A$.

Remark. Note that $D = \sigma^2/\gamma^2$, where γ is the friction and σ^2 is the diffusion coefficient in the Ornstein-Uhlenbeck process (Theorem 9.1). Furthermore, $\nu = (\gamma M^*)^{-1} = (m\omega_L)^{-1}$.

Proof. In the harmonic system the Einstein relation appears in a trivial way: look at (11.2) and from (10.5)

$$(11.3) \qquad \lim_{t\to\infty} \frac{c(t)}{t} = M(m\omega_L)^{-1} = \tfrac{1}{2}\beta M D = \nu M$$

moreover,

$$c(t) = \int_0^t du \int_0^u dv\, a(u-v).$$

Thus $Z_A(t) = X_A(t) + M^{-1} F A^{-1} c(At)$. Since by Theorem 10.1, $X_A \Rightarrow D^{1/2}W$, the theorem follows by virtue of (11.3) using standard weak convergence arguments [19]. ∎

Theorem 11.2. Let $F_A(x) = A^{-1/2}F(A^{-1/2}x)$, where $F(x)$ is a bounded Lipschitz continuous function with Lipschitz constant L ($\geq \sup F(x); x \in \mathbb{R}$).

If $M > m$, $Z_A \Rightarrow Z^*$, where Z^* is the solution of the stochastic differential equation

$$dy(t) = \nu\, F(y(t))\, dt + D^{1/2}\, dW(t), \qquad y(0) = 0;$$

ν, D as in Theorem 11.1, and $Z_A(t) = A^{-1/2} Z(At)$, $Z(t)$ being solution of (11.2) with $f(x) \equiv F_A(x)$.

Proof. We shall use the fact that for $M > m$, $||a||_1 = \int_0^\infty |a(t)|dt < \infty$ (Lemma 8.1). Recall that in this case

$$\lim_{t\to\infty} \frac{c(t)}{t} = \int_0^\infty a(t)dt = \nu M.$$

Consider the map G: $C[0,T] \to C[0,T]$ given by

$$G(\xi)(t) = \xi(t) - \nu\int_0^t F(\xi(s))ds, \qquad \xi\in C[0,T]$$

Since F is globally Lipschitz, the inverse mapping G^{-1} is continuous (see, e.g. [20], Theorem 2). Therefore, the family of processes $\hat{Z}_A = G^{-1}(X_A)$, i.e.,

$$\hat{Z}_A(t) = X_A(t) + \int_0^t F(\hat{Z}_A(s))ds, \qquad \hat{Z}_A(0) = 0$$

converges weakly to Z^* by Theorem (5.1) of [19].

By Skhorohod's embedding [21] there exists a probability space allowing for simultaneous representation of the family ($\hat{Z}_A, Z^*$) such that for these versions $\hat{Z}_A$ converges almost surely to Z^*. We shall use the same notations for these versions.

By (11.2), with $f(x) = A^{-1/2}F(A^{-1/2}x)$,

$$Z_A(t) - \hat{Z}_A(t) = \int_0^t du\,[\int_0^u dv\ M^{-1}a_A(u-v)\,F(Z_A(v)) - \nu\,F(\hat{Z}_A(u))]$$

where $a_A(t) \equiv Aa(At)$.

Suppose we can show that for any $\varepsilon > 0$ and A large enough

$$(11.4)\quad I_A \equiv \sup_{t\in[0,T]} \left| \int_0^t du\,[\int_0^u dv\ M^{-1}a_A(u-v)\,F(\hat{Z}_A(v)) - \nu\,F(\hat{Z}_A(u))] \right| < \varepsilon,$$

then for A large enough

$$\varphi_A(T) \equiv \sup_{t\in[0,T]} |Z_A(t) - \hat{Z}_A(t)| \le \sup_{t\in[0,T]} \left| \int_0^t du \int_0^u dv\ M^{-1}a_A(u-v)\,(F(Z_A(v)) - F(\hat{Z}_A(v))] \right| + \varepsilon,$$

or

$$\varphi_A(T) \le \varepsilon + L \sup_{t\in[0,T]} \int_0^t du \sup_{v\in[0,u]} |Z_A(v) - \hat{Z}_A(v)| \int_0^u dv\ M^{-1}|a_A(u-v)|$$

Noting that

$$\int_0^u dv\ M^{-1}|a_A(u-v)| = \int_0^{Au} dv\, M^{-1}|a(v)| \le M^{-1}\,\|a\|_1$$

we obtain

$$\varphi_A(T) \le \varepsilon + L M^{-1}\,\|a\|_1 \int_0^T du\, \varphi_A(u)$$

and therefore by Gronwall's inequality: $\varphi_A(T) \le \varepsilon \exp\,(LM^{-1}\,\|a\|_1 T)$.

Since ε is arbitrary,

$$\lim_{A\to\infty} \varphi_A(T) = 0$$

i.e., for every $\varepsilon > 0$

$$\lim_{A\to\infty} \text{Prob}\,\{\sup_{t\in[0,T]} |Z_A(t) - \hat{Z}_A(t)| > \delta\} = 0$$

and since $\hat{Z}_A \Rightarrow Z^*$, the theorem follows by standard weak convergence results [19].

Therefore we need only prove (11.4). Since

$$\lim_{A\to\infty} \hat{Z}_A = Z^* \qquad \text{a.s.}$$

we have that for every $\varepsilon > 0$ and A large enough $\sup_{t\in[0,T]} |\hat{Z}_A(t) - Z^*(t)| < \varepsilon$, and thus

$$\sup_{t\in[0,T]} |F(Z_A(t) - F(Z^*(t))| < L\,\varepsilon\ .$$

Therefore

$$I_A \le \sup_{t\in[0,T]} |\int_0^t du\,[\int_0^u dv\ M^{-1}a_A(u-v)\,F(Z^*(v)) - \nu\,F(Z^*(u))]\,| +$$

$$+ L\,\varepsilon \sup_{t\in[0,T]} |\int_0^t du \int_0^u dv\ |a_A(u-v)|\,| + T\nu L\varepsilon$$

or

$$I_A \le \sup_{t\in[0,T]} |\int_0^t du\,[\int_0^{Au} dv\ M^{-1}a(v)\,g(u - A^{-1}v) - \nu\,g(u)]\,| + T\,L\,\varepsilon\,(\|a\|_1 + \nu)$$

where $g(t) \equiv F(Z^*(t))$ is a bounded continuous function ($\sup g(t) \le L$, $t\in[0,T]$) since $Z^* \in C_0[0,T]$ a.s. and

$g(t) \equiv 0$ for $t < 0$. But

$$\sup_{t\in[0,T]} \left| \int_0^t du \left[\int_0^{Au} dv\; M^{-1}a(v)\, g(u - A^{-1}v) - \nu\, g(u) \right] \right| \le$$

$$\sup_{t\in[0,T]} \int_0^t du \left| \int_0^{\infty} dv\; M^{-1}a(v)\, g(u - A^{-1}v) - \nu\, g(u) \right| \le$$

$$\int_0^T du \left| \int_0^{\infty} dv\; M^{-1}a(v)\, g(u - A^{-1}v) - \nu\, g(u) \right| = \int_0^T du \left| \int_0^{\infty} dv\; M^{-1}a(v)[\, g(u - A^{-1}v) - g(u)] \right|,$$

where we used the fact that $\int_0^{\infty} dv\, M^{-1}a(v) = \nu$. Now,

$$\int_0^T du \left| \int_0^{\infty} dv\; M^{-1}a(v)[\, g(u - A^{-1}v) - g(u)] \right| \le$$

$$2T M^{-1}L \int_B^{\infty} dv|a(v)| + \int_0^T du \left| \int_0^B dv\; M^{-1}a(v)[\, g(u - A^{-1}v) - g(u)] \right|$$

for any finite B. Taking the limit $A\to\infty$ we obtain:

$$\lim_{A\to\infty} \int_0^T du \left| \int_0^{\infty} dv\; M^{-1}a(v)[\, g(u - A^{-1}v) - g(u)] \right| \le 2T M^{-1}L \int_B^{\infty} dv|a(v)|.$$

Since $a(t)$ is absolutely integrable and B is arbitrary, we obtain

$$\lim_{A\to\infty} \int_0^T du \left| \int_0^{\infty} dv\; M^{-1}a(v)[\, g(u - A^{-1}v) - g(u)] \right| = 0.$$

From this (11.4) easily follows. ∎

Remarks.

1. In Theorem 11.2 the condition that F is Lipschitz is purely technical. Moreover, the theorem should also hold for $M \le m$, but in this case $a(t)$ is not absolutely integrable and a proof would require a fine analysis of oscillatory integrals.

2. A natural problem is to study (11.2) with f a gradient of a bounded periodic potential U in the diffusive scaling (note that now f remains unscaled!) Then one expects that $Z_A \Rightarrow (\tilde{D})^{1/2}\, W(t)$ where $\tilde{D}$ depends on the spatial average of U.

S 12. Diffusion in a random mass chain.

We address informally the problem of the diffusion of the tp when the masses m_k's of the harmonic chain depend on k deterministically or in a completely random way. A more detailed discussion of this will appear elsewhere.

Since long, random mass harmonic chains have been studied (see, e.g.[22] and references therein) and attract recently much attention, always in connection with spectral properties of the system. For example, the three dimensional random mass harmonic lattice is conjectured to exhibit Fourier law for heat conduction. For i.i.d. masses in the one-dimensional nearest neighbor chain it has been shown that the spectrum is pure point a.s. with exponentially localized modes for eigenvalues strictly larger than zero [14]. In fact, the localization length diverges, as it should be, as the spectrum approaches zero. It is this part of the spectrum which determines the diffusive properties of the tp. Here we are only concerned with the diffusion constant of the tp; we leave open the question of the convergence of the tp process.

We found the surprising, but very nice fact, that the diffusion constant of the tp for a very large class of mass distributions $\{m_k\}$ can be given explicitly. It only depends on the "tales" of the $\{m_k\}$, which also shows a deeper reason for the diffusion constant to be independent of M (the mass of the tp) as we stressed already earlier for the special case when all m_k, $k\neq 0$ are the same. The theory is in fact a beautiful application of Krein's theory of strings with its implications on generalized diffusion processes [9].

To start, recall that

$$D = \lim_{t\to\infty} \frac{E_0(X(t)^2)}{t} = 2\lim_{t\to\infty} \int_0^t (1-\frac{u}{t})E_0(Y(u)Y(0))du$$

$$= 2(\beta M)^{-1}\, \mathcal{C}\text{-}\int_0^\infty a(t)\,dt,$$

where $\mathcal{C}\text{-}\int$ refers to the Ceasaro mean.

The quantity we have at hand however is

$$(12.1)\qquad \mathcal{A}\text{-}D = \lim_{\lambda\to 0} D(\lambda) = 2(\beta M)^{-1} \lim_{\lambda\to 0} \int_0^\infty e^{-\lambda t}\, a(t)\,dt.$$

where $\mathcal{A}$ refers to the Abel mean. To identify $\mathcal{A}$-D with D needs extra checking in terms of Tauberian theorems. But [23] $\mathcal{A}\text{-}D = D$ or $D=\infty$. The case $D=\infty$ may not be immediately excluded from the analytical expression for a(t), but it seems physically unrealistic. We are here only concerned with $\mathcal{A}$-D.

We always assume $\inf\{m_k\} > 0$ and $\sup\{m_k\} < \infty$ a.s.

Theorem 12.1. Suppose that there exist constants $0 < m_+ < \infty$, $0 < m_- < \infty$ such that

$$(12.2)\qquad \begin{aligned}\lim_{L\to\infty} \frac{1}{L}\sum_{k=0}^{L} m_k &= m_+ \quad \text{a.s.}\\ \lim_{L\to\infty} \frac{1}{L}\sum_{k=0}^{L} m_{-k} &= m_- \quad \text{a.s.}\end{aligned}$$

Then

$$\mathcal{A} - D = \frac{1}{\beta\sqrt{K}} \; \frac{2}{\sqrt{m_+} + \sqrt{m_-}}$$

Before we sketch the proof of the theorem we give some examples.

Example 1. $m_k = m$ for all but finitely many k. Then

$$\mathcal{A} - D = \frac{1}{\beta\sqrt{Km}}$$

Example 2. $m_k = m$ for $k > 0$ and $m_k = M$ for $k \le 0$. Then

$$\mathcal{A} - D = \frac{1}{\beta\sqrt{K}} \; \frac{2}{\sqrt{m} + \sqrt{M}}$$

Example 3. $m_k = m(1 + \varepsilon\cos\alpha k)^{-1}$ for all k, $0 < \varepsilon < 1$.

If α is rational multiple of 2π, say p/q, then $\{m_k\}$ is periodic with period q and

$$m_+ = m_- = \frac{1}{q}\sum_{k=0}^{q-1} m_k$$

If α is irrational multiple of 2π, then $\{m_k\}$ arises from an irrational rotation of the circle and by Weyl's theorem

$$m_+ = m_- = \overline{m} = \frac{m}{2\pi}\int_{-\pi}^{\pi} dx \; \frac{1}{1 + \varepsilon\cos x}$$

Note that in this case $\mathcal{A} - D$ is independent of the particular value of α.

Example 4. Suppose $\{m_k\}$ is a stationary ergodic sequence with $E(m_k) = \overline{m}$. Then by the ergodic theorem $m_+ = m_- = \overline{m}$ and

$$\mathcal{A} - D = \frac{1}{\beta\sqrt{K\overline{m}}}$$

Proof of the Theorem 12.1. From (12.1)

$$D(\lambda) = 2(\beta M)^{-1}\int_0^\infty e^{-\lambda t} a(t)\, dt = 2(\beta M)^{-1}\int_0^\infty e^{-\lambda t} \langle e_0, \cos(A^{1/2}t)e_0\rangle\, dt =$$

$$2(\beta M)^{-1}\int_0^\infty e^{-\lambda t}\int_{\sigma(A^{1/2})} \cos\omega t\, \langle e_0, P_{A^{1/2}}(d\omega)e_0\rangle\, dt = 2(\beta M)^{-1}\lambda\int_{\sigma(A^{1/2})} (\lambda^2 + \omega^2)^{-1}\langle e_0, P_{A^{1/2}}(d\omega)e_0\rangle =$$

$$= 2\,(\beta M)^{-1}\ \lambda\,\langle e_0, (\lambda^2 + A)^{-1}\, e_0\rangle .$$

Consider the unitary map $U: l_2(\mathbf{Z}) \to L^2(\mathbf{Z}, \mathbf{m})$ defined by $(U\xi)(k) = (\mathbf{M}^{-1/2}\xi)_k$ where the measure $\mathbf{m}$ is given by $\mathbf{m}(k) = m_k$. Under this mapping the operator $A = \kappa\mathbf{M}^{-1/2}(-\Delta)\mathbf{M}^{-1/2}$ becomes $\hat{\mathbf{A}} = -\,\kappa\,\mathbf{M}^{-1}\Delta$. Note that the scalar product in $L^2(\mathbf{Z}, \mathbf{m})$ can be expressed as $\langle\xi, \eta\rangle_{\mathbf{m}} = \langle\xi, \mathbf{M}\eta\rangle$. Therefore

$$D(\lambda) = 2\,(\beta M)^{-1}\ \lambda\,\langle e_0, (\lambda^2 + A)^{-1}\, e_0\rangle = \langle Ue_0, (\lambda^2 + \hat{\mathbf{A}})^{-1} Ue_0\rangle_{\mathbf{m}} =$$

$$2\,(\beta M)^{-1}\ \lambda\,\langle \mathbf{M}^{-1/2}e_0, \mathbf{M}(\lambda^2 + \hat{\mathbf{A}})^{-1}\,\mathbf{M}^{-1/2}e_0\rangle = 2\,(\beta M)^{-1}\ \lambda\,\langle e_0, (\lambda^2 + \hat{\mathbf{A}})^{-1}\, e_0\rangle =$$

$$2(\beta\kappa)^{-1}\lambda\,\kappa\,M^{-1}\,\langle e_0, (\lambda^2 + \hat{\mathbf{A}})^{-1}\, e_0\rangle = 2(\beta\kappa)^{-1}\lambda\, g_{\lambda^2}(0,0)$$

where $g_{\lambda^2}(x,y)$ is the kernel of the resolvent operator $(\lambda^2 + \hat{\mathbf{A}})^{-1}$ with respect to the "speed measure" $\kappa^{-1}\mathbf{m}$. In fact, $\hat{\mathbf{A}}$ is the generator of a generalized diffusion process, H_t (birth and death process with jump rate κm_k^{-1}), in the sense of [9], see also [24], i.e., a Wiener process time changed with the discrete speed measure $\kappa^{-1}\mathbf{m}$.

Thus

(12.3) $$\mathcal{A} - D = 2(\beta\kappa)^{-1}\lim_{\lambda\to 0} \lambda\, g_{\lambda^2}(0,0).$$

Now Krein's theory enters in the asymptotics of $g_{\lambda^2}(0,0)$. In fact [9]

(12.4) $$\lim_{\lambda\to 0} \lambda\, g_{\lambda^2}(0,0) = \lim_{\lambda\to 0} \lambda\, h(\lambda^2)$$

where

(12.5) $$[h(\lambda^2)]^{-1} = [h_+(\lambda^2)]^{-1} + [h_-(\lambda^2)]^{-1},$$

and h_+, h_- are the Krein correspondences to the measures $\mathbf{m}_+ = \kappa^{-1}\,\chi_{[0,\infty)}\,\mathbf{m}$ and $\mathbf{m}_- = \kappa^{-1}\,\chi_{(-\infty,0)}\,\mathbf{m}$. (12.4) with (12.5) holds if H_t is normal, in the sense of [9], which is insured by (12.2) as we shall see below.

Let $\mu_+(L) = \mathbf{m}_+(L)L$ and $\mu_-(L) = \mathbf{m}_-(L)L$ and denote by $u_+(x)$ the inverse of $x\to\mu_+(x)$ and by $u_-(x)$ the inverse of $x\to\mu_-(x)$. Then as $L\to\infty$, by virtue of (12.2)

$$\lim_{x\to\infty} \frac{u_-(x)}{u_+(x)} = \frac{\sqrt{m_+}}{\sqrt{m_-}}$$

which is equivalent to H_t being normal.

The point is now that we obtain the asymptotics in (12.4) from (12.5) by the following [9]:

If for some $\gamma > 0$ and some slowly varying function $L_+(x)$,

$$u_+(x) \sim x^{\gamma} L_+(x), \qquad x\to\infty$$

then

$$h_+(\lambda^2) \sim c(\gamma)\, \lambda^{-2\gamma}\, L_+(\lambda^{-2}), \qquad \lambda\to 0$$

with a constant $c(\gamma)$ depending only on γ. Similarly,

$$h_-(\lambda^2) \sim c(\gamma)\, \lambda^{-2\gamma}\, L_-(\lambda^{-2}), \qquad \lambda\to 0$$

if

$$u_-(x) \sim x^{\gamma} L_-(x), \qquad x\to\infty.$$

Again by (12.2), in our case $\gamma = ½$ and

$$\lim_{x\to\infty} L_+(x) = \sqrt{K/m_+} \qquad \text{and} \qquad \lim_{x\to\infty} L_-(x) = \sqrt{K/m_-}$$

so that

$$\lim_{\lambda\to 0} \lambda\, h_\pm(\lambda^2) = c(½)\sqrt{K/m_\pm}$$

and thus by (12.5), (12.4) and (12.3)

$$\mathcal{A}\text{-}D = \frac{2}{\beta K}\, c(½)\, \frac{\sqrt{K}}{\sqrt{m_+} + \sqrt{m_-}} = \frac{2}{\beta\sqrt{K}}\, \frac{c(½)}{\sqrt{m_+} + \sqrt{m_-}} .$$

The constant $c(½) = 1$, since for the case $m_k = m$ for all k

$$\mathcal{A}\text{-}D = \frac{1}{\beta\sqrt{Km}}$$

∎

Remark. If in (12.2) we require also uniformity, namely that

$$\lim_{L\to\infty} \frac{1}{L}\sum_{i=k}^{k+L} m_i = m_+$$

uniformly in k and similarly for m_-, then the result may be seen starting from (12.3) in a straightforward way using an averaging approximation theorem [25] in the resulting equations, changing lattice spacing by $1/\lambda$. This was communicated to us by G.Papanicolaou.

S 13. The heavy mass limit in two dimensions.

In two dimensions the motion of the tp with sufficiently large mass on an "appropriate time scale" appears as the motion of a harmonically bounded particle. This result is quite surprising since the non-existence of the Gibbs measure in two dimensions indicates that the tp performs an unbounded motion. "Appropriate time scale" therefore has to be understood as "before escape to infinity sets in".

Considering $a(t)$ given by (8.26), the only non-trivial limit occurs for the following scaling:

$$M = AM^* \qquad (M^* \text{ a unit of mass, henceforth } M^*=1 \text{ for simplicity});$$

$$V_A(t) = A^{1/2}V(\varepsilon^{-1}(A)t) \tag{13.1}$$

$$X_A(t) = A^{1/2}\varepsilon(A)X(\varepsilon^{-1}(A)t),$$

where $\varepsilon(A)$ satisfies (8.24) with $M=A$.

Theorem 13.1. Let x be an independent centered Gaussian random variable with $Ex^2=(\beta\omega_L{}^2)^{-1}$. Let (X^*,V^*) be given by

$$\dot{X}^*(t) = V^*(t)$$

$$\dot{V}^*(t) = -\omega_L{}^2(X^*(t)+x)$$

with $\qquad V^*(0) = V_A(0)= v$ and $X^*(0) = 0$, i.e.,

$$X^*(t) = \omega_L{}^{-1}v\sin\omega_L t + x\cos\omega_L t - x; \qquad V^*(t) = v\cos\omega_L t - \omega_L x\sin\omega_L t.$$

Then $(X_A,V_A) \Longrightarrow (X^*,V^*)$.

Proof. To prove tightness, we verify (7.3) for $E_0(V_A(t)V_A(0)) = \beta^{-1}a(\varepsilon^{-1}(A)t)$, i.e., we need to show: $|\varepsilon^{-1}(A)\dot{a}(\varepsilon^{-1}(A)t)| \le$ Const. This estimate can be verified by expressing $\varepsilon^{-1}(A)\dot{a}(\varepsilon^{-1}(A)t)$ as the inverse Laplace transform of $\tau\varepsilon(A)\tilde{a}(\varepsilon(A)\tau)-1$, where $\tilde{a}(\tau)$ is given by (8.23) with $M=A$,

$$\varepsilon^{-1}(A)\dot{a}(\varepsilon^{-1}(A)t) = \frac{1}{2\pi i}\int_L \frac{A^{-1}m\tau^2 - [A^{-1}m\tau^2+\varepsilon^{-2}(A)A^{-1}\omega_L^2]F^{-1}}{[A^{-1}m\tau^2+\varepsilon^{-2}(A)A^{-1}\omega_L^2]F^{-1} + \tau^2[1-A^{-1}m]} e^{t\tau} d\tau ,$$

$$\text{where } F^{-1} \equiv F^{-1}\left(\tfrac{1}{2}, \tfrac{1}{2}; 1; \left[\frac{\omega_L^2}{\varepsilon^2(A)\tau^2+\omega_L^2}\right]^2\right).$$

Since the denominator of the integrand in the last formula is the same as in (8.23) with $M=A$, and τ substituted by $\varepsilon(A)\tau$, $\quad \varepsilon^{-1}(A)\dot{a}(\varepsilon^{-1}(A)t) = \mathrm{Res}(\tau_+)+\mathrm{Res}(\tau_-) + (\text{Integral along the cut}) + O(A^{-1})$ and each of the terms in the last identity is bounded.

For pointwise convergence, notice that from (8.24) and (8.25) with $M=A$ as $A \to \infty$, $\varepsilon(A) \to 0$, $A\varepsilon^2(A) \to 0$, $\delta(A) \to 0$, thus $\cos\delta(A) \to 1$, $\sin\delta(A) \to 0$. Then from (8.26), (8.28) we obtain:

$$\lim_{A\to\infty} a(\varepsilon^{-1}(A)t) =$$

$$\lim_{A\to\infty}\Big[\exp(-\omega_L t\sin\delta(A))\frac{\cos(\omega_L t\cos\delta(A)) - \varepsilon^2(A)\pi^{-1}\cos(\omega_L t\cos\delta(A)-\delta(A))}{1-2m^{-1}A\varepsilon^2(A)\pi^{-1}\cos\delta(A)+(m^{-1}A\varepsilon^2(A)\pi^{-1})^2} -$$

$$- \frac{2A\varepsilon^2(A)}{\pi\omega_L^2 t^2}\Big] = \cos\omega_L t .$$

Therefore $E(V_A(t)V_A(0)) \to E(V^*(t)V^*(0)) = \beta^{-1}\cos\omega_L t$. Invoking the remark of S 7 the complete proof of the theorem follows. ▮

Remark. Note that contrary to the one dimensional case, we find in the heavy mass limit a deterministic process describing the motion of the heavy tp on the macroscopic scale.

S 14. Long time behaviour and Einstein relation in two dimensions.

From (8.29) it is easily seen that the long time behaviour of $X(t)$, for M sufficiently big but finite, is determined by the contribution of $c_{(0)}(t)$ in $c(t)$, since the contribution from the poles (the second term in (8.29)) is negligible. Then from (8.30)

$$(14.1) \qquad c(t) \sim M(\pi m\omega_L^2)^{-1}\ln\omega_L t.$$

Clearly, $A^{-1/2}X(At) \Longrightarrow 0$ and hence the diffusion constant in two dimensions is zero.

(14.1) suggests that $X_A(t) \equiv (\ln A)^{-1/2}X(At)$ converges weakly. But for $t>0$ and M sufficiently big

$$\lim_{A\to\infty}(\ln A)^{-1}c(At) = \lim_{A\to\infty} M(\pi m\omega_L^2)^{-1}(\ln A)^{-1}\ln\omega_L At = M(\pi m\omega_L^2)^{-1}$$

since the logarithm is a slowly varying function, whereas, for $t=0$, $X_A(0)=0$. Therefore, in this scaling we obtain a left continuous process, which jumps at time zero to the constant value $(\beta M)^{-1}(M(\pi m\omega_L^2)^{-1})^{1/2}$.

It is a remarkable feature of the two dimensional model that the escape to infinity of the tp can not be seen on a macroscopic level by choosing a linear time scale. In fact, considering the following scaling:

$$(14.2) \qquad X_A(t) \equiv A^{-1/2}X(\omega_L^{-1}(\omega_L t+1)^A),$$

we have the following theorem:

Theorem 14.1. Let X^* be a mean zero Gaussian process with covariance

$$E(X^*(t)X^*(s)) = (\beta M)^{-1}[c^*(t)+c^*(s) - c^*(|t-s|)]$$

where $c^*(t) = M(\pi m \omega_L{}^2)^{-1}\ln(\omega_L t+1)$. Then $X_A \Rightarrow X^*$.

We omit the proof of this theorem, i.e., the proof of pointwise convergence and tightness. It follows in a straightforward way from the formulae (8.29) and (8.30).

Remark. $D^* \equiv 2(\beta\pi m\omega_L{}^2)^{-1}$ plays the role of a generalized diffusion constant for $X^*(t)$. Note that for small times $X^*(t) \cong D^{1/2}W(t)$ with $D = \omega_L D^*$.

As in S11, we may now study the motion of a charged tp, subjected to a small constant electric field. Our reference scale is determined by (14.2), thus the force is $F_A \equiv A^{-1/2}F$. Like in one dimension we obtain as a direct consequence of Theorem 14.1 the following

Theorem 14.2. Let $Z_A(t) = A^{-1/2}Z(\omega_L{}^{-1}(\omega_L t+1)^A)$ where $Z(t)$ is the solution of

$$Z(t) = X(t) + M^{-1}\int_0^t du \int_0^u dv\, a(u-v)\, A^{-1/2}F.$$

Let $Z^*(t)$ be given by

$$Z^*(t) = \nu^* F \ln(\omega_L t+1) + \quad X^*(t) \quad \text{with} \quad \nu^* = \tfrac{1}{2}\beta D^*.$$

Then $Z_A \Rightarrow Z^*$.

Remark. For small t, $Z^*(t) \cong \nu^* F\omega_L t + (D^*\omega_L)^{1/2}W(t) = \nu F t + D^{1/2}W(t)$ with $\nu = \tfrac{1}{2}\beta D$. (cfr. Theorem 11.1).

S 15. The heavy mass limit in three dimensions.

Knowing the result in the two dimensional case we are prepared for a harmonically bounded Brownian particle also in three dimensions under an appropriate scaling of the tp process. What we have more is that in three dimensions (and all higher dimensions) also the Gibbs measure $\hat{\mathbf{P}}$ exists, i.e., the tp position has finite variance. This give us the chance to compare the tp motion under $\mathbf{P}_0$ with its equilibrium motion under $\hat{\mathbf{P}}$.

Since $(\hat{X}, \hat{V})$ is stationary, it will remain so under scaling. (^ refers to the system initially distributed according to $\hat{\mathbf{P}}$). Therfore we may only expect a non-trivial limit if

$$M = AM^{*} \qquad (M^{*} \text{ a unit of mass, henceforth } M^{*}=1 \text{ for simplicity})$$

(15.1) $$\hat{\mathcal{V}}_A(t) = A^{1/2}\,\hat{\mathcal{V}}(A^{1/2}t)$$

$$\hat{\mathcal{X}}_A(t) = \hat{\mathcal{X}}(A^{1/2}t).$$

Thus both $\hat{\mathbf{E}}(\hat{\mathcal{V}}_A(t)^2) = \hat{\mathbf{E}}(\hat{\mathcal{V}}_A(0)^2) = \beta^{-1}$ and $\hat{\mathbf{E}}(\hat{\mathcal{X}}_A(t)^2) = \hat{\mathbf{E}}(\hat{\mathcal{X}}_A(0)^2) = (\beta\kappa)^{-1}\langle e_0, -\Delta^{-1}e_0\rangle =$

$= (\beta\kappa)^{-1}\,\tfrac{1}{4}\zeta_0$ remain fixed (see (8. 34)).

As we shall see, and this will consume most of this section, the convergence

$$V_A \Rightarrow V^{*} \qquad\qquad (\text{under } \hat{\mathbf{P}} \text{ and } \mathbf{P}_0)$$

may be understood as some kind of "law of large numbers", namely, we are able to couple V_A and V^* in such a way that for all $t\in[0,T]$ $\mathbf{E}((V_A(t)-V^*(t)^2)\to 0$, i.e., $V_A(t) \to V^*(t)$ in L_2-sense, which in turn enables us, since we deal with Gaussian variables, to determine the convergence rate: we shall show that the "fluctuation process" $\xi_A = A^{1/4}(V_A-V^*)$ converge weakly towards a nonsingular process. Note that $A^{1/4}$ is just the Central Limit Theorem type scaling one expects if $(V_A - V^*)$ is a well mixing process on the time scale $A^{1/2}$.

Theorem 15.1. Let x be an independent centered Gaussian random variable with

$$\mathbf{E}\,x^2 = (\beta\kappa)^{-1}\tfrac{1}{4}\zeta_0 \equiv (\beta\omega^2)^{-1} \qquad \text{where } \omega = 2(\kappa/\zeta_0)^{1/2}.$$

(i) Let $(\hat{\mathcal{X}}^*, \hat{\mathcal{V}}^*)$ be given by

$$\dot{\hat{\mathcal{X}}}^*(t) = \hat{\mathcal{V}}^*(t),$$

$$\dot{\hat{\mathcal{V}}}^*(t) = -\,\omega^2\,\hat{\mathcal{X}}^*(t)$$

with $\hat{\mathcal{V}}^*(0)=\hat{\mathcal{V}}_A(0)\equiv v$ and $\hat{\mathcal{X}}^*(0)= x$, i.e., $\hat{\mathcal{X}}^* =\omega^{-1}v\sin\omega t + x\cos\omega t$, $\hat{\mathcal{V}}^*(t)= v\cos\omega t - \omega\, x\sin\omega t$.

Then $(\hat{\mathcal{X}}_A, \hat{\mathcal{V}}_A) \Rightarrow (\hat{\mathcal{X}}^*, \hat{\mathcal{V}}^*)$.

(ii) Let (X^*, V^*) be given by

$$\dot{X}^*(t) = V^*(t),$$

$$\dot{V}^*(t) = -\,\omega^2(X^*(t) + x)$$

with $V^*(0)= v$ and $X^*(0)=0$, i.e., $X^*(t)=\omega^{-1}v\sin\omega t + x(\cos\omega t-1)$, $V^*(t)= v\cos\omega t - \omega\, x\sin\omega t$.

Then $(X_A, V_A) \Rightarrow (X^*, V^*)$.

Remark. Recall (8.36):

$$a(t) \doteq e^{-\frac{2}{\pi}(\kappa m)^{1/2}\zeta_0^{-2}M^{-1}t}\left[\cos\omega M^{-1/2}t - (m^{1/2}\pi^{-1}\zeta_0^{-3/2})M^{-1/2}\sin\omega M^{-1/2}t\right].$$

thus

$$|a(t)| \le e^{-\frac{2}{\pi}(\kappa m)^{1/2}\zeta_0^{-2}M^{-1}t}$$

and then

$$|a(At)| \le e^{-\frac{2}{\pi}(\kappa m)^{1/2}\zeta_0^{-2}t} \xrightarrow[t\to\infty]{} 0$$

which shows that our scaling result holds before relaxation sets in.

Proof. Since both $\hat{V}_A$ and V_A are stationary and $\hat{E}(\hat{V}(t)\hat{V}(s))=E_0(V(t)V(s))=(\beta M)^{-1}a(t-s)$, besides tightness, we need only check pointwise convergence of $\beta^{-1}a(A^{1/2}t)$ to $E(\hat{V}^*(t)\hat{V}^*(0))=E(V^*(t)V^*(0))=$ $=\beta^{-1}\cos\omega t$. But note that $E_0(V_A(t)V_A(0))=E_0((V_A(t)-V^*(t))v)+E_0(V^*(t)v)$ and the same is true for the "^ - process". Hence, if for all t $V_A(t)\to V^*(t)$ and $\hat{V}_A(t)\to\hat{V}^*(t)$ in L_2-sense, then we are done, and this is precisely the subject of the next section.

To check tightness we need to verify (7.3), i.e., we need to show: $|A^{1/2}\dot{a}(A^{1/2}t)|\le$ Const. Since the formula (8.34) for $a(t)$ is only asymptotic, it is convenient to return to the inversion formula (8.12) with $\tilde{a}(\tau)$ given by (8.32) and M=A. Then, using the properties of the Laplace transform,

$$A^{1/2}\dot{a}(A^{1/2}t) = \frac{1}{2\pi i}\int_L \frac{mA^{-1}\tau^2 - mI^{-1}(A^{-1/2}\tau)}{mI^{-1}(A^{-1/2}\tau)+(1-mA^{-1})\tau^2}\, e^{t\tau}\, d\tau \tag{15.2}$$

To show that (15.2) is bounded, we notice that the denominator of the expression in (15.2) is the same as in (8.32) with M=A. Therefore, as before, $A^{1/2}a(A^{1/2}t) = \mathrm{Res}(\tau_+) + \mathrm{Res}(\tau_-) + O(A^{-1})$ for A large enough, uniformly in t. Using (8.35), it is easy to see that $\mathrm{Res}(\tau_+)$ and $\mathrm{Res}(\tau_-)$ are bounded and therefore $A^{1/2}\dot{a}(A^{1/2}t)$ is bounded. ∎

S 16. Fluctuation process in three dimensions.

In both two and three dimensions we obtain in the heavy mass limit deterministic evolution with however stochastic initial conditions, contrary to one dimension where the limit motion is genuinely stochastic. Hence there is some hope that convergence rates (or fluctuations) can be determined. Besides the scale ($A^{1/4}$ in d=3 as we remarked earlier) there is some wisdom as to what to expect given the deterministic equation: the fluctuations should be Gaussian and governed by the linearized deterministic equation with an additional Gaussian noise. This is also what we obtain, but the fluctuation processes under $\mathbf{P}_0$ and $\hat{\mathbf{P}}$ are different.

On the way we shall see that the situation in two dimensions is different , however we shall leave as an open problem the study of the convergence rates in two dimensions.

To begin with recall that $V^*(t) = v \cos\omega t - \omega x \sin \omega t$ with x independent Gaussian and

$$(16.1) \qquad E(x^2) = (\beta\omega^2)^{-1}$$

and recall (6.2): $V(t) = \sum_j M^{-1/2} m_j^{1/2} \dot{a}_{0j}(t) x_j + \sum_j M^{-1/2} m_j^{1/2} a_{0j}(t) v_j$ with $m_j = m$ for all $j \neq 0$ and $m_0 = M$.

We wish to realize V_A and V^* on some probability space $(\Xi, \mathrm{F}, \mathbf{P})$ such that

$$(16.2) \qquad E((V_A(t) - V^*(t))^2) \to 0.$$

This is what we need to get started with the scaled fluctuation process ξ_A. Since V is already defined on $(\Omega, \mathrm{B}(\Omega), \mathbf{P}_0)$ or $(\Omega, \mathrm{B}(\Omega), \hat{\mathbf{P}})$, one naturally tries to put V^* on the same space and that means to realize x on $(\Omega, \mathrm{B}(\Omega), \mathbf{P}_0)$ or $(\Omega, \mathrm{B}(\Omega), \hat{\mathbf{P}})$ ($v = V_A(0)$, of course).

We look now at the crucial term

$$(16.3) \qquad E(V(t)V^*(t)) = -\omega \sin\omega t \sum_j M^{-1/2} m_j^{1/2} \dot{a}_{0j}(t) E(x_j x) + (\beta M^{1/2})^{-1} a(t) \cos\omega t$$

where we used the trivial facts $E(v_j v) = \delta_{j0} (\beta M^{1/2})^{-1}$ and $E(v_j x) = 0$ for all j (recall that $M = AM^*$ and we put $M^* = 1$).

So we need to know $E(x_j x)$ and that is easy if $E = \hat{E}$: then the natural candidate is $x = x_0$ i.e., the tp position, $X(0)$, at t=0 (then (16.1) holds trivially) and from (4.8)

$$\hat{E}(x_j x) = \hat{E}(x_j x_0) = (\kappa\beta)^{-1} \langle e_j, -\Delta^{-1} e_0 \rangle$$

and hence

$$\sum_j M^{-1/2} m_j^{1/2} \dot{a}_{0j}(t) E(x_j x) = \sum_j M^{-1/2} m_j^{1/2} \dot{a}_{0j}(t) (\kappa\beta)^{-1} \langle e_j, -\Delta^{-1} e_0 \rangle =$$

$$= \sum_j M^{-1/2} m_j^{1/2} \langle e_0, -A^{1/2} \sin(A^{1/2} t) e_j \rangle (\kappa\beta)^{-1} \langle e_j, -\Delta^{-1} e_0 \rangle =$$

$$= \sum_j M^{-1/2} \langle e_0, -A^{1/2} \sin(A^{1/2} t) \mathbf{M}^{1/2} e_j \rangle (\kappa\beta)^{-1} \langle e_j, -\Delta^{-1} e_0 \rangle =$$

$$= M^{-1/2} (\kappa\beta)^{-1} \langle -\mathbf{M}^{1/2} A^{1/2} \sin(A^{1/2} t) e_0, -\Delta^{-1} e_0 \rangle =$$

$$= -(M\beta)^{-1}\int_0^t a(u)du,$$

and for (16.3) we obtain

$$\hat{E}(V(t)V^*(t)) = (M\beta)^{-1}\omega \sin\omega t \int_0^t a(u)du + (M^{1/2}\beta)^{-1}\cos\omega t$$

and hence

$$\hat{E}(A^{1/2}V(A^{1/2}t)V^*(t)) = (\beta)^{-1}(A^{1/2}\omega \sin\omega t \int_0^t a(u)du + a(A^{1/2}t)\cos\omega t) =$$

$$= (\beta)^{-1}(\omega \sin\omega t \int_0^t a(A^{1/2}u)du + a(A^{1/2}t)\cos\omega t).$$

Now from (8.36) with $M=A$:

$$\lim_{A\to\infty} \int_0^t a(A^{1/2}u)\, du = \omega^{-1}\sin\omega t$$

and

$$\lim_{A\to\infty} \hat{E}(V_A(t)V^*(t)) = (\beta)^{-1}$$

so (16.2) follows.

Assume now that $E = E_0$. Then $X(0) = 0$ a.s., but suppose we still want to find x such that

(16.4) $\qquad E_0(x^2) = (\beta\kappa)^{-1}\langle e_0, -\Delta^{-1}e_0\rangle$ (this does not even exist in d=2!),

(16.5) $\qquad E_0(x_jx) = (\beta\kappa)^{-1}\{\langle e_j, -\Delta^{-1}e_0\rangle - \langle e_0, -\Delta^{-1}e_0\rangle\}.$

By virtue of (5.5), the desired result follows as before.

However, we do not know apriori whether such x exists; indeed a choice of the type: $x = \sum_i c_i x_i$ is not compatible with (16.5).

Fortunately, we can go another way. Because of (5.5) we have with the ansatz

(16.6) $\qquad E_0(x_jx) = B,\quad$ a constant, $\quad j \neq 0$

that in (16.3)

$$\sum_j M^{-1/2} m_j^{1/2} \dot{a}_{0j}(t) E_0(x_jx) = -B\, a(t)$$

and thus $E_0(A^{1/2}V(A^{1/2}t)V^*(t)) = A^{1/2}\omega \sin\omega t\, B\, a(A^{1/2}t) + \beta^{-1}a(A^{1/2}t)\cos\omega t.$

But $\quad \lim_{A\to\infty} A^{1/2}a(A^{1/2}t) = -\omega^{-1}\sin\omega t,$

so that $\lim_{A\to\infty} E_0(V_A(t)V^*(t)) = -B\,\omega^2 \sin^2 \omega t + (\beta)^{-1}\cos^2\omega t = (\beta)^{-1}$

if $B = -(\beta\omega^2)^{-1} = -(4\beta\kappa)^{-1}\,\zeta_0 = -(\beta\kappa)^{-1}\langle e_0, -\Delta^{-1} e_0\rangle$ (which does not exist in d=2!).

Let us see what x satisfying (16.6) looks like. Write $B = E_0(x_j x) = (\beta\kappa)^{-1}\langle e_j - e_0, -\Delta^{-1}\xi\rangle$ for all $j \neq 0$ then $\Delta^{-1}\xi \perp e_j$ for all $j \neq 0$, hence $-\Delta^{-1}\xi = \frac{1}{4}\zeta_0 e_0$ or $\xi = -\frac{1}{4}\zeta_0 \Delta e_0 = -\frac{1}{4}\zeta_0(e_1 - 2e_0 + e_{-1})$, therefore try $x = -\frac{1}{4}\zeta_0(x_1 + x_{-1})$ and see whether (16.4) is satisfied. We have:

$$(16.7)\qquad E_0(x^2) = 1/16\,\zeta_0^2\,E_0((x_1 + x_{-1})^2)) = \tfrac{1}{2}\zeta_0\,(\beta\omega^2)^{-1} < (\beta\omega^2)^{-1},$$

since $\frac{1}{2}\zeta_0 = 0.505\ldots$. Thus we see that the conditions (16.4) and (16.6) can not be satisfied on the same probability space. However by the virtue of the inequality (16.7), we may now enlarge our probability space to a product space $(\Xi, \mathbf{F}, \mathbf{P}) = (\Omega, \mathbf{B}(\Omega), \mathbf{P}_0) \times (\Omega, \mathbf{F}, \tilde{\mathbf{P}})$ and take $\tilde{x} \in (\Omega, \mathbf{F}, \tilde{\mathbf{P}})$ Gaussian with $\tilde{\mathbf{E}}(\tilde{x}) = 0$ and $\tilde{\mathbf{E}}(\tilde{x}^2) = (\beta\omega^2)^{-1}(1 - \frac{1}{2}\zeta_0)$. Now for $x = -\frac{1}{4}\zeta_0(x_1 + x_{-1}) + \tilde{x}$ with $B = (\beta\omega^2)^{-1}$ (16.4) and (16.6) are satisfied.

It is now clear that we have a coupling of V_A and V^* on $(\Xi, \mathbf{F}, \mathbf{P})$ for which (16.2) holds: $\mathbf{E}((V^* - V_A)^2) \to 0$, i.e., $V_A(t) \to V^*(t)$ in L_2-sense.

In the following study of the fluctuation process, $\tilde{x}$ plays no significant role.

Theorem 16.1. (i) Let $(\hat{\eta}, \hat{\xi})$ be given by

$$d\hat{\eta}(t) = \hat{\xi}(t)\,dt$$
$$d\hat{\xi}(t) = -\omega^2\,\hat{\eta}(t)dt + \sigma\,dW(t)$$

with $\sigma^2 = (\beta\pi\zeta_0^{3/2})^{-1} 4 m^{1/2}\omega$ and $\hat{\eta}(0) = \hat{\xi}(0) = 0$, i.e., $\hat{\xi}(t) = \sigma \int_0^t \cos\omega(t-s)\,dW(s)$.

Let $\hat{\eta}_A = A^{1/4}(X_A - X^*)$ and $\hat{\xi}_A = A^{1/4}(V_A - V^*)$ with $x = X(0)$ in (X^*, V^*). Then $(\hat{\eta}_A, \hat{\xi}_A) \Rightarrow (\hat{\eta}, \hat{\xi})$.

(ii) Let (η, ξ) be given by

$$d\eta(t) = \xi(t)\,dt$$
$$d\xi(t) = -\omega^2\,\eta(t)dt + \sigma\omega\,W(t)dt$$

with $\eta(0) = \xi(0) = 0$, i.e., $\xi(t) = \sigma \int_0^t \sin \omega (t-s)\, dW(s)$.

Let $\eta_A = A^{1/4}(X_A - X^*)$ and $\xi_A = A^{1/4}(V_A - V^*)$ with $x = -\frac{1}{4}\zeta_0(x_1 + x_{-1}) + \aleph$ in (X^*, V^*). Then $(\eta_A, \xi_A) \Rightarrow (\eta, \xi)$.

Remark. One should remark the difference between ξ and $\hat{\xi}$. ξ has differentiable paths whereas the paths of $\hat{\xi}$ inherit the Holder continuity of the Wiener process. We shall not expand on why the difference arises (it has probably to do with $\aleph$ being independent) but one might expect that if x may be realized on $(\Omega, \mathrm{B}(\Omega), \mathbf{P}_0)$ such that $V_A(t) \to V(t)$ in $L_2(\mathbf{P}_0)$, the fluctuation processes $\hat{\xi}_A$ and ξ_A are the same. But observe also the truth of the general wisdom concerning the fluctuation law.

Proof. We start with (i). From the discussion above, for $t \ge s$

$$\hat{\mathbf{E}}(\hat{\xi}_A(t)\, \hat{\xi}_A(s)) = A^{1/2}\, \hat{\mathbf{E}}(V_A(t)V_A(s) + V^*(t)V^*(s) - V_A(s)V^*(t) - V_A(t)V^*(s)) =$$

$$= A^{1/2}\beta^{-1}(a(A^{1/2}(t-s)) + \cos\omega(t-s) - \omega\sin\omega s \int_0^t a(A^{1/2}u)du -$$

$$- a(A^{1/2}t)\cos\omega s - \omega\sin\omega t\int_0^t a(A^{1/2}u)du - a(A^{1/2}s)\cos\omega t).$$

We have to prove tightness and pointwise convergence of the above.

For pointwise convergence observe that

$$(16.8) \quad a(A^{1/2}t) = \exp\{2(\pi A^{1/2}\zeta_0^{2})^{-1}(\kappa m)^{1/2}t\}[\cos\omega t - (\pi\zeta_0^{3/2})^{-1} m^{1/2} A^{1/2} \sin\omega t] + o(A^{-1/2}) =$$

$$= \cos\omega t - 2(\pi\zeta_0^{2})^{-1}(\kappa m)^{1/2}A^{-1/2} t\cos\omega t - (\pi\zeta_0^{3/2})^{-1}m^{1/2}A^{-1/2}\sin\omega t + o(A^{-1/2})$$

and

$$\int_0^t a(A^{1/2}u)du \doteq \omega^{-1}\sin\omega t - A^{-1/2}[2(\pi\zeta_0^{2})^{-1}(\kappa m)^{-1/2}\int_0^t u\cos\omega u\, du - (\pi\zeta_0^{3/2})^{-1}m^{1/2}\omega^{-1}(\cos\omega t - 1)]\,.$$

Now,

$$\hat{\mathbf{E}}(\hat{\xi}_A(t)\, \hat{\xi}_A(s)) = \beta^{-1}[2A^{1/2}\cos\omega(t-s) - 2A^{1/2}\sin\omega s\sin\omega t - 2A^{1/2}\cos\omega t\cos\omega s -$$

$$-2(\pi\zeta_0^{2})^{-1}(\kappa m)^{1/2}(t-s)\cos\omega(t-s) - (\pi\zeta_0^{3/2})^{-1}m^{1/2}\sin\omega(t-s) +$$

$$+ \omega\sin\omega s\{2(\pi\zeta_0^{2})^{-1}(\kappa m)^{1/2}\int_0^t u\cos\omega u\, du - (\pi\zeta_0^{3/2})^{-1}m^{1/2}\omega^{-1}(\cos\omega t - 1)\} +$$

$$+ \omega \sin\omega t\{2(\pi\zeta_0^2)^{-1}(km)^{1/2} \int_0^t u\cos\omega u\,du - (\pi\zeta_0^{3/2})^{-1}m^{1/2}\omega^{-1}(\cos\omega s-1)\} +$$

$$+2(\pi\zeta_0^2)^{-1}(\kappa m)^{1/2}\{(t+s)\cos\omega s\cos\omega t\} + (\pi\zeta_0^{3/2})^{-1}m^{1/2}\{\sin\omega t\cos\omega s+\sin\omega s\cos\omega t\}].$$

Next observe that

$$2\omega(\pi\zeta_0^2)^{-1}(km)^{1/2} \int_0^t u\cos\omega u\,du = 2(\pi\zeta_0^2)^{-1}(km)^{1/2}t\sin\omega t + (\pi\zeta_0^{3/2})^{-1}m^{1/2}(\cos\omega t-1)$$

so that

$$\lim_{A\to\infty} \hat{\mathbf{E}}(\xi_A(t)\xi_A(s)) = \beta^{-1}\{4(\pi\zeta_0^2)^{-1}(\kappa m)^{1/2} s\cos\omega(t-s) + (\pi\zeta_0^{3/2})^{-1}m^{1/2}[\sin\omega(t+s)-\sin\omega(t-s)]\}$$

which is the covariance of $\hat{\xi}$. Let us see how σ comes out: $\hat{\xi}(t) = \sigma \int_0^t \cos\omega(t-s)\,dW(s)$,

hence $\mathbf{E}(\hat{\xi}(t)^2) = \sigma^2 \int_0^t \cos^2\omega(t-s)\,ds = \sigma^2 \int_0^t \cos^2\omega u\,du = \sigma^2(2\omega)^{-1}\sin\omega t\cos\omega t + \tfrac{1}{2}t\sigma^2$

and hence $\sigma^2 = (\beta\pi\zeta_0^2)^{-1}\,8(\kappa m)^{1/2}$.

(ii) Note that $\sigma^2 \int_0^t \sin^2\omega u\,du = -\sigma^2(2\omega)^{-1}\sin\omega t\cos\omega t + \tfrac{1}{2}t\sigma^2$ and watch for the minus sign in the following.

From the discussion after (16.6) clearly

$$\mathbf{E}(\xi_A(t)\xi_A(s)) = = A^{1/2}\beta^{-1}(a(A^{1/2}(t-s)) + \cos\omega(t-s) + \omega\sin\omega s\,(\omega)^{-2}a(A^{1/2}t) -$$

$$-a(A^{1/2}t)\cos\omega s + \omega\sin\omega t\,(\omega)^{-2}a(A^{1/2}s) - a(A^{1/2}s)\cos\omega t).$$

Now from (16.7)

$$A^{1/2}a(A^{1/2}t) \doteq -\omega\sin\omega t - 2(\pi\zeta_0^2)^{-1}(\kappa m)^{1/2}A^{-1/2}\cos\omega t + 2(\pi\zeta_0^2)^{-1}(\kappa m)^{1/2}A^{-1/2}t\omega\sin\omega t -$$

$$-(\pi\zeta_0^{3/2})^{-1}m^{1/2}A^{-1/2}\omega\cos\omega t$$

and

$$\mathbf{E}(\xi_A(t)\xi_A(s)) \doteq \beta^{-1}[2A^{1/2}\cos\omega(t-s) - 2A^{1/2}\sin\omega s\sin\omega t - 2A^{1/2}\cos\omega t\cos\omega s -$$

$$-2(\pi\zeta_0^2)^{-1}(\kappa m)^{1/2}(t-s)\cos\omega(t-s) - (\pi\zeta_0^{3/2})^{-1}m^{1/2}\sin\omega(t-s) -$$

$$-(\omega)^{-1}2\sin\omega s\,(\pi\zeta_0^2)^{-1}(\kappa m)^{1/2}\cos\omega t - (\omega)^{-1}2(\pi\zeta_0^2)^{-1}(\kappa m)^{1/2}\sin\omega t\cos\omega s +$$

$$+ 2t\sin\omega s\,(\pi\zeta_0^2)^{-1}(\kappa m)^{1/2}\sin\omega t + 2s(\pi\zeta_0^2)^{-1}(\kappa m)^{1/2}\sin\omega t\sin\omega s -$$

$$-\sin\omega s\,(\pi\zeta_0^{3/2})^{-1}(m)^{1/2}\cos\omega t - (\pi\zeta_0^{3/2})^{-1}(m)^{1/2}\sin\omega t\cos\omega s +$$

$$+ 2(\pi\zeta_0^2)^{-1}(\kappa m)^{1/2}(t+s)\cos\omega(t-s) + (\pi\zeta_0^{3/2})^{-1}(m)^{1/2}\sin\omega(t+s)].$$

Thus,

$$\lim_{A\to\infty} \mathbf{E}(\xi_A(t)\,\xi_A(s)) = \beta^{-1}\{4(\pi\zeta_0^2)^{-1}(\kappa m)^{1/2}\, s\cos\omega(t-s) - $$
$$-(\pi\zeta_0^{3/2})^{-1}m^{1/2}[\sin\omega(t+s)+\sin\omega(t-s)]\}$$

and there is the minus sign in front of the second parenthesis.

For tightness, one has to follow the same route as in Theorem 14.1. ∎

REFERENCES .

1. Hemmen, J.L. van.: *Dynamics and ergodicity of the infinite harmonic crystal*, Thesis, University of Groningen (1976).
2. Lanford, O.E., Lebowitz, J.L.: Time evolution and ergodic properties of harmonic systems. in: Lecture Notes in Physics, 38, 144-177, Springer (1975).
3. Rubin, R.J. : J. of Math. Phys. 1, 309 (1960).
4. Rubin, R.J. : J. of Math. Phys. 2, 373 (1961).
5. Morita, T., Mori, H. : Prog.Theor. Phys. 56, 498 (1976).
6. Dürr, D., Goldstein, S., Lebowitz, J.L.: Comm.Math.Phys. 78, 507 (1981).
7. Nelson, E.: *Dynamical theories of Brownian motion*, Princeton University Press (1967).
8. Smoluchowski, M. von. : Bull. Acad. Sci. Cracovie, 577 (1906).
9. Kotani S., Watanabe S.: Krein's spectral theory of strings and generalized diffusion processes. in: Lecture Notes in Math. 923, 235-259, Springer (1982).
10. Ford, G.W., Kac, M., Mazur, P.: J. of Math. Phys. 6, 504 (1965).
11. Krein, S. : *Lineinee differentzialnie uravnenia v Banachovom prostranstve*. Nauka (1967).
12. O'Connor, A.J., Lebowitz, J.L.: J. of Math. Phys. 15, 692 (1974).
13. Casher, A., Lebowitz, J.L.: J. of Math. Phys. 8, 1701 (1971).
14. Delyon, F., Kunz, H., Souillard, B. : J.Phys. A 16, 25 (1983).
15. Lighthill, M. : *Introduction to Fourier analysis and generalized functions*, Cambridge University Press (1958).
16. Berlin, T.H., Kac, M. : Phys. Rev. 86, 821 (1952).
17. Ferrari, P.A., Goldstein, S., Lebowitz, J.L. : *Diffusion, mobility and the Einstein relation*. Preprint (1984).
18. Calderoni, P., Dürr, D. : BiBoS Preprint (1985).
19. Billingsley, P. : *Convergence of probability measures*. John Wiley and Sons (1968).
20. Sussmann, H.J. : Ann. Probab. 6, 19 (1978).

21. Ikeda, N., Watanabe, S. : *Stochastic differential equations and diffusion processes*. North Holland/Kodansha (1981).

22. Marudin, A.A., Montroll, E.W., Weiss, G.H. (with Ipatova I.P.) : *Theory of lattice dynamics in the harmonic approximation*. Academic Press (1963, 1971).

23. Hardy, G.H. : *Divergent series*. Oxford University Press (1949).

24. Stone, C. : Illinois J. of Math. 7, 638 (1963).

25. Freidlin, M.I., Wentzell, A.D.: *Random perturbation of dynamical systems*. Springer (1983).

QUANTUM STOCHASTIC INTEGRATION IN CERTAIN PARTIAL *-ALGEBRAS

G.O.S. EKHAGUERE

Department of Mathematics
University of Ibadan
Ibadan

1. Introduction

In the spirit of the Hudson-Parthasarathy formulation [1] of Boson quantum stochastic calculus, we discuss quantum stochastic integration and state some generalizations of the Ito formula [2] in certain partial *-algebras [3,4]. By adopting an algebraic approach, we are able to circumvent the usual difficulties associated with the domains or adjoints of unbounded linear maps on Hilbert spaces. Consequently, in the results described below, the operators appearing in them are not assumed to be bounded, as has sometimes been done in [1]. Proofs of all results listed here may be found in [5].

In [6,7], we have applied our algebraic formulation to discuss certain properties of solutions of quantum stochastic integral equations and to initiate the study of quantum stochastic control theory.

Acknowledge

The work reported here was done during my tenure as Visiting Professor to the Forschungszentrum Bielefeld-Bochum-Stochastik, Universität Bielefeld. I am grateful to Professors S. Albeverio, Ph. Blanchard and L. Streit for their kind invitation. Furthermore, a Research Fellowship of the Alexander von Humboldt-Stiftung is thankfully acknowledged.

2. Preliminaries

Let $I \subseteq \mathbb{R}_+ \equiv [0,\infty)$ and $\Gamma(L^2(I,ds))$ be the Boson Fock space [1] over the Hilbert space $L^2(I,ds)$. It is known that the linear submanifold of $\Gamma(L^2(I,ds))$ generated by the set $\{\Omega(f) \equiv \bigoplus_{h=0}^{\infty} (h!)^{-1/2}(f\hat{\otimes} f\hat{\otimes} \ldots \hat{\otimes} f : f \in L^2(I,ds)\}$ of coherent vectors is dense in $\Gamma(L^2(I,ds))$. Here, $(f\hat{\otimes} f\hat{\otimes} \ldots \hat{\otimes} f)_0 \equiv 1$ and $(f\hat{\otimes} f\hat{\otimes} \ldots \hat{\otimes} f)_n$ is the n-fold algebraic tensor product of f with itself.

For $f \in L^2(I,ds)$, let $a(f)$ and $a^*(f)$ denote the Boson annihilation and creation operators. These operators are densely defined on the dense linear submanifold describe above but polynomials in the operators $\{a^*(f): f \in L^2(I,ds)\}$ do not leave that dense domain invariant. However, it is easy to construct a linear submanifold, denoted in the sequel by $\mathcal{S}(I)$, $I \subseteq \mathbb{R}_+$, which contains the linear submanifold generated by $\{\Omega(f): f \in L^2(I,ds)\}$ and is left invariant by polynomials in the operators $\{a(f), a^*(f): f \in L^2 I,ds)\}$. We shall use the following abbreviations: $\mathcal{S}([0,t)) \equiv \mathcal{S}_{\{t\}}$, $\mathcal{S}([t,\infty)) \equiv \mathcal{S}^{\{t\}}$, $t \in \mathbb{R}_+$, and $\mathcal{S}(\mathbb{R}_+) = \mathcal{S}$.

In the sequel, R is some fixed Hilbert space and X is defined by $X \equiv R \otimes \Gamma(L^2(\mathbb{R}_+,ds))$. Since $\Gamma(L^2(\mathbb{R}_+,ds)) = \Gamma(L^2([0,t),ds)) \otimes \Gamma(L^2([t,\infty),ds))$, for each $t \in \mathbb{R}_+$, it follows that $X = X_{\{t\}} \otimes \Gamma(L^2([t,\infty),ds))$, where $X_{\{t\}} \equiv R \otimes \Gamma(L^2([0,t),ds))$, $t \in \mathbb{R}_+$. We identify $X_{\{0\}}$ with R and call it the initial space.

Definition: Let Z be a set. Then, we call a subset W of $Z \times Z$ diagonally balanced provided that $\underline{w} \in W$, with $\underline{w} = (w_1 w_1)$, implies $\underline{w}_1 \equiv (w_1,w_2) \in W$ and $\underline{w}_2 \equiv (w_2,w_2) \in W$.

Remark: (i) Throughout the discussion, S is a subset of $L^2(\mathbb{R}_+,ds) \cap L^\infty(\mathbb{R}_+,ds)$, $\mathbb{R}$ and $\mathbb{H}$ are diagonally balanced subsets of $R \times R$ and $S \times S$, respectively, $\mathbb{H}_{\{t\}} \equiv \{(\mathbb{P}_t h_1, \mathbb{P}_t h_2): (h_1,h_2) \in \mathbb{H}\}$, and $\mathbb{H}^{\{t\}} \equiv \{(\mathbb{P}^t h_1, \mathbb{P}^t h_2): (h_1,h_2) \in \mathbb{H}\}$, where $\mathbb{P}_t$ (resp. $\mathbb{P}^t$) is the orthogonal projection of $L^2(\mathbb{R}_+,ds)$ onto $L^2([0,t),ds)$ (resp. $L^2([t,\infty),ds)$), $t \in \mathbb{R}_+$.

(ii) If $(\underline{u},\underline{h}) \in \mathbb{R} \times \mathbb{H}$, with $\underline{u} = (u_1,u_2)$ and $\underline{h} = (h_1,h_2)$, define $\underline{u}_1$, $\underline{u}_2$ $\underline{h}_1$, $\underline{h}_2$ thus: $\underline{u}_j = (u_j,u_j)$ and $\underline{h}_j = (h_j,h_j)$, $j = 1,2$.

(iii) If W is a Cartesian product of two sets, we write $\mathbb{W}$ for the diagonal of W.

3. The Algebraic Setting

The notion of an Op*-algebra [8] is now generally well-known.

If F is a dense linear submanifold of a Hilbert space H, we write $\mathbb{A}(F)$ for the maximal Op*-algebra of linear operators associated with F. Notice that $\mathbb{A}(F)$ is a unital *-algebra. We denote the algebraic dual of $\mathbb{A}(F)$ by $\mathbb{A}(F)^*$.

The set $\mathbb{A}(E)^{*\mathbb{R} \times \mathbb{H}}$. Let D be some dense linear submanifold of R and E be the dense linear submanifold of X with the property that $E = E_t \hat{\otimes} \mathcal{S}^{\{t\}}$, with $E_t = D \hat{\otimes} \mathcal{S}_{\{t\}}$, for each $t \in \mathbb{R}_+$. Then E_t is dense in $X_{\{t\}}$, for each $t \in \mathbb{R}_+$. Furthermore,

$$\mathbb{A}(E) = \mathbb{A}(E_t) \bar{\otimes} \mathbb{A}(\mathcal{S}^{\{t\}}), \text{ for each } t \in \mathbb{R}_+, \text{ where } \hat{\otimes}, \tag{3.1}$$

$\bar{\otimes}$ denote algebraic tensor products. We write $\mathbb{1}$, $\mathbb{1}_t$ and $\mathbb{1}^t$ for the identities of $\mathbb{A}(E)$, $\mathbb{A}(E_t)$ and $\mathbb{A}(\mathcal{S}^{\{t\}})$, respectively, for each $t \in \mathbb{R}_+$.

In the sequel, $\mathbb{A}_{\{a,a^*\}}(\mathcal{S}^{\{t\}})$ denotes the Op*-subalgebra of $\mathbb{A}(\mathcal{S}^{\{t\}})$ generated by the set $\{a(f), a^*(h): f , h \in L^2([t,\infty),ds)\}$, $t \in \mathbb{R}_+$.

In order to introduce certain topologies of interest to us on $\mathbb{A}(E)$, we need the set $\mathbb{A}(E)^{*\mathcal{R}\times\mathcal{H}}$ defined as follows.

<u>(3.2) Definition</u>: $\mathbb{A}(E)^{*\mathcal{R}\times\mathcal{H}}$ is the set of all $\mathbb{A}(E)^*$-valued maps on $\mathcal{R}\times\mathcal{H}$

$$\mu: \mathcal{R}\times\mathcal{H} \longrightarrow \mathbb{A}(E)^*$$

$$(\underline{u},\underline{h}) \longrightarrow \mu_{(u,h)}(\cdot)$$

with the following properties:

(i) $\mu_{(\underline{u},\underline{h})}(\cdot)$ is a <u>positive</u> member of $\mathbb{A}(E)^*$, for each $(\underline{u},\underline{h}) \in \mathcal{R}\times\mathcal{H}$;

(ii) for each $t \in \mathbb{R}_+$ and $(\underline{u},\underline{h}) \in \mathcal{R}\times\mathcal{H}$, the linear functional $\mu_{(\underline{u},\underline{h})}$ factorizes as follows relative to the factorization (3.1) of $\mathbb{A}(E)^*$:

$$\mu_{(\underline{u},\underline{h})}(\cdot) = \mu_{(\underline{u},\underline{h}_{\{t\}})}(\cdot) \otimes \mu_{\underline{h}^{\{t\}}}(\cdot)$$

with $\underline{h}_{\{t\}} \in \mathcal{H}_{\{t\}}$, $\underline{h}^{\{t\}} \in \mathcal{H}^{\{t\}}$, and $\underline{h} = \underline{h}_{\{t\}} + \underline{h}^{\{t\}}$, $t \in \mathbb{R}_+$;

(iii) for each $t \in \mathbb{R}_+$ and $h \in \mathcal{H}$, with $\underline{h} = (h_1,h_2)$, the linear functional $\mu_{\underline{h}^{\{t\}}}(\cdot)$ in (ii) is such that its restriction to $\mathbb{A}_{\{a,a^*\}}(\mathcal{S}^{\{t\}})$ is $\langle \Omega(h_1^{\{t\}}), \cdot\, \Omega(h_2^{\{t\}})\rangle_{\Gamma(L^2([t,\infty),ds))}$;

(iv) for each $(\underline{u},\underline{h}) \in \mathcal{R}\times\mathcal{H}$, with $\underline{u} = (u_1,u_2)$ and $\underline{h} = (h_1,h_2)$, then

a) $|\mu_{(\underline{u},\underline{h})}(b^*c)| \le (\mu_{(\underline{u}_1,\underline{h}_1)}(b^*b))^{1/2}(\mu_{(\underline{u}_2,\underline{h}_2)}(c^*c))^{1/2}$, and

b) $|\mu_{\underline{h}^{\{t\}}}(d^*e)| \le (\mu_{\underline{h}_1^{\{t\}}}(d^*d))^{1/2}(\mu_{\underline{h}_2^{\{t\}}}(e^*e))^{1/2}$,

for all $b,c \in \mathbb{A}(E)$, $d,e \in \mathbb{A}(\mathcal{S}^{\{t\}})$, where $\underline{u}_j \equiv (u_j,u_j) \in \mathcal{R}$, $\underline{h} \equiv (h_j,h_j) \in \mathcal{H}$ and $\underline{h}_j^{\{t\}} = (h_j^{\{t\}}, h_j^{\{t\}}) \in \mathcal{H}^{\{t\}}$, $j = 1,2$.

<u>(3.3) Example</u>: Let P,Q be two mappings of $\mathcal{R}$ into $\mathbb{R}_+$ and R be a mapping of $\mathcal{R}$ into itself such that $\underline{u} = (u_1,u_2) \to R(u_1), R(u_2))$ is a transformation of $\mathcal{R}$ onto itself. For each $(\underline{u},\underline{h}) \in \mathcal{R}\times\mathcal{H}$, with $\underline{u} = (u_1,u_2)$ and $\underline{h} = (h_1,h_2)$, define $\mu_{(\underline{u},\underline{h})}(\cdot)$ thus:

$$\mu_{(\underline{u},\underline{h})}(\cdot) = \langle R(u_1) \otimes \Omega(h_1), \cdot\, R(u_2) \otimes \Omega(h_2)\rangle_X \ \exp(P(u_1) + Q(u_2)).$$

Then, it is straightforward to show that $(\underline{u},\underline{h}) \to \mu_{(\underline{u},\underline{h})}(\cdot)$ lies in $\mathbb{A}(E)^{*\mathbb{R} \times \mathbb{H}}$.

(3.4) Remark: If $P = 0 = Q$; R = the identity operator on R, $\mathbb{R} \equiv R \times R$ and $\mathbb{H} = \tilde{L} \times \tilde{L}$ in (3.3), where $\tilde{L} = L^{\infty}(\mathbb{R}_+, ds) \cap L^2(\mathbb{R}_+, ds)$, then

(*) $$\mu_{(\underline{u},\underline{h})}(\cdot) = \langle u_1 \otimes \Omega(h_1), \cdot\, u_2 \otimes \Omega(h_2)\rangle_X .$$

The map $(\underline{u},\underline{h}) \to \mu_{(\underline{u},\underline{h})}(\cdot)$ given by (*) is essentially the one employed throughout in [1]. Hence, one may regard the formulation in [1] as a particular case of the present more general setting.

The topology τ_2^{μ} on $\mathbb{A}(E)$. Let $\mu \in \mathbb{A}(E)^{*\mathbb{R} \times \mathbb{H}}$. Then, in the sequel, τ_2^{μ} denotes the locally convex topology on $\mathbb{A}(E)$ whose family of semi-norms is the following:

$$\{b \to \|b\|_{\mu,(\underline{u},\underline{h})} = (\mu_{(\underline{u},\underline{h})}(b^*b))^{1/2},\ b \in \mathbb{A}(E) : (\underline{u},\underline{h}) \in \mathbb{R} \times \mathbb{H}\}.$$

Notation: We write $\mathbb{A}(E,\tau_2^{\mu})$ for the completion of $\mathbb{A}(E)$ in the topology τ_2^{μ}. We remark that $\mathbb{A}(E,\tau_2^{\mu})$ is a partial *-algebra of, in general, unbounded linear operators [4].

4. Stochastic Processes and Stochastic Integrals

By a stochastic process, we refer to an $\mathbb{A}$-valued map on $\mathbb{R}_+$. Such a map X will be called adapted or non-anticipating provided that $X(t) \in \mathbb{A}(E_t) \bar{\otimes} \mathbb{1}^t$, for each $t \in \mathbb{R}_+$. We denote the collection of all adapted stochastic processes by $Ad(E)$. The following classes of stochastic processes are of interest.

(4.1) Definition: A member b of $Ad(E)$ will be called

(i) simple, provided that b has a representation of the form $b(\cdot) = \sum_{n=0}^{\infty} \chi_{(t_n,t_{n-1}]}(\cdot) b_n$ where $0 = t_o < t_1 < \ldots < t_n$, with $t_n \to \infty$ and $n \to \infty$, $b_n \in \mathbb{A}(E_{t_n}) \otimes \mathbb{1}^{t_n}$ and χ_I is the indicator function of the set $I \subseteq \mathbb{R}_+$; and

(ii) μ-locally square integrable, in case $\mu \in \mathbb{A}(E)^{*\mathbb{R} \times \mathbb{H}}$, the map $t \to \|b(t)\|_{\mu,(\underline{u},\underline{h})}$, from $\mathbb{R}_+$ into itself, is Lebesgue measurable for each $(\underline{u},\underline{h}) \in \mathbb{R} \times \mathbb{H}$ and

$$\int_0^t ds\ \|b(s)\|^2_{\mu,(\underline{u},\underline{h})} < \infty$$

for each $(\underline{u},\underline{h}) \in \mathfrak{R} \times \mathfrak{H}$ and each $t > 0$.

Notation: (i) Let $\mu \in \mathbb{A}(E)^{*\mathfrak{R} \times \mathfrak{H}}$. Then, the collection of all members of $\mathrm{Ad}(E)$ which are simple will be denoted by $\mathrm{Ad}(E)_{sim}$.

(ii) Write $L^2(E,\tau^{\mu}_{2,loc})$ for the completion of the linear manifold of all μ-locally square integrable members of $\mathbb{A}(E)$ in the locally convex topology $\tau^{\mu}_{2,loc}$ included by the family $\{\|\cdot\|_{\mu,(\underline{u},\underline{h}),t} : (\underline{u},\underline{h}) \in \mathfrak{R} \times \mathfrak{H}, t \in \mathbb{R}_+\}$ of semi-norms, where

$$\|b\|^2_{\mu,(\underline{u},\underline{h}),t} = \int_0^t ds \, \|b(s)\|^2_{\mu,(\underline{u},\underline{h})} .$$

Remark: The following is a useful approximation result.

(4.2) Proposition: Let $\mu \in \mathbb{A}(E)^{*\mathfrak{R} \times \mathfrak{H}}$ and $b \in L^2(E,\tau^{\mu}_{2,loc})$. Then, there exists a sequence of members of $\mathrm{Ad}(E)_{sim}$ which converges in $L^2(E,\tau^{\mu}_{2,loc})$ to b .

Notation: We introduce the following notation:

$$A(t) = a(\chi_{[0,t)}) \quad \text{and} \quad A^*(t) = a^*(\chi_{[0,t)}),\ t \in \mathbb{R}_+ .$$

Remark: (i) The operators $A(t)$ and $A^*(t)$ lie in $\mathbb{A}(E_t)$, for each $t \in \mathbb{R}_+$, but in the sequel, we regard them as members of $\mathbb{A}(E)$ through the natural identification of $\mathbb{A}(E_t)$ with $\mathbb{A}(E_t) \otimes \mathbb{1}^t$, $t \in \mathbb{R}_+$. In this way, the maps $t \to A(t)$ and $t \to A^*(t)$, $t \in \mathbb{R}_+$, lie in $\mathrm{Ad}(E)$.

(ii) Since $A(t) - A(s) = a(\chi_{[s,t)})$ and $A^*(t) - A^*(s) = a^*(\chi_{[s,t)})$, $0 \neq s < t$, these operators lie in $\mathbb{A}(\mathcal{S}^{\{s\}})$. Hence, in the sequel, we shall regard them as members of $\mathbb{A}(E)$ through the identification of $\mathbb{A}(\mathcal{S}^{\{s\}})$ with $\mathbb{1}_s \bar{\otimes} \mathbb{A}(\mathcal{S}^{\{s\}})$, $s \in \mathbb{R}_+$.

(iii) The operators $A(t)$, $A^*(t)$, $t \in \mathbb{R}_+$, are noncommutative analogues of classical Brownian motion. Let us now define integration with respect to them.

Definition: Let F,G,H be members of $\mathrm{Ad}(E)_{sim}$ with $F(t) = \sum_{n=0}^{\infty} F_n \chi_{(t_n,t_{n+1}]}(t)$, $G(t) = \sum_{n=0}^{\infty} G_n \chi_{(t_n,t_{n+1}]}(t)$ and $H(t) = \sum_{n=0}^{\infty} H_n \chi_{(t_n,t_{n+1}]}(t)$, $t \in \mathbb{R}_+$, for some $\{F_n,G_n,H_n\} \subset \mathbb{A}(E_{t_n}) \bar{\otimes} \mathbb{1}^{t_n}$, $n = 0,1,2,\ldots$, where $0 = t_o < t_1 < \ldots < t_n$ and $t_n \to \infty$ as $n \to \infty$.

Then, we define X as follows

$X(0) = 0$ and

$$X(t) = X(t_n) + F_n(A(t) - A(t_n)) + G_n(A^*(t) - A^*(t_n)) + H_n(t-t_n),$$

for $t \in (t_n, t_{n+1}]$, $n = 0,1,2,\ldots$.

Defined in the above way, we shall write X symbolically as follows:

$$X(t) = \int_0^t (F(s)dA(s) + G(s)dA^*(s) + H(s)ds),\ t \in \mathbb{R}_+ \ . \tag{4.3}$$

We can give estimates for $X(t)$ and $X(t) - X(s)$, $s,t \in \mathbb{R}_+$, with $s \le t$.

(4.4) Theorem: Let $\mu \in \mathbb{A}(E)^{*\mathbb{R}\times\mathbb{H}}$ and $F,G.H$ be members of $Ad(E)_{sim}$. Then, for each $\tau > 0$ and all $(\underline{u},\underline{h}) \in \mathbb{R}\times\mathbb{H}$,

(i) $\|X(t)\|^2_{\mu,(\underline{u},\underline{h})}$

$$\le \alpha_\tau(\underline{h}) \int_0^t ds\ e^{t-s} \left\{\|H(s)\|^2_{\mu,(\underline{u},\underline{h})} + \|F(s)\|^2_{\mu,(\underline{u},\underline{h})} + \|G(s)\|^2_{\mu,(\underline{u},\underline{h})}\right\},$$

$0 < t \le \tau$;

(ii) $\|X(t) - X(s)\|^2_{\mu,(\underline{u},\underline{h})}$

$$\le \alpha_\tau(\underline{h}) \int_0^t dr\ e^{t-r} \left\{\|H(s)\|^2_{\mu,(\underline{u},\underline{h})} + \|F(s)\|^2_{\mu,(\underline{u},\underline{h})} + \|G(s)\|^2_{\mu,(\underline{u},\underline{h})}\right\}$$

$0 < t \le \tau$, where $\alpha_\tau(\underline{h})$ is some positive constant;

(iii) $X \in L^2(E,\tau^\mu_{2,loc})$.

Remark: Using Proposition (4.2) and Theorem (4.4), we may now extend the stochastic integral (4.3) so as to apply to integrands F,G,H lying in $L^2(E,\tau^\mu_{2,loc})$. In the sequel, we assume that the relevant extension has been implemented. We remark that Theorem (4.4) remains valid in the case where F,G,H lie in $L^2(E,\tau^\mu_{2,loc})$.

5. The Ito Formula

We shall give a generalization of the well-known Ito formula [2] in the present setting involving noncommutative stochastic processes which take values in partial *-algebras of operators.

Throughout, $\mu \in \mathbb{A}(E)^{*\mathbb{R}\times\mathbb{H}}$.

(5.1) Notation: (i) If A is an index set, we write $Fin(A)$ for the collection of all finite subsets of A.

(ii) For $\mathbb{H} \in Fin(\mathbb{R}\times\mathbb{H})$, we define $\|\circ\|_{\mathbb{H}}$ on $\mathbb{A}(E,\tau^\mu_2)$ by

$$\|x\|_{\mathbb{H}} = \sup_{(\underline{u},\underline{h})\in\mathbb{H}} \|x\|_{\mu,(\underline{u},\underline{h})},\quad x \in \mathbb{A}(E,\tau^\mu_2).$$

(iii) Let $L(\mathbb{A}(E,\tau_2^{\mu}))$ denote the linear space of all continuous linear maps from $\mathbb{A}(E,\tau_2^{\mu})$ into itself. For $\eta \in L(\mathbb{A}(E,\tau_2^{\mu}))$, we write $\eta[x]$ for the image of x in $\mathbb{A}(E,\tau_2^{\mu})$ under η.

In the sequel, $L_b(\mathbb{A}(E,\tau_2^{\mu}))$ denotes $L(\mathbb{A}(E,\tau_2^{\mu}))$ equipped with the locally convex topology whose family

$$\left\{\|\circ\|_{\mu,(\underline{u},\underline{h}),\mathbb{H},\Theta} : (\underline{u},\underline{h}) \in \mathcal{R} \times \mathcal{H}, \mathbb{H} \in \text{Fin}(\mathcal{R}\times\mathcal{H}), \Theta = \text{bounded subset of } \mathbb{A}(E,\tau_2^{\mu})\right\}$$

of semi-norms is specified thus:

$$\|\eta\|_{\mu,(\underline{u},\underline{h}),\mathbb{H},\Theta} = \sup\left\{\frac{\|\eta[x]\|_{\mu,(\underline{u},\underline{h})}}{\|x\|_{\mathbb{H}}} : x \in \Theta\right\}$$

(iv) Define $L_b((\mathbb{A}(E,\tau_2^{\mu}))^m, \mathbb{A}(E,\tau_2^{\mu}))$, $m = o,1,2,\ldots$, by $L_b((\mathbb{A}(E,\tau_2^{\mu}))^o, \mathbb{A}(E,\tau_2^{\mu})) \equiv \mathbb{A}(E,\tau_2^{\mu})$, and

$$L_b((\mathbb{A}(E,\tau_2^{\mu}))^n, \mathbb{A}(E,\tau_2^{\mu})) = L_b(\mathbb{A}(E,\tau_2^{\mu}), L_b((\mathbb{A}(E,\tau_2^{\mu}))^{n-1}, \mathbb{A}((E,\tau_2^{\mu}))),$$

$n = 1,2,\ldots,m$, where $L_b(\mathbb{A}(E,\tau_2^{\mu}), \mathbb{A}(E,\tau_2^{\mu})) \equiv L_b(\mathbb{A}(E,\tau_2^{\mu}))$.

(5.2) Definition: Let $C(\mathbb{A}(E,\tau_2^{\mu}), \mathbb{A}(E,\tau_2^{\mu}))$ be the linear space of all the continuous mappings from $\mathbb{A}(E,\tau_2^{\mu})$ into $\mathbb{A}(E,\tau_2^{\mu})$. Suppose that $\psi \in C(\mathbb{A}(E,\tau_2^{\mu}), \mathbb{A}(E,\tau_2^{\mu}))$. Then, by the derivative of ψ on $\mathbb{A}(E,\tau_2^{\mu})$, if it exists, we refer to a continuous map ψ' from $\mathbb{A}(E,\tau_2^{\mu})$ into $L_b(\mathbb{A}(E,\tau_2^{\mu}))$ such that the expression $\frac{1}{\lambda}(\psi(x+\lambda y)-\psi(x)-\psi'(x)[y]$ $(0 \neq \lambda \in (-\infty,\infty), y,x \in \mathbb{A}(E,\tau_2^{\mu}))$ converges, for each x in $\mathbb{A}(E,\tau_2^{\mu})$, to the zero members of $\mathbb{A}(E,\tau_2^{\mu})$ as λ tends to zero, uniformly with respect to each $y \in \mathbb{A}(E,\tau_2^{\mu})$.

Remark: (i) Higher order derivatives on $\mathbb{A}(E,\tau_2^{\mu})$ are analogously defined.

(ii) Let $C^m(\mathbb{A}(E,\tau_2^{\mu}), \mathbb{A}(E,\tau_2^{\mu}))$ be the linear space of all the members of $C(\mathbb{A}(E,\tau_2^{\mu}), \mathbb{A}(E,\tau_2^{\mu}))$ which are m-times differentiable on $\mathbb{A}(E,\tau_2^{\mu})$.

(iii) If $\psi \in C^m(\mathbb{A}(E,\tau_2^{\mu}), \mathbb{A}(E,\tau_2^{\mu}))$, we write $\psi^{(m)}$ for its m-th derivative. Then, $\psi^{(m)}$ is a continuous map from $\mathbb{A}(E,\tau_2^{\mu})$ into $L_b((\mathbb{A}(E,\tau_2^{\mu}))^m, \mathbb{A}(E,\tau_2^{\mu}))$, $m = 1,2,\ldots$.

(iv) The symbol $C^{1,2}(I \times \mathbb{A}(E,\tau_2^{\mu}), \mathbb{A}(E,\tau_2^{\mu}))$ denotes the linear space of all continuous mappings ψ from $\mathbb{R}_+ \times \mathbb{A}(E,\tau_2^{\mu})$ into $\mathbb{A}(E,\tau_2^{\mu})$ with the properties that

a) for each $x \in \mathbb{A}(E,\tau_2^{\mu})$, the map $t \to \psi(t,x)$ is differentiable in $\mathbb{A}(E,\tau_2^{\mu})$; and

b) for each $t \in I \subseteq \mathbb{R}_+$, the map $x \to \psi(t,x)$ lies in $C^2(\mathbb{A}(E,\tau_2^{\mu}), \mathbb{A}(E,\tau_2^{\mu}))$.

(v) We require the following notion of adaptedness of maps.

<u>Definition</u>: We call a map $\theta: \mathbb{R}_+ \times \mathbb{A}(E,\tau_2^\mu) \to L_b((\mathbb{A}(E,\tau_2^\mu))^m, \mathbb{A}(E,\tau_2^\mu))$ <u>adapted</u> provided that

(i) for each $t \in \mathbb{R}_+$, $\theta(t,x)(y_1,y_2,\ldots,y_m)$ lies in the τ_2^μ-completion $\mathbb{A}_t(E,\tau_2^\mu)$ of $\mathbb{A}(E_t) \otimes \mathbb{1}^t$ whenever $y_j, x \in \mathbb{A}_t(E,\tau_2^\mu)$, $j = 1,2,\ldots,m$, and

(ii) for each $t \in \mathbb{R}_+$, $x \in \mathbb{A}_t(E,\tau_2^\mu)$ and $u_j = y_j z_j \in \mathbb{A}(E)$ with $y_j \in \mathbb{A}(E_t) \bar{\otimes} \mathbb{1}^{t^+}$ and $z_j \in \mathbb{1}_t \bar{\otimes} \mathbb{A}(\mathcal{S}^{\{t\}})$, $j = 1,2,\ldots,m$, we have $\theta(t,x)(u_1,u_2,\ldots,u_m) = \theta(t,x)(y_1,y_2,\ldots,y_m) \cdot z_1 z_2 \ldots z_m$.

<u>Remark</u>: In the case of a map $\theta: \mathbb{A}(E,\tau_2^\mu) \to L_b((\mathbb{A}(E,\tau_2^\mu))^m, \mathbb{A}(E,\tau_2^\mu))$, the notion of adaptedness is analogous to that just introduced.

<u>(5.3) Theorem (the Ito formula)</u>: Let $\mu \in \mathbb{A}(E)^{*\mathbb{R}\times\mathbb{H}}$, $\tau > 0$ be fixed and $\psi \in C^{1,2}([0,\tau] \times \mathbb{A}(E,\tau_2^\mu), \mathbb{A}(E,\tau_2^\mu))$. Suppose that

(i) the maps ψ' and ψ'' are adapted;

(ii) the maps $t \to F(t)$, $t \to G(t)$, $t \to H(t)$ are continuous from $\mathbb{R}_+$ into $\mathbb{A}(E,\tau_2^\mu)$;

(iii) X_o is a fixed member of $\mathbb{A}(E,\tau_2^\mu)$ and

$$X(t) = X_o + \int_o^t (F(s)dA(t) + G(s)dA^*(s) + H(s)ds), \quad t \in [0,\tau] .$$

Then

$$d\psi(t,X(t)) = \Big(\frac{\partial\psi}{\partial t}(t,X(s)) + \psi'(t,X(t))[H(t)] + $$

$$+ \psi''(t,X(t))(F(t),G(t))\Big)\, dt \; +$$

$$+ \psi'(t,X(t))[F(t)]dA(t) + \psi'(t,X(t))[G(t)]dA^*(t) ,$$

$t \in [0,\tau]$.

<u>(5.4) Theorem</u>: Let $\mu \in \mathbb{A}(E)^{*\mathbb{R}\times\mathbb{H}}$ and $\xi \in C^2(\mathbb{A}(E,\tau_2^\mu), \mathbb{A}(E,\tau_2^\mu))$.
Suppose that ξ' and ξ'' are adapted.
Then

$$d\xi(\beta A(t) + \gamma A^*(t))$$

$$= \beta\gamma\xi''(\beta A(t) + \gamma A^*(t))dt + \beta\xi'(\beta A(t) + \gamma A^*(t))dA(t) +$$

$$+ \gamma\xi'(\beta A(t) + \gamma A^*(t))dA^*(t), \quad t \in [0,\tau] .$$

(5.5) Theorem (Integration by parts): Let $\mu \in \mathbb{A}(E)^{*\mathbb{R}\times\mathbb{H}}$ and $\tau > 0$ be fixed. Suppose that

(i) the maps $t \to F_j(t)$, $t \to G_j(t)$ and $t \to H_j(t)$, are continuous from $\mathbb{R}_+$ into $\mathbb{A}(E,\tau_2^\mu)$, $j = 1,2$; and

(ii) $X_j^o \in \mathbb{A}(E,\tau_2^\mu)$ and $X_j(t) = X_j^o + \int_0^t (F_j(s)dA(s) + G_j(s)dA^*(s) + H_j(s)ds$, $j = 1,2$.

Furthermore, define $[X_1,X_2]_t$ by

$$[X_1,X_2]_t = \int_0^t ds\Big(F_1(s)G_2(s) + F_2(s)G_1(s)\Big)\ , \quad t \in [0,\tau]\ .$$

Then

$$X_1(t)X_2(t) = X_1^oX_2^o + [X_1,X_2]_t + \int_0^t \Big(dX_1(s)X_2(s) + X_1(s)dX_2(s)\Big)\ , \quad t \in \mathbb{R}_+\ .$$

□

Remark: (i) Proofs of Theorems (5.3) - (5.5) in a more general setting than presented here appear in [5].

(ii) A result similar to Theorem (5.5) has been established in [1, Theorem 4.5]. But there, it is assumed that $X_1(t)$, $X_2(t)$, $t \in [0,\tau]$ are bounded operators. Recall that the operators featuring in our presentation are not necessarily bounded. Thus, Theorem (5.5) is a generalization of [1, Theorem 4.5].

References:

[1] Hudson, R.L. and Parthasarathy, K.R.: Quantum Ito's formula and stochastic evolutions, Commun. Math. Phys. 93, 301-323 (1984)

[2] Ito, K.: On a formula concerning stochastic differentials, Nagoya Math. J. 3, 55-65 (1951)

[3] Borchers, H.J.: in RCP 25 (Strasbourg) 22, 26 (1975)

[4] Antoine, J.-P. and Karwowski, W.: Partial *-algebras of closed linear operators in Hilbert space, Publ. RIMS, Kyoto Univ.

[5] Ekhaguere, G.O.S.: Quantum stochastic integration and the Ito formula, BiBoS Bielefeld Preprint (1985)

[6] ______________ : Properties of solutions of quantum stochastic integral equations, BiBoS Bielefeld Preprint (1985)

[7] ______________ : A quantum stochastic maximum principle, BiBoS Bielefeld Preprint (1985)

[8] Lassner, G.: Topological algebras of operators, Rep. Mathematical Phys. 3, 279-293 (1972)

A non-renormalizable planar field theory

Giovanni Felder
Theoretische Physik
ETH-Hönggerberg
8093 Zürich, Switzerland

Abstract

We solve the ultraviolet problem of the planar diagram ϕ_4^4 theory with propagator $1/p^{2-\varepsilon/2}$. For small $\varepsilon>0$ the theory is shown to have a non-trivial ultraviolet stable fixed point at negative coupling. The vicinity of the fixed point is discussed.

1. Introduction

The renormalization group [1] has changed the picture of renormalizability of field theory: in the old approach a renormalizable theory is a theory which can be made finite in perturbation theory by adding counterterms to a finite number of coupling constants in the bare Lagrangean.

In the renormalization group approach one looks at the problem from a different point of view: the crucial observation is that only a finite number of terms in a bare Lagrangean (the "relevant" terms), which is a perturbation of a free field, can be seen at low energy. These terms are the ones corresponding to eigenvalues ≥ 1 of the renormalization group transformation. This means that the theory has only a finite number of parameters, and can be parametrized e.g. by the value of the effective coupling constants of the relevant directions at some fixed energy scale. From this point of view, in a non-renormalizable field theory one tries to parametrize the model by more parameters than one is allowed to, i.e. by imposing the value of some irrelevant effective coupling constants as well as the relevant ones. Of course this analysis is based on the study of the vicinity of a Gaussian fixed point. If another fixed point of the renormalization group is present there can be other relevant directions appearing and a non-renormalizable theory can become renormalizable.

A typical example where these general heuristic discussions can be made concrete is the ϕ^4 model in $d>4$ dimensions, with euclidean action

$$S = \int (\tfrac{1}{2} Z (\nabla\phi(x))^2 + \tfrac{1}{2} m^2 \phi^2(x) + g{:}\phi^4(x){:})d^d x \;. \qquad (1.1)$$

The $:\phi^4:$ term is irrelevant in more than four dimensions and the renormalization group tells us that the theory tends to a free field as the cut-off is removed (at least if g is small). This is in fact true for all $g \geqslant 0$ as was proved by Aizenman [2] and Fröhlich [3] using a lattice cut-off.

On the other hand a second order beta function calculation

$$\mu\frac{d}{d\mu} \lambda(\mu) = \varepsilon\lambda(\mu)+\beta_2\lambda(\mu)^2, \quad \varepsilon = d-4, \quad \beta_2=\beta_2(\varepsilon)>0, \qquad (1.2)$$

where $\lambda(\mu)$ is the dimensionless running coupling constant, predicts the existence of a non-trivial fixed solution of the flow equation $\lambda(\mu) = -\varepsilon/\beta_2 \equiv \lambda^*(\varepsilon)$ at negative ("wrong sign") coupling constant. This fixed point is ultraviolet stable, i.e. the $:\phi^4:$ term has a <u>relevant</u> component at λ^* and the theory becomes renormalizable if expanded around this fixed point.

In fact, as it stands, this argument is not very conclusive even at the perturbative level: the perturbation theory of the beta function for non-renormalizable theories <u>does not make sense</u>: higher order coefficients are ultraviolet divergent!

However there is a way out from this problem: Gallavotti and Nicolò introduced [4] a beta <u>functional</u> for renormalizable theories

$$\mu \frac{d\,\underline{\lambda}(\mu)}{d\mu} = \underline{\beta}(\{\underline{\lambda}(\mu')\}_{\mu'>\mu}) \tag{1.3}$$

where $\underline{\lambda}(\mu)$ is the set of running coupling constants on scale μ (in fact (2.3) is formulated as a difference equation: we will be more precise below). This beta functional coincides with the usual beta function up to second order but to higher order it couples $\lambda(\mu)$'s on different scales.

It then turned out [5] that even for non-renormalizable theories the beta functional is finite order by order in perturbation theory.

This observation is the basis of the rigorous construction [6] of a planar ϕ^4 theory which is similar to (1.1): a ϕ^4 model in 4 dimensions but with propagator $1/p^{2-\varepsilon/2}$. This model is non-renormalizable and has the same second order beta function (1.2) as the $\phi^4_{4+\varepsilon}$ model, but is simpler to treat because one can keep ε small without going to non-integer dimensions.

Another model which can be handled along these lines is the Gross - Neveu model in two dimensions with propagator $\not{p}/p^{2-\varepsilon/2}$. In this model the Pauli principle plays the role of the planarity of the ϕ^4 model. This non-renormalizable

Gross-Neveu model has been recently studied by Gawędzki and Kupiainen [7].

Of course none of these models can lead to physically reasonable quantum field theories. We find, however, that it is interesting to see that ultraviolet fixed points indeed exist. Moreover we wait to emphasize that these models have no anomalous dimensions at the non-trivial fixed point. To see these methods at work for theories with anomalous dimensions one has to go to non-integer space time dimension by means of some analytic continuation prescription, but this makes all estimates more complicated.

2. Definition of the model, main concepts

We consider a four-dimensional euclidean field formally defined by the "measure"

$$e^{-V(\phi)}\ dP(\phi), \tag{2.1}$$

where dP is a Gaussian measure with mean zero and covariance

$$C(x,y) = \int \phi(x)\phi(y)\,dP(\phi) = \frac{1}{(2\pi)^4}\int \frac{1}{p^{2-\varepsilon/2}}\, e^{i\,p\,(x-y)}\,d^4 p. \tag{2.2}$$

We introduce a momentum decomposition with scale parameter $\gamma>1$ by writing

$$\frac{1}{p^{2-\varepsilon/2}} = \sum_{j=-\infty}^{+\infty} \hat{C}^{(j)}(p^2) \tag{2.3}$$

where, e.g.

$$\hat{C}^{(j)}(p^2) = \int_{\gamma^{-2j}}^{\gamma^{-2(j-1)}} e^{-\alpha p^2} \frac{\alpha^{-\varepsilon/4} d\alpha}{\Gamma(1-\varepsilon/4)} . \tag{2.4}$$

Let now $\{\phi^{(j)}\}_{j=-\infty}^{+\infty}$ be independent Gaussian fields with covariance $\hat{C}^{(j)}$. We can write a cut-off version of (2.1)

$$e^{-V(\phi^{\leq N})} dP^{(\leq N)}(\phi^{\leq N}), \tag{2.5}$$

where $\phi^{\leq N} = \sum_{j\leq N} \phi^{(j)}$ is Gaussian field with ultraviolet cut-off γ^N. The problem is to remove the cut-off by keeping the <u>effective potentials</u>

$$V^{(k)}(\phi^{\leq k}) = - \ell n E_{k+1} \cdots E_N \exp(-V(\phi^{\leq N})), \tag{2.6}$$

(where E_j denotes integration over the distribution of $\phi^{(j)}$) finite (in some sense). In our case the bare potential is

$$\begin{aligned} V(\phi^{\leq N}) &= \lambda_{2'}(N)\gamma^{-\varepsilon N/2}\int :(\partial\phi)^2: d^4x \\ &+ \lambda_2(N)\gamma^{-(2-\varepsilon/2)N} \int :\phi^2: d^4x + \lambda_4(N)\gamma^{-\varepsilon N}\int :\phi^4: d^4x \ , \end{aligned} \tag{2.7}$$

where $\lambda_\alpha(N)$ are the dimensionless bare coupling constants. The effective potentials, which we view as formal power series in the fields

$$V^{(k)}(\phi^{\leq k}) = \sum_{m\geq 0}\int d^4x_1 \ldots d^4x_m V_m^{(k)}(x_1,\ldots,x_m) :\phi^{\leq k}(x_1)\ldots\phi^{\leq k}(x_m): \tag{2.8}$$

(with Wick-ordering with respect to the covariance $C^{\leq k}$) can be split into two parts

$$V^{(k)} = L_k V^{(k)} + (1-L_k) V^{(k)}, \tag{2.9}$$

where L_k is a (finite dimensional) projector onto the space spanned by $\int :(\partial\phi)^2:$, $\int :\phi^2:$, $\int :\phi^4:$. We define L_k to be the zero momentum Taylor operator defined on formal power series of the type (2.8) as

$$L_k \int V(\underline{x}) : \prod_{i=1}^{m} \phi(x_i) : = \begin{cases} 0 \quad \text{if } m>4 \\ (\int V(\underline{x})\,dx_2 \ldots dx_4) \int :\phi^4(x): \text{ if } m=4 \end{cases}$$

$$L_k \int V(x,y) : \phi(x)\phi(y) : = (\int V(x,y,)\,dy \int :\phi^2(x):$$

$$- (\int \frac{(x-y)^2}{8} V(x,y)\,dy) \int :(\partial\phi)^2: \quad . \qquad (2.10)$$

This linear operator has the properties

$$L_k^2 = L_k,\ L_k\, E_{k+1} = E_{k+1}\, L_{k+1}\ . \qquad (2.11)$$

We define the (dimensionless) <u>running coupling constants</u> $\{\lambda_\alpha(k)\}_{k\in\mathbb{Z}}$ (or form factors) by

$$L_k V^{(k)} = \lambda_{2'}(k)\gamma^{-\varepsilon k/2} \int :(\partial\phi)^2: d^4x + \lambda_2(k)\gamma^{-(2-\varepsilon/2)k}$$

$$\int :\phi^2: d^4x + \lambda_4(k)\gamma^{-\varepsilon k} \int :\phi^4: d^4x. \qquad (2.12)$$

The <u>planar theories</u> (see [8] and references therein) can be thought of, in our case, as the $M\to\infty$ limit of a $\mathrm{tr}\phi^4$ model, where ϕ is an MxM matrix field. If this limit is taken in perturbation theory, only planar diagrams (i.e. diagrams which can be drawn on a plane without intersections of lines) survive to leading order in a $\frac{1}{M}$ expansion. The only property we will need here is that there exist less than const^n unlabelled planar diagrams (instead of n! const^n) to n'th order. This means that the theory can be defined directly in perturbation theory in presence of the cut-off and all manipulations we described so far are to be thought of as manipulations on the perturbative expansion of the kernels $V_m^{(k)}$ of (2.8). In fact the distribution $V_m^{(k)}$ are closely related to the Schwinger function and we identify our model with the sequences $\{V_m^{(k)}\}_{m\geq 0}$. These will be constructed in the $M\to\infty$ limit in the next sections. The detailed proof is contained in [6].

3. The tree expansion and the construction of the model

The starting point is the recursion relation between effective potentials

$$V^{(k)} = -\ell n\, E_{k+1} \exp(-V^{(k+1)}). \tag{3.1}$$

The irrelevant point of $V^{(k)}$ is expanded in cumulants

$$V^{(k)} = L_k V^{(k)} + (1-L_k) \sum_{s=1}^{\infty} \frac{(-)^{s+1}}{s!} E^T_{k+1}(V^{(k+1)},\ldots,V^{(k+1)}). \tag{3.2}$$

The $V^{(k+1)}$'s on the r.h.s. can be expanded the same way and so on. The resulting expansion if an expression of $V^{(k)}$ in terms of $L_h V^{(h)}$ with $h\geqslant k$ and by (2.12), it is a power series in the running coupling constants on all scales $h>k$. It is the <u>tree expansion</u> [4]. In terms of the kernels $V_m^{(k)}$ of (2.8) it reads

$$V_m^{(k)}(\underline{x}) = \sum_{\underline{n}} V^{(k)}_{m,\underline{n}}(\underline{x})\ \lambda^{\underline{n}}, \tag{3.3}$$

with the short-hand notation $\underline{n} = \{n_\alpha(h)\}_{\alpha=2,2',4,h\in\mathbb{Z}'}$
$\underline{\lambda}^{\underline{n}} = \prod_{\alpha,h} \lambda_\alpha(h)^{n_\alpha(h)}$.

If we insert the tree expansion (3.3) for $V^{(k+1)}$ in the r.h.s. of the cumulant expansion of the "local" terms

$$L_k V^{(k)} = E_k L_{k+1} V^{(k+1)} + \sum_{s=2}^{\infty} \frac{(-)^{s+1}}{s!} L_k E^T_{k+1}(V^{(k+1)},\ldots,V^{(k+1)}), \tag{3.4}$$

we get a recursion relation between the running coupling constants

$$\lambda_\alpha(k) = \gamma^{-\sigma(\alpha)}\lambda_\alpha(k+1) + \beta_\alpha(\{\underline{\lambda}(k+h)\}_{h\geqslant 1})$$
$$\beta_\alpha(\{\lambda_\alpha(k+h)\}_{h\geqslant 1}) = \sum_{\underline{n}} \beta^{(k)}_{\alpha,\underline{n}}\, \underline{\lambda}^{\underline{n}}, \tag{3.5}$$

where $\sigma(2') = \varepsilon/2$, $\sigma(2) = -2+\varepsilon/2$, $\sigma(4) = -\varepsilon$. The point is now that the expansions (3.3) and (3.5) are absolutely convergent, if $||\lambda_\alpha(k)||_\infty$ is small, uniformly in the cut-off N and in $0\leqslant\varepsilon\leqslant\varepsilon_o$. Moreover, the dependence of $V^{(k)}, \lambda_\alpha(k)$ on $\lambda_\alpha(k+h)$ is exponentially small in h. The bounds are [6], for the beta functional,

$$|\beta_{\alpha,\underline{n}}| \leqslant C^{|\underline{n}|}\, \rho^{-(h_{max}(\underline{n})-k)}, \quad C>0,\ \rho>1, \tag{3.6}$$

where $h_{max}(\underline{n}) = \max\{h|n_\alpha(h) \neq 0 \text{ some } \alpha\}$, and $|\underline{n}| = \sum_{\alpha,h} n_\alpha(h)$. Similar bounds are valid for the kernels $V^{(k)}_{m,\underline{n}}$. The proof is essentially based on power counting and the observation that $(1-L_k)$ in (3.2) kills all terms in the Feynman diagram expansion of E^T_{k+1} which have relevant power counting.

The reader might wonder at this point where the ultraviolet divergences of this non-renormalizable theory have disappeared. In fact these divergences reappear when one wants to parametrize the theory by the coupling constants on a fixed scale, say $k = 0$, by solving (3.5) in a power series in $\underline{\lambda}(0)$. This expansion has divergent coefficients to all (sufficiently high) orders (see [6] where this point is discussed).

But one can solve (3.5) by the fixed point ansatz $\lambda_\alpha(k) = \lambda^*_\alpha$ for all k:

$$\begin{aligned} \lambda^*_\alpha &= \gamma^{-\sigma(\alpha)} \lambda^*_\alpha + \overline{\beta}_\alpha(\underline{\lambda}^*) \\ \overline{\beta}_\alpha(\underline{\lambda}^*) &= \beta_\alpha(\underline{\lambda}^*,\underline{\lambda}^*,\underline{\lambda}^*,\ldots) \end{aligned} \tag{3.7}$$

$\overline{\beta}_\alpha(\underline{\lambda}^*)$ is an analytic function in the three variables $\{\lambda^*_\alpha\}_\alpha = 2',2,4$ for $|\underline{\lambda}|<R$; (3.7) coincide with the beta function up to second order, but $\overline{\beta}_\alpha$ is <u>not</u> the usual beta function, the latter being infinite in perturbation theory as we already pointed out. The fact that $\overline{\beta}_\alpha(\underline{\lambda}^*)$ is analytic implies that we can trust the second order calculation (1.2) and an implicit function theorem shows that there exists a fixed point solution of (3.7) if ε is small enough. The ε dependence is

$$\lambda^*_{2'} = O(\varepsilon),\ \lambda^*_2 = O(\varepsilon^2),\ \lambda^*_4 = O(\varepsilon). \tag{3.8}$$

The linearization of (3.7) at $\underline{\lambda}^*$ has two eigenvalues $\geqslant 1$ (at the trivial fixed point only $:\phi^2:$ is relevant) and one can find a two parameter family of solutions of (3.5) with $k \geqslant 0$ with $\lambda_\alpha(k) \to \lambda^*_\alpha$ as $k \to \infty$. These solutions can be inserted in (3.3) and we obain all effective potentials $V^{(k)}$ with $k > 0$. This solves the ultraviolet problem for the planar ϕ^4_4 theory with propagator $1/p^{2-\varepsilon/2}$.

References

[1] K. Wilson: Renormalization group and critical phenomena, I and II, Phys. Rev. B4, 3174-3183 and 3184-3205 (1971).

[2] M. Aizenman: Geometric analysis of ϕ^4 fields and Ising models I and II, Commun. Math. Phys. 86, 1-48 (1982).

[3] J. Fröhlich: On the triviality of $\lambda\phi_d^4$ theories and the approach to the critical point in $d \underset{(=)}{\geq} 4$ dimensions; Nucl. Phys. B200 FS4 , 281-296 (1982).

[4] G. Gallavotti, F. Nicolò: Renormalization theory in four dimensional scalar fields, to appear in Commun.Math.Phys. G. Gallavotti: Renormalization theory and ultraviolet stability for scalar fields via renormalization group methods, Rev.Mod.Phys. 57, 471-562 (1985).

[5] G. Felder, G. Gallavotti: Perturbation theory and non-renormalizable scalar fields, to appear in Commun.Math. Phys.

[6] G. Felder; Construction of a non-trivial planar field theory with ultraviolet stable fixed point, to appear in Commun. Math. Phys.

[7] K. Gawędzki, A. Kupiainen: Renormalizing the non-renormalizable, Phys. Rev. Lett. 55, 363-365 (1985), Renormalization of a nonrenormalizable quantum field theory, Preprint 1985, Helsinki University.

[8] G. 't Hooft: Planar diagram field theoreis, lectures given at the 1983 Cargèse Summer School "Progress in Gauge Field Theories".

An Invariant Torus for Nearly Integrable Hamiltonian Systems with Infinitely Many Degrees of Freedom

Jürg Fröhlich

Theoretical Physics, ETH - Zürich

CH-8093 Zürich

Thomas Spencer*

Courant Institute of Mathematical Sciences

NYU, 251 Mercer Street

New York, NY 10012

C. Eugene Wayne**

Department of Mathematics

The Pennsylvania State University

University Park, PA 16801

*Supported in part by NSF Grant DMR-8401225

**Supported in part by NSF Grant DMS-8403664

Abstract. Infinite dimensional invariant tori are constructed for some nearly integrable Hamiltonian systems arising in condensed matter physics. Trajectories lying on these tori represent localized states in the sense that the initial conditions concentrate most of the energy of the state in a relatively small number of modes of the system, and the energy remains primarily in these modes for all time.

Introduction

This note concerns the persistence of ordered motions in Hamiltonian systems with infinitely many degrees of freedom. Although our results are more generally applicable we will focus on a classical mechanical model of a layer of atoms deposited on a crystal surface. Crucial to our results is the assumption that the crystal surface contains some imperfections or randomness. For certain initial configurations of the deposited atoms we show that the trajectory of the system lies on a torus in the phase space. We provide here only a sketch of the proof. For a complete description of our results and methods the reader should consult [FSW].

During this conference we learned from J. Bellissard that he and M. Vittot had obtained similar results [VB] for a system of coupled classical rotators.

The Model

Consider the following model for the deposition of atoms on a crystal surface. On the surface of the crystal there are regions of low potential energy and it is in these potentials wells that the deposited atoms typically lie. To a first approximation, in which the atoms do not interact with each other and the potential energy of the crystal surface is fixed, the (classical) Hamiltonian for the system is

$$H(p,q) = \sum_{i\in\mathbb{Z}^d} h(p_i,q_i) = \sum_{i\in\mathbb{Z}^d} \frac{1}{2}(p_i^2+\omega_i^2 q_i^2) + \text{terms quartic in } p_i,q_i \quad (1)$$

In (1), the sum runs over all sites in the d-dimensional lattice $\mathbb{Z}^d$. In our present example $d=2$, but our results are more generally true, so we allow other values of d. In the second equality in (1) we have expanded $h(p_i,q_i)$, assuming that our potential wells are symmetric (so that no terms with odd powers of p_i and q_i appear) and set the mass of our deposited atoms equal to one. At each site of the lattice there are really two degrees of freedom--i.e. p_i and q_i should have two components. Our methods easily handle this complication, but to simplify the notation and exposition we ignore this fact.

<u>We assume that the crystal lattice is not a perfect lattice</u>, and to model these imperfections we <u>choose the ω_i's to be random variables</u>.

We now allow for interactions between the deposited atoms at various sites on the surface. We will assume that these interactions depend only on nearest neighbors, and in addition that they depend only on the relative positions of the atoms. Our Hamiltonian then takes the form,

$$\begin{aligned} H(p,q) = {} & \sum_{i\in\mathbb{Z}^d} \frac{1}{2}(p_i^2+\omega_i^2 q_i^2) + \mathcal{O}(p_i^4,q_i^4,(p_iq_i)^2) \\ & + \sum_{\langle i,j\rangle}\left[a(q_i-q_j)^2+b(q_i-q_j)^4+\dots\right] \end{aligned} \quad (2)$$

Here, the sum over $\langle i,j\rangle$ runs over all nearest neighbor pairs in the lattice $\mathbb{Z}^d$. Gathering the quartic and higher order terms together, and assuming that the displacements of the atoms from their equilibrium positions are small so that the higher order terms are weak, we rewrite (2) as

$$H(p,q) = \sum_{i\in\mathbb{Z}^d} \frac{1}{2}(p_i^2+\omega_i^2 q_i^2) + \sum_{\langle i,j\rangle}\left[a(q_i-q_j)^2 + \varepsilon f_{\langle i,j\rangle}(p_i,q_j)\right], \qquad (3)$$

where ε is small, and $f_{\langle i,j\rangle}$ is of fourth order or higher in each of its arguments.

We wish eventually to understand the nature of the trajectories of the system with the full non-linear Hamiltonian (3). In the present case, though, even the linearized problem with Hamiltonian

$$H^2(p,q) = \sum_{i\in\mathbb{Z}^d} \frac{1}{2}(p_i^2+\omega_i^2 q_i^2) + \sum_{\langle i,j\rangle} a(q_i-q_j)^2 \qquad (4)$$

is nontrivial, so we first analyze its behavior.

The equations of motion for the system with Hamiltonian (4) may be written as

$$\begin{aligned}\ddot{q}_i &= -a \sum_{j:|i-j|=1} (q_i-q_j) - \omega_i q_i \qquad i\in\mathbb{Z}^d \\ &= -[(-a\Delta \underline{q})_i+(V(\omega)\underline{q})_i] \equiv -(\mathcal{H}\underline{q})_i .\end{aligned} \qquad (5)$$

In (5), Δ is the dicretized Laplacian, $\underline{q} \in \mathbb{R}^{\mathbb{Z}^d}$, with $(\underline{q})_i=q_i$, and $V(\omega)$ the multiplication operator $(V(\omega)\underline{q})_i = \omega_i q_i$.

For a finite number of degrees of freedom, N, we know that $\mathcal{H}$ has N eigenvectors, $\underline{\psi}^j$, $j=1,\dots,N$, with eigenvalues $\tilde{\omega}_j$, from which one obtains N periodic solutions (normal modes) of (4) by setting $\underline{q}^j(t) = e^{i\sqrt{\tilde{\omega}_j}\,t}\,\underline{\psi}_j$. These normal modes allow one to represent (4) as a sum of uncoupled harmonic oscillators.

In general, for infinitely many degrees of freedom, $\mathcal{H}$, (considered as an operator on $\ell^2(\mathbb{Z}^d)$ say) will have some continuous spectrum, and the above picture breaks down. However, if the ω_i's are sufficiently random the picture remains valid. This is the famous <u>Anderson</u> <u>localization</u> phenomenon.

Let δ measure the disorder of the system. For instance, if the ω_i's are independent, identically distributed, r.v.'s with smooth distribution $\rho(\omega_i)$, set $\delta^{-1}=\sup \rho(\omega_i)$. One then has the following important result.

<u>Theorem 1</u>. ([A],[DLS],[FMSS],[SW]). *If δ is sufficiently large, $\mathcal{H}$ has pure point spectrum almost surely. Furthermore if $\{\underline{\psi}^j\}$ are the eigenvectors of $\mathcal{H}$, each $(\underline{\psi}^j)_\ell$ decays exponentially as $|\ell| \to \infty$.*

<u>Remark</u>: The rate of decay of $(\underline{\psi}^j)_\ell$ can be increased by increasing δ.

If we choose the (normalized) eigenvectors $\underline{\psi}^j$ as a basis for $\mathbb{R}^{\mathbb{Z}^d}$, we can write the quadratic Hamiltonian (4) in terms of new canonical variables P,Q (where $\underline{q} = \sum_j Q_j \underline{\psi}^j$ and similarly for P) and we find

$$H^2(P,Q) = \sum_{i\in\mathbb{Z}^d} \frac{1}{2} (P_i^2+\tilde{\omega}_i^2 Q_i^2) \tag{6}$$

with $\tilde{\omega}_i$ the points in the spectrum of $\mathcal{H}$. Thus, just as in the finite dimensional case the quadratic problem can be represented as a sum of uncoupled harmonic oscillators. We remark that since each $\underline{\psi}^j$ decays exponentially fast it will be localized in some finite region of the lattice, and if it decays very fast (i.e. δ is large) we will assume that it can be associated with a particular site $j \in \mathbb{Z}^d$. (This identification may be somewhat ambiguous.) Then Q_j is the coefficient of $\underline{\psi}^j$, and $\tilde{\omega}^j$ the eigenvalue of $\underline{\psi}^j$.

Let us now ask how our nonlinear Hamiltonian (3) looks, in terms of the new variables P and Q. The quadratic part of (3) will be the same as (6), so we obtain

$$H(P,Q) = \sum_{i\in\mathbb{Z}^d} \frac{1}{2} (P_i^2+\tilde{\omega}_i^2 Q_i^2) + \varepsilon \sum_{\langle i,j\rangle} f_{\langle i,j\rangle}(P,Q) \tag{7}$$

The interaction terms $f_{<i,j>}(P,Q)$ will still be fourth order in the arguments P and Q, but they will not in general depend only on the variables P_i, P_j and Q_i, Q_j. When we express $\underline{p}$ and $\underline{q}$ in terms of $\underline{\Psi}^\ell$, the exponential decay of the eigenfunctions implies that p_i and q_i will depend only exponentially weakly on eigenfunctions $\underline{\Psi}^\ell$ with $|\ell-i|$ large. Hence $f_{<i,j>}(P,Q)$ will depend only exponentially weakly on P_ℓ, Q_ℓ, if $|\ell-i|$ is large, a fact we express by the inequality

$$\left|\frac{\partial^2 f_{<i,j>}}{\partial x_\ell \partial x_k}\right| \leq C\ e^{-m|\ell-k|} \tag{8}$$

where x_i can be either P_ℓ or Q_ℓ, and similarly for x_k. The decay rate m can be made larger by increasing δ, and if the disorder is large enough we make the assumption that the $f_{<i,j>}$'s depend only on a finite number of P_ℓ's and Q_ℓ's with ℓ "close" to $<i,j>$. In fact, for simplicity we go even farther and assume that the interaction terms in (7) once again become nearest neighbor in nature.

Remark: This is an important assumption. Our methods easily encompass interaction terms of any finite range, but they do not allow us to treat exponentially decaying interactions of the form (8).

We make two further assumptions about the Hamiltonian (7). First, we assume that the interaction terms $f_{<i,j>}$ are analytic functions. This is a quite reasonable assumption for the sort of systems we are interested in.

Second, we note that the eigenvalues $\tilde{\omega}_i$ will be complicated functions of the original random variables ω_i. We model this complicated dependence by assuming that the $\tilde{\omega}_i$ are themselves i.i.d. random variables. Our methods work for essentially any smooth distribution $\rho(\tilde{\omega}_i)$ and would even permit weak correlations between $\tilde{\omega}_i$'s, but for definiteness take

$$\rho(\tilde{\omega}_i) = \begin{cases} 0 \quad \text{if} \quad \tilde{\omega}_i \leq 0 \\ \frac{2}{\sqrt{\pi}}\, e^{-\tilde{\omega}_i^2} \quad \text{if} \quad \tilde{\omega}_i > 0. \end{cases} \tag{9}$$

Results

Note that the system, with quadratic Hamiltonian (4) has the following important localization property. If we choose initial conditions $(\underline{p}^0, \underline{q}^0)$ such that most of the energy of the system is in a finite number of modes, then the majority of the energy of the system will remain in a finite number of modes of the system for all time, rather than being shared among all the (infinite number of) modes. This is easily seen by writing down the solution to the equations motion in terms of the eigenvectors $\underline{\psi}^j$ of $\mathcal{H}$ and noting that because of their exponential decay modes $\underline{\psi}^j$ localized far from the region of the system into which we put the initial energy essentially never participate in the motion.

The question we wish address is whether or not this phenomenon persists for the non-linear system with Hamiltonian (7). We show that it does, at least for certain special initial conditions. This is somewhat surprising since "conventional wisdom" holds that the nonlinear couplings lead to equipartition of energy among all the modes of the system.

Before giving a precise statement of our results we note that there is another physical system; illustrated in Figure 1, to which our model applies very well; namely a bed spring. This system contains a collection of harmonic oscillators located at sites of a (finite) two dimensional lattice, with frequencies that may be somewhat random, if the manufacturer of our bed was not sufficiently careful. These oscillators are coupled to their nearest neighbors and after a little calculation we arrive at (7) as the Hamiltonian for our system. The question of localized vibrations then becomes a crucial one since one wishes to know "If I roll over in bed will the vibrations I set up remain localized or will they spread out and wake up the person sleeping next to me?" This important question would seem to merit experimental investigation.

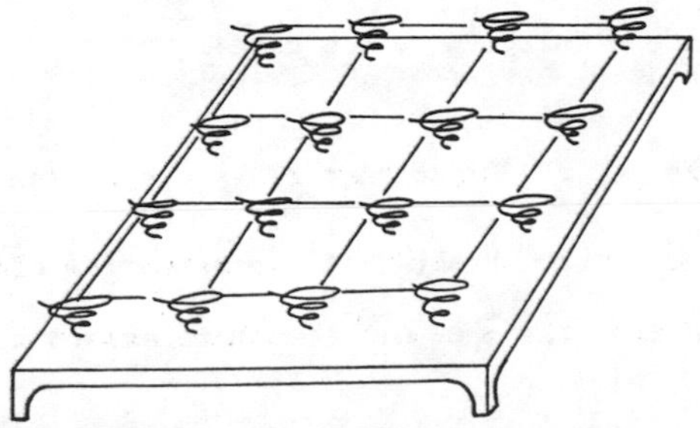

Figure 1. An important system of coupled oscillators

In order to study the trajectories of the system with Hamiltonian (7) it is convenient to introduce action-angle variables, (I_i, φ_i), defined by

$$Q_i = \sqrt{I_i/\tilde{\omega}_i}\ \cos \varphi_i \qquad\qquad P_i = -\sqrt{\tilde{w}_i I_i}\ \sin \varphi_i \tag{10}$$

for the harmonic oscillators. In terms of these new canonical variables (7) takes the form

$$H(I,\varphi) = \sum_{i\in\mathbb{Z}^d} \tilde{\omega}_i I_i + \varepsilon \sum_{\langle i,j\rangle} f_{\langle i,j\rangle}(I_i, I_j; \varphi_i, \varphi_j) \tag{11}$$

with $f_{\langle i,j\rangle}$:

a) $\mathcal{O}(I^2)$

b) analytic except at $I_i = 0$, $i \in \mathbb{Z}^d$.

Since we want to choose initial conditions that put most of the energy into only a few modes, and since except for small corrections due to the nonlinearities, the energy is proportional to the action, we define

$$(I^0)_j = \exp(-|j|^{d+\alpha}) \tag{12}$$

where α is any positive constant, $j \in \mathbb{Z}^d$, and $|j| = \sum_{i=1}^{d} |j_i|$.

We note that the exact form of these initial conditions is unimportant. Inside a finite region we could choose them to be essentially anything we like. What is necessary for the present proof is the very strong decay as $|j| \to \infty$ that this choice displays. We now have:

Theorem 2: *There exists* $\varepsilon_0 > 0$ *such that if* $\varepsilon < \varepsilon_0$, *there is a set* $\Omega(I^0)$ *of frequencies* $\tilde{\omega}$, *with* $\mathrm{Prob}(\Omega(I^0))$ *arbitrarily close to one (depending on* ε) *such that if* $\tilde{\omega} \in \Omega(I^0)$, *there exists a point* $\tilde{I}$ *with*

$$|\tilde{I}_j - I_j^0| < \tfrac{1}{4} I_j^0 \qquad\qquad j \in \mathbb{Z}^d \tag{13}$$

and $\tilde{\varphi} \in T^{\mathbb{Z}^d}$ *such that the trajectory of the system with Hamiltonian (11), and initial conditions* $(\tilde{I}, \tilde{\varphi})$ *lies on an infinite dimensional invariant torus.*

Remark: One can also show that the trajectory $\tilde{I}(t)$ satisfies

$|\tilde{I}_j(t) - I_j^0| < \frac{1}{4} I_j^0$, for all times t, not just at t=0.

This theorem implies that near any strongly localized initial condition (like (12)) there is a trajectory which lies on an invariant torus. Furthermore the estimate in the remark following the theorem shows that the energy of this trajectory is concentrated in a finite number of modes for all times.

If our system had only finitely many degrees of freedom such a result would not be surprising since the Kolmogorov-Arnol'd-Moser [KAM] theory guarantees that small perturbations of integrable systems possess many trajectories that lie on invariant tori. However, classical proofs of the KAM theorem:

(i) do not apply to systems with infinitely many degrees of freedom, and

(ii) they demand certain "anisochronicity" conditions apply to the integrable system, which our harmonic oscillators do not possess.

Thus, while our proof uses the KAM idea of an iterated sequence of canonical transformations it contains two novel ideas:

(i)' One uses the strong decay of the initial conditions to reduce the problem at each state in the iterative process to one of a finite number of degrees of freedom, and then shows that one can control the limit when the number of degrees of freedom becomes infinite.

(ii)' One uses the randomness of the $\tilde{\omega}$'s to remove the restriction that $(\partial^2 h/\partial I \partial I)^{-1}$ exists, where h is the integrable part of the Hamiltonian.

Proof

We sketch the first of the inductive steps in the proof of Theorem 2. Once again the reader interested in more details is urged to consult [FSW].

In order to show that a system contains invariant tori one usually tries to solve the Hamilton-Jacobi equation

$$H(I' + \frac{\partial S}{\partial \varphi}(I',\varphi),\varphi) = \tilde{h}(I') \tag{14}$$

If one finds a function S satisfying (14), one constructs a canonical transformation $C : (I',\varphi') \leftrightarrow (I,\varphi)$ via

$$I' = I + \frac{\partial S}{\partial \varphi}(I',\varphi) \quad ; \quad \varphi = \varphi' + \frac{\partial S}{\partial I'}(I',\varphi) \tag{15}$$

which transforms the Hamiltonian $H(I,\varphi)$ into $h(I')$. The latter Hamiltonian has all of its trajectories lying on tori, and since canonical transformations take solutions of Hamilton's equations into solutions of Hamilton's equations one gets a lot of invariant tori. Unfortunately, (14) is a very complicated nonlinear partial differential equation which in general cannot be solved.

On the other hand since our original system differs from an integrable one only by terms of $\mathcal{O}(\varepsilon)$, we can hope that the difference between the canonical transformation, C, and the identity is also $\mathcal{O}(\varepsilon)$. This difference is determined by $S(I',\varphi)$. We assume S is $\mathcal{O}(\varepsilon)$, expand (14) using Taylor's theorem, and discard terms that are at least formally of $\mathcal{O}(\varepsilon^2)$, whereupon we arrive at the equation

$$\begin{aligned} &\sum_{i\in\mathbb{Z}^d}\left[\tilde{\omega}_i I_i' + \tilde{\omega}_i \frac{\partial S}{\partial \varphi_i}(I',\varphi)\right] + \varepsilon \sum_{<i,j>} f_{<i,j>}(I',\varphi) \\ &= \sum_{i\in\mathbb{Z}^d}\left[\tilde{\omega}_i I_i' + \tilde{\omega}_i \frac{\partial S}{\partial \varphi}(I',\varphi)\right] + \varepsilon \sum_{\nu} f_\nu(I')e^{i\nu\cdot\varphi} \\ &= \tilde{h}(I'). \end{aligned} \tag{16}$$

The first equality in (16) just used the periodicity of $f_{<i,j>}$ to expand it in a Fourier series. From equation (16) we could easily write down a formal expression for $S(I',\varphi)$ as a Fourier series. We first make two further modifications though. Recall that the interaction terms $f_{<i,j>}$ are analytic functions. Thus, Cauchy's theorem implies that the Fourier coefficients satisfy;

$$|f_\nu(I)| < Ke^{-\delta|\nu|},$$

where K is some constant, and δ measures the size of the analyticity domain of $f_{<i,j>}$ in the angular variables. Since we have already discarded terms of $\mathcal{O}(\varepsilon^2)$ in (16) we make a further approximation by restricting the sum over ν to terms with $|\nu| \leq M$. If we choose $M = c|\ell n\ \varepsilon|$, then (for c appropriately chosen) the discarded terms will be $\mathcal{O}(\varepsilon^2)$ and we can hope that we have not worsened the approximation. The sum over ν still contains an infinite number of terms because of the infinite spatial extent of our system. However, the fact that $f_{<i,j>} \sim \mathcal{O}(I^2)$, and the fact that $I_j^0 \sim e^{-|j|^{d+\alpha}}$ implies that for I near I^0,

$$|f_\nu(I)| \sim \exp\{-2[\mathrm{dist}(\mathrm{supp}\ \nu, \mathrm{origin})]^{d+\alpha}\}.$$

Here $\mathrm{supp}\ \nu$ = support of ν considered as an integer valued function on $\mathbb{Z}^d$. Thus, we can discard terms $f_\nu(I')$, with $\mathrm{dist}(\mathrm{supp}\ \nu, \mathrm{origin}) \geq L = c'|\ell n\ \varepsilon|^{1/d+\alpha}$, and once again the terms we throw away will be $\mathcal{O}(\varepsilon^2)$.

Having made these two approximations the solution $S(I',\varphi)$ of (16) takes the form

$$S(I',\varphi) = i\varepsilon \sum_{\substack{\mathrm{supp}\ \nu \subset B_L \\ |\nu| < M}} \frac{f_\nu(I')e^{i\nu\cdot\varphi}}{\tilde{\omega}\cdot\nu}, \tag{17}$$

with, $B_L = \{j \in \mathbb{Z}^d \mid |j| \leq L\}$.

The sum in (17) contains only a finite number of terms and thus can fail to be well defined only if the denominator in (17) vanishes. We insure that this does not occur by <u>excluding</u> frequencies $\tilde{\omega}$ such that there is some ν with $|\nu| < M$ and $\mathrm{supp}\ \nu \subset B_L$ such that $|\tilde{\omega}\cdot\nu| < \varepsilon^\gamma$, where γ is some fixed, small, positive constant. The complement of the set of excluded frequencies gives a first approximation to the set $\Omega(I^0)$ in Theorem 2, and it is easy to show that is probability is close to one if ε is small.

It is now easy to estimate $S(I',\varphi)$, since each term is bounded by $K\varepsilon^{1-\gamma}$ (for some $K > 0$) and there are at most $(2M)^2(2L)^d \lesssim |\ell n\ \varepsilon|^3$ terms in the sum. Thus,

$$|S(I',\varphi)| < \mathcal{O}(\varepsilon^{1-\gamma'}), \tag{18}$$

for some small positive γ' -- almost as small as we assumed it would be in deriving the linearized equation (16).

We have been somewhat cavalier in failing to state precisely on which neighborhoods our various bounds apply. We will content ourselves with observing that (18) holds for I' "near" I^0 and φ "near" T^∞ the infinite dimensional torus. Again, precise statements are contained in [FSW].

The bound in (18), plus the implicit function theorem and bounds on derivatives of S that follow from Cauchy's theorem are sufficient to insure that (15) can be inverted to obtain a canonical transformation

$$C^0 : (I',\varphi') \to (I,\varphi) = (I' + \Xi(I',\varphi'),\ \varphi' + \Delta(I',\varphi')).$$

Note that because of the restrictions on the sum in (17), S does not depend on variables (I_j',φ_j) with $|j| > L$. Thus, <u>our canonical transformation</u> C^0 <u>reduces to the identity outside</u> B_L.

We then define $H^1(I',\varphi') = H \circ C^0(I',\varphi')$. Because our canonical transformation C^0 is an approximate solution of the Hamilton-Jacobi equation we hope that H^1 will be "closer" to an integrable system than the original Hamiltonian H.

One can write out an explicit form for H^1 and we find (see [FSW])

$$H^1(I',\varphi') = \sum_i \tilde{\omega}_i I_i' + h^1(I') + f^1(I',\varphi') + \varepsilon \sum_{\substack{<i,j> \\ \mathrm{dist}(<i,j>,\ \mathrm{origin}) > L}} f_{<i,j>}(I',\varphi'). \tag{19}$$

A little more work then shows:

a) h^1 and f^1 depend only on the variables (I_j',φ_j') with $|j| \le L$.

b) $|f'(I',\varphi')| < \mathcal{O}(\varepsilon^{2(1-\gamma')})$

From b), and the observation if $\mathrm{dist}(<i,j>, \mathrm{origin}) > L$, $\varepsilon f_{<i,j>}(I',\varphi') \sim \mathcal{O}(\varepsilon^2)$ we see that H^1 <u>is</u> much closer to an integrable system than our original Hamiltonian.

One now iterates this procedure, including at the second stage of the iteration all those parts of the interaction which lie inside a box $B_{L'}$, much bigger than our original box B_L, and also including Fourier coefficients $f_\nu(I)$ with $|\nu| < M'$, where $M' >> M$. Continuing this process with larger and larger boxes one can show that the sequence of canonical transformations one constructs converges to give an invariant torus.

Concluding Remarks

Many interesting questions remain to be answered about the systems described above. From the physical point of view the most pressing is the following. For the linearized problem with Hamiltonian (4), any initial condition for which the energy is localized will remain localized for all time, by the superposition principle. In the nonlinear problem on the other hand we have shown only that certain special initial conditions (i.e. those lying on invariant tori) lead to localized states. Can one show that a general initial condition leads to a localized state, or at least give bounds on the rate at which energy escapes from some large but finite region?

As a second point note that the linearized problem possesses (infinitely) many periodic solutions, while the trajectories we constructed for the nonlinear system are quasi-periodic. It would be interesting to know whether or not the nonlinear systems also possess periodic solutions.

Acknowledgements

We wish to thank the organizers of the conference on Stochastic Processes in Classcial and Quantum Systems for the invitation to present this talk and the Theoretical Physics department of the ETH-Zurich for hospitality during its preparation.

References

[A] Anderson, P.: Absence of diffusion in certain random lattices, Phys. Rev. 109, p.1492 (1958).

[DLS] Delyon, F., Levy, Y.-E., and Souillard, B.: "Approach a la Borland to multidimensional localization." Phys. Rev. Lett. 55, p.618 (1985).

[FMSS] Fröhlich, J., Martinelli, F., Scoppola, E., and Spencer, T.: Constructive Proof of Localization in the Anderson Tight Binding Model, Comm. Math. Phys. (1985), in press.

[FSW] Fröhlich, J., Spencer, T. and Wayne, C.E.: Localization in Disordered, Nonlinear Dynamical Systems (preprint).

[KAM] Kolmogorov, A.N.: On conservation of conditionally periodic motions under small perturbations of the Hamiltonian. Dokl. Akad. Nauk. 98, p.527 (1954).

Arnol'd, V.I.: Small divisor problems in classical and celestial mechanics. Usp. Mat. Nauk. 18(#6) p.91 (1963).

Moser, J.: On invariant curves of area-preserving mappings of an annulus. Nachr. Akad. Wiss., Göttingen, Math. Phys. Kl., p.1 (1962).

[SW] Simon, B. and Wolff, T.: Singular continuous spectrum under rank one perturbations and localization for random Hamiltonians, Comm. Pure Appl. Math., to appear.

[VB] Vittot, M. and Bellisard, J.: Invariant Tori for an Infinite Lattice of Coupled Classical Rotators, (preprint).

The problem of energy partition in the light of classical perturbation theory and the possibility of introducing a critical action in the classical theory of the electromagnetic field

Luigi GALGANI
Dipartimento di Matematica dell'Universitá
via Saldini 50 - 20133 MILANO, Italia

1. The problem of relaxation times and the 'freezing' of degrees of freedom according to Boltzmann.

Everyone agrees, in discussing about specific applications of physics, that the relaxation times characteristic of the considered subject should be taken into account: for example, if one puts a piece of iron on a flame and then extracts it, the piece of iron will keep a proper temperature well different from room temperature up to rather long times, and so it would be inappropriate to use the microcanonical or the canonical ensembles to discuss from the point of view of statistical mechanics such a situation, up to the time necessary to have an equilibrium of the iron with the air of the room. However, even if the piece of iron and the air molecules are in mutual equilibrium, no one would use the actual room temperature to discuss the state of the nucleons constituting the nuclei of the gas molecules of the room, or the state of the interstellar matter, or the state of the gas of point particles (stars) constituting a certain galaxy in the same moment. So we speak of situations of partial equilibria; and not only can there be different temperatures in different places, but also there exist in fact different temperatures in the same place, at different space scales, in the same sense in which there exist different densities at different space scales.

A similar situation of nonequipartition of energy obtains also for the internal degrees of freedom of molecules: if temperature is sufficiently small, the average energy decreases in passing from the translational degrees of freedom to the rotational and the vibrational ones. Analogously, considering the vibrational degrees of freedom of a solid or of the electromagnetic field in a cavity (blackbody), the average energy decreases when passing from the low frequencies to the high frequencies; one can say that one has in such cases a *ultraviolet cutoff*, in the sense that the high frequencies don't have the share of energy (equipartition) that classical mechanics is usually assumed to predict: the high frequencies are, as one usually also says, frozen.

The obvious explanation should be that in such cases too one is concerned with a situation of the kind described above: each degree of freedom should have a characteristic relaxation time to equilibrium, such time should be a rapidly increasing function of the frequency, and so there would in fact be no time to produce equilibrium, up to the common observation times. And this is in fact the explanation proposed by Boltzmann, as one can find in his book on gas theory, and even more clearly in a very beautiful short letter [1] published in Nature in the year 1895, where he speaks explicitly of relaxation times of days or centuries, which would be needed in order to explain the phenomena. In particular, Boltzmann considers his beloved example of hard spheres: on encounters, the spheres clearly exchange momentum, so that one can expect to find equipartition for the translational degrees of freedom at least after a sufficiently long time; but the problem is very different for the energy related to angular momentum, because, if the spheres are perfectly smooth, there is no energy exchange at all. Thus one has to expect that the equilibrium for angular momentum in the case of rough spheres could possibly occur on a time scale which is larger than that characteristic for equilibrium of momentum.

In this connection, I cannot refrain from quoting an even more shocking example. For the point particles describing the stars in a galaxy, Chandrasekhar [2] calculated the average collision time to be typically of the order of magnitude of the age of the universe; that's why in such case one uses, even for the translational degrees of freedom, not the complete Boltzmann equation, but rather the corresponding equation with the collision term neglected, namely the Vlasov equation. So, in particular, one does not make use of the standard ensembles for the statistical mechanics of galaxies.

However, the common opinion is that the ultraviolet cutoff which freezes the high frequencies in the blackbody corresponds to a real equilibrium situation, appropriately described by quantum statistics, which leads to Planck law. Instead, several reasons that I will try to illustrate below have convinced me that it is worthwhile to investigate carefully the following thesis: that Boltzmann was right, that in the ultraviolet cutoff one is concerned with a situation of metaequilibrium, that such a situation is described by the (static) Planck law only in a first approximation, and that more in general quantum mechanics might provide a first approximation to the classical description.

2. Nekhoroshev's theorem on Arnold's diffusion as a support to Boltzmann's dynamical interpretation of the ultraviolet cutoff, and the physical relevance of critical parameters in perturbation theory.

Why did Boltzmann think that the high frequency degrees of freedom should be frozen up to long times? Although I didn't have time to study carefully the problem, it should be obvious that the reason was just his understanding of perturbation theory, and in particular of what we now call the averaging principle, because he repeatedly in his works discussed the so called cyclic motions of Helmholtz, namely the internal motions characterized by fast angles, i.e. high frequencies.

Let us thus come to some relevant results of modern perturbation theory. One considers a slightly perturbed integrable system, with a Hamiltonian

$$H(I,\varphi) = h(I) + \epsilon f(I,\varphi,\epsilon)$$

where ϵ is a small real parameter, $I = (I_1, \cdots, I_n)$, $\varphi = (\varphi_1, \cdots, \varphi_n)$ are action angle variables ($I \in \mathcal{B}, \varphi \in \mathbf{T}^n$, $\mathcal{B}$ being an open connected domain of $\mathbf{R}^n$ and $\mathbf{T}^n$ the $n-$dimensional torus), h and f are smooth, for example analytic. For $\epsilon = 0$ the system is integrable, i.e. one has $I(t) - I(0) = 0$ and $\varphi(t) - \varphi(0) = \omega(I(0))t$, $\omega = \frac{\partial h}{\partial I}$, namely, as Boltzmann would say, the actions are frozen for all times, while the angles have fast motions. For $\epsilon \neq 0$ one clearly has the a priori estimate $\dot{I} = \epsilon \frac{\partial f}{\partial \varphi}$, namely

$$|I(t) - I(0)| \leq \epsilon \; \|\frac{\partial f}{\partial \varphi}\|$$

for $|t| \leq 1$ (with a suitable norm $\|\cdot\|$), i.e. the actions are frozen (move little) up to times of order 1. Perturbation theory aims at giving informations for longer times. In order to do this, one looks for canonical transformations $(I,\varphi) \mapsto (I',\varphi')$ which eliminate the angles up to higher orders, for example by reducing the Hamiltonian to the form

$$H^{(r)}(I',\varphi') = h^{(r)}(I',\epsilon) + \epsilon^r f^{(r)}(I',\varphi',\epsilon)$$

for a positive integer r, so that one would have

$$|I'(t) - I'(0)| \leq \epsilon \; \|\frac{\partial f^{(r)}}{\partial \varphi}\|$$

for $|t| \leq \epsilon^{-r-1}$, i.e. a freezing of the new actions (and essentially also of the old ones) up to times of the order ϵ^{-r-1}. Without entering into details, which are discussed for example in the talk by Benettin in the present conference [3], I only want to quote the recent theorem of Nekhoroshev [4] , which provides uniform estimates in the domain $\mathcal{B}$ if ϵ is sufficiently small: there exist positive constants a, b and ϵ_0, such that one has

$$|I(t) - I(0)| \leq \mathcal{I}\epsilon^b \; , \text{ for } \; t \leq \tau \frac{1}{\epsilon} \exp{(\frac{\epsilon_0}{\epsilon})^a} \; ,$$

if $\epsilon \leq \epsilon_0$, where $\mathcal{I}$ and τ are dimensional constants. So one has indeed a freezing of the actions up to vey long times, which increase essentially in an exponential way with $1/\epsilon$ as $\epsilon \to 0$ (for an explanation of such exponential dependence, one can see also ref.[5]). For what concerns the way in which the quantities a and b depend on the number n of degrees of freedom, the recent works of Wayne and others and of Vittot and Bellissard in connection with KAM theorem give us good hope that such dependence can be reasonably controlled possibly even in the thermodynamic limit [6].

Moreover, I would like to point out the significance of the 'critical value' ϵ_0 of the perturbative parameter ϵ, below which perturbation theory can be applied. From a technical point of view the finite value of ϵ_0 comes about because, in performing the necessary canonical transformations, for example in the standard way using mixed variables, one has to make use of the implicit function theorem; from another (essentially equivalent) point of view, the canonical tranformation, even at the first step, will necessarily be a series in ϵ which should be required to converge. So one has the following picture. Above ϵ_0 one cannot even perform a single step of perturbation theory, and one has just no freezing, apart from the a priori one, which is effective just up to times of order 1; below ϵ_0, instead, the actions are frozen up to times which become larger and larger the more ϵ approaches 0. In this sense, ϵ_0 can be considered as a first estimate of some stochasticity threshold, above which the fluctuations of the actions are essentially free, while below ϵ_0 the actions become more and more frozen as if there were integrals of motion. More precisely, there are in general integrals of motion in some generalized sense, i.e. for very special initial conditions (on KAM tori), and the possible 'Arnold diffusion' in the complement is very slow, being just estimated by Nekhoroshev theorem, and thus requiring exponential times.

In particular, let us come now to the case of weakly coupled harmonic oscillators. In such case, the unperturbed Hamiltonian $h(I)$ is linear in the actions, $h(I) = \sum_j \omega_j I_j$, $\omega = (\omega_1, \cdots, \omega_n) = \text{const}$, where $I_j = \frac{p_j^2+q_j^2}{2}$, if q_j is the displacement of the j-th oscillator from the equilibrium position and p_j its conjugate momentum. The Hamiltonian has in general the form $H = \sum_j \omega_j \frac{p_j^2+q_j^2}{2} + H^{(3)} + H^{(4)} + \cdots$, where $H^{(k)}$ is a polynomial of degree k in $q_1, \cdots, q_n$; namely, one is in fact considering a Taylor expansion about an (elliptic) equilibrium point, and in a sense there is no parameter ϵ, the role of ϵ being taken by the 'distance' $|I|$ from the origin. So, now the analogue of diminishing ϵ is to restrict I to balls of decreasing radius about the origin. This can be seen formally by introducing the trivial rescaling (blowing up) $\epsilon p' = p, \epsilon q' = q$, which allows to consider the actions I' still defined as before in a fixed domain $\mathcal{B}$ (for example the ball of radius 1) with an Hamiltonian (neglecting accents) $H(I,\varphi) = \sum_j \omega_j I_j + \epsilon H^{(3)}(I,\varphi) + \epsilon^2 H^{(4)}(I,\varphi) + \cdots$.

So one has now, instead of the critical parameter ϵ_0, a critical action A_0 estimating the onset of stochasticity: for $|I(0)| \le A_0$ one can apply perturbation theory which guarantees a freezing of the actions for longer and longer times the more $|I(0)|$ tends to zero, while for $|I(0)| > A_0$ one can expect large fluctuations. Recalling that the energies E_j of the oscillators are given in a first approximation by $E_j = \omega_j I_j$, one can also say that there are critical energies $E_j^{(c)} = A_0 \omega_j$, such that one has frozen motions for $E_j < E_j^{(c)}(j = 1, \cdots, n)$, and possilbly chaotic motions for $E_j > E_j^{(c)}(j = 1, \cdots, n)$. Moreover, let us consider an initial condition in which one excites many oscillators all essentially of the same frequenncy ω with energy $E_j(0) < E_j^{(c)}$; then, in the energy exchanges, each of them will be frozen up to a time of the order $\exp(\frac{A_0}{I_j(0)}) = \exp(\frac{A_0\omega}{E_j(0)})$, which increases exponentially with ω. And this seems strongly to support the opinion expressed by Boltzmann, concerning the freezing of the high frequency oscillators.

3. Planck's second theory and Nernst's deduction of Planck law.

History of science is a very strange subject: reading of it in books one usually has the impression of dealing with dead things, but now I don't know whether what I'm going to say will be old or new, dead or alive.

In 1911 Planck for the first time conceived of zero-point energy [7]: as one knows, the energy levels of a harmonic oscillator of frequency ν (or angular frequency or pulsation $\omega = 2\pi\nu$) are considered to be $E_n = (n + \frac{1}{2})h\nu = (n + \frac{1}{2})\hbar\omega$, h being the Planck constant and $\hbar = \frac{h}{2\pi}$. So, according to standard quantum mechanics, using the quantum Gibbs ensemble at zero absolute temperature (or zero-point, from the german *nullpunkt*) all oscillators should have the zero-point energy $\frac{1}{2}\hbar\omega$. Let us not discuss here whether the zero-point energy according to quantum mechanics should be $\frac{1}{2}\hbar\omega$ or $\hbar\omega$ (or $\alpha\hbar\omega$ with any positive $\alpha \leq 1$ as Enz and Thellung [8] would say), and whether such energy is measurable or not, which would lead us into a rather complicated subject.

What is quite astonishing in any case, is that Planck conceived of $\hbar\omega$ as a stochasticity threshold more or less in the sense described above, with $\hbar$ in place of A_0. Indeed, he assumes that an oscillator of frequency ω absorbs energy in a kind of diffusive process, requiring a time $\exp\frac{\hbar\omega}{kT}$ in order to reach the level $\hbar\omega$. On reaching such level, it could emit the complete energy $\hbar\omega$ or proceed by absorbing energy in a continuous way as before, according to some probabilistic law. In his words: "This will not be regarded as implying that there is no causality for emission; but the processes which cause the emission will be assumed to be of such a concealed nature that for the present their laws cannot be obtained by any but statistical methods. Such an assumption is not at all foreign to physics; it is e.g. made in the atomistic theory of chemical reactions and in the disintegration theory of radioactive substances."

Let us pause for a moment: he says that one is not allowed to use the standard methods of statistical mechanics if $E < \hbar\omega$, i.e., as we said above, that zero-point energy is an energy threshold for the onset of stochasticity. Moreover, the diffusion time for reaching such energy is exponentially increasing with frequency, as essentially comes out of Nekhoroshev theorem.

Planck then proceeds, deducing his law in a way that I don't intend to follow here; in addition, he quite stangely ascribes zero-point energy only to material oscillators and not to the oscillators of the electromagnetic field. More interesting from the present point of view are the ideas introduced four years later by Walter Nernst [9], the inventor of the third principle of thermodynamics. First of all, he reconfirms Planck's interpretation of $h\nu$ as a stochasticity threshold in an even more direct way; he says in fact explicitly that the motions of the oscillators are ordered (*geordnete*) below $h\nu$ and disordered (*ungeordnete*) above $h\nu$. His reason for such an idea is quite interesting in itself. According to the third principle, in lowering temperature one eventually reaches a situation where the internal energy coincides with the free energy. Now, free energy is just that part of internal energy which according to thermodynamics can be used to do macroscopic work, and so it has, according to Nernst, an ordered character. That's why, with an intuition coming from thermodynamics, he comes to the striking proposal that the microscopic motions too have an ordered character below $h\nu$, by introducing the conception of a stochasticity threshold as we are accustomed to conceive now, after the impressive evidence coming from the numerical works started by Hénon and Heiles [10]. He also explicitly ascribes the threshold to the oscillators of the electromagnetic field too, and furthermore conceives of h as a constant deduced from other elementary quantities. Namely, thinking of the equations of motion of the electromagnetic field interacting with an electron of charge e, which also are the equations for a system of weakly coupled harmonic oscillators, assume that one can find a critical action such as the action A_0 described above. Then by dimensional considerations one clearly has $A_0 = \frac{e^2}{c}\mathcal{A}$, where c is the velocity of light and $\mathcal{A}$ a dimensionless quantity. If one finds $\mathcal{A} = 137$, then one has $A_0 = \hbar$.

Then Nernst proceeds to deduce Planck law, in a very impressive elementary way that howevere took to me ten years of repeated meditations to be understood[11]. Assume that the initial conditions of the oscillators are distributed at random, and consider more precisely the case in which they are distributed according to a normal, i.e. Gauss or Maxwell, law at absolute temperature T; so, the probability density for the energy E of each oscillator $p_{\beta,\nu}(E) = p_\beta(E)$ is independent of the frequency ν and is given by

$$p_\beta(E) = \beta e^{-\beta E} \ , \quad 0 \le E < \infty$$

where $\beta = \frac{1}{kT}$ and k is the Boltzmann constant. Clearly one has normalization $\int_0^{+\infty} p_\beta(E)dE = 1$ and equipartition $\hat{E}_\beta \equiv \int_0^{+\infty} E\ p_\beta(E)dE = \frac{1}{\beta}$, i.e. an average energy independent of frequency. But now, due to the dynamical properties of motions as described by the existence of an energy threshold $E^{(c)}(\nu) = h\nu$, one has, in the spirit of Boltzmann's ideas (think of the case of the rotational energy for perfectly smooth hard spheres), to separate the mechanical energy into two parts: the energy which can be exchanged, pertaining to oscillators having energy $E > h\nu$, and the energy which is frozen, pertaining to oscillators with energy $E < h\nu$. For a given frequency ν one will have a fraction $n_1(\beta,\nu)$ of oscillators above threshold, and a fraction $n_0(\beta,\nu)$ of oscillators below threshold, with

$$n_1 = \int_{h\nu}^{\infty} p_\beta(E)dE \quad , \quad n_0 = \int_0^{h\nu} p_\beta(E)dE \ ,$$

and $n_0 + n_1 = 1$; moreover, the average energy of the oscillators above threshold will be $E_1(\beta,\nu)$, while the average energy of the oscillators below threshold will be $E_0(\beta,\nu)$, where

$$E_1 = \frac{1}{n_1}\int_{h\nu}^{\infty} E\, p_\beta(E)dE \quad , \quad E_0 = \frac{1}{n_0}\int_0^{h\nu} E\, p_\beta(E)dE \ ,$$

and one has clearly $n_0E_0 + n_1E_1 = \frac{1}{\beta} \equiv kT$. By elementary integrations one finds

$$n_1 = \exp\left(-\beta h\nu\right), \quad n_0 = 1 - n_1, \quad E_1 = kT + h\nu \ , \quad E_0 = kT - \frac{h\nu}{e^{\beta h\nu} - 1} \ .$$

The most elementary model for the thermodynamic energy u, or the energy available for thermal exchanges in Boltzmann's sense, is then clearly

$$u(\beta,\nu) = n_1(E_1 - E_0) \ ;$$

indeed one thinks that only the n_1 oscillators above threshold can loose energy, and in fact each of them just the quantity $E_1 - E_0$, because it would be frozen in falling to the lower energy level E_0. Thus, with the expressions reported above, one gets immediately

$$u(\beta,\nu) = \frac{h\nu}{e^{\beta h\nu} - 1} \ ,$$

namely exactly Planck law (and without zero-point energy, of course). In the original paper of Nernst, one finds for u the expression $u = kT - E_0$, which, using $kT = n_0E_0 + n_1E_1$ and $n_0 + n_1 = 1$, is immediately checked to coincide with $n_1(E_1 - E_0)$.

4. Possible corrections to Planck law due to Arnold diffusion, and on the experimental verification of the blackbody radiation law.

So, the conception of the zero-point energy $h\nu$ as a stochasticity threshold immediately leads to Planck law for the energy u exchangeable in the sense of Boltzmann, due to the fact that only the n_1 oscillators above threshold (on the average on the level E_1) can exchange energy, while the n_0 oscillators below threshold (on the average on the level E_0) are frozen. Now, in such a reasoning, the oscillators below threshold were considered to be frozen for all times, while, in the spirit of Nekhoroshev's theorem, as also predicted by Planck, they are frozen only up to a time of the order $\exp\left(\frac{h\nu}{kT}\right)$, and this is large for the large frequencies but not for the low ones. Thus, if one fixes an observation time t, it is clear that to a better approximation one can conceive that there exists a frequency $\hat{\nu} = \hat{\nu}(t)$, such that the large frequencies ($\nu > \hat{\nu}$) are frozen, while the low frequencies ($\nu < \hat{\nu}$) are not at all frozen up to that time (see the appendix of the Jeans contribution at the 1912 Solvay Conference [12]). In such a way, for the thermodynamic energy u one should have a plateau $u = kT$ for $\nu < \hat{\nu}$, followed by an exponential tail, for example just a planckian $\frac{h\nu}{e^{\beta' h\hat{\nu}}-1}$ for $\nu > \hat{\nu}$; the effective inverse temperature $\beta' = \beta'(\hat{\nu}, \beta)$, which is the temperature apparent from the side of the high frequencies, is then determined by the matching condition $\frac{h\nu}{e^{\beta' h\hat{\nu}}-1} = \frac{1}{\beta}$, which gives $\beta' h\hat{\nu} = \log(1 + \beta h\hat{\nu})$.

Now, as time goes on, the plateau front at $\hat{\nu}(t)$ also advances towards the high frequencies; however, due to the fact that the Arnold diffusion time increases exponentially with the frequency, such an advancement should be negligible on a linear time scale at any given time, giving the impression of a stationary distribution. Moreover, this phenomenon of apparent stationarity should be enhanced if one looks at the distribution from the side of the high frequencies and if the energy u is plotted versus the relevant quantity, i.e. the adimensional parameter $x' = \beta' h\nu$; indeed the inflection point occurs at $x' = \beta' h\hat{\nu} = \log(1 + \beta h\hat{\nu})$, which depends only logarythmically on $\hat{\nu}$.

So far the reasoning was of 'canonical' type, with a fixed inverse temperature β. Analogous considerations can also be made for an isolated system, with a fixed energy E_0. In such a case, the height of the plateau should diminish as $\hat{\nu}$ increases, due to energy conservation. In fact, the numerical computations performed up to now refer to the latter case. Particularly impressive are the computations on the Bocchieri-Loinger model for a blackbody cavity [13]: see especially fig.6, with a very nitid plateau followed by an exponential tail, and fig.7, where the exponential time for the invasion of the high frequencies is very beautifully exhibited. For some analytical results in a similar context see also ref. In this connection, a very illuminating contribution came from Parisi et al. [14], who transported to Hamiltonian systems some techniques previously used by Frisch and Morf in connection with the problem of turbulence in fluids, on which I don't have time to enter here.

Now, what about the experimental verification of the blackbody radiation law? Here, one should first remind that the energy density observed is not u, but $\nu^2 u$ (apart from a constant factor), because of the factor $\nu^2 d\nu$ which gives the number of oscillators between ν and $\nu + d\nu$ in a cavity; so the observed energy tends to zero for $\nu \to 0$, and the corrections alluded to above should not be easy to observe. Furthermore, one should point out that the observations on the spectrum of the blackbody radiation law are incredibly poor: essentially, there are no (no, means no one) observations after the year 1921 [15], and such observations fit Planck law only within 3 (three) per cent [16]; moreover, they all refer to $\frac{h\nu}{kT} > 0.2$ (for a history of the problem see [17]). It is curious to notice that for the cosmic background radiation too one has data only for $\frac{h\nu}{kT} > 0.2$. Data for lower values of $\frac{h\nu}{kT}$ are available for the sun (which very well might not be a good blackbody), and they are just a kind of exponential tail at high frequencies with a very nitid plateau at low frequencies, the inflection point being around $\beta' h\nu = 0.2$.

References

1] L.Boltzmann, Nature 51,413-415 (1895); see also G.Benettin, L.Galgani and A.Giorgilli, Nature 311,444-445(1984)

2] S. Chandrasekhar, *Principles of stellar dynamics*, The University of Chicago Press (1942)

3] G.Benettin, this conference

4] N.N.Nekhoroshev, Russian Math.Surv. 32,1-65 (1977); G.Benettin, L.Galgani and A.Giorgilli, Celestial Mechanics, in print

5] A.Giorgilli and L.Galgani, Celestial Mechanics, in print

6] E.Wayne, this conference; M.Vittot and Bellissard, preprint; G.Benettin, L.Galgani, A.Giorgilli and M.Vittot, in preparation

7] M.Planck, Ann.d.Phys. 37,642-656(1912); *The theory of heat radiation*, Dover (1959)

8] C.P.Enz and A.Thellung, Helv.Phys.Acta 33,839(196); C.P. Enz, *Is zero-point energy real ?*, contribution to a book dedicated to Jauch

9] W.Nernst, Verh.d.Deutsch.Phys.Ges. 4,83(1916)

0] M.Hénon and C.Heiles, Astron.J. 69,73(1964); M.Hénon, in Les Houches summer school, 1982

.] L.Galgani and A.Scotti, Phys.Rev.Lett. 28,1173 (1972); C.Cercignani,L.Galgani and A.Scotti, Phys.Lett. A38,403(1972); L.Galgani and A.Scotti, Rivista Nuovo Cim. 2,189(1972); L.Galgani, Nuovo Cim. B62,306(1981); L.Galgani, Lett.Nuovo Cim. 31,65-72(1981); L.Galgani and G.Benettin, Lett.Nuovo Cim. 35,93-96(1982)

] P.Langevin and M.de Broglie eds., *La théorie du rayonnement et les quanta*,(Paris, 1912)

] G.Benettin and L.Galgani, J.Stat.Phys. 27,153(1982)

] F.Fucito et al., J. de Physique 43,707(1982); R.Livi et al., Phys.Rev. A28,3544(1983)

] H.Rubens and G.Michel, Phys.Zeitschr. 22,569(1921)

] L.Crovini and L.Galgani, Lett.Nuovo Cim. 39,210(1984)

] L.Galgani, Annales Fond.L.de Broglie 8,19(1983)

ON THE φ_4^4 - PROBLEM

Giovanni GALLAVOTTI

Dipartimento di Matematica
II Università di Roma
Via Raimondo, I-00173 Roma/Italy

Abstract

In this paper we illustrate the recent techniques developed to treat renormalizable interactions by developing an example which, although implicit in the literature, has not been pointed out. We consider the formal perturbation expansion of $\lambda\varphi_4^4$-hierarchical with $\lambda > 0$ (i.e. the "unstable" case) and show that one can construct a one parameter family P_λ, $\lambda \in [0,\lambda_o]$, of real stochastic processes whose effective potential (and Schwinger functions) admit the formal renormalized series as asymptotic series: this shows that P_λ can be a family of probability measure and does not have to be necessarily complex valued as it is in the constructions based on analytic continuation from $\lambda < 0$ to $\mathrm{Re}\lambda > 0$.

The construction seems to be generalizable to more interesting hierarchical models (i.e. having non-trivial S-matrix): however as it stands, it is bound to produce in the Euclidean case a theory violating the Osterwalder-Schrader positivity (which would be kept only in the hierarchical cases).

§1 The Model: "Non-Perturbative Formulation"

In this paper, the hierarchical φ_4^4 model is considered.

The hierarchical model was introduced by Dyson [1] in a Statistical Mechanics context and by Wilson [2] in Field Theory.

It played a major role in the development of the renormalization group methods both from the Theoretical Physics' viewpoint [3] and from the Mathematical Physics' [4,5,6,7,8,9].

In [10], appendix G, a concise introduction to the model is given, together with its renormalizability properties.

The free field with cut-off γ^N, $\gamma = 2$ (say) is, in dimension $d > 2$:

$$\varphi_x^{(\leq N)} = \sum_{j=0}^{N} \varphi_x^{(j)} \qquad x \in R^d \ , \ d > 2 \ . \tag{1.1}$$

The fields $\varphi^{(j)}$ have to be thought of as gaussian random fields independently distributed over j. Their x-dependence is specified by

$$\varphi_x^{(j)} = \sqrt{\gamma^{(d-2)j}} \quad z_\Delta \qquad \text{if} \quad x \in \Delta \tag{1.2}$$

where Δ is a tessera of a pavement Q_j of the unit cube U built with cubes of side size γ^{-j}. The z_Δ is a gaussian random variable with covariance $\frac{1}{2}$ if $j > 0$: if $j = 0$, i.e. $\Delta \equiv U$, we take the covariance to be some $c \neq \frac{1}{2}$, and not $c = \frac{1}{2}$, in order to simplify some formulas.

The φ_d^4-problem is related to the family of stochastic processes (i.e. probability measures on the space of the fields $\varphi_x^{(\leq N)}$) defined by

$$\exp\left(\sum_{j=0}^{2} \int_U r^{(j)}(N) \quad \varphi_x^{(\leq N)2j} \, dx \right) P(d\varphi^{(\leq N)}) \tag{1.3}$$

where $P(d\varphi^{(\leq N)})$ is the probability distribution of $\varphi^{(\leq N)}$, i.e. by (1.1), (1,2):

$$P(d\varphi^{(\leq N)}) = \left(\prod_{j>0}^{N} \prod_{\Delta \in Q_j} e^{-z_\Delta^2} \frac{dz_\Delta}{\sqrt{\pi}} \right) \left(e^{-\frac{z_U}{2c}} \frac{dz_U}{\sqrt{2\pi c}} \right) \tag{1.4}$$

(as said above, the case $j = 0$, $U \equiv \Delta$, is treated differently to simplify later formulae).

The $r^{(j)}(N)$ are called "bare couplings".

More generally, one could consider expressions like

$$e^{V^{(N)}} dP = (\exp \int_U w_D(\varphi_x^{(\leq N)}) d^d x) \, P(d\varphi^{(\leq N)}) \tag{1.5}$$

for w_D arbitrary (bounded above).

The φ_d^4-problem, "ultraviolet problem", is to find, and analyze in some detail, the set of probability measures on the fields which can be reached as limit points of sequences of measures like (1.3) when $N \to \infty$: the general "ultraviolet" problem of scalar field theories is to find the limit points of sequences of measures like (1.5) when $N \to \infty$.

Although it is known that if $d = 1,2,3$ such set of limit points is rather large and consists of non-trivial objects (i.e. of non-gaussian stochastic processes), this is not the case if $d = 4$ (or $d > 4$), where sometimes it has even been conjectured that only gaussian measures build up the set of limit points ("strong triviality conjecture", see [11]).

To study the limit as $N \to \infty$ of (1.3), (1.5), one defines $V^{(K)}(\varphi^{(\leq K)})$ as

$$\exp V^{(K)}(\varphi^{(\leq K)}) = \int \exp V^{(N)}(\varphi^{(\leq N)}) \, P(d\varphi^{(K+1)}) \ldots P(d\varphi^{(N)}) \tag{1.6}$$

and $V^{(K)}$ will be called the "effective potential" on scale K, or "renormalized potential on scale K corresponding to the bare potential $V^{(N)}$ on the cut-off scale N.

Using the fact that $\varphi^{(\leq N)}$ is constant over the tesserae Δ of size γ^{-N}, $\Delta \in Q_N$, the integral defining $V^{(N)}$ in (1.5) can obviously be written as a sum:

$$\int_U w_D(\varphi_x^{(\leq N)})d^dx \equiv \sum_\Delta \gamma^{-dN} w_D(\gamma^{\frac{d-2}{2}N} x_\Delta) \equiv \sum_\Delta w^{(N)}(x_\Delta) \tag{1.7}$$

where the "normalized field" corresponding to Δ has been introduced as

$$X_\Delta = \frac{\varphi_x^{(\leq N)}}{\gamma^{\frac{d-2}{2}N}} \quad \text{if} \quad x \in \Delta \in Q_N . \tag{1.8}$$

The field X_Δ is called normalized because $E(\varphi_x^{(\leq N)z}) = \text{const.}\ \gamma^{(d-2)N}$ (the constant being $1/2(\gamma^{d-2}-1)$ if c is chosen conveniently: $c = 1/2(\gamma^{d-2}-1)$).

The $w^{(N)}$ defined in (1.7) will be called the "dimensionless potential" on scale N (the subscript D in w_D stands, in fact, for "dimensional").

The identity $\varphi_x^{(\leq N)} = \varphi_x^{(\leq N-1)} + \varphi_x^{(N)}$ can be written, for dimensionless fields, as:

$$X_\Delta = \alpha z_\Delta + \beta X_\Delta , \tag{1.9}$$

if $x \in \Delta \subset \Delta'$, $\Delta \in Q_N$, $\Delta' \in Q_{N-1}$, $N \geq 1$, and

$$\alpha^2 + \beta^2 = 1 , \quad \beta = \gamma^{-\frac{d-2}{2}} \tag{1.10}$$

provided c in (1.4) is conveniently chosen as $c = 1/2(\gamma^{d-2}-1)$. If $c = 1/2$, then $\beta = \gamma^{-\frac{d-2}{2}} + O(\gamma^{-N})$ a change which would only result in messier expressions.

The main property of the hierarchical model is that, if $V^{(N)}$ is given by (1.7), then $V^{(N-1)}$ is also given by the r.h.s. of (1.7) with $w^{(N)}$ replaced by a new function $w^{(N-1)}$ defined by

$$e^{w^{(N-1)}(x)} = \left(\int e^{-z^2} \frac{dz}{\sqrt{\pi}}\, e^{w^{(N)}(x\beta+2\alpha)}\right)^{\gamma^d} \tag{1.11}$$

expressing the "strict locality" of the hierarchical model.

The proof of (1.11) is straightforward from (1.4), (1.8), (1.9), (1.10) (see [6], [7] and [11] appendix G).

We call N the operator (1.11) on $f = e^w$:

$$N\,f(x) = (\Gamma(\beta)f(x))^{\gamma^d}$$

$$\Gamma(\beta)f(x) = \int e^{-z^2}\, f(\alpha z + \beta x)\,\frac{dz}{\sqrt{\pi}} \tag{1.12}$$

and $\Gamma(\beta)$ is a well-known linear operator ("hypercontractive operator") which acts on f by multiplying its n-th Hermite coefficient by β^n :

$$\Gamma(\beta)H_n(x) = \beta^n\, H_n(x) \qquad \forall n = 0,1,\ldots \tag{1.13}$$

where H_n are the Hermite polynomials defined by:

$$e^{-\frac{\alpha^2}{4}+\alpha x} = \sum_{n=0}^{\infty} \frac{\alpha^n}{n!}\, H_n(x) \qquad \forall \alpha, x \in R\,. \tag{1.14}$$

This remark implies that the linearization of N near $f = 1$, which is a trivial fixed point of N, is

$$D_1 N\, F(x) = \gamma^d\, \Gamma(\beta)\, F(x) \qquad \text{so that}$$

$$D_1 N\, H_n(x) = \gamma^d\, \beta^n\, H_n(x) \equiv \gamma^{\sigma(n)}\, H_n(x) \quad \sigma(n) = d - \frac{d-2}{2}n \tag{1.15}$$

suggesting representing w as a Hermite series, as we shall often do (this is called a "Wick ordered representation" of $w(x)$).

The general ultraviolet problem can be rephrased as follows: describe the set of points $w^{(0)}$ of the form

$$\exp w^{(0)}(x) = \lim_{N\to\infty} N^N\, w^{(N)}(x) \tag{1.16}$$

and the problem of φ_d^4 can be put in the same way with the extra restriction that $w^{(N)}$ is a fourth order polynomial:

$$w^{(N)}(x) = \sum_{j=0}^{2} \lambda^{(j)}(N)\; H_{2j}(x)\,. \tag{1.17}$$

Here $\lambda^{(j)}(N)$ will be called the "dimensionless bare couplings".

The above formulation of the φ_d^4 ultraviolet problem will be called "non-perturbative" following a trend become recently widespread.

In [11] such a formulation of the φ_d^4 problem has been criticized (in the corresponding Euclidean version) as being too restrictive. In fact, the "perturbative" formulation defined below will be richer.

§ 2 Form Factors and the Perturbative Formulation of the φ_d^4-Problem

The effective potential on scale k is described by the "dimensionless" function $w^{(k)}$ related to $w^{(N)}$ by

$$w^{(k)} = \log N^{N-k} (\exp w^{(N)}) . \tag{2.1}$$

We define the form factors of $w^{(k)}$ by considering the Hermite expansion for $w^{(k)}$

$$w^{(k)}(k) = \sum_{j=0}^{2} \lambda^{(j)}(k)\, H_{2j}(x) + \sum_{j=3}^{\infty} \lambda^{(j)}(k)\, H_{2j}(x) \tag{2.2}$$

and the three coefficients $\underline{\lambda}(k) = (\lambda^{(0)}(k), \lambda^{(1)}(k), \lambda^{(2)}(k))$ will be called the "form factors" on scale k.

Then in [12], [10], [13] it has been proved that $\forall d \geq 4$:

(1) if $j \geq 3$ then $\lambda^{(j)}(k)$ is a formal power series in terms of $\underline{\lambda}(k+1),\ldots,\underline{\lambda}(N)$ and $\underline{\lambda}(N+1) \equiv \underline{0}$, $\underline{\lambda}(N+1) \equiv \underline{0}$, ... with N-independent coefficients. Such coefficients are non-negative and will be denoted $\beta^{(j)}(h_1,\ldots,h_p;\, \alpha_1,\ldots,\alpha_p)$ so that

$$\lambda^{(j)}(k) = \sum_{p=2}^{\infty} \sum_{\substack{\underline{h}=(h_1,\ldots,h_p \\ h_i \geq k+1}} \sum_{\alpha_1,\ldots,\alpha_p}^{0,2} \beta^{(j)}(\underline{h};\underline{\alpha})\lambda^{(\alpha_1)}(h_1) \ldots \lambda^{(\alpha_p)}(h_p). \tag{2.3}$$

In fact, a very detailed bound on β can be provided, as described below.

(2) If θ denotes a tree 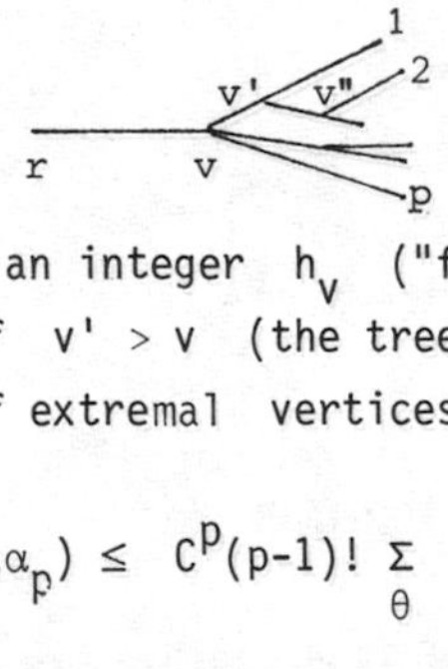

and if to each of its vertices v, non-extremal, one associates an integer h_v ("frequency or scale of the vertex v") so that $h_r \equiv k$, $h_{v'} > h_v$ if $v' > v$ (the tree being oriented from r upwards) then, if p is the number of extremal vertices of θ:

$$\beta^{(j)}(h_1,\ldots,h_p;\, \alpha_1,\ldots,\alpha_p) \leq C^p (p-1)! \sum_{\theta} \sum_{\underline{h}}^{*} \prod_{v>r} \gamma^{-\bar{\rho}(h_v - h_w)} \tag{2.4}$$

where the sum runs over all the ways to associate "frequency labels" h_v to the vertices $v \in \theta$ which are not extremal; furthermore the p extremal vertices are, respectively, directly attached to vertices of θ carrying labels $h_1,\ldots,h_p$; $\bar{\rho}$ is a suitably chosen positive number and w is the vertex immediately preceding v in θ.

(3) The $\underline{\lambda}(k)$ themselves obey a formal power series relation; $\alpha = 0,1,2$:

$$\lambda^{(\alpha)}(k) = \gamma^{\sigma(\alpha)} \lambda^{(\alpha)}(k+1) + \sum_{p=2}^{\infty} \sum_{\substack{\underline{h}=(h_1,\ldots,h_p) \\ N \geq h_i \geq k+1}} \sum_{\underline{\alpha}=(\alpha_1,\ldots,\alpha_p)}^{0,1,2} \beta^{(\alpha)}(\underline{h};\underline{\alpha}) \prod_{j=1}^{p} \lambda^{(\alpha_j)}(h_j) \tag{2.5}$$

and $\beta^{(\alpha)}(\underline{h};\underline{\alpha}) \geq 0$ obey a bound like (2.4); the $\sigma(\alpha)$'s $\sigma(\alpha) = d - 2\alpha(d-2)/2$. The $\beta^{(\alpha)}$ depend only on $h_v - k$ $v \in \theta$.

(4) The Eq. (2.5) can be thought of as an equation for $\underline{\lambda}(k)$. As such it is "inhomogeneous" if $\underline{\lambda}(0) \equiv \underline{\lambda}$ is considered known and, if $d = 4$, it admits a recursive solution in the form of a formal power series in $\underline{\lambda} \equiv \underline{\lambda}(0)$, with coefficients $\underline{\ell}^{(n)}(k) = (\ell^{(\underline{n})0}(k), \ell^{(\underline{n})1}(k), \ell^{(\underline{n})2}(k))$:

$$\lambda^{(\alpha)}(k) = \gamma^{-\sigma(\alpha)k}\,\lambda^{(\alpha)} + \sum_{\substack{n_0,n_1,n_2\\ |\underline{n}|\geq 2}} \ell^{(n_0,n_1,n_2)\alpha}(k) \prod_{j=0}^{3} (\lambda^{(j)})^{n_j} \tag{2.6}$$

or, more compactly

$$\underline{\lambda}(k) = \gamma^{-\underline{\sigma}k}\,\underline{\lambda} + \sum_{|\underline{n}|\geq 2} \ell^{(\underline{n})}(k)\;\underline{\lambda}^{\underline{n}} \tag{2.7}$$

and for all N

$$|\underline{\ell}^{(n)}(k)| \leq (|\underline{n}|-1)!\;C^{|\underline{n}|-1} \sum_{j=0}^{|\underline{n}|-1} \frac{(\beta k)^j}{j!} \tag{2.8}$$

which follows from (2.4), (2.5) and $\sigma(\alpha) = d - \alpha\,\frac{d-2}{2} \leq 0$ (because $d = 4$), alone [12], [10].

(5) The explicit form of (2.5), "to second order", is

$$\lambda^{(2)}(k) = \lambda^{(2)}(k+1) + \beta\,\lambda^{(2)}(k+1)^2 + \beta_1\,\lambda^{(2)}(k+1)\,\lambda^{(1)}(k+1) + \dots$$

$$\lambda^{(2)}(k) = \gamma^2\,\lambda^{(1)}(k+1) + \beta_2\,\lambda^{(2)}(k+1)^2 + \beta_3\lambda^{(1)}(k+1)^2 + \beta_4\lambda^{(1)}(k+1)\lambda^{(2)}(k+1) + \dots$$

$$\lambda^{(0)}(k) = \gamma^4\,\lambda^{(0)}(k+1) + \beta_5\,\lambda^{(2)}(k+1)^2 + \beta_6\,\lambda^{(1)}(k+1)^2 + \dots \tag{2.9}$$

where $\beta, \beta_1, \beta_2, \dots$ are (computable) positive constants and d has been taken 4 (if $d > 4$ the first equation is modified by multiplying the linear term by γ^{4-d} and the third by replacing γ^4 by γ^d).

(6) The same results hold if $d \geq 4$ and $w^{(N)}$ has the form

$$w^{(N)}(k) = \sum_{j=0}^{n} \lambda^{(j)}(N)\;H_{2j}(x) \tag{2.10}$$

provided one now introduces the dimensionless form factors on scale k by a formula like (2.2) with 2 replaced by n and 3 by $n+1$; furthermore, in the analogue of (2.5), (2.3) one chooses $\alpha, \alpha_1, \dots, \alpha_p$ to vary in $0, 1, \dots, n$ and j in $n+1, n+2, \dots$. However, there is <u>no</u> obvious analogue of (4) above because (2.5) no longer admits a formal solution as a power series in $\underline{\lambda}(0)$ if $n > 2$ or if $d > 4$.

Nevertheless, an analogue of (4) can be formulated as follows [13]: if $d=4$, $n>2$, Eq. (2.5) admits a formal power series solution in powers of $\lambda^{(0)}(0)$, $\lambda^{(1)}(0)$, $\lambda^{(2)}(0)$, $\lambda^{(3)}(N),\dots,\lambda^{(n)}(N)$. But the resulting formal series has the remarkable property that its coefficients involving non-trivially $\lambda^{(j)}(N)$, $j\geq 3$, vanish as $N\to\infty$ [13]. If $d>4$ also $\lambda^{(2)}(0)$ has to be replaced by $\lambda^{(2)}(N)$ and $j\geq 3$ by $j\geq 2$.

The latter property says that it is not different, from a formal viewpoint, to consider (2.10) with $n > 2$ rather than (1.17), if $d = 4$: "formally all polynomial theories in $d = 4$ coincide with the φ_4^4-theories".

This suggests that the appropriate way to define φ_4^4 seems to be the old-fashioned way ("perturbative definition") of defining φ_4^4 via the result (4) above. In other words, one defines φ_4^4-theory a family $P_{\lambda,\mu,\nu}$ of stochastic processes parametrized by three parameters $(\lambda,\mu,\nu) \equiv (\lambda^{(2)}(0), \lambda^{(1)}(0), \lambda^{(0)}(0))$ varying in a set Ω such that $\underline{0} \in \partial\Omega$ and such that the effective potential $w^{(k)}(x)$ on scale k has an asymptotic expansion in (λ,μ,ν) near $\underline{0}$ agreeing to all orders with the one constructed formally when $N\to\infty$ via (4), see [10], [11], for each fixed x .

We say that $P_{\lambda,\mu,\nu}$, $(\lambda,\mu,\nu) \in \Omega$, is "trivial" if $(\lambda,\mu,\nu) \in \Omega$ implies $\lambda \equiv 0$, [11].

Observe that this definition neither prescribes the sign of λ nor the form of $w^{(N)}$: this is in contrast with the definition ("non-perturbative") of § 1 which prescribes $w^{(N)}$, see (1.11), and also fixes the sign of $\lambda^{(2)}(N)$ to be ≤ 0 .

In spite of what the wording seems to suggest to many, the perturbative approach is harder (in fact much harder, probably) than the non-perturbative one.

In this paper, it is proved that a family $P_{\lambda,\mu,\nu}$ exists, and is non-trivial, in a region Ω containing a vicinity of the origin restricted by the condition $\lambda>0$.

For instance, one can show the existence of a family $P_{\lambda,0,0}$ for small $\lambda > 0$ with $\lambda^{(j)}(k)$ given, for $j \geq 3$, by a C^∞-function of λ admitting the usual perturbation series as asymptotic expansion at $\lambda = 0$.

A similar result was proved in [14] to low order of perturbation theory: however, in [14] $P_{\lambda,0,0}$ is constructed by analytic continuation from the $\lambda < 0$ cut-off case with $w^{(N)}$ given exactly by (1.17): this ultimately implies, at least in [14], see, however, [15], that $P_{\lambda,0,0}$ is probably not a probability measure (being probably complex as it can be defined only if $\mathrm{Re}\,\lambda > 0$, $\mathrm{Im}\,\lambda \neq 0$ and taking the limit $\mathrm{Im}\,\lambda \to 0$: it remains unclear whether the result is real, leaving aside the harder positivity problem).

On the other hand, the techniques of [14], [9] are extensively used in this work as they proved a good scheme to treat renormalizable theories: they are combined with the general theory of the "beta-function" developed in [12], [11], [13] to show the validity of perturbation theory to all orders. This work can be considered as a simple example of the renormalization group approach to constructive field theory in the renormalizable cases which follows closely the schemes already successfully developed in the constructions of φ^4_d, $d = 2,3$ in [6], [7], [8] based on the detailed analysis of only few orders of perturbation theory. As shown in [14], the new idea of the "control of remainders" by the use of analyticity properties, proposed in [9] allows to carry the techniques of superrenormalizable theories to the renormalizable cases.

That scalar fields could exist in $d = 4$ and be non-trivial for $\lambda > 0$ has been hinted (even very recently) by many authors [16], [11], [18], [15]: the proposal based on adding higher order powers of φ to the "bare action" $w^{(N)}$ with dimensionally appropriate bare constants seem to have failed to realize that the resulting theory might be φ^4_4 (a remark in [13], see iii) of theorem 3). If the theory discussed in [17] is non-gaussian, it might just be the full Euclidean φ^4_4.

§ 3 Construction of a Scalar Field with $\lambda > 0$

Let $\bar{\lambda}_k > 0$ be a sequence obeying

$$\bar{\lambda}_{k-1} = \bar{\lambda}_k + \beta\, \bar{\lambda}_k^2 + \kappa_1\, \bar{\lambda}_k^{3-\varepsilon_1} \qquad k = 1,2,... \tag{3.1}$$

where β is the positive coefficient appearing in (2.9) and $\kappa_1 > 0$, $\varepsilon_1 > 0$ will be fixed later.

Assume also that for some $\bar{\lambda} > 0$:

$$\bar{\lambda}_k = \frac{\bar{\lambda}}{1+\beta\, \bar{\lambda} k} \left(1 + 0\left(\left(\frac{\bar{\lambda}}{k+1}\right)^{1-\varepsilon_1}\right)\right) \qquad k = 0,1,... . \tag{3.2}$$

It is easy to show that (3.1) implies that if $\bar{\lambda}_o$ is small enough, then (3.2) holds for some $\bar{\lambda} = 0(\bar{\lambda}_o)$; vice versa if $\bar{\lambda}_o$ is given a priori, positive and small enough, then one can define $\bar{\lambda}_2, \bar{\lambda}_2, ...$ so that (3.1), (3.2) hold for $k = 1,2,...$.

Let, for some $\varepsilon_o > 0$ to be fixed later:

$$B_k = \bar{\lambda}_k^{-\varepsilon_o} . \tag{3.3}$$

Then, fixed $k \in [0,N]$, consider a function f_k defined for $|x| \le B_k$, $x \in \mathbb{C}$

$$f_k(x) = \exp\left(\sum_{j=0}^{3} \tilde{\lambda}^{(j)}(k)\, H_{2j}(x) + \nu_k(x) \right) \tag{3.4}$$

with

$$(a)\quad |\tilde{\lambda}^{(2)}(k)| \le \lambda_k$$

$$(b)\quad |\tilde{\lambda}^{(j)}(k)| \le \kappa_o\, \bar{\lambda}_k^{2} \qquad j = 0,1,3 \tag{3.5}$$

(c) $\nu_k(x)$ is holomorphic in $|x| \le B_k$, divisible by x^8 and

$$|\nu_k(x)| \le \kappa_o\, \bar{\lambda}_k^{3-\varepsilon_1}$$

where κ_o will be fixed later.

We now consider the stochastic process (here $\chi(|x|<B)=1$ if $|x|<B$ and $= 0$ otherwise):

$$P(d\varphi) = \underset{N\to\infty}{\text{"lim"}} \left(\prod_{\Delta\in Q_N} f_N(x_\Delta)\right)\left(\prod_{k=0}^{N}\prod_{\Delta\in Q_N} \chi(|x_\Delta| \le B_k)\, e^{-z_\Delta^2}\frac{dz_\Delta}{\sqrt{\pi}}\right) \tag{3.6}$$

where f_N is a function verifying (a), (b), (c) with $\nu_N \equiv 0$. We want to show that if $\tilde{\lambda}^{(0)}(N)$, $\tilde{\lambda}^{(1)}(N)$ are conveniently chosen, then the limit in (3.6) exists in the sense that the distribution of the zero scale field in (3.6) converges to some $f_o(x)\ \chi(|x| < B_o)$ with f_o of the form (3.4) obeying (3.5). The " " mean that possibly one has to consider a subsequence of $N \to \infty$ in (3.6).

The presence of the field cut-offs in (3.6) changes the above ultraviolet problem formulated in terms of the map N. If $\chi_k(x) \equiv \chi(|x| < B_k)$ let

$$N_k\, f(x) \equiv \chi_k\, N(\chi_{k+1} \cdot f)(x), \tag{3.7}$$

then the effective potentials on scale k for (3.6) are given by

$$f_k(x) = N_k\, N_{k+1} \cdots N_{N-1}\, f_N(x) \tag{3.8}$$

(rather than by $f_k = N^{N-k} f_N$) .

The limit in (3.6) will exist, thus defining a stochastic process, if f_N can be so chosen that the limit in (3.8) exists for all k's and x's .

We show first that $N_k f_k$ has the form (3.4), (3.5) with k replaced by $k-1$ and (b) replaced:

$$|\tilde{\lambda}^{(j)}(k-1)| \le 2\gamma^{\sigma(j)}\kappa_o\, \bar{\lambda}_{k-1}^{-2} \qquad j = 0,1,3 \tag{3.9}$$

where $\sigma(j) = d-j(d-2)$ and $d = 4$.

Furthermore, let $\{\le 2\}$ denote a truncation to second order in $\bar{\lambda}_k$ of a polynomial in $\tilde{\lambda}^{(j)}(k)$, $j = 0,1,2,3$, when $\tilde{\lambda}^{(2)}(k)$, $j = 0,1,3$, are regarded of second order (see (3.5), (a), (b) for motivation on this point). Then

$$\sum_{j=0}^{3} \tilde{\lambda}^{(j)}(k-1)\, H_{2j}(x) = \left[\gamma^{d} \sum_{p=1}^{2} \frac{E^{T}}{p!}\left(\sum_{j=0}^{3} \tilde{\lambda}^{(j)}(k)\, H_{2j}(d\cdot+\beta x);p\right)\right]^{\{\leq 2\}} + \tag{3.10}$$

$$+ \text{"higher orders in } \bar{\lambda}_k\text{"}$$

where E, E^T denote, respectively, the expectation (i.e. integration) and the truncated expectation with respect to the measure $e^{-z^2} \frac{dz}{\sqrt{\pi}}$.

The (3.10) can be written explicitly:

$$\tilde{\lambda}^{(2)}(k-1) = \tilde{\lambda}^{(2)}(k) + \beta\, \tilde{\lambda}^{(2)}(k)^2 + O(\bar{\lambda}_k^{3-\varepsilon_1})$$

$$\tilde{\lambda}^{(1)}(k-1) = \gamma^2\, \tilde{\lambda}^{(2)}(k) + \beta_2\, \tilde{\lambda}^{(2)}(k)^2 + O(\bar{\lambda}_k^{3-\varepsilon_1})$$

$$\tilde{\lambda}^{(0)}(k-1) = \gamma^4\, \tilde{\lambda}^{(0)}(k) + \beta_5\, \tilde{\lambda}^{(2)}(k)^2 + O(\bar{\lambda}_k^{3-\varepsilon_1})$$

$$\tilde{\lambda}^{(3)}(k-1) = \frac{1}{\gamma^2}\, \tilde{\lambda}^{(3)}(k) + \beta_7\, \tilde{\lambda}^{(2)}(k)^2 + O(\bar{\lambda}_k^{3-\varepsilon_1}) \tag{3.11}$$

where $\beta_7 > 0$ and the other coefficients $\beta, \beta_2, \ldots$ have been introduced in (2.9) and, furthermore:

$$|O(\bar{\lambda}_k^{3-\varepsilon_1})| \leq \kappa_1 \frac{\bar{\lambda}_k^{3-\varepsilon_1}}{2} \tag{3.12}$$

provided $\varepsilon_o, \varepsilon_1$ are chosen conveniently and $\bar{\lambda}_o$ is small enough.

Assume for the time being that $N_k f_k$ has the properties (3.9) through (3.12). We first show how this allows us to complete the proof.

First we fix the value of the free parameter κ_o so that

$$\gamma^2\kappa_o - \beta_2 > \kappa_o, \quad \gamma^4\kappa_o - \beta_5 > \kappa_o, \quad \frac{1}{\gamma^2}\kappa_o + \beta_7 < \kappa_o \tag{3.13}$$

and then we suppose that $\bar{\lambda}_o$ (hence $\bar{\lambda}$ and $\bar{\lambda}_k$, see (3.2)) is so small that (3.13) remains true even if the r.h.s. are increased or decreased by $\frac{\kappa_1}{2}\, \bar{\lambda}_k^{3-\varepsilon_1}$, $\forall k \geq 0$. Then it follows from the "expansivity" of the $\tilde{\lambda}^{(1)}$, $\tilde{\lambda}^{(0)}$ linear terms in (3.11) that the square

$$D_N = [-\kappa_o\, \bar{\lambda}_N^2, \kappa_o\, \bar{\lambda}_N^2]^2 \tag{3.14}$$

in the plane $(\lambda_N^{(0)}, \lambda_N^{(1)})$ will have an image under N_N covering D_{N-1} in the sense that the $(\tilde{\lambda}^{(0)}_{N-1}, \tilde{\lambda}^{(1)}_{N-1})$ will cover D_{N-1} as $\tilde{\lambda}^{(0)}_N, \tilde{\lambda}^{(1)}_N$ cover D_N at fixed $\tilde{\lambda}^{(2)}_N, \tilde{\lambda}^{(3)}_N, \nu_N$ obeying (a), (b), (c) in (3.5).

Iterating this remark and assuming the above properties of $\mathcal{N}_k f_k$, $f \sim f_k$ verifying (3.4), (3.5), it follows the existence of a sequence of subsets of D_N:

$$D_N > \mathcal{D}_{N-1} > \mathcal{D}_{N-2} > \ldots > \mathcal{D}_o \tag{3.15}$$

such that

$$\mathcal{N}_k \mathcal{N}_{k+1} \cdots \mathcal{N}_{N-1} \mathcal{D}_{N-k} = D_{N-k} . \tag{3.16}$$

This proves that for each choice of $\tilde{\lambda}^{(2)}(N) \in [0,\bar{\lambda}_N]$ it is possible to choose $\tilde{\lambda}^{(0)}(N)$, $\tilde{\lambda}^{(1)}(N)$ and $\tilde{\lambda}^{(3)}(N) = 0$ (say), $\nu_N(x) \equiv 0$ (say) so that (3.4), (3.5) hold for all $k \le N$ and $\tilde{\lambda}^{(0)}(0) = \nu$, $\tilde{\lambda}^{(1)}(0) = \mu$ are prescribed in D_o (e.g. $\nu = \mu = 0$).

It is then easy to infer that this actually implies the existence of the limit (3.6), possibly considering a subsequence.

Therefore, it remains to show that $\kappa_1, \varepsilon_o, \varepsilon_1$ can be fixed so that $\mathcal{N}_k f_k$ has the properties listed between (3.9) and (3.12) if f_k has the properties (3.4), (3.5).

Fix $\eta > 0$ so that (recall $d = 4$, $\gamma = 2$, $\beta = \gamma^{-\frac{d-z}{2}}$)

$$\tau \equiv 2\,\gamma^d \left(\frac{\beta}{1-\eta}\right)^8 \left(-1 + \frac{1-\eta}{\beta}\right) < 1 . \tag{3.17}$$

Then for $|x| < (1-\eta)B_k\beta^{-1}$:

$$\mathcal{N}\chi_k f_k(x) = \left(\int_{|\alpha z + \beta x| < B_k} f_k(dz + \beta x)\, e^{-z^2} \frac{dz}{\sqrt{\pi}} \right)^{\gamma^d} =$$

$$= \left(\int_{|z| < \eta B_k/\alpha} f_k(\alpha z + \beta x)\, e^{-z^2} \frac{dz}{\sqrt{\pi}} + \int_{\substack{|z| > \eta B_k/\alpha \\ |\alpha z + \beta x| < B_k}} f_k(\alpha z + \beta x)\, e^{-z^2} \frac{dz}{\sqrt{\pi}} \right)^{\gamma^d} =$$

$$= (1-\rho_k)^{\gamma^d}\, \hat{E}(f_k(\alpha\cdot + \beta x))^{\gamma^d} \left(1 + \frac{\int_{\substack{|z| > \eta B_k/\alpha \\ |\alpha z + \beta x| < B_k}} f_k(\alpha z + \beta x) e^{-z^2} \frac{dz}{\sqrt{\pi}}}{(1-\rho_k)\, \hat{E}(f_k(\alpha\cdot + \beta x))} \right)^{\gamma^d}$$

where $\hat{E}(\cdot)$ denotes the expectation with respect to the measure

$\chi(|z| < \eta B_k/\alpha) e^{-z^2} \frac{dz}{\sqrt{\pi}}$ /norm and $E^T(\cdot)$ will later denote the truncated expectation with respect to the same measure; finally $(1-\rho_k)$ is the normalization constant

$$\rho_k = \int_{|z|>\eta B_k/\alpha} e^{-z^2} \frac{dz}{\sqrt{\pi}} = O(e^{-(\eta B_k \alpha)^2/z}) . \tag{3.19}$$

Using the bounds (3.4), (3.5), (3.19), (3.3) that for $|x| < (1-\eta)B_k\beta^{-1}$

$$N\chi_k f(x) = \hat{E}(f_k(\alpha\cdot + \beta x))^{\gamma^d} \left(1-\rho_k+\theta\rho_k\, e^{2(\bar{\lambda}_k B_k^4 + 4\kappa_0 \bar{\lambda}_k^2 B_k^6)T}\right) \tag{3.20}$$

where T is such that $|H_{2j}(x)| \le T\, B^{2j}$ for all $|x| \le B$, $(B > 1)$, $j = 0,1,2,3$ and θ is an unspecified number between 0 and 1 (introduced to keep (3.20) an equality rather than an inequality).

By using the definition of the truncated expectations $\hat{\varepsilon}^T$ we see that

$$\hat{E}^T(f_k(\alpha\cdot + \beta x)) = \exp\left[\sum_{p=1}^{2} \frac{1}{p!} \hat{E}^T \left(\sum_{j=0}^{2} \tilde{\lambda}^{(j)}(k)\, H_{2j}(\alpha\cdot + \beta x) + \nu_k(\alpha\cdot + \beta x);p\right) + R\right] \tag{3.21}$$

where for some $\bar{\kappa} > 0$

$$\begin{aligned} |R| &\le \bar{\kappa}(\bar{\lambda}_k B_k^4 + 3\kappa_0\, \bar{\lambda}_k^2\, B_k^6 + \kappa_0\, \bar{\lambda}_h^{3-\varepsilon_1})^3\, T^3 \le \\ &\le \delta\, \kappa_0\, \bar{\lambda}_k^{3-\varepsilon_1} \end{aligned} \tag{3.22}$$

where the estimate of the remainder of the cumulant expansion has been made by simply estimating $\sum_{j=0}^{2} \tilde{\lambda}^{(j)}(k)\, H_{2j}(\alpha z + \beta x) + {}_k(\alpha z + \beta x)$ by its maximum in $|x| < (1-\eta)B_k\beta^{-1}$, $|z| < \eta B_k/\alpha$, using (3.5); the (3.22) holds provided

$$3 - 12\varepsilon_0 > 3-\varepsilon_1 , \quad \varepsilon_1 < 1 \tag{3.23}$$

e.g. if $\varepsilon_0 = \frac{\varepsilon_1}{13}$, $\varepsilon_1 = \frac{1}{2}$.

The number δ in (3.22) can be fixed a priori once (3.23) holds, if $\bar{\lambda}_0$ is taken small enough (depending on δ): we take $\delta = \frac{1}{2}$, say.

The sum of the truncated expectations in (3.21) can be rewritten as, $(|\theta_\alpha| < 1)$:

$$\sum_{p=1}^{2} \frac{1}{p!}\, \varepsilon^T \left(\sum_{j=0}^{3} \tilde{\lambda}^{(j)}(k)\, H_{2j}(\alpha\cdot + \beta x);p\right) + \hat{E}(\nu_k(\alpha\cdot + \beta x) +$$

$$+ \theta_1\, T_1\, \bar{\lambda}_k^{4-\varepsilon_1}\, B_k^4 \equiv \theta_2(T_1\, \bar{\lambda}_k^{4-\varepsilon}\, B_k^4 + T_2 \rho_k\, \bar{\lambda}_k\, B_k^4) +$$

$$+ \hat{E}(\nu_k(\alpha\cdot + \beta x) + \sum_{p=1}^{2} \frac{1}{p!} E^T\Big(\sum_{j=0}^{3} \tilde{\lambda}^{(j)}(k)\, H_{2j}(\alpha\cdot + \beta x);p\Big) \qquad (3.24)$$

because replacing E^T by E^T changes the expectation value of a polynomial of degree ≤ 6 by a quantity involving ρ_k times the maximum of the polynomial in the integration domain specified in E^T which, in our case, is of the order of $\bar{\lambda}_k B_k^4 << 1$ in the region $|z| < \eta B_k/\alpha$, $|x| < (1-\eta)B_k/\beta$.

Therefore, (3.24) can be written for $|x| < (1-\eta)B_k/\beta$ as:

$$\Big[\sum_{p=1}^{2} \frac{1}{p!} E^T\Big(\sum_{j=0}^{3} \tilde{\lambda}^{(j)}(k)\, H_{2j}(\alpha\cdot + \beta x);p\Big)\Big]^{\{\leq 2\}} + \gamma^{-d}\, \tilde{\nu}_{k-1}(x)$$

and (3.25)

$$|\nu_{k-1}(x)| \leq \kappa_o\, \bar{\lambda}_k^{3-\varepsilon_1} (1+2\delta)\gamma^d < 2\gamma^d\, \kappa_o\, \bar{\lambda}_k^{3-\varepsilon_1}$$

(recalling the choice of $\delta < \frac{1}{2}$) and here one might again have to restrict further $\bar{\lambda}_o$ to be small so that

$$\kappa_o\, \delta\, \bar{\lambda}^{3-\varepsilon_1} + \bar{\kappa}_o\, \bar{\lambda}^{3-\varepsilon_1} + T_1\, \bar{\lambda}_k^{4-\varepsilon_1}\, B_k^4 + T_2\, \bar{\lambda}_k\, B_k^4 \rho_k \leq$$

$$\leq \kappa_o\, \bar{\lambda}^{3-\varepsilon_1} (1+2\delta)\ . \qquad (3.26)$$

The factor γ^{-d} in (3.25) has been inserted because f_{k-1} is the exponential of the first of (3.25) raised to the power γ^d.

We now observe that $(N\chi_k\, f_k)(x)$ is an entire function of x because:

$$N\chi_k f_k(x) = \int_{|y|<B_k} f_k(y)\, e^{-(y-\beta x)^2/\alpha^2} \frac{dy}{\alpha\sqrt{\pi}}\ . \qquad (3.27)$$

Hence it easily follows from our bounds that $\tilde{\nu}_{k-1}$ is holomorphic in $|x| < B_k(1-\eta)/\beta$ and therefore we can consider its first 6 Taylor coefficients

$$t_j = \frac{1}{2\pi i} \oint \tilde{\nu}_{k-1}(\zeta)\, \frac{d\zeta}{\zeta}\, \frac{1}{\zeta^{2j}} \qquad j = 0,1,2,3 \qquad (3.28)$$

where the contour of integration is any circle C_r around the origin and radius $r \leq B_k(1-\eta)/\beta$; we choose $r = 1$: hence (3.25) implies

$$|t_j| \leq (\kappa_o\, \bar{\lambda}_k^{3-\varepsilon_1}\, \gamma^d\, 2)\ . \qquad (3.29)$$

Therefore the coefficients of the Hermite polynomial of order < 8 in the representation of type (3.4) of $f_{k-1}(x)$ are given by (3.11) with the $O(\cdot)$ bounded by

$$2\gamma^d \kappa_o \bar{\lambda}_k^{3-\varepsilon_1} T_3 \equiv \frac{\kappa_1}{2} \bar{\lambda}_k^{3-\varepsilon_1} \tag{3.30}$$

for some T_3, a numerical constant: this determines κ_1.

The "remainder"

$$\nu_{k-1}(x) = \frac{1}{2\pi i} \oint \frac{d\zeta}{\zeta - x} \left(\frac{x}{\zeta}\right)^8 \tilde{\nu}_{k-1}(\zeta) \tag{3.31}$$

can be estimated by choosing $|\zeta| = B_k(1-\eta)/\beta$ as integration contour and $|x| < B_{k-1} \le B_k$: it is

$$|\nu_{k-1}(x)| \le 2\kappa_o \gamma^d \bar{\lambda}_k^{3-\varepsilon_1} \left(\frac{\beta}{1-\eta}\right)^8 \left(\frac{1-\eta}{\beta} - 1\right) = \tau \kappa_o \bar{\lambda}_k^{3-\varepsilon_1} < \kappa_o \bar{\lambda}_{k-1}^{3-\varepsilon_1} . \tag{3.32}$$

This proves (3.12), (3.11) and (c) in (3.5). Property (a) of (3.5) follows from (3.12) and the first of (3.11) by (3.1).

Property (b) in (3.5) with k replaced by $(k-1)$ follows from the last of (3.11), for $j = 3$, and (3.12) if $\bar{\lambda}_o$ is taken small enough.

Hence our construction of the measures in (3.6) is complete and such measures will have, by construction, effective potentials analytic on their support (bounded, because $|x| \le B_k$ is the support of f_k): in fact, they are, by our construction, uniformly bounded (as $N \to \infty$) on each fixed scale k. This allows us to use Vitali's theorem to find a subsequence $N_j \to \infty$ such that the limit in (3.6) exists.

Actually, it would not be difficult to prove that there is no need to consider subsequences, but we leave aside this (minor) question.

We can pick $\tilde{\lambda}^{(0)}(N)$, $\tilde{\lambda}^{(1)}(N)$ so that $\tilde{\lambda}^{(0)}(0), \tilde{\lambda}^{(1)}(0) = 0$: with this choice, the measures in (3.6) can be thought of as parametrized by $\lambda \equiv \tilde{\lambda}^{(2)}(0)$: the resulting family of stochastic processes will be denoted $P_{\lambda,0,0}(d\varphi)$. Note that we still have to check that $\lambda \neq 0$ if $\tilde{\lambda}^{(2)}(N)$ is taken conveniently.

§ 4 Proof that the Scalar Field Constructed in § 3 is φ_4^4 with $\lambda > 0$

To prove that the field in § 3 is non-trivial and "admits an asymptotic expansion in $\lambda^{(2)}(0) \equiv \lambda$, $\lambda^{(1)}(0) \equiv \mu \equiv 0$, $\lambda^{(0)}(0) \equiv \nu \equiv 0$ identical to that of φ_4^4" we proceed as follows.

Fix a sequence of bare constants $\lambda^{(2)}(N), \lambda^{(1)}(N), \lambda^{(0)}(N)$ such that $(\lambda^{(0)}(0), \lambda^{(1)}(0), \lambda^{(0)}(0))$ have a limit, as $N \to \infty$, $(\lambda,0,0)$.

If we choose

$$\lambda^{(2)}(N) \equiv \frac{\bar{\lambda}/2}{1+\beta\frac{\bar{\lambda}}{2} N} < \bar{\lambda}_N = \frac{\bar{\lambda}}{1+\beta\bar{\lambda}N} \left(1 + 0((N+1)^{-(1+\varepsilon_1)}\right) \tag{4.1}$$

where the inequality holds if N is large enough and $\bar{\lambda}$ is small enough (independently on N), then (3.11) implies

$$\tilde{\lambda}^{(2)}(k-1) \geq \tilde{\lambda}^{(2)}(k) + \beta\tilde{\lambda}^{(2)}(k)^2 - \frac{\kappa_1}{2} \bar{\lambda}_k^{3-\varepsilon} \tag{4.2}$$

which easily implies, if $\bar{\lambda}_o$, i.e. $\bar{\lambda}$, is small enough

$$\tilde{\lambda}^{(2)}(0) \geq \frac{1}{4} \bar{\lambda} \tag{4.3}$$

proving that $\lambda > 0$.

We show now the asymptoticity of perturbation theory and the identity of the family $P_{\lambda,0,0}(d\varphi)$ of stochastic processes with the formal perturbation expansion of φ_4^4.

Consider (2.5) and its formal power series solution (2.6).

Since the coefficients $\beta^{(\alpha)}(\underline{h},\underline{\alpha})$ are "translation invariant" in their frequency dependence (i.e. they are functions of h_v-k) it follows that, if $N \to \infty$,

$$\lambda(k+p) = \gamma^{-\underline{\sigma}(p-1)} \underline{\lambda}(k+1) + \sum_{|\underline{n}|\geq 2} \ell^{(\underline{n})}(p) \underline{\lambda}(k+1)^{\underline{n}} \tag{4.4}$$

where K+1 plays now the role of 0 in (2.6).

This expression can be reinserted into (2.5) to obtain a formal relation between $\underline{\lambda}(k)$ and $\underline{\lambda}(k+1)$ of the type:

$$\underline{\lambda}(k) = \gamma^{\underline{\sigma}} \underline{\lambda}(k+1) + \sum_{|\underline{n}|\geq 2} L^{\underline{n}} (\underline{\lambda}(k+1))^{\underline{n}} . \tag{4.5}$$

The reader can check that by substituting (4.4) into (2.5) and using the bound (2.8) on $\ell^{\underline{n}}(p)$ one falls exactly on the same expressions met in the proof that (2.8) holds, see § 19 of [10]; this immediately implies a bound on $L^{\underline{n}}$ of the form:

$$0 \leq |L^{\underline{n}}| \leq (|\underline{n}|-1)! \, \bar{C}^{|\underline{n}|-1} \tag{4.6}$$

the details are in [10].

The formula (4.5) gives us a formal function

$$\gamma^{\underline{\sigma}}\underline{\lambda} + \underline{B}(\underline{\lambda}) \equiv \gamma^{\underline{\sigma}} \underline{\lambda} + \sum_{|\underline{n}|\geq 2} L^{\underline{n}} \underline{\lambda}^{\underline{n}} \tag{4.7}$$

of three variables: it is the "beta function" of φ_4^4.

We now assume that for any $p \geq 2$, $|x| \leq B_k$:

$$f_k(x) = \exp \sum_{j=0}^{p+1} \tilde{\lambda}_p^{(j)}(k)\, H_{2j}(x) + \nu_{k,p}(x) \qquad (4.8)$$

where for some $\kappa_p > 0$

$$|\tilde{\lambda}_p^{(j)}(k)| \leq \kappa_p \quad \bar{\lambda}_k^{j-1} \qquad 2j > 4$$

$$|\tilde{\lambda}_p^{(2)}(k)| \leq \kappa_p \quad \bar{\lambda}_k$$

$$|\tilde{\lambda}_p^{(j)}(k)| \leq \kappa_p \quad \bar{\lambda}_k^{2} \qquad j = 0,1$$

$$|\ _{k,p}(x)| \leq \kappa_p \quad \bar{\lambda}_k^{p+1-\varepsilon_p} \qquad 0 < \varepsilon_p = 1 . \qquad (4.9)$$

Then, proceeding as in § 3, it follows that

$$\sum_{j=0}^{p+1} \tilde{\lambda}_p^{(j)} (K-1)\, H_{2j}(x) = \left[\sum_{q=1}^{p} \frac{\gamma^d}{q!} E^T\left(\sum_{j=0}^{p+1} \tilde{\lambda}_p^{(j)}(k)\, H_{2j}(\beta x + \alpha\cdot);q \right) \right]^1 + \qquad (4.10)$$

$$+ \text{"higher order terms"}$$

and "higher order terms" means $O(\bar{\lambda}_k^{p+1-\varepsilon_p})$, $0 < \varepsilon_p < 1$.

As a matter of fact we can replace $\tilde{\lambda}_p^{(j)}(k)$ by "p-independent" quantities: in fact, it follows from (4.8) that if $f_k(x)$ is defined $\equiv 1$ for $|x| > B_k$ and

$$\log f_k(x) = \sum_{j=0}^{\infty} \lambda^{(j)}(k)\, H_{2j}(x) \qquad (4.11)$$

is the Hermite expansion of $\log\ f_k$, then the (4.9) imply:

$$\tilde{\lambda}_p^{(j)}(k) = \lambda^{(j)}(k) + O(\bar{\lambda}_k^{p+1-\varepsilon_p}) .$$

The (4.9) also imply that

$$f_k(v) = \exp \sum_{j=0}^{p+1} \lambda^{(j)}(k)\, H_{2j}(x) + \bar{\ }_{\kappa,p}(x) \qquad (4.12)$$

and

$$|\bar{\nu}_{k,p}(x)| \leq \bar{\kappa}_p \quad \bar{\lambda}_k^{p+1-\varepsilon_p} . \qquad (4.13)$$

Finally it is clear that, by the uniqueness of the formal perturbation series the relation (4.10) <u>must</u> coincide with

$$\underline{\lambda}(k-1) = \gamma^{\underline{\sigma}} \; \underline{\lambda}(k) + \{B\,\underline{\lambda}(k)\}^{\{\leq p\}} + O(\bar{\lambda}_k^{p+1-\varepsilon_p}) \qquad (4.14)$$

where $\{\cdot\}^{\{\leq p\}}$ is the truncation of the formal power series defining the beta-function (4.7) to the order p .

The (4.14) implies that the dependence of $\underline{\lambda}(k)$ on $\underline{\lambda}(0)$ has to start as prescribed by perturbation theory for φ_4^4 : in fact, one just has to iterate (4.14) at fixed k a finite number of times, X_0 express $\underline{\lambda}(k)$ in terms of $\underline{\lambda}(0)$ and of functions of $\underline{\lambda}(p)$ of formal degree higher than p .

This shows that all the form factors admit an expansion in $\underline{\lambda}(0)$ which is asymptotic and coincides with that of φ_4^4 .

It remains to analyze the $f_k(x)$ fixed k,x and the Schwinger functions: we do not enter into the details of the proof that, as a consequence of the above asymptotic properties of the form factors, also the effective potentials and the Schwinger functions are expressed by an asymptotic series in $\underline{\lambda}(0)$ coinciding with the one of φ_4^4 .

Acknowledgements:

I am indebted to Giovanni Felder, Joel Feldman, Konrad Osterwalder and Lon Rosen for many discussions. This work has been partially supported by NSF grant # NSF DMS 85-03333 and by "Ministero della Pubblica Istruzione".

References:

[1] Dyson, F.: Comm. Math. Phys. 21, 269 (1971)

[2] Wilson, K.: Phys. Rev. D2, 1438 (1970)

[3] Wilson, K., Kogut, J.: Phys. Rep. 12, 75 (1974)

[4] Bleher, P., Sinai, Y.: Comm. Math. Phys. 45, 147 (1975)

[5] Collet, P., Eckmann, J.P.: Lecture Notes in Physics, vol. 74, Springer-Verlag, Berlin (1978)

[6] Gallavotti, G.: Mem. Accad. Lincei 15, 23 (1978) and Annali Mat. Pura e Applicata 120, 1 (1979)

[7] Gallavotti, G.: in Bielefeld Rencontres in Physics and Mathematics, ed. L. Streit, Springer-Vienna (1979), p. 407-440

[8] Benfatto, G., Cassandro, M., Gallavotti, G., Nicolò, F., Olivieri, E., Presutti, E., Scacciatelli, E.: Comm. Math. Phys. 59, 143 (1978) and 71, 95 (1980); Benfatto, G., Gallavotti, G., Nicolò, F.: Comm. Math. Phys. 83, 387 (1982); Nicolò, F.: Comm. Math. Phys. 88, 581 (1983)

[9] Gawędzki, K., Kupiainen, A.: J. Stat. Phys. 29, 683 (1982), 35, 267 (1981)

[10] Gallavotti, G.: Rev. Mod. Phys. 57, 471 (1985)

[11] Gallavotti, G., Rivasseau, V.: Ann. Inst. H. Poincaré B40, 185 (1984)

[12] Gallavotti, G., Nicolò, F.: Comm. Math. Phys. 100, 545 (1985) and 101, 247 (1985)

[13] Felder, G., Gallavotti, G.: Renormalization and Non-Renormalizable Field Theories, preprint IAS (1985), in print in Comm. Math. Phys.

[14] Gawędzki, K., Kupiainen, A.: Lectures in the Proceedings of the 1984 Les Houches Summer School, ed. K. Osterwalder, in print at North Holland

[15] Khuri, N.: Rockefeller Univ. preprint (1985)

[16] Symanzik, K.: in Lecture Notes in Physics, vol. 153, ed. R. Schrader, R. Seiler (1982)

[17] Baker, G.: preprint at Los Alamos N.L. (1985)

[18] Stevenson, P.M.: The gaussian effective potential II, $\lambda\varphi^4$ field theory. Preprint Univ. of Wisconsin, Madison

[19] Nelson, E.: in Lecture Notes in Physics, vol. 25, ed. G. Velo, A. Wightman (1973)

[20] Guerra, F., Rosen, L., Simon, B.: Annals of Mathematics 101, 111 (1975)

[21] Glimm, J.: Comm. Math. Phys. 10, 111 (1975)
Glimm, J., Jaffe, A.: Fort. Phys. 21, 327 (1973)

[22] Glimm, J., Jaffe, A.: Quantum Physics, Springer-Verlag (1981)

INDETERMINACY RELATIONS IN STOCHASTIC MECHANICS

Simon Golin
Theoretische Physik, Fakultät für Physik
Universität Bielefeld
and
Forschungszentrum Bielefeld-Bochum-Stochastik
Postfach 8640
D-4800 Bielefeld 1
Federal Republic of Germany

I. INTRODUCTION

The theory of stochastic mechanics provides a probabilistic description of non-relativistic quantum phenomena. The representation of quantum systems in terms of stochastic processes was discussed by Fényes [1] in 1952, and was rediscovered by Nelson [2,3] in 1966. Nelson accomplished a rigorous diffusion theoretic set-up of stochastic mechanics and claims that it provides a naively realistic, objective picture of physical events [4]. The classical character of stochastic mechanics comes from the interpretation of the trajectories associated to the stochastic mechanical diffusions as actual particle paths in a fluctuating background field.

One is then immediately faced with the question of equivalence: does stochastic mechanics make the same predictions as ordinary quantum mechanics?

We will look at this question from the point of view of the indeterminacy relations. Although the introduction of non-configurational variables (such as momentum or orbital angular momentum) into the stochastic framework poses serious difficulties [5], it is possible to establish uncertainty relations which involve them. In the sequel we will look at position-momentum, angle variables - orbital angular momentum, and time - energy indeterminacy. It turns out that these relations give larger bounds on the uncertainties than those determined by the Heisenberg-like indeterminacy relations. There is, however, a stronger form of indeterminacy relations in quantum mechanics due to Schrödinger [6]. For the case of the position-momentum indeterminacy we proved in [7] that the stochastic mechanical result is identical to Schrödinger's generalization. We will show that this holds true for other pairs of operators.

It is often maintained that the appearance of indeterminacy relations is a generic feature of quantum theories. From the standpoint of stochastic mechanics, however, this proposition seems to be questionable. The Heisenberg position-momentum uncertainty relation derived via stochastic mechanics corresponds to a purely kinematical fact about diffusion processes, namely the non-differentiability of their sample path. Moreover, uncertainty relations can be established for general diffusions which are not related to quantum processes. This supports the view [8] that the indeterminacy relations are merely a result and a measure of the stochasticity of quantum systems and do not express a specifically quantum mechanical property.

Our analysis reveals agreement between stochastic mechanics and conventional quantum mechanics on the level of indeterminacy relations. However, as Nelson [9] has pointed out, there may be serious trouble in the correspondence of the two theories.

II. INDETERMINACY RELATIONS IN QUANTUM MECHANICS

There is vast variety of indeterminacy relations in quantum mechanics, some of them are reviewed in [10]. In this section we will only make mention of those necessary for comparison with stochastic mechanics.

The earliest version of an indeterminacy relation is due to Heisenberg in 1927 [11]. It states that if the commutator of two Hermitian operators A and B is a multiple of the identity,

$$[A,B] := AB - BA = c\,\mathbf{1}\,, \tag{1}$$

then this determines a lower bound on the uncertainty

$$\mathrm{Var}\,A \cdot \mathrm{Var}\,B \geq \frac{1}{4}\,|c|^2\,, \tag{2}$$

where $\mathrm{Var}\,A := \langle (A-\langle A\rangle)^2\rangle$ and $\langle\cdot\rangle$ denotes the quantum expectation. More generally, if the commutator is not of the form (1), i.e. if we deal with non-conjugate operators, the Heisenberg-like uncertainty relations are given by

$$\mathrm{Var}\,A \cdot \mathrm{Var}\,B \geq \frac{1}{4}|\langle [A,B]\rangle|^2. \tag{3}$$

In 1930, Schrödinger [6] established a generalization of (3). If one defines the covariance of A and B by

$$\mathrm{Cov}(A,B) := \frac{1}{2}\langle AB + BA\rangle - \langle A\rangle\langle B\rangle \tag{4}$$

taking care of a potential non-commutativity of the two operators, then Schrödinger's version of indeterminacy relations assumes the form

$$\mathrm{Var}\,A \cdot \mathrm{Var}\,B \geq \mathrm{Cov}^2(A,B) + \frac{1}{4}|<[A,B]>|^2 \quad . \tag{5}$$

Clearly, it gives a stronger bound on the uncertainty. The reason why the indeterminacy relations à la Schrödinger are not particularly well-known, is that one normally makes use of the uncertainty relations in the interpretation of the non-commutativity of observables: non-commuting observables cannot simultaneously be measured within arbitrary accuracy. And for this statement, of course, the Heisenberg version is sufficient.

Davidson [12] pointed out that the usual proofs of such uncertainty relations may lead to paradoxes, since they have the deficiency of not taking care of the domains of Hermiticy of the operators involved. His idea was taken up by Jackiw [13], who presents a rigorous derivation of (5) based on an Euler-Lagrange variational principle. We will not go into this matter in more detail.

It is worth mentioning that for non-commuting operators there is no consistent way to generalize the definition of covariance to a definition of higher moments [14]. If this could have been accomplished, we would have obtained a non-negative joint probability distribution. But this is not possible, of course; a fact that is expressed by the von Neumann-Nelson theorem [3] on the non-existence of joint distributions related to non-commuting observables.

III. INDETERMINACY RELATIONS IN STOCHASTIC MECHANICS

1. Several indeterminacy relations can be derived in the stochastic framework. There existence is in no way confined to Nelson diffusions, where the diffusion coefficient is a constant $\sqrt{2\nu} = \sqrt{\hbar/m}$; but it is rather a characteristic of diffusion processes with arbitrary diffusion coefficients. In 1933, Fürth [15] derived a position-velocity uncertainty relation for the heat equation, i.e. for Brownian motion; but - of course - at that time he did not think of it as a quantum expression. Fényes [1] was the first to obtain a stochastic mechanical position-momentum indeterminacy relation. Its general form is due to de La Peña-Auerbach and Cetto [8], and de Falco, De Martino, and De Siena [16]. Time-energy indeterminacy was later considered in [17], and the case of orbital angular momentum will be established in the sequel. As a matter of fact, the stochastic mechanical indeterminacy relations are fully equivalent to Schrödinger's version. This was noticed in [7].

2. We will now present an explicit exposition of all this. The notation and conventions will be in accordance with Nelson [2-4]. Unless otherwise noted we restrict ourselves to one dimension - the generalization to higher dimensions being trivial. Consider a function $f = f(x,t)$ of space and time, and let $E[f] \equiv E[f(\xi_t(\cdot),t)]$. The following useful formula is obtained by partial integration,

$$E[fu] = -\nu E[\frac{\partial}{\partial x} f] \tag{6}$$

A handy tool for the derivation of uncertainty relations in stochastic mechanics is then easily derived:

<u>Osmotic Velocity Indeterminacy Relation</u> (De Martino, De Siena [17]):

$$\frac{\text{Var } f}{E^2[\frac{\partial}{\partial x}f]} \text{ Var } u \geq \nu^2. \tag{7}$$

<u>Proof:</u> Apply the Schwarz inequality and note that the osmotic velocity has zero mean,

$$\begin{aligned} \text{Var } f \text{ Var } u &= E[(f-E[f])^2] \cdot E[u^2] \\ &\geq E^2[(f-E[f])u] = E^2[fu] \\ &= \nu^2 E[\frac{\partial}{\partial x} f] \,. \qquad \square \end{aligned}$$

If we set $f(x) = x$, we obtain

$$\text{Var } \xi \text{ Var } u \geq \nu^2 , \tag{8}$$

and by means of the Schwarz inequality

$$\text{Var } \xi \text{ Var } v \geq \text{Cov}^2(\xi,v). \tag{9}$$

This now yields the

<u>Position-Momentum Indeterminacy Relation</u>

$$\text{Var } \xi(\text{Var } u + \text{Var } v) \geq \text{Cov}^2(\xi,v) + \nu^2 . \tag{10}$$

The distributions of the diffusion ξ and of the quantum mechanical operator X coincide, and the momentum P satisfies

$$\text{Var } P = m^2(\text{Var } u + \text{Var } v), \tag{11}$$
$$\text{Cov}(X,P) = m \text{ Cov}(\xi,v). \tag{12}$$

Therefore (10) is equivalent to Schrödinger's form of the position-momentum uncertainty relation

$$\text{Var } X \text{ Var } P \geq \text{Cov}(X,P) + \frac{\hbar^2}{4} \tag{13}$$

Remarks:

a) The Heisenberg uncertainty relation follows already from (8), i.e. it can be traced back to the non-differentiability of the sample paths of the diffusion ξ, which shows up in $u \neq o$. This is a purely kinematical quality: the dynamics of the system under consideration does not enter (8).

b) The relation $\nu = \hbar/2m$ is not essential for the validity of (8,10). In fact, ν could be any positive constant or even need not be a constant, i.e. uncertainty relations are a general feature of stochastic systems (diffusions).

c) The inequality (9) appears already in Fényes' work [1,(19)]; however, he concludes from this that $\text{Var } \xi \cdot \text{Var } v \geq \nu^2$ [1,(20)] . This, of course, is incorrect (e.g. stationary states are characterized by a zero current velocity).

d) The uncertainty relation (10) can be generalized by introducing $f = f(x,t)$ instead of x again. For instance, ma = - grad V (V is the potential) yields the force-momentum uncertainty relation (see [7]).

3. To deal with angular momentum we pass over to three dimensions. The azimuthal angle φ and the z-component L_z of the orbital angular momentum are commonly regarded as conjugate observables,

$$[\varphi, L_z] = [\varphi, \frac{\hbar}{i}\frac{\partial}{\partial\varphi}] = i\,\hbar, \tag{14}$$

$$\text{Var } \varphi \quad \text{Var } L_z \geq \frac{\hbar^2}{4} . \qquad \text{(wrong!)} \tag{15}$$

It was noted by Jordan [18] that (15) must be wrong, since Var L_z may be arbitrarily close to zero (choosing a state close to an eigenstate of L_z), and thus Var φ would have to be very large. But this is in contradiction to the boundedness of φ [Var $\varphi \leq (2\pi)^2$]. In fact, a careful treatment of L_z shows that its domain of Hermiticity can only contain functions periodic in φ. Since φ itself is not periodic, it is clear that (15) cannot be established.

There have been several attempts of replacing the azimuthal angle by other variables [19, and references therein]. One suggestion due to Louisell [20] is to use the two continuous periodic functions sin φ and cos φ instead of φ itself. This idea was implemented by Carruthers and Nieto [19]. They established the corresponding Heisenberg-like indeterminacy relations and pointed out that for well-localized wave packets these relations reduce to (15).

Let $f = f(x,y,z,t)$ be again a function of space and time. By means of the Schwarz inequality

$$\mathrm{Var}\, f\, \mathrm{Var}[\xi_x u_y - \xi_y u_x] \geq \mathrm{Cov}^2(f, \xi_x u_y - \xi_y u_x) = \nu^2 E^2[\xi_x \frac{\partial}{\partial y} f - \xi_y \frac{\partial}{\partial y} f] , \tag{16.a}$$

$$\mathrm{Var}\, f\, \mathrm{Var}[\xi_x v_y - \xi_y v_x] \geq \mathrm{Cov}^2(f, \xi_x v_y - \xi_y v_x) . \tag{16.b}$$

Tanking $\sin \varphi$ or $\cos \varphi$ for f, we obtain the

Angle Variables - Orbital Angular Momentum Indeterminacy Relations

$$\mathrm{Var}\,[\sin\varphi]\{\mathrm{Var}[\xi_x u_y - \xi_y u_x] + \mathrm{Var}\,[\xi_x v_y - \xi_y v_x]\} \geq \mathrm{Cov}^2(\sin\varphi, \xi_x v_y - \xi_y v_x) + \nu^2 E^2[\cos\varphi] , \tag{17.a}$$

$$\mathrm{Var}\,[\cos\varphi]\{\mathrm{Var}\,[\xi_x u_y - \xi_y u_x] + \mathrm{Var}\,[\xi_x v_y - \xi_y v_x]\} \geq \mathrm{Cov}^2(\cos\varphi, \xi_x v_y - \xi_y v_x) + \nu^2 E^2[\sin\varphi], \tag{17.b}$$

or in a symmetric form

$$\frac{\mathrm{Var}[\sin\varphi]+\mathrm{Var}[\cos\varphi]}{E^2[\sin\varphi]+E^2[\cos\varphi]}\{\mathrm{Var}\,[\xi_x u_y - \xi_y u_x] + \mathrm{Var}[\xi_x v_y - \xi_y v_x]\} \geq \frac{\mathrm{Cov}^2(\sin\varphi, \xi_x v_y - \xi_y v_x) + \mathrm{Cov}^2(\cos\varphi, \xi_x v_y - \xi_y v_x)}{E^2[\sin\varphi]+ E^2[\cos\varphi]} + \nu^2 . \tag{17.c}$$

It is an easy matter to compare this result with quantum mechanics because in similarity to the case of momentum

$$\mathrm{Var}\, L_z = m^2(\mathrm{Var}[\xi_x u_y - \xi_y u_x] + \mathrm{Var}\,[\xi_x v_y - \xi_y v_x]), \tag{18}$$

$$\mathrm{Cov}(\sin\varphi, L_z) = m\, \mathrm{Cov}(\sin\varphi, \xi_x v_y - \xi_y v_x), \tag{19.a}$$

$$\mathrm{Cov}(\cos\varphi, L_z) = m\, \mathrm{Cov}(\cos\varphi, \xi_x v_y - \xi_y v_x). \tag{19.b}$$

As a result of this the stochastic mechanical indeterminacy relations (17a.-c.) coincide with Schrödinger's version

$$\mathrm{Var}[\sin\varphi]\, \mathrm{Var}\, L_z \geq \mathrm{Cov}^2(\sin\varphi, L_z) + \frac{\hbar^2}{4} < \cos\varphi >^2, \tag{20.a}$$

$$\mathrm{Var}[\cos\varphi]\, \mathrm{Var}\, L_z \geq \mathrm{Cov}^2(\cos\varphi, L_z) + \frac{\hbar^2}{4} < \sin\varphi >^2, \tag{20.b}$$

$$\frac{\mathrm{Var}[\sin\varphi]+\mathrm{Var}[\cos\varphi]}{\langle\sin\varphi\rangle^2+\langle\cos\varphi\rangle^2} \geq \frac{\mathrm{Cov}^2(\sin\varphi,L_Z)+\mathrm{Cov}^2(\cos\varphi,L_Z)}{\langle\sin\varphi\rangle^2+\langle\cos\varphi\rangle^2} + \frac{\hbar^2}{4}. \tag{20.c}$$

4. We now turn to the time-energy indeterminacy. The time dependence of the mean of $f = f(x,y,z,t)$ is

$$\frac{d}{dt} E[f] = E[\frac{\partial}{\partial t} f] + E[f\frac{\partial}{\partial t} \ln \rho]. \tag{21}$$

f may be viewed as representing a clock measuring the time dependence of the stationarity of the state. A generic time for the process to spend in a state related to the density ρ, is the time one must wait for the expectation of f to change by an amount of the order of the standard deviation. Thus the characteristic time of f is defined by

$$\tau_f := \frac{\sqrt{\mathrm{Var}\, f}}{|\frac{d}{dt} E[f]-E[\frac{\partial}{\partial t} f]|}\ . \tag{22}$$

Now remember that $v = \frac{\hbar}{m}$ grad S. Then an application of the Schwarz inequality yields the

Time-Energy Indeterminacy Relation

$$\tau_f^2 \{\frac{1}{4} E[(\frac{\partial}{\partial t} \ln \rho)^2]+\mathrm{Var}[\frac{\partial}{\partial t} S]\} \geq \left[\frac{\mathrm{Cov}(f,\frac{\partial}{\partial t} S)}{E[f\frac{\partial}{\partial t} \ln \rho]}\right]^2 + \frac{1}{4}. \tag{23}$$

The Hamiltonian satisfies

$$\mathrm{Var}\, H = \hbar^2\{\frac{1}{4} E[(\frac{\partial}{\partial t} \ln \rho)^2] + \mathrm{Var}\, [\frac{\partial}{\partial t} S]\}\ , \tag{24}$$

$$\mathrm{Cov}(f,H) = - \hbar\, \mathrm{Cov}(f, \frac{\partial}{\partial t} S), \tag{25}$$

$$\langle[H,f]\rangle = -i\, \hbar\, E[f \frac{\partial}{\partial t} \ln \rho]\ , \tag{26}$$

and again the stochastic uncertainty relation is nothing but a Schrödinger-type relation

$$\tau_f^2\, \mathrm{Var}\, H \geq \hbar^2|\frac{\mathrm{Cov}(f,H)}{\langle[H,f]\rangle}|^2 + \frac{\hbar^2}{4}. \tag{27}$$

Remarks:

a) Time-energy indeterminacy has a spirit different from the previous uncertainty relations because of the non-operational character of time.

b) The inequality

$$\tau_f^2 \, E\,(\frac{\partial}{\partial t} \ln \rho)^2] \geq \frac{1}{4} \tag{28}$$

is due to De Martino and De Siena [17]. The mean temporal change of ρ, $|E[\rho^{-1} \frac{\partial}{\partial t} \rho]|$, is a measure of the non-stationarity of the state. If it is very small, the system must exhibit large characteristic times.

c) In the quantum mechanical framework one is not restricted to considering functions f of position and time alone, but equation (27) may also be established for an f depending on non-configurational variables as e.g. momentum. In order to get an equality sign in

$$\tau_f^2 <(\frac{\partial}{\partial t} \ln \rho)^2> \geq \frac{1}{4}, \tag{29}$$

it is in fact necessary to admit such functions. This amounts to determining the optimal clock (minimal characteristic time) to measure the time-variability of the system. In stochastic mechanics where f may not be of this general form it was suggested by De Martino and De Siena [17] to consider functions depending on several times.

5. There are more uncertainty relations to be looked at. For instance, one could consider the pair (X,X_t), where X_t is the Heisenberg position operator at time t. The case of general potential has not yet been treated. But for the simple case of a particle without interaction and for the harmonic oscillator both stochastic mechanics and quantum mechanics give the same bounds on the uncertainty. This follows from a simple Taylor expansion.

Another common time-energy uncertainty relation involves the lifetime

$$\tau := \frac{1}{2} \int dt \, |<e^{-i\frac{t}{\hbar}H}>|^2. \tag{30}$$

This concept is useful in the description of resonances and metastable states. So far the lifetime τ has not found a representation in stochastic terms.

6. The viewpoint of the preceding paragraphs can be reversed and the following question asked: Given the quantum mechanical indeterminacy relation, what can we infer about the motion of the quantum particle? In an article by Abbott and Wise [21] it was shown that the Heisenberg uncertainty principle is reflected in the fractal nature of quantum mechanical paths,* viz. the paths have Hausdorff dimension D = 2.

---

* I would like to thank M.Berry for having pointed out this reference to me.

But this is exactly a regularity property of the sample paths of diffusion processes. which are everywhere continuous and nowhere differentiable (with probability one). Thus the quantum mechanical indeterminacy gives a hint as to what stochastic processes would be of use in the description of quantum systems.

This idea can be generalized to the relativistic case where the uncertainty principle yields Hausdorff dimension D = 1. Roughly speaking, this corresponds to differentiability of the quantum mechanical paths. In fact, the probabilistic solution of the Dirac equation obtained by Blanchard, Combe, Sirugue, and Sirugue-Collin [22] is in terms of jump processes, and their paths are constant up to random jumps.

After having noted the interrelation of the uncertainty principle and the fractal nature of the stochastic mechanical sample paths it becomes clear that indeterminacy relations for the stochastic mechanics on manifolds can also be established.

References

[1] I.Fényes: Eine wahrscheinlichkeitstheoretische Begründung und Interpretation der Quantenmechanik, Z.Physik 132, 81 (1952)

[2] E.Nelson: Derivation of the Schrödinger Equation from Newtonian Mechanics, Phys.Rev. 150, 1079 (1966)

[3] E.Nelson: Dynamical Theories of Brownian Motion, Princeton University Press, Princeton (1967)

[4] E.Nelson: Quantum Fluctuations, Princeton University Press, Princeton (1985)

[5] S.Golin: Comment on Momentum in Stochastic Mechanics, Bielefeld preprint, BI-TP 85/13, BiBoS 43 (1985)

[6] E.Schrödinger: Zum Heisenbergschen Unschärfeprinzip, Sitzungsber.Preuss.Akad. Wiss., Phys.-Math.Klasse, 296 (1930)

[7] S.Golin: Uncertainty Relations in Stochastic Mechanics, to appear in: J.Math.Phys. 26 (1985)

[8] L. de La Peña-Auerbach and M.Cetto: Stronger Form for the Position-Momentum Uncertainty Relation, Phys.Lett. 39A, 65 (1972)

[9] E.Nelson: Field Theory and the Future of Stochastic Mechanics, contribution to this issue

[10] W.G.Faris: Inequalities and Uncertainty Principles, J.Math.Phys. 19, 461 (1978)

[11] W.Heisenberg: Über den anschaulichen Inhalt der quantentheoretischen Kinematik und Mechanik, Z.Physik 43, 172 (1927)

[12] E.R.Davidson: On Derivations of the Uncertainty Principle, J.Chem.Phys. 42, 1461 (1965)

[13] R.Jackiw: Minimum Uncertainty Product, Number-Phase Uncertainty Product and Coherent States, J.Math.Phys. 9, 339 (1968)

[14] H.Margenau and R.N.Hill: Correlation between Measurements in Quantum Theory, Prog.Theor.Phys. 26, 722 (1961)

[15] R.Fürth: Über einige Beziehungen zwischen klassischer Statistik und Quantenmechanik, Z.Physik 81, 143 (1933)

[16] D. de Falco, S. De Martino, and S. De Siena: Position-Momentum Uncertainty in Stochastic Mechanics, Phys.Rev. Lett. 49, 181 (1982)

[17] S. De Martino and S. De Siena: Quantum Uncertainty Relations and Stochastic Mechanics, Nuovo Cimento 79B, 175 (1984)

[18] P.Jordan: Über eine neue Begründung der Quantenmechanik.II., Z.Physik 44, 1 (1927)

[19] P.Carruthers and M.M.Nieto: Phase and Angle Variables in Quantum Mechanics, Rev.Mod.Phys. 40, 411 (1968)

[20] W.H.Louisell: Amplitude and Phase Uncertainty Relations, Phys. Lett. 7, 60 (1963)

[21] L.F.Abbott and M.B.Wise: Dimension of a quantum-mechanical path, Am.J.Phys. 49, 37 (1981)

[22] Ph.Blanchard, Ph.Combe, M.Sirugue and M.Sirugue-Collin: Probabilistic Solution of the Dirac Equation, Bielefeld preprint, BiBoS 44 (1985)

GIBBS STATES AND SPONTANEOUS

SYMMETRY BREAKDOWN

Christian Gruber
Institut de Physique Théorique
Ecole Polytechnique Fédérale de Lausanne
PHB-Ecublens
CH-1015 Lausanne, Switzerland

1. INTRODUCTION

It is well known that equilibrium properties of macroscopic systems are described by means of "Gibbs states", also called Gibbs Random Fields. The fundamental problem in this domain is to obtain a description of all possible Gibbs states at a given temperature and to characterize their properties.

In this note we shall be interested in those properties which can be analysed by means of symmetry group. As we shall see one can achieve a rather complete description of all periodic Gibbs states in the case where the temperature is "regular" (Sec. 3). We shall then mention a result due to Ch. Pfister which shows that for ferromagnetic systems, almost all temperature are regular (Sec. 4). In Sec. 5, we briefly discuss extensions to other systems. All definitions are given in Sec. 2. Proofs of the results stated in Sec. 3 can be found in ref. [1], where the reader will find more references to related work; proofs of the results given in Sec. 4 are given in ref. [2].

2. DEFINITIONS

We consider the lattice $\mathcal{L} = \mathbb{Z}$; at each site x of $\mathcal{L}$ is associated a random variable θ_x with value in some measure space Ω_0 (Hausdorff-Metrizable-Compact) with probability measure $d\nu_0$.

1) The configuration space is $\Omega = \Omega_0^{\mathcal{L}} = \{\underline{\theta}\}$ i.e. $\underline{\theta} : \mathcal{L} \to \Omega_0$, $x \mapsto \theta_x$

   For all $\Lambda \subset \mathcal{L}$ we denote by $\underline{\theta}_\Lambda$ the projection of $\underline{\theta}$ on $\Omega_\Lambda = \Omega_0^\Lambda$ and $\underline{\theta} = (\underline{\theta}_\Lambda, \underline{\theta}_{\Lambda^c})$ where $\Lambda^c = \mathcal{L} \setminus \Lambda$.

2) The interactions are defined by $\{\Phi_B\}$, family of real functions on Ω, indexed by the finite subsets B of $\mathcal{L}$, which satisfy:

$$\Phi_B(\underline{\theta}) = \Phi_B(\underline{\theta}_B) \quad ; \quad \sum_{B \ni x_0} \int_{\Omega_B} d\nu_B \, |\Phi_B| < \infty .$$

   The hamiltonian of the system is then formally expressed as

$$H = \sum_B \Phi_B$$

   i.e. for any finite $\Lambda \subset \mathcal{L}$, the hamiltonian of the finite system Λ

with boundary condition $\underline{\vartheta}$ outside of Λ is given by the function $H_{\Lambda,\underline{\vartheta}}$ on Ω_Λ :

$$H_{\Lambda,\underline{\vartheta}}(\underline{\theta}_\Lambda) = \sum_{B:\, B\cap\Lambda \neq \phi} \phi_B(\underline{\theta}_\Lambda, \underline{\vartheta}_{\Lambda^c})$$

We shall assume that the interactions are <u>invariant under translations, i.e.</u>

$$\forall a \in \mathcal{L} \qquad \begin{cases} \phi_B(\underline{\theta}) = \phi_{B+a}(a\cdot\underline{\theta}) \\ (a\circ\underline{\theta})_x = \theta_{x-a} \qquad B+a = \{x+a;\, x\in B\} \end{cases}$$

3) The <u>internal symmetry group</u> of the system G^{int} is then introduced in the following way :

Let $G_0 = \{g\}$ be a topological group of transformations on Ω_0 which leaves the measure $d\nu_0$ invariant :

$$\begin{array}{cccc} g: & \Omega_0 & \rightarrow & \Omega_0 \\ & \cup\!\!\!\!\shortmid & & \cup\!\!\!\!\shortmid \\ & \theta & \mapsto & g\cdot\theta \end{array}$$

and $G = G_0^{\mathcal{L}} = \{\underline{g}\}$ be the corresponding group of transformations on Ω, i.e. $(\underline{g}\cdot\underline{\theta})_x = g_x\cdot\theta_x$.

Then :

$$G^{int} = \{\underline{g} \in G;\ \phi_B(\underline{g}\cdot\underline{\theta}) = \phi_B(\underline{\theta}) \quad \forall B\}$$

There is a natural action of $\mathbb{Z}^\nu$ on G^{int} given by :

$$(T_a\,\underline{g})_x = g_{x-a} \qquad \forall a \in \mathbb{Z}^\nu$$

The <u>Gauge Group</u> is the subgroup of G^{int} defined by :

$$G_f^{int} = \{\underline{g} \in G^{int};\ g_x \neq \mathbb{1} \text{ for finitely many } x\}$$

4) The <u>Gibbs states</u> are introduced first for finite systems Λ with boundary conditions $\underline{\vartheta}$ by the probability measure on Ω_Λ :

$$P_{\Lambda,\underline{\vartheta}}[d\theta_\Lambda] = Z^{-1} \exp\{-\beta H_{\Lambda,\underline{\vartheta}}(\underline{\theta}_\Lambda)\} \prod_{x\in\Lambda} d\nu_0(\theta_x)$$

The family $\Delta(\beta)$ of Gibbs states at inverse temperature β is then defined as the closed, convex hull, of probability distributions on Ω, obtained as weak limits of $P_{\Lambda,\underline{\vartheta}}$ as Λ tends to $\mathcal{L}$. We shall represent a state by ω, positive, linear functional on the algebra of local observables; the following result is well known.

Property 1

$\Delta(\beta)$ is a non-empty, convex set, which is a Choquet simplex.

The symmetry groups $\mathbb{Z}^\nu$ and G^{int} act in a natural way on $\Delta(\beta)$, e.g. $\tau_{\underline{g}}\, \omega_{\underline{\nu}} = \omega_{\underline{g}.\underline{\nu}}$ where $\omega_{\underline{\nu}}$ is the state associated with the boundary conditions $\underline{\nu}$.

Property 2

i) $\forall \underline{g} \in G^{int}$ and $\omega \in \Delta(\beta)$ then $\tau_{\underline{g}}\, \omega \in \Delta(\beta)$; furthermore if ω is extremal in $\Delta(\beta)$ then $\tau_{\underline{g}}\, \omega$ is extremal.

ii) $\tau_{\underline{g}}\, \omega = \omega$ for all $\underline{g} \in G_f^{int}$

5) At high temperature $\Delta(\beta)$ contains only one state which is thus invariant under $\mathbb{Z}^\nu$ and G^{int} .

By definition there exists a "Spontaneous Symmetry Breakdown" if there exist Gibbs states which are not invariant under $\mathbb{Z}^\nu$ or G^{int}.

3. RESULTS

Let $\mathcal{S}$ be some compact abelian subgroup of G^{int} ; we introduce the "internal symmetry group $\mathcal{S}_\omega$ of ω "

$$\mathcal{S}_\omega = \{ s \in \mathcal{S};\ \tau_s\, \omega = \omega \} \qquad (= \text{little group of } \omega)$$

and the "translation symmetry group $\mathcal{T}_\omega$ of ω "

$$\mathcal{T}_\omega = \{ a \in \mathbb{Z}^\nu;\ \tau_a\, \omega = \omega \}$$

Property 3

1) $\forall s \in \mathcal{S}$, the Gibbs states ω and $\tau_s\, \omega$ have the same internal symmetry group, but in general not the same translation group, i.e.

$$\forall \omega \in \Delta(\beta),\ \mathcal{S}_{\tau_s \omega} = \mathcal{S}_\omega \quad \text{but} \quad \mathcal{T}_{\tau_s \omega} \neq \mathcal{T}_\omega \qquad \text{(in general)}$$

2) $$\left.\begin{array}{l} \forall a \in \mathcal{T}_\omega \\ \forall \omega \in \Delta(\beta) \end{array}\right\} \Rightarrow T_a\, \mathcal{S}_\omega \subset \mathcal{S}_\omega$$

Therefore all states on the orbit of ω under $\mathcal{S}$ have the same internal symmetry group $\mathcal{S}_\omega$ and they are all extremal in $\Delta(\beta)$ if ω is extremal. The only subgroups $\mathcal{S}_0$ of $\mathcal{S}$ which can appear as internal symmetry group for $\mathbb{Z}^\nu$-invariant states are those which are stable under $\mathbb{Z}^\nu$ (i.e. $T_a \mathcal{S}_0 = \mathcal{S}_0$ for all $a \in \mathbb{Z}^\nu$).

Let us introduce the family $\Delta_{\mathcal{S}}(\beta)$ of "symmetric states"

$$\Delta_{\mathcal{S}}(\beta) = \{ \omega \in \Delta(\beta) ; \quad \tau_s \omega = \omega \quad \forall s \in \mathcal{S} \}$$

(which is non empty, compact, convex, Choquet simplex) and for any ω in $\Delta(\beta)$ we define

$$\bar{\omega} = \int_{\mathcal{S}/\mathcal{S}_\omega} ds \; \tau_s \omega$$

where ds is the normalised Haar measure on $\mathcal{S}/\mathcal{S}_\omega$.

Property 4

i) $\forall \omega \in \Delta(\beta)$, then $\bar{\omega} \in \Delta_{\mathcal{S}}(\beta)$

ii) $\forall \omega$ extremal in $\Delta(\beta)$, then $\bar{\omega}$ is extremal in $\Delta_{\mathcal{S}}(\beta)$

iii) $\forall \omega_1, \omega_2$ extremal in $\Delta(\beta)$ such that $\bar{\omega}_1 = \bar{\omega}_2$, then ω_1 and ω_2 are on the same orbit with respect to $\mathcal{S}$.

iv) $\forall \omega_s$ extremal in $\Delta_{\mathcal{S}}(\beta)$, then there exists ω_0 extremal in $\Delta(\beta)$ such that $\bar{\omega}_0 = \omega_s$.

Therefore, the set of extremal Gibbs states in $\Delta(\beta)$ decomposes into orbits with respect to $\mathcal{S}$; each orbit is mapped on one extremal symmetric state and each extremal symmetric state is the image of exactly one orbit.

Let ω_s be an extremal state of $\Delta_{\mathcal{S}}(\omega)$ and define

$$\Delta_{\omega_s}(\beta) = \{ \omega \in \Delta(\beta) ; \quad \bar{\omega} = \omega_s \}$$

which is a convex set.

Property 5

Let ω_0 be extremal in $\Delta(\beta)$ such that $\omega_0 = \bar{\omega}_s$; then

1) The extremal states in $\Delta_{\omega_p}(\beta)$ are precisely those on the orbit of ω_0 under $\mathcal{S}/\mathcal{S}_{\omega_0}$.

2) For any state ω in $\Delta_{\omega_p}(\beta)$, there exists a unique probability measure $d\lambda$ on $\mathcal{S}/\mathcal{S}_{\omega_0}$ such that

$$\omega = \int_{\mathcal{S}/\mathcal{S}_{\omega_0}} d\lambda(\rho)\, \tau_\rho \omega_0$$

and $\mathcal{S}_\omega \supset \mathcal{S}_{\omega_0}$.

We thus arrive at the following picture :

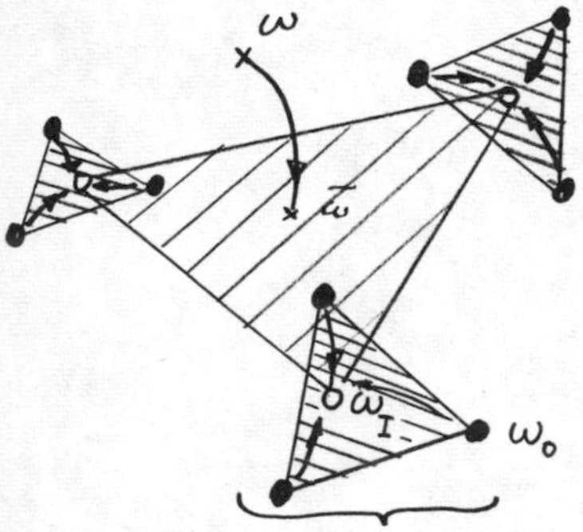

If β is regular all periodic states are in this set $= \Delta_{\omega_I}(\beta)$.

x : Gibbs state
• : Extremal Gibbs state
o : Extremal symmetric state
/// : Symmetric States $= \Delta_{\mathcal{S}}(\omega)$
(dense hatching) : Convex set generated by the states on the orbit of $\omega_0 \equiv$ $\equiv \Delta_{\omega_p}(\beta)$ (where $\bar{\omega}_0 = \omega_p$)

Definition

The inverse temperature β is "regular" (with respect to $\mathcal{S}$) if there exists a unique, extremal state ω_I of $\Delta_{\mathcal{S}}(\beta)$ which is $\mathbb{Z}^\nu$-invariant; ω_I is then an "invariant state".

Theorem

Let β be regular and ω_0 extremal in $\Delta(\beta)$ such that $\bar{\omega}_0 = \omega_I$, then:

1) $\forall a \in \mathbb{Z}^\nu$, $\tau_a \omega_0$ is on the orbit of ω_0 with respect to $\mathcal{S}$

2) $\mathcal{S}_{\omega_0}$ is stable under $\mathbb{Z}^\nu$

3) $\Delta_{\omega_I}(\beta)$ contains all periodic states

4) The set of extremal Gibbs states in $\Delta_{\omega_I}(\beta)$ is precisely the orbit of ω_0 and they all have the same internal symmetry group $\mathcal{S}_{\omega_0}$.

5) Every Gibbs state in $\Delta_{\omega_I}(\beta)$ is of the form :

$$\omega = \int_{\mathcal{S}/\mathcal{S}_{\omega_0}} d\lambda(\rho)\ \tau_\rho \omega_0$$

Conclusion

If β is regular we have thus the general structure of the set of all periodic Gibbs states. If $\Delta_{\mathcal{S}}(\beta) = \{\omega_I\}$ we have the structure of all Gibbs states.

Problems

1) For what group $\mathcal{S}$ can we expect that (almost) all temperatures are regular ? [One could expect that it is the smallest group which generates the set of ground states (= states at zero temperature)].

2) Given a concrete model then

   i) show the existence - or absence - of non regular β (i.e. temperature at which several invariant states can coexist)

   ii) show the existence - or absence - of states which are non periodic; i.e. is $\Delta_{\omega_I}(\beta) \neq \Delta(\beta)$ or $\Delta_{\omega_I}(\beta) = \Delta(\beta)$?

An answer to these problems can be given in the case of ferromagnetic systems.

4. FERROMAGNETIC SYSTEMS

Let $\Omega_0 = G_0$ be a compact, abelian, metrizable group and $d\nu_0$ be the Haar measure. In this case, the configuration space is a group $\mathcal{G}_{\mathcal{L}} = \Omega_0^{\mathcal{L}}$; introducing the dual group $\mathcal{G}_{\mathcal{L}}^{\wedge} = \{\underline{\chi}\}$, which is the group of characters, we can express the Hamiltonian as :

$$\beta H = - \sum_{\underline{\chi} \in \mathcal{G}_{\mathcal{L}}^{\wedge}} K(\underline{\chi})\ \underline{\chi}$$

The translation invariance of the interactions imply :

$$K(\underline{\chi} \circ a) = K(\underline{\chi}) \qquad \forall a \in \mathbb{Z}^\nu$$

where :

$$(\underline{\chi} \circ a)(\underline{\theta}) = \underline{\chi}(a \circ \underline{\theta}) .$$

By definition the system is "ferromagnetic" if

$$K(\underline{\chi}) = K(\underline{\chi}^{-1}) \geq 0 \qquad \forall\ \underline{\chi} \in \mathcal{G}_{\mathcal{L}}^{\wedge} .$$

$\mathcal{G}_{\mathcal{L}}$ acts on itself by translation, i.e.

$$\forall\ \underline{\varphi} \in \mathcal{G}_{\mathcal{L}} : \quad \underline{\theta} \mapsto \underline{\theta} + \underline{\varphi}$$

and the "internal symmetry group $\mathcal{S}$ " is defined by :

$$\mathcal{S} = \{ \underline{s} \in \mathcal{G}_{\mathcal{L}} ;\ \underline{\chi}(\underline{s}) = 1 \quad \forall\ \underline{\chi} \text{ s.t. } K(\underline{\chi}) \neq 0 \}$$

Property 6

1) The internal symmetry group $\mathcal{S}$ of ferromagnetic systems is precisely the set of ground states .

2) $\omega \in \Delta_{\mathcal{S}}(\beta)$ iff $\omega[\underline{\chi}] = 0 \quad \forall\ \underline{\chi} \in \mathcal{S}^{\perp}$

3) ω is invariant under $\mathcal{S}_0 \subset \mathcal{S}$ iff $\omega[\underline{\chi}] = 0 \quad \forall\ \underline{\chi} \in \mathcal{S}_0^{\perp}$

Theorem

1) The Gibbs state $\omega_0(\beta)$ defined by the boundary condition $\vartheta_x = 0$[1] $\forall\ x \in \mathcal{L}$, is extremal, $\mathbb{Z}^{\nu}$-invariant, and

 i) $\omega_0[\underline{\chi}] \geq \omega_f[\underline{\chi}] \qquad \forall\ \underline{\chi} \text{ s.t. } K(\underline{\chi}) \neq 0$

 ii) $\omega_0[\underline{\chi}] \geq |\omega[\mathrm{Re}\,\underline{\chi}]| \qquad \forall\ \underline{\chi}$ and $\omega \in \Delta(\beta)$

 where ω_f is the Gibbs state defined by the "free" boundary condition (i.e. $\phi_B = 0$ for all B not in Λ)

2) For all Gibbs states $\omega \in \Delta(\beta)$, $\mathcal{S}_{\omega} \supset \mathcal{S}_{\omega_0(\beta)}$ '

3) If $\beta_1 > \beta_2$ then $\mathcal{S}_{\omega_0(\beta_1)} \subset \mathcal{S}_{\omega_0(\beta_2)}$

4) Non regular β are at most countable

5) The following are equivalent:

 i) β_0 is regular

 ii) $\omega_0[\underline{\chi}] = \omega_f[\underline{\chi}]$ $\Big\}\ \forall\ \underline{\chi} \text{ s.t. } K(\underline{\chi}) \neq 0$

 iii) $\omega_0[\underline{\chi}]$ is continuous in β at β_0 $\Big\}$

 iv) the free energy is differentiable in β at β_0.

---

(1) identity in the group G_0

Remarks

1) If $\mathcal{S}$ is finite, then $\mathcal{S}_{\omega_0(\beta)} = \{ 1 \}$ for $\beta > \beta_1$
i.e. there is a complete symmetry breakdown at low temperatures.

2) All phase transitions are in the relation from group to subgroup. Therefore, to describe phase transition with symmetry breakdown which are not in the relation from group to subgroup, we need systems which are not ferromagnetic.

3) The above discussions and results cannot be applied to systems with hard core or diluted systems.

5. EXTENSIONS

1) Continuous Systems

The existence of phase transitions for continuous systems was established by Ruelle (1971)[3] and Lieb and Lebowitz (1972)[4] for the "Widom-Rowlinson" model. Extension of such models to include several type of particles were recently published by Bricmont-Kuroda-Lebowitz (1985)[5], using Pirogov-Sinaï theory. The interest of this work is that it yields a discussion of phase transitions which are not associated with a spontaneous symmetry breakdown; however, they are always restricted to the "Widom-Rowlinson" condition , i..e the hard core between different particles is always much larger than the hard core between identical particles. Another interesting aspect of this approach is that it gives a possibility to investigate phase transitions for systems with an infinite number of ground states.

2) Ferromagnetic fluids (Continuous or lattice)

A large literature has appeared concerning continuous or lattice systems of particles with magnetic and non-magnetic interactions. However, most of the results have been obtained within the mean field approximation and only few properties are rigorously known. However, the mean field results suggest that these systems are very interesting to study. In a recent work, it was established that such systems do indeed exhibit a ferromagnetic phase transition[6].

REFERENCES

[1] Gruber Ch., Pfister C.E., "Introduction to spontaneous symmetry breakdown in classical lattice systems". To appear in the Proceedings of the 21st Karpacz Winter School (1985)

[2] Pfister C.E., 1) Comm. Math. Phys. 59, 97 (1978). 2) Proceeding of the Sixth International Symposium on Information Theory, Tashkent, 1984, part. III, p. 259. 3) Infinite dimensional analysis and stochastic processes, p. 98, Ed. S. Albeverio, Res. Notes, Pitman, Maths. 1985

[3] Ruelle D., Phys. Rev. Lett. 27, 1040 (1971)

[4] Lebowitz J.L., Lieb E.H., Phys. Lett. 39A, 98 (1972)

[5] Bricmont J., Kuroda K., Lebowitz J.L., "First order phase transition in lattice and continuous systems : Extension of Pirogov. Sinaï theory"

[6] Griffiths R., Gruber Ch., in preparation.(To appear).

STOCHASTIC EQUATIONS FOR SOME EUCLIDEAN FIELDS

Z. Haba
Research Center Bielefeld-Bochum-Stochastics*
Bielefeld University, D-4800 Bielefeld 1, FRG
and
Institute of Theoretical Physics
University of Wroclaw, Poland

The Euclidean functional integral has become a powerful tool in the rigorous construction of models of quantum field theory, especially $P(\varphi)$ interactions. The usefulness of the functional integral in the quantum mechanics is well-known. However, the conventional functional approach to the quantum mechanics on a manifold, although possible (e.g. through the lattice approximation) appears less promising. This is so, because there is no natural decomposition of the functional measure on the manifold into Gaussian (free) part and a perturbation. Fields with values in a manifold appear in models aspiring to a unification and geometrization of interactions. The Yang-Mills theory, which is of geometric origin, is the most important example of the relevance of geometry to quantum physics. It appears that the infrared difficulties in gauge theories result from the use for quantization of improper geometrical objects.

The stochastic equations seem to be the proper tool for a study of the (imaginary time) quantum mechanics on a manifold [1]. We derive stochastic equations for Euclidean Markov fields with values in a manifold. We believe that a deep understanding of the geometry of these fields (including the gauge fields) can lead to a solution of the stochastic equations and to results of physical significance.

I. Quantum Mechanics on a Manifold

We illustrate in this section some aspects of the stochastic description, which are relevant to quantum field theories. Consider the stochastic process generated by the Laplace-Beltrami operator Δ_M on the Riemannian manifold M. In some coordinates ξ

---

* Supported by Stiftung Volkswagenwerk

$$d\xi_\mu = \frac{1}{2} g^{\alpha\beta}(\Gamma_{\mu\alpha\beta} - e_{a\beta}\, \partial_\alpha\, e_{a\mu})dt + e_{a\mu}\, db^a \qquad \text{(I.1)}$$

where $e_{a\mu}$ is the vierbein $(e_{a\alpha}\, e_{a\beta} = g_{\alpha\beta})$ and b^a is the Wiener process

$$E[b^a_t\, b^{a'}_{t'}] = \delta^{aa'} \min(t,t') \qquad \text{(I.2)}$$

$f db$ denotes in this paper the Stratonovitch differential [1] defined by

$$\int f\, db = \lim \sum_i f(\tfrac{1}{2}(t_{i+1} + t_i))(b(t_{i+1}) - b(t_i)) \ .$$

The stochastic equations simplify on a class of complex manifolds called Kähler manifolds. The tangent space of a complex manifold is an orthogonal sum of holomorphic $(\frac{\partial}{\partial z})$ and antiholomorphic $(\frac{\partial}{\partial \bar{z}})$ vectors

$$TM = (TM)^+ + (TM)^- \ . \qquad \text{(I.3)}$$

On a Kähler manifold this decomposition of the tangent space is preserved during the parallel transport. The non-covariant term in eq. (I.1) vanishes in the complex coordinates w^α. Then

$$dw_\alpha = e_{a\alpha}(w)\, db^a \qquad \text{(I.4)}$$

where b^a is the complex Brownian motion.

Consider now a compact Lie group G. Eq. (I.1) on the group can be expressed in the form

$$g^{-1} dg = db \qquad \text{(I.5)}$$

where b is a matrix.

The solution of eq. (I.5) has the form of the time-ordered exponential

$$g_t = T(\exp \int^t db) \ . \qquad \text{(I.6)}$$

As an application of the formula (I.6) consider $SU(N)$ for large N. Then

$$E[\mathrm{Tr}(g_t^+ g_{t'})] \simeq \exp \frac{1}{2} \mathrm{Tr}\, E[(\int_t^{t'} db)^2] = \exp - c\, |t-t'| . \qquad (I.7)$$

So, we get the mass gap.

Let now $M = G/H$ be a symmetric homogeneous space. Consider the bundle $\Pi: G \to M$ with the group $H \subset G$ as the fiber. We can write $g = vh$, where $h \in H$ and $v \in G/H$ (we embed G/H in G). The Lie algebra $L(G)$ of G is a direct sum

$$L(G) = L(H) + L(G/H)$$

with

$$[L(H), L(G/H)] \subset L(G/H).$$

Let P_v be the projection of $L(G)$ onto $L(G/H)$. Then, eq. (I.5) can be decomposed into two equations

$$\begin{aligned} h^{-1} dh &= (1 - P_v) db \\ v^{-1} dv &= h\, P_v db\, h^{-1} . \end{aligned} \qquad (I.8)$$

Eq. (I.8) may be considered as a Brownian motion on the bundle $\Pi: G \to G/H$ with the connection P_v.

As an important example consider $G = SU(n+1)$ and $G = Sp(n+1)$ (the symplectic group, which can be described as a unitary group with quaternionic matrix elements) with $H = SU(n)$ and $H = Sp(n)$, respectively. In this case v can be parametrized as follows [2]

$$v = \gamma^{-1} \begin{pmatrix} 1 & -w^+ \\ w & \alpha(w) \end{pmatrix} \qquad (I.9)$$

where $\gamma = (1 + w^+ w)^{1/2}$ and $\alpha = \gamma (1 + w^+ w)^{-1/2}$, w is a column and $w^+ = (\bar{w}_1, \ldots, \bar{w}_n)$. w's are the complex coordinates of the $CP(n)$ ($G = SU(n+1)$) and the quaternionic coordinates of the $HP(n)$ manifolds.

From eq. (I.8) we get the equation for w (h can be absorbed into the definition of w)

$$(1 + w^+ w)^{-1}\, \alpha(w)\, dw = db \qquad (I.10)$$

where b is the complex (quaternionic) Brownian motion.

In the search for solutions so other descriptions can be useful, e.g. the Brownian motion on the sphere $S^2 = SU(2)/U(1)$ can be described by an equation defined on a linear space (R^3), whose solutions stay on a submanifold (S^2) [3]

$$d\vec{n} = P(n)\, d\vec{b} \tag{I.11}$$

where $P(n)$ is a matrix with matrix elements

$$P(n)_{ij} = \delta_{ij} - n_i n_j / n^2 \,, \quad n^2 = \Sigma n_i n_i \,. \tag{I.12}$$

$P(n)$ projects the vector $d\vec{b}$ onto the tangent space of S^2, so that $d\vec{n}$ is tangent to S^2, hence $\vec{n}d\vec{n} = 0$ implies that $\vec{n}^2 = \text{const.}$ The generalization of eq. (I.11) to the CP(n) model described by a Hermitian matrix φ with $\mathrm{Tr}\,\varphi^2 = 1$ [4] reads

$$d\varphi = (\mathrm{Tr}\varphi^2)^{-1}[\varphi,[\varphi,db]] \,. \tag{I.13}$$

All the models of Brownian motion on a symmetric space can immediately be solved using the solution of the Brownian motion on a group (I.6). It is sufficient to extract the coset G/H from the group. The solution of the CP(n) model can be expressed by elementary functions, e.g. the Brownian motion on the sphere (I.11) is solved by $\vec{n} = \vec{b}\,|\vec{b}|^{-1}$. Note that it would be difficult to solve the nonlinear equations (I.1) directly in coordinates.

II. Two-Dimensional Fields with Values in a Complex Manifold

There exists in the two-dimensional Euclidean space an analogue to the complex Brownian motion - the complex massless scalar free field. This is the Gaussian random field with the covariance

$$E[\varphi_o^a(z)\ \overline{\varphi_o^b(z')}] = -\frac{1}{4\pi}\ln|z-z'|^2\,\delta^{ab} \tag{II.1}$$

(other two-point correlation functions vanishing). The complex scalar field can be considered as a random map $\varphi_o: \mathbb{C} \to \mathbb{C}^n$. $T\mathbb{C}^n$ splits into the holomorphic $(T\mathbb{C}^n)^+$ and antiholomorphic $(T\mathbb{C})^-$ parts. The pull-back to $T^*\mathbb{C}$ of a basis $\{e^a\}$ of $(T^*\mathbb{C}^n)^+$ has the form

$$d\varphi_o^a(z) = \partial\varphi_o^a\, dz + \bar{\partial}\varphi_o^a(z)\, d\bar{z} \tag{II.2}$$

where $\bar{\partial} = \frac{\partial}{\partial \bar{z}}$. It is easy to check that $\bar{\partial}\varphi_o$ (as well as $\partial\varphi_o$) is a complex white noise, i.e.

$$E[\bar{\partial}\varphi_o^a(z) \; \overline{\bar{\partial}\varphi_o^b(z')}] = \delta(z-z')\delta^{ab} \; . \tag{II.3}$$

So, $\bar{\partial}\varphi_o$ is a generalization of $\frac{d}{dt} b_t$.

Consider now a map $\varphi: \mathbb{C} \to M$, where M is a symmetric space G/H with a complex structure, i.e. the cotangent space $(T^*M)_g$ is the direct sum of holomorphic $(T^*M)_g^+$ and antiholomorphic $(T^*M)_g^-$ parts. Let L_g be the left translation on G from the unit element 1 to g and $\{e^a\}$ a basis of $(T^*M)_1^+ \sim (T^*\mathbb{C})^+$. Then, we can compare the $(T^*\mathbb{C})^-$ part of the pull-back of $\{e^a\}$ by the composition of the maps $L_g^{-1}\varphi$ to the $(T^*\mathbb{C})^-$ part of the pull-back of $\{e^a\}$ by φ_o (II.2). This leads to the equation

$$(1 + w^+w)^{-1} \; \alpha(w) \; \bar{\partial}w = \bar{\partial}\varphi_o \tag{II.4}$$

which is a generalization of eq. (I.10) to two dimensions.

Eq. (II.4) is invariant under the Euclidean group

$$z \to e^{i\alpha}z + c \; . \tag{II.5}$$

Solutions of stochastic equations, which are of first order in time t , have the Markov property in the t-direction [1]. Now, the Markov property and the Euclidean invariance are sufficient for a construction of relativistic fields from Euclidean fields according to Nelson's reconstruction theorem [5]. A direct interpretation of the Euclidean field in the physical space-time may also be possible [6].

In our paper [7] we have obtained eq. (II.4) as a stochastic equation on the manifold $F(R,M)$ of maps $R \to M$. F is a Hilbert manifold modelled on $L^2(R)$ with the scalar product in $(TF)_\sigma$ (the tangent space at $\sigma \in F$) defined by

$$(v,v') = \int dx \; (v(x), \, v'(x))_{\sigma(x)} \tag{II.6}$$

where $(\, , \,)_\sigma$ is the Riemannian structure in $(TM)_\sigma$. The two-dimensional white noise $\bar{\partial}\varphi_o$ may be considered as a time derivative $\dot{b}$ of an $L^2(R)$-valued Wiener process b_t defined by

$$E[b_t(f)\ b_{t'}(f')] = \min(t,t')(f,f') \tag{II.7}$$

where $(f,f') = \int dx\ \bar{f}(x)\ f'(x)$.

We modify eq. (I.10) (which could also be considered as an equation for a Brownian motion on F) by an addition of a drift term β. The drift should fulfil the following requirements: i) the solutions of the modified equation should also stay on M, ii) the exponential decay of correlations (mass gap) should be preserved. The preservation of some correlation functions means that the generator of the stochastic process can be modified only by an addition of the generator of an isometry [8]. If we treat the process (I.10) as defined on F, then its generator is the Laplace-Beltrami operator defined by the metric (II.6). Hence, the drift has to be a generator of an isometry of the metric (II.6), i.e. its <u>Killing vector</u>. The metric (II.6) has many Killing vectors. The choice of $K = (i\partial_x w, -i\partial_x \bar{w})$ as the drift β in eq. (II.4) comes from the requirement of the Euclidean invariance. The vector K is the generator of the isometry $R_\alpha T_a R_\alpha^{-1}$, where R_α is the rotation $w \to e^{i\alpha} w$ and T_a is the translation $w(x) \to w(x+a)$.

These two, a priori different, interpretations of the random field, either as a Euclidean covariant random map $R^2 \to M$ or as a stochastic process on the manifold $F(R,M)$ of maps, admit different regularization schemes. In the first interpretation we may use the covariant regularization, whereas the second interpretation requires the preservation of the Markov property, i.e. only a regularization in space coordinates is admissible, e.g. $b_t(x) \to (-\varepsilon\partial_x^2 + 1)^{-1} b_t(x)$ or the lattice regularization in space. If the stochastic equation (II.4) is regularized only in the spatial coordinate, then w_t can be treated as a Markov process with values in a Hilbert space. In such a case the functional measure corresponding to the solution w_t of eq. (II.4) is determined by the Girsanov formula (see [1], [9]-[11])

$$d\mu = d\mu_o \ \exp[-\frac{1}{2}\int g_{\alpha\bar{\beta}}(w)\ \partial_x w \ \ \overline{\partial_x w^\beta} + Q] \tag{II.8}$$

where $d\mu_o$ is the functional measure corresponding to the stochastic process w_t without the drift $\partial_x w$ and Q is the topological charge.

The measure $d\mu_o$ can be obtained from the short-time propagator for the stochastic process (I.10). We can conclude in this way that the stochastic equation (II.4) describes a field theory with the Lagrangian

$$L_B = \frac{1}{2} g_{\alpha\bar{\beta}}(w)\ \partial_\mu w^\alpha\ \overline{\partial_\mu w^\beta} - Q\ . \qquad \text{(II.9)}$$

On the other hand, eq. (II.4) could be treated as a prescription for a non-linear transformation of the Gaussian measure corresponding to the free field φ_o. From the Jacobian of this transformation we get a fermionic contribution to the total Lagrangian L

$$L = L_B + L_F = L_B + \bar{\psi}\ \not{D}\ \psi \qquad \text{(II.10)}$$

where $\not{D} = \gamma^\mu D_\mu$ and D_μ is the covariant derivative along w. If a spatial lattice regularization is applied, then the formulas (II.8) - (II.9) and (II.10) do not contradict each other (see [11]). In fact, the Girsanov formula (II.8) (with the lattice regularization of the exponential factor) is a rigorous version of the functional transformation [12]. So, the fermionic determinant is absent (det $\not{D} = 1$). The only way to determine, whether eq. (II.4) describes the σ-model with fermions or without, is to study the removal of the ultraviolet regularization. We have shown [11] in a model with a holomorphic potential [13] that the spatial regularization cannot be removed, whereas the covariant one can. It is more difficult to resolve this problem in the model (II.4). It appears that the spatial regularization as well as the covariant one can be removed in the perturbation theory (at least in the S^2-model) with the proper renormalization of the coupling constant. It remains unclear whether det $\not{D} \neq 1$ on the support of the functional measure after a rigorous removal of the ultraviolet regularization.

We can obtain a straightforward generalization of eq. (II.4) by an addition of a random connection χ. Then,

$$(1 + w^+ w)^{-1}\ \alpha(w)\ (\bar{\partial} + \bar{\chi}) w = \bar{\partial}\varphi_o \qquad \text{(II.11)}$$

where χ is a complex white noise independent of $\bar{\partial}\varphi_o$. In such a case we get the four-fermion interaction $\bar{\psi}\psi\bar{\psi}\psi$ in the Lagrangian. We are studying this model now (such models can be ultraviolet finite).

Eq. (II.4) can be embedded back in the group G. As $d\omega_o = \bar{\partial}\varphi_o\, d\bar{z}$ is an (L(G)-valued) 1-form it can be integrated along a curve γ. We are looking for a certain generalization of eq. (I.6) that could solve eq. (II.4) (see refs. [14], [15] for another generalization of the formula (I.6)). The integral $T(\exp \int_\gamma d\omega_o)$ depends on the curve γ. Hence, it cannot be a solution of eq. (II.4). $d\omega_o$ must be rotated during the integration along γ in such a way that the integral does not depend on the curve.

Other forms of eq. (II.11) can be useful in a search for solutions. So, the generalization of eq. (I.11) to two dimensions has the form

$$d\vec{n} = p(n)\ \partial_x \vec{n}\ dt + p(n) d\vec{\chi} + P(n)\ d\vec{b} \tag{II.12}$$

where the matrix $(p(n))_{ij} = \varepsilon_{ijk}\, n_{k/n}$ is the square root of P ($p^2 = P$). The analogue of eq. (I.13) for $CP(n)$ reads

$$d\varphi = i[\varphi,\partial_x\varphi]dt + i[\varphi,d\chi] + (Tr\varphi^2)^{-1}[\varphi,[\varphi,db]]. \tag{II.13}$$

The additional Brownian motion χ in eqs. (II.12) - (II.13) leads to the four-fermion terms in the Lagrangian.

III. Gauge Theories in Four Dimensions

It appears that a generalization of the stochastic equations of Section II to four dimensions should be related to the quaternionic structure of $R^4 = \mathbb{C} \times \mathbb{C}$. A point $x \in R^4$ can be expressed in the quaternion basis $\{e_\mu\}$

$$x = \sum_{\mu=0}^{3} x_\mu\, e_\mu$$

where the quaternion algebra

$$e_i e_j = -\delta_{ij} + \varepsilon_{ijk} e_k\,,\quad e_o e_i = e_i e_o = e_i,\ e_i^2 = -e_o$$

can be realized by means of the Pauli matrices.
The action of the Euclidean group $x \to U_1\, x U_2^{-1} + a$, where $U_i \in SU(2)$ and $a \in GL(2,C)$, is a generalization of eq. (II.5). We can also define a first order differential operator (the Hamilton operator [2])

$$\mathcal{D} = \Sigma\, e_\mu \frac{\partial}{\partial x_\mu}$$

which is a generalization of $\frac{\partial}{\partial z}$. Let A_μ be a vector potential and $A = \Sigma A_\mu\, e_\mu$. Then the equation

$$\mathcal{D} A = \dot{b} \tag{III.1}$$

where $\dot{b} = \Sigma \dot{b}_\mu e_\mu$ and $\dot{b}_\mu$ is the four-dimensional white noise, defines the electromagnetic field in the Feynman gauge. In fact, it is easy to check that

$$E[f(A(b))] = \int d\mu_o(A) f(A) \tag{III.2}$$

where μ_o is the Gaussian measure with the covariance

$$\int d\mu_o(A)\ A_\mu(x)\ A_\nu(x') = \delta_{\mu\nu}(-\Delta)^{-1}(x,x'). \tag{III.3}$$

Eq. (III.1) is the analogue of $\bar{\partial}\varphi_o = \dot{b}$ (Sec. II) and $\frac{d}{dt} b = \dot{b}$ (Sec. I). However, we are unable to generalize directly eqs. (III.1) - (III.3) (with the preservation of the Euclidean invariance) to the non-abelian case, because the problem of gauge degrees of freedom is more involved there. A possible way of generalization is to consider the path-dependent phase factors [16] (with $\mathcal{D} \to \Sigma\, e_\mu \frac{\delta}{\delta \xi_\mu}$) or the quaternionic σ-models [2], [17].

We pursue here a more conventional formulation in terms of the potentials, which is a generalization of our description of the random field as a Brownian motion on a manifold of maps. The formulation is non-covariant with respect to the Euclidean group, but this dose not preclude the possibility that we get covariant equations through a change of variables (cp. eqs. (II.11) and (II.12)).

First we need to introduce some notions from differential geometry. Let $\Pi: P \to M$ be a principal fiber bundle with a group G as a fiber. Let $\mathcal{B}$ be the space of (irreducible) connections ω on P and $\mathcal{G}$ an infinite dimensional Lie group of gauge transformations

$$\omega \to \omega^g = g^{-1}\omega g + g^{-1} dg\ . \tag{III.4}$$

Consider the coset $\mathcal{M} = \mathcal{B}/\mathcal{G}$. Then, $\Pi: \mathcal{B} \to \mathcal{M}$ is a principal fiber bundle [18]. Let Λ^o be the space of $L(G)$-valued functions on M. Then, the vertical subspace V_ω of $T\mathcal{B}$ consists of functions of the form $\nabla_\omega \lambda$, where $\lambda \in \Lambda^o$ and ∇_ω denotes the covariant derivative. The horizontal subspace of $T\mathcal{B}$ can be defined as the orthogonal complement of V_ω in $\mathcal{B}$. This horizontal subspace is determined by the connection form

$$\Omega = (\nabla_\omega^* \nabla_\omega)^{-1} \nabla_\omega^*\ . \tag{III.5}$$

The connection allows to identify H_ω with $(TM)_{\Pi(\omega)}$ and embed M as a submanifold in B. In particular, if $\bar{X},\bar{Y}$ are vectors in TB, then their horizontal parts correspond to vectors X,Y in $(TM)_{\Pi(\omega)}$ with the scalar product

$$g(X,Y) = (\bar{X},P_\omega\bar{Y}) \tag{III.6}$$

where $(\ ,\ )$ is the L^2-scalar product in B and

$$P_\omega = 1 - \nabla_\omega(\nabla^*_\omega \nabla_\omega)^{-1} \nabla^*_\omega . \tag{III.7}$$

A stochastic process A_t, which is to describe the quantum Yang-Mills theory should take its values in M rather than in B, because $\mathrm{Tr}F^2$ does not depend on the gauge degrees of freedom. This is similar to the case of fields with values in a sphere (Secs. I-II), where the Lagrangian does not depend on the radial component of $\vec{n} \in R^3$. We would like to write down a stochastic equation in a form independent of coordinates. Such an approach is inspired by eqs. (I.11) and (II.12) (see also [3]). So, we would like to find a stochastic equation for $A \in B$, whose solutions stay on a submanifold $\bar{M}$ being an embedding of M in B.

If the curve A_t is to be the lift to B of $\Pi(A_t) \in M$ with respect to the connection Ω (III.5), then its tangent $\frac{d}{dt} A_t$ must be an element of H_A. This leads to the equation (cp. with eq. (I.11))

$$dA_t = P_A\, db_t \tag{III.8}$$

which can also be expressed as an equation on the fiber bundle $\Pi: B \to B/G$ (cp. with eq. (I.8))

$$\begin{aligned} d\omega^g &= g^{-1}\, db\, g \\ g^{-1}dg &= \Omega db \end{aligned} \tag{III.9}$$

where ω^g is defined in eq. (III.4) and $\Omega db = (\nabla^*\nabla)^{-1} \nabla^*_j db_j$.

Following the discussion of Sec. II we may still modify the Brownian motion on M by an addition of a Killing vector corresponding to an isometry of the metric (III.6). It is easy to see that the scalar product (III.6) is invariant under a rotation of the potential A_k. Moreover, it is invariant under the translation of the fiber (it is not invariant under the ordinary translations)

$$A(x) \to \exp(iA_k(x)\Delta x_k)\ A(x+\Delta x_k)\ \exp(-iA_k(x)\Delta x_k).$$

The sum of commutators $\Sigma[R_k,P_k]$ of the generators of the above mentioned transformations (R_k is the generator of the rotation around the k-th axis) is equal to

$$\varepsilon_{ijk}\ F_{jk}\ \frac{\delta}{\delta A_i}\ .$$

The addition of this Killing vector as a drift to eq. (III.8) leads to the stochastic equation

$$dA_t = {}^*F\ dt + P_A\ db_t$$

where (III.10)

$$ {}^*F_i = \frac{1}{2}\ \varepsilon_{ijk}\ F_{jk}\ .$$

Consider now the functional measure $d\mu(A)$ corresponding to the solution of eq. (III.10). Let $d\mu_o(A)$ be the probability measure corresponding to the solution of eq. (III.8). Then, from the Girsanov formula, we get

$$\begin{aligned} d\mu(A) &= d\mu_o(A)\ \exp[-\frac{1}{2}\int P_A^{-1}\ {}^*F\ \ P_A^{-1}\ {}^*F + \int P_A^{-1}\ {}^*F\ db] \\ &= d\mu_o(A)\ \exp[-\frac{1}{4}\int F_{jk}\ F_{jk} + Q] \end{aligned} \tag{III.11}$$

where Q is the topological charge.

In the derivation of eq. (III.11) the horizontality of ${}^*F$ $(P_A{}^*F = {}^*F)$ and the equality of Ito and Stratonovitch integrals in Q were used. The measure $d\mu_o$ can be obtained from the short-time propagator for the process (III.8). This problem can be treated rigorously on the lattice, where the propagator on M can be derived from the propagator on B (the Cartesian product of groups attached to bonds of the lattice). We get as a result that the functional measure (III.11) coincides (up to the topological charge) with the standard functional measure for the pure Yang-Mills theory in any spatial gauge (see [19] and a paper in preparation).

In the temporal gauge eq. (III.10) has been derived earlier by Nicolai [20] (without P_A) and interpreted as an equation for the Yang-Mills theory with fermions. Stochastic equations for gauge fields have been studied by Asorey and Mitter [21] (see also [22]). These authors write the stochastic equation in coordinates and treat the spatial part of $F_{\mu\nu} F_{\mu\nu}$ as a potential. Then, the stochastic equation has the form of the ground state equation [23].

The form of the equation (III.10) suggests that the solution for the Wilson loop $\exp i \int A_\mu \, d\xi^\mu$, expressed by $F_{\mu\nu}$ through the Stokes theorem, could be obtained in a form of a surface integral over the white noise (see [14], [15] for another approach to such integrals). We suggest here an elementary approach to the solution of eq. (III.10) originating from Yang's formulation of the self-duality equation [24]. In Yang's complex coordinates eq. (III.10) reads

$$\begin{aligned} F_{yz} &= \eta_2 - i\eta_1 \\ \frac{1}{2}(F_{y\bar{y}} + F_{z\bar{z}}) &= -i\eta_3 \end{aligned} \qquad \text{(III.12)}$$

where $\eta = P_A \dot{b}$. When we introduce a new variable $g \in GL(n,C)$ such that after a complex gauge transformation implemented by g $A'_y = 0$, then the non-local part of η drops out from the equation for g. So, we get a simple linear perturbation by noise of Yang's equations.

By means of the dimensional reduction [25] we get from eq. (III.10) the equation for the two-dimensional abelian Higgs model (with the φ^4 interaction) discussed in our earlier papers [7], [11] and an equation for the three-dimensional non-abelian Higgs model (with fermions resulting from the Jacobian)

$$\begin{aligned} dA_i &= \varepsilon_{ij} \nabla_j \varphi \, dt - \nabla_i G \varphi \, db' + (\delta_{ij} - \nabla_i G \nabla_j^*) db_j \\ d\varphi &= \varepsilon_{ij} F_{ij} \, dt + (1 - \varphi G \varphi) db' - \varphi G \nabla_j^* \, db_j \end{aligned} \qquad \text{(III.13)}$$

where $G = (\nabla^* \nabla + \varphi\varphi)^{-1}$.

The mechanism of dimensional reduction leading to eq. (III.13) suggests that it might be possible to get in this way an interaction of gauge fields with scalar and Fermi fields in four dimensions. A stochastic equation for R^2-gravity (which has instantons) can be derived following the argument leading to eq. (III.10). It may be that some simple stochastic partial differential equations describe unified models of particle interactions.

References

[1] N. Ikeda and S. Watanabe, Stochastic Differential Equations and Diffusion Processes, North Holland, 1981

K.D. Elworthy, Stochastic Differential Equations on Manifolds, Cambridge Univ. 1981

[2] F. Gürsey and H.C. Tze, Ann. Phys. 128, 29 (1980)

[3] M. van den Berg and J.T. Lewis, Bull. Lond. Math. Soc. 17. 144 (1985)

[4] A.M. Perelomov, Physica 4D, 1 (1981)

[5] E. Nelson, Journ Funct. Anal. 12, 97 (1973)

[6] E. Nelson, these Proceedings

[7] Z. Haba, Journ. Phys. A18, L347 (1985)

[8] E. Seiler, Acta Phys. Austr., Supp. XXVI, p. 259, 1984

[9] Z. Haba, Journ. Phys. A18, 1641 (1985)

[10] G. Jona-Lasinio, these Proceedings

[11] Z. Haba, BiBoS preprint Nr. 18 , 1985

[12] L. Gross, Tran. Amer. Math. Soc. 94, 404 (1960)

[13] G. Parisi and N. Sourlas, Nucl. Phys. B206, 321 (1982)

S. Cecotti and L. Girardello, Ann. Phys. 145, 81 (1983)

[14] S. Albeverio and R. Høegh-Krohn, in Stochastic Analysis and Applications, M. Pinsky, Ed., p. 1, 1984

S. Albeverio, R. Høegh-Krohn and H. Holden, Acta Phys. Austr. Supp. XXVI, p. 211 (1984)

[15] H. Holden, these Proceedings

[16] S. Mandelstam, Ann. Phys. 19, 1 (1962)

I. Bialynicki-Birula, Bull. l'Acad. Pol. Sci. 11, 135 (1963)

[17] J. Lukierski, in Field Theoretical Methods in Particle Physics, W. Rühl, Ed., 1980

[18] O. Babelon and C.M. Viallet, Phys. Lett. 85B, 246 (1979)

I.M. Singer, Physica Scripta 24, 817 (1981)

[19] Z. Haba, BiBoS preprint No. 58, 1985

[20] H. Nicolai, Phys. Lett. 117B, 408 (1982)

[21] M. Asorey and P.K. Mitter, Comm. Math. Phys. 80, 43 (1981)

[22] B. Gaveau and P. Trauber, Journ. Funct. Anal. 38, 324 (1980)

[23] S. Albeverio and R. Høegh-Krohn, Z. Wahr. verw. Gebiete 40, 1 (1977)

[24] C.N. Yang, Phys. Rev. Lett. 38, 1377 (1977)

[25] C.H. Taubes, Comm. Math. Phys. 75, 207 (1980)

A CLASS OF MEAN-FIELD-LIKE MODELS OF DISORDERED SYSTEMS

J. Jędrzejewski and A. Komoda

Institute of Theoretical Physics, University of Wrocław
50-205 Wrocław, Poland

Abstract

Exactly solvable, equivalent-neighbour type Ising models whose interactions are functions of site, vector, random variables are considered. Using symmetry arguments a class of models is selected. A question of dependence of phase diagrams on probability distributions of site random variables is addressed and a problem of obtaining an infinite number of pure phases is studied.

The need of description of interesting properties of regular systems with very complicated interactions, which are long range, change sign and disordered systems like alloys (spin glasses), where magnetic atoms are randomly distributed over crystal sites, led physicists to consider statistical-mechanical models with random interactions.

Following the experience accumulated in investigations of regular systems with simple interactions, the first step towards understanding of phase diagrams of random systems, seems to be a construction of equivalent-neighbour type (e.n.t) models, called also mean-field like-models. In such models all particles interact with the same "strength", scaled properly to quarantee the existence of the thermodynamic limit. In case of regular systems e.n.t. models are exactly solvable, i.e. their free energy density f can be obtained analytically and one can study stable (global minima of f) and metastable (local minima of f) states of such systems.

A first attempt to construct an exactly solvable e.n.t. model has been presented by Sherrington and Kirkpatrick [1,2] . The model can be defined as follows: let Λ be a finite set containing N elements, $\{J_{ij}\}_{i,j\in\Lambda}$ a family of independent, identically distributed random variables (i.i.d.r.v.) whose distribution is Gaussian with mean

$\tilde{J}_o = \frac{J_o}{N}$ and variance $\tilde{J}^2 = \frac{J^2}{N}$, where J_o, J are N - independent, then the Hamiltonian reads

$$H_\Lambda = -\frac{1}{2} \sum_{i,j\in\Lambda} J_{ij} S_i S_j - h\sum_i S_i . \tag{1}$$

In (1) S_i, $i\in\Lambda$ stand for Ising spins and h is an external magnetic field.

The model was intended to describe properties of magnetic materials called spin glasses, therefore here and in the following we use magnetic terminology. However, this sort of models can of course be interpreted in many ways.

Despite substantial efforts of many authors [3] the model (1) has not been solved. However a vast literature concerning properties of the model has been created with most of results obtained on heuristic grounds. Among them Parisi's replica symmetry breaking scheme [4,5] is very interesting and a lot of attention is paid to this construction [3] (it is supposed to lead to the exact solution of the SK model). The SK model is classified in physics literature as random-bond model. Another sort of e.n.t. models of disordered systems, called random-site models, have been proposed by Mattis [6] and Luttinger [7] . A general e.n. random-site (e.n.r.s.) model is defined by Hamiltonian (1), where couplings J_{ij} are:

$$J_{ij} = \frac{1}{N} (J_o + Q_{ij}^{(2)} + Q_{ij}^{(1)}), \tag{2a}$$

$$Q_{ij}^{(2)} = \sum_{\mu,\nu=1}^{n} Q^{\mu\nu} \xi_{i,\mu}\xi_{j,\nu} , \tag{2b}$$

$$Q_{ij}^{(1)} = \sum_{\mu=1}^{n} L^\mu (\xi_{i,\mu} + \xi_{j,\mu}) , \tag{2c}$$

where Q is a real symmetric matrix, what guarantees symmetry $J_{ij}=J_{ji}$, L^μ are arbitrary real parameters, $\xi_{i,\mu}$ $\mu=1,\dots,n$ are components of a random vector $\bar{\xi}_i$. $\bar{\xi}_i$, $i\in\Lambda$ are assumed to be i.i.d.r.v. with finite second order moments. Particular examples of e.n.r.s. models defined by (2a,2b,2c) have been studied by many authors, see [8] and references quoted there, mostly as possible models of spin glasses. However, in [8,9] one can find a discussion of a relation between SK-model and e.n.r.s. models.

In contradistinction to SK-model, e.n.r.s. models are exactly solvable. An elegant way proposed in [12] is to use a theory of large deviations.

Let

$$m_N = N^{-1} \sum_{i=1}^{N} S_i, \qquad q_{\mu,N} = N^{-1} \sum_{i=1}^{N} \xi_{i,\mu} S_i = (\overline{q_N})_\mu . \tag{3}$$

Quantities $q_{\mu,N}$ and $q_\mu = \lim_{N\to\infty} q_{\mu,N}$ are called random modes. $m = \lim_{N\to\infty} m_N$ and q_μ, $\mu=1,\dots,n$ are fundamental order parameters of e.n.r.s. models. In terms of (3)

$$H_\Lambda = -\frac{N}{2}\left(J_o m_N^2 + 2m_N \sum_{\mu=1}^{n} L^\mu q_{\mu,N} + \bar{q}_N Q \bar{q}_N + 2hm_N\right) + O(N) \equiv$$

$$\equiv - Ne(m_N, q_{1,N}, \dots, q_{n,N}) + O(N). \tag{4}$$

The free energy density f of e.n.r.s. models in inverse temperature β is given in the form of the following variational principle

$$- \beta f(\beta) = \sup_{\mathbb{R}^{n+1}} (e(\bar{n}) - c^*(\bar{n})), \tag{5}$$

where c^* is an adjoint function of c [13] ,

$$c(\bar{t}) = \langle \ln \operatorname{ch} (t_1 + \sum_{\mu=1}^{n} \xi_{i,\mu} t_{\mu+1}) \rangle , \tag{6}$$

with probability one with respect to a distribution of $\bar{\xi}_i$.

There are claims that e.n.r.s. models posses no typical behaviour: they have many parameters and changes of relations between them and changes of probability distributions of $\bar{\xi}_i$, induce large and hard to predict changes of thermodynamic properties. The models are also criticized for the finite number of pure phases-global maxima of $(e - c^*)$ (in the SK-model an infinite number of pure phases with a very special ultrametric structure is expected [5]).

Here we present some results obtained (using ideas of [9,12]) in [11], which are concerned with stated above objections. $\xi_{i,\mu}$, $i\in\Lambda$, $\mu=1,\dots,n$ are assumed to be i.i.d.r.v. with a discrete probability distribution, which is symmetric in zero. An important role in a study of a low temperature part of a phase diagram is played by the effective domain of c*-domc* [13]. domc* is a bounded, closed, convex set, which in case of discrete probability distributions of $\xi_{i,\mu}$ is a polytope [11]. To illustrate its use, let us consider for simplicity a one-mode case with convex function e, $e(m,q) = J_o m^2 + Jq^2$, h=0, (see discussion below). Lines of constant energy are ellipses. The one of the form $q_{max}^2 m^2 + q^2 = q_{max}^2$, where $q_{max} = E(|\xi_{i,1}|)$ we call the stability ellipse. We have the following equilibrium condition: If domc* is contained in the stability ellipse, then the ground states of the system are of the form $m=\pm 1$, $q=0$ (ferromagnetic phases) and $m=0$, $q=\pm q_{max}$ (random phases). It is obvious that in the opposite case we can have in general many mixed phases, where m and q are nonzero. Distributions, for which domc* is contained in the stability ellipse we call typical.

In order to choose a function e we impose the following symmetry requirements on J_{ij}: a) distribution of J_{ij} should be symmetric at zero [12], b) J_{ij} should be invariant under permutation of indices . Under these conditions

$$e(\bar{q}_N) = \frac{1}{2}\left(J_o m_N^2 + J\, s_\alpha(\bar{q}_N) + 2hm_N\right), \quad \text{where } s_\alpha(\bar{q}_N), \quad \alpha=1,2,3$$

are quadratic forms, invariant under permutation of random modes. Parameter J can be assumed to be positive without any loss of generality, while $J_o>0$, since in magnetic problems it represents a ferromagnetic exchange. Using convexity and invariance under permutation of n last variables of function c^* one can prove that in cases $S_1=\left(\sum_{\mu=1}^{n} q_{\mu,N}\right)^2$ and $S_2=\sum_{\mu<\nu=1}^{n} q_\mu q_\nu$ the global maximum of $(e-c^*)$ is attained in points with $q_1=q_2=\ldots=q_n$. So, in case of typical probability distributions there are only few pure phases. Only in the case $S_3=\sum_{\mu=1}^{n} q_{\mu,N}^2$ the symmetry between random modes can be broken and eventually in the limit $n\to\infty$ we can have an infinite number of pure random phases in the system. Using an obvious generalization of the equilibrium condition it can be proven, for example in the case $\xi_{i,\mu}=\pm 1$ with equal probability, that at low temperatures there are 2 ferromagnetic phases and 2n random phases, while the number of metastable states (local maxima of $e-c^*$) grows exponentially with n, for large n. In general the following proposition holds:

if the common probability distribution of $\xi_{i,\mu}$ is typical, then the ground state phase diagram of the multi-mode model whose function e is $e=J_o m^2+J\sum_{\mu=1}^{n} q_\mu^2$ consists of ferromagnetic phases: $m=\pm 1$ and $q_\mu=0$, $\mu=1,\ldots,n$ and $2n$ random phases: $m=0$ and $q_\mu=\pm q_{max}$ for one μ.

REFERENCES

[1] Sherrington, D., Kirkpatrick S. Phys.Rev.Lett.35,1792(1975)

[2] Sherrington, D., Kirkpatrick S. Phys.Rev.B17,1384(1978)

[3] Chowdhury, D., Mookerjee, A.: Phys.Rep.114(1984)

[4] Parisi G.: J.Phys.A13,1101(1980)

[5] Mezard, M., Parisi G., Sourlas, N., Toulouse, G. and Virasoro, M.:J.Physique 45,843(1984)

[6] Mattis D.C.: Phys.Lett.56A, 421(1976)

[7] Luttinger J.M.: Phys.Rev.Lett.37,778(1976)

[8] Benamira R., Provost J.P., Vallée G.: J.Physique 46,1269(1985)

[9] Provost, J.P., Vallée G.: Phys.Rev.Lett.50,598(1983)

[10] Choy, T.C., Sherrington, D., J.Phys.C17,739(1984)

[11] Jędrzejewski J., Komoda A.: Preprint ITP UWr 85/694, September 1985

[12] Van Hemmen I.L., Van Enter A.C.D., Canisius J.: Z.Phys.B50,311(1983)

[13] Rockafellar, R.T.: Convex analysis, Princeton, New Jersey, Princeton University Press, 1970

THE GRAND-CANONICAL SURFACE TENSION AND ITS CONVERGENCE TO THE SOS LIMIT IN THE TWO-DIMENSIONAL ISING MODEL

Steinar Johannesen, Danilo Merlini

The relation between the Ising model and the corresponding solid on solid (SOS) model (to be defined in Remark 1) involves interesting problems which are still unsolved. In particular, it has been expected that in two dimensions, the surface tension computed in the SOS limit will coincide with the exact value at low temperature. I will give a proof of this conjecture for the Ising model, and I expect that by similar methods, the result may also be extended to a more general class of two-dimensional models. This is part of a work together with F.J.L.C. Calheiros and D. Merlini, and a more detailed proof will be contained in [1].

Consider a finite rectangular box Λ of length $L+1$ and height $2M$ in $\mathbb{Z}^2$ with an Ising spin variable σ_i at each lattice site. At each bond (i.e. two-point nearest neighbour subset) B of $\mathbb{Z}^2$ with $B \cap \Lambda \neq \emptyset$ we have a ferromagnetic interaction J and we let $\sigma_B = \prod_{i \in B} \sigma_i$. The Hamiltonian is then given by $H_\Lambda = \sum_B J\,\sigma_B$ and it depends on the boundary conditions on Λ. Let Z_{++} (resp. Z_{+-}) be the usual partition function with plus (resp. mixed) boundary conditions. By mixed boundary conditions we mean that $\sigma_i = 1$ for $i = (a,b) \in \partial\Lambda$, $b < 0$ and $\sigma_i = -1$ when $b > 0$.

The canonical surface tension τ is then given by

$$e^{-\tau \cdot L} = \frac{Z_{+-}}{Z_{++}} = \langle \sigma_{i_1} \sigma_{i_2} \rangle_{\Lambda^*}(K^*) \tag{1}$$

where $i_1 = (-L/2,0)$ and $i_2 = (L/2,0)$, Λ^* is the dual lattice of Λ and $\tanh K^* = e^{-2K}$ $(K = \beta J,\ \beta = \frac{1}{kT})$ is the low-high temperature duality transformation (see [2]). By a refinement of the Sherman theorem on paths [1] it can be shown that

$$\langle \sigma_{i_1} \sigma_{i_2} \rangle_{\Lambda^*}(K^*) = \sum_{P_{1,2}} (-1)^N e^{-2K\cdot n} \tag{2}$$

where the sum is over all paths $P_{1,2}$ from i_1 to i_2, N is the number of self crossings and n the number of bonds in $P_{1,2}$.

In order to study the relation with the SOS model, we now introduce the grand canonical surface tension $\bar{\tau}$ which can be proved [1] to coincide with τ when $T < T_c$ (T_c being the critical temperature). $\bar{\tau}$ is given by

$$\Phi = e^{-\bar{\tau}\cdot L} = \lim_{M\to\infty} \sum_{i\in\mathbb{Z}} \frac{Z^i_{L,M,+-}}{Z_{L,M,++}} = \sum_{i\in\mathbb{Z}} \langle \sigma_{(-L/2,0)} \sigma_{(L/2,i)} \rangle^{\circ}_{L,\infty} \tag{3}$$

where $Z^i_{L,M,+-}$ is the partition function with mixed boundary conditions, but where the separation on one side between + and - is at hight i (see Fig. 1). From (2) and (3) we see that $e^{-\bar{\tau}\cdot L}$ is obtained as a sum over all paths from $(-L/2,0)$ to $(L/2,i)$ for any $i \in \mathbb{Z}$.

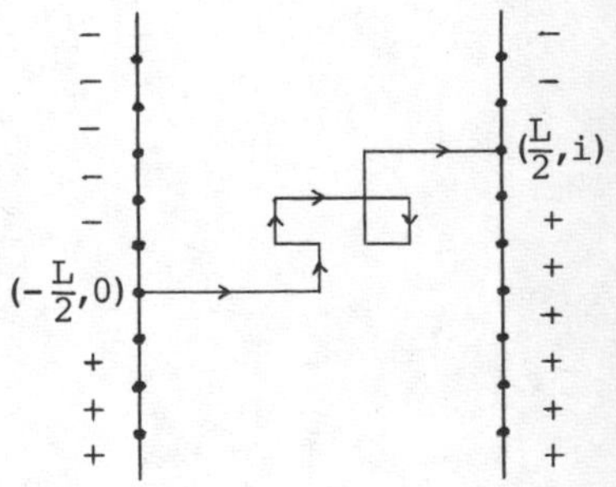

Fig. 1

<u>Theorem</u>: All paths having at least four bonds at some point or which are coming back will cancel exactly in the formula for $\bar{\tau}$ when $T < T_c$.

<u>Remark 1</u>: Considering only the remaining paths is called the SOS model.

<u>Proof</u>: Let M be the propagator for trajectories in Fourier space:

$$M(k_1,k_2) = \begin{bmatrix} x\,e^{-ik_1} & x\,e^{-ik_2-i\frac{\pi}{4}} & 0 & x\,e^{ik_2+i\frac{\pi}{4}} \\ x\,e^{-ik_1+i\frac{\pi}{4}} & x\,e^{-ik_2} & x\,e^{ik_1-i\frac{\pi}{4}} & 0 \\ 0 & x\,e^{-ik_2+i\frac{\pi}{4}} & x\,e^{ik_1} & x\,e^{ik_2-i\frac{\pi}{4}} \\ x\,e^{-ik_1-i\frac{\pi}{4}} & 0 & x\,e^{ik_1+i\frac{\pi}{4}} & x\,e^{ik_2} \end{bmatrix}$$

where $x = \tanh K^* = e^{-2K}$. From (3) we then obtain

$$\Phi = e^{-\bar{\tau}\cdot L} = \int_0^{2\pi} dk_1 \text{ Trace} \sum_{l=L-1}^{\infty} M^l(k_1,0)\cdot e^{ik_1(L-1)}$$

$$= \int_0^{2\pi} dk_1\, e^{ik_1(L-1)} \text{ Trace } \frac{M^{L-1}}{I-M}(k_1,0) = \int_0^{2\pi} dk_1\, e^{ik_1(L-1)} \sum_{i=1}^{4} \frac{\lambda_i^{L-1}}{1-\lambda_i} \tag{4}$$

λ_i are the eigenvalues of $M(k_1,0)$, and we have the characteristic equation

$$\left(z + \frac{\xi(1-\xi)}{1+\xi}\right)\left(z + \frac{1+\xi}{\xi(1-\xi)}\right) = 0 \tag{5}$$

where $\frac{\lambda}{x} = \xi$, $e^{ik_1} = z$.

In the SOS model we have

$$M(k_1,k_2) = \begin{bmatrix} x\,e^{-ik_1} & x\,e^{-ik_2-i\frac{\pi}{4}} & 0 & x\,e^{ik_2+i\frac{\pi}{4}} \\ x\,e^{-ik_1+i\frac{\pi}{4}} & x\,e^{-ik_2} & 0 & 0 \\ 0 & 0 & 0 & 0 \\ x\,e^{-ik_1-i\frac{\pi}{4}} & 0 & 0 & x\,e^{ik_2} \end{bmatrix}$$

and the characteristic equation is

$$\xi(\xi-1)\left(z + \frac{1+\xi}{\xi(1-\xi)}\right) = 0 \tag{6}$$

The last factor is the same in (5) and (6) and gives the same eigenvalues λ_3 and λ_4 in the two models. In the SOS model the first two eigenvalues $\lambda_1 = 0$ $(\xi_1=0)$ and $\lambda_2 = x$ $(\xi_2=1)$ do not give any contribution to the integral for Φ. For the Ising model we must compute

$$\tilde{\Phi} = \int_0^{2\pi} dk_1\, e^{ik_1(L-1)} \left(\frac{\lambda_1^{L-1}}{1-\lambda_1} + \frac{\lambda_2^{L-1}}{1-\lambda_2}\right) = \int_0^{2\pi} dk_1\, e^{ik_1(L-1)} \left(\frac{\xi_1^{L-1}}{1-x\xi_1} + \frac{\xi_2^{L-1}}{1-x\xi_2}\right) \quad (7)$$

As k_1 runs from 0 to 2π, ξ_1 will run from the point $P_1 = (1+\sqrt{2},0)$ to the point $P_2 = (1-\sqrt{2},0)$, and ξ_2 from P_2 back to P_1 counterclockwise on the circle C with center $(1,0)$ and radius $\sqrt{2}$ (see Fig. 2). From (7) we then obtain

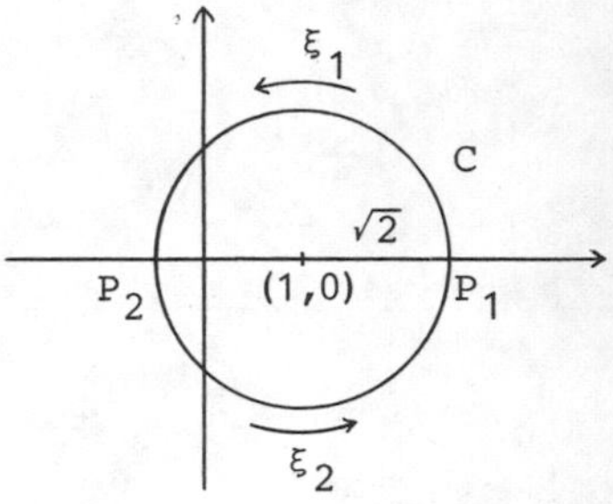

Fig. 2

$$\tilde{\Phi} = \int_C \frac{d\xi}{i}(\xi^2+2\xi-1)\cdot x^{L-1} \cdot \frac{\xi^{L-1}(1-\xi)^{L-1}}{(1+\xi)^{L+1}(1-x\xi)} = 0 \quad (8)$$

since the integrand is a meromorphic function with no pole inside the circle when $T < T_c$ (i.e. $|x| < \sqrt{2}-1$). This completes the proof that $\bar{\tau} = \tau_{SOS}$ for $T < T_c$.

Remark 2: Computing the integral corresponding to λ_3 and λ_4 shows that the SOS model also gives the well known Onsager formula for the surface tension:

$$\bar{\tau} = 2(K-K^*) \qquad (T < T_c) \quad (9)$$

References:

[1] F.J.L.C. Calheiros, S. Johannesen, D. Merlini: A refinement of the Sherman theorem and the grand-canonical surface tension in the two-dimensional Ising model, submitted to J. Stat. Phys.

[2] C. Gruber, A. Hinterman, D. Merlini: Lecture Notes in Physics No. 60, Springer Verlag, 1977.

STOCHASTIC QUANTIZATION

G.Jona-Lasinio
Dipartimento di Fisica - Università "La Sapienza",
GNSM and INFN - Roma

1. Rigorous Results on Simple Models

In this report I would like to briefly outline some of the mathematical problems encountered in a rigorous implementation of the program of stochastic quantization first proposed by Parisi and Wu Yong-Shi/1/ and then developed in its formal aspects by several authors/2/.

We recall that the basic idea of stochastic quantization consists in considering the Euclidean measure associated to a quantum mechanical system with finite or infinite degrees of freedom, as the stationary state of some stochastic process.

The standard proposal for the construction of such a process is to solve the following stochastic differential equation

$$\frac{\partial \phi(\underline{x},t)}{\partial t} = - \frac{\delta S(\phi)}{\delta \phi(\underline{x},t)} + \frac{\partial W(\underline{x},t)}{\partial t} \tag{1.1}$$

where $S(\phi)$ is the Euclidean action describing the system and $W(\underline{x},t)$ in the Wiener process characterized by the covariance

$$E\,(W\,(\underline{x},t)\;W\,(\underline{x}',t')) = \min\,(t,t')\;\delta(\underline{x} - \underline{x}') \tag{1.2}$$

The typical form of the functional $S(\phi)$ is

$$S(\phi) = \int d^{\nu}x \left(\frac{1}{2}\left[(\nabla\phi)^2 + \phi^2\right] + V(\phi)\right) \tag{1.3}$$

where $V(\phi)$ is a local polynomial in ϕ of even degree and ν is the dimension of thc space. Introducing (1.3) in (1.1) we obtain

$$\frac{\partial\phi}{\partial t} = \Delta\phi - \phi - V'(\phi) + \frac{\partial W}{\partial t} \tag{1.4}$$

Δ is the Laplacian.

As it is eq.(1.4) is only formal because the Wiener process is non differentiable. This is a well known difficulty already in the case of ordinary stochastic differential equations where it is overcome by integrating with respect to the time and transforming the equation into an integral equation/3/.

The natural thing to do in the case of (1.4) is to obtain an integral equation by using the Green function of the linear part, that is

$$\phi(t,\underline{x}) = -\int d^{\nu}x' \int_0^t dt'\; G(t,t',\underline{x},\underline{x}')\, V'(\phi(t',\underline{x}')) + Z(t,\underline{x}) \tag{1.5}$$

where G satisfies

$$\frac{\partial G}{\partial t} - \Delta G + G = \delta(t'-t)\,\delta(\underline{x}'-\underline{x}) \tag{1.6}$$

and Z is the Gaussian process

$$Z(t,\underline{x}) = \int d^{\nu}x' \int_0^t dt'\; G(t,t',\underline{x},\underline{x}')\,\frac{\partial W(t',\underline{x}')}{\partial t'} + \phi_0(t,\underline{x}) \tag{1.7}$$

where ϕ_0 is a solution of the linear homogeneous part of (1.4). The next step depends crucially on the dimensionality ν .

ν = 1. - In this case (1.5) is a meaningful equation. This depends on the circumstance that the typical trajectories of the process $Z(t,x)$ are continuous functions in both variables. (1.5) can then be solved for each continuous realization of the input $Z(t,x)$. A rather complete treatment of this case can be found in ref./4/. The ν =1 theory covers the stochastic quantization of systems with a finite number of degrees of freedom, that is the case of Quantum Mechanics. It is interesting to note however that its relevance, goes beyond quantum mechanical applications. In recent years in fact the theory developed in /4/ has been useful in entirely different domains/5/-/6/.

ν = 2. - At ν =2 the typical difficulties of Quantum Field Theory appear. The free field $Z(t,\underline{x})$ is not anymore a continuous function but a distribution. If one evaluates for example the expectation value $E_w\,(Z^2(t,x))$ this diverges logarithmically. E_w means expectation with respect to the Wiener process (1.2).
Eq.(1.5) has therefore to be modified by introducing counterterms. In this way however, since in the end the counterterms become infinite, the equation itself does not have a mathematical meaning. The way out to this problem taken in the physical literature consists in developing the solution in perturbation theory and then adjusting the renormalization terms in such a way that expectations of the form

$$E_w\,(\phi(t_1, x_1)\,\phi(t_2, x_2) - - \phi(t_n, x_n))$$

make sense. For a rigorous mathematical treatment this is not sufficient and one has to resort to a non perturbative approach. Therefore the problem facing us consists in defining a "solution" of (1.5) in spite of the fact that the equation does not have a meaning. To solve this problem we appeal to what probabilists call a weak solution of a stochastic differential equation. The basic idea is as follows. Let us first regularize (1.5) by introducing the counter terms. In the present situation this means taking the Wick product of the nonlinear term $V'(\phi)$ and then introducing a cut-off κ in evaluating it. That is the nonlinear term will be: $V'(\phi_\kappa)$: where ϕ_κ is the cut-off field. The Wick product can be taken with respect to the covariance of the free field $C(\underline{x},\underline{y}) = (-\Delta+1)^{-1}$. If for example $V(\phi) = \frac{\lambda}{4}\phi^4$, $:V'(\phi): = \lambda(\phi^3 - 3C(\underline{x},\underline{x})\phi)$. With these modifications (1.5) becomes

$$\phi = -G *: V'(\phi_\kappa): + Z \tag{1.8}$$

and as long as $\kappa < \infty$ this is a meaningful equation which can be solved for each imput Z. The process Z will now induce a measure μ_ϕ^κ on the solutions of (1.8). <u>If now μ_ϕ^κ converges to a limiting measure</u> μ_ϕ (in the sense of weak convergence of measures) <u>as $\kappa \to \infty$ we shall say</u> that (1.8) <u>has a weak</u> solution when the cut-off in removed. Our goal therefore consists in implementing non perturbatively this idea. In stochastic calculus there is a well known formula, the Girsanov-Cameron-Martin formula, which provides the Radon-Nikodym derivative of the measure μ_ϕ^κ with respect to μ_Z. This is[3]

$$\frac{d\mu_\phi^\kappa}{d\mu_Z} = \exp\left\{-\int_0^T(:V'(Z_\kappa):, dW) - \frac{1}{2}\int_0^T dt' \,\| :V'(Z_\kappa): \|^2\right\} \tag{1.9}$$

where

$$(:V'(Z_\kappa):, dW) = \int_\Lambda d^2x :V'(Z_\kappa(t,\underline{x})): dW(t,\underline{x})$$

is a scalar product in the space variables and $\|\cdot\|$ is the norm induced by it. We work in the finite volume Λ. The stochastic integral appearing in (1.9) is a Ito integral, that is it must be considered as a limit of sums

$$\lim_{n\to\infty}\sum_{i=0}^{\infty} (:V'(Z_\kappa(t_i):, W(t_{i+1}) - W(t_i)) \tag{1.10}$$

where the t_i represent a partition of $[o, T]$. Notice that with this definition the increment is uncorrelated with the integrand due to the Markov property of the Wiener process. This integral, very natural probabilistically, does not obey as it is well known to the usual rules of differential calculus/3/.

Our basic problem now consists in showing that when $\kappa \to \infty$ (1.9) is a good stochastic variable and in particular

$$E_{Z_o} \left(\frac{d\mu_\phi}{d\mu_Z}\right) = 1 \tag{1.11}$$

that is, the measure μ_ϕ is normalized.

Z_o means that the expectation is taken with $Z(o, \underline{x}) = Z_o(x)$.

The problem now reminds of constructive field theory, only a rather special lagrangian is involved. To make the connection even more explicit we notice that by the rules of the Ito calculus it follows

$$\int_0^T (:V'(Z):, dW) = \frac{1}{4} \int_\Lambda : Z^4(T, \underline{x}): d^2x - \frac{1}{4} \int_\Lambda :Z^4(o, \underline{x}): d^2x + \tag{1.12}$$

$$+ \frac{1}{2} \int_0^T dt : (Z^3, (-\Delta + 1)Z):$$

Using (1.12), the exponential in (1.9) takes a less exotic form.

At this point everything seems to be ready to apply the methods of constructive field theory, in particular the rather straight forward methods by which $P(\phi)_2$ was constructed/7/. One realizes immediately however that our problem is more difficult. In fact neither term in the exponent of (1.9) is a well defined stochastic variable. For example the expectation of the second term diverges. The remarkable thing is that this type of divergence does not show up in perturbation theory! The divergence we just mentioned is cancelled by the square of the first term in the expansion of the exponential and a similar mechanism operates with higher order contributions. The reason is the special structure of (1.9) which is such as to insure in any case the normalization condition $E\left(\frac{d\mu_\phi}{d\mu_2}\right) = 1$. This reminds of the cancellation mechanisms in supersymmetric theories(*). These divergences however constitute a difficulty in a non perturbative approach.

At this stage there are two possibilities. If we insist on the specific form of eq.(1.8) as the basis for stochastic quantization we must conclude that the methods devised for $P(\phi)_2$ are not sufficient to treat its stochastic counterpart. We must in such a case look for more powerful methods like for example the phase space cell expansion or more generally the renormalization group methods which led to the construction of ϕ_3^4. In fact the above difficulties of stochastic $P(\phi)_2$ seem of a similar nature as those encountered in ϕ_3^4.

The other possibility consists in modifying eq.(1.8) in such a way that the usual $P(\phi)_2$ Euclidean theory still represents its equilibrium state. This was the way followed recently by Jona-Lasinio and Mitter/9/. There is in fact a whole family of stochastic differential equations which admit the same equilibrium measure. The one considered in/9/ is

$$d\phi(t,\underline{x}) = dW(t,\underline{x}) - \frac{1}{2}\left(C^{-\varepsilon}\phi(t,\underline{x}) + C^{1-\varepsilon} :V'(\phi(t,\underline{x})):\right) dt \qquad (1.13)$$

with $0<\varepsilon<1$ and

$$E(W(t,\underline{x})\,W(t',\underline{x}')) = C^{1-\varepsilon}(\underline{x},\underline{x}')\min(t,t') \qquad (1.14)$$

In/9/ it was shown that for $\varepsilon < \frac{1}{10}$ the methods used for $P(\phi)_2$ are sufficient to prove the existence of an ergodic weak solution of (1.13). The previous equation (1.8) corresponds to $\varepsilon = 1$. The approach to equilibrium is slower for (1.13).

(*) The connection between stochastic calculus and supersymmetry has been considered by many authors/8/.

2. Perspectives

In this section I will briefly discuss some topics in (or connected with) stochastic quantization on which progress not only would be desirable but can be expected in a near future. These are: the extension of the previous existence proof to non abelian gauge models and the dovclopment of a large fluctuation theory for $P(\phi)_2$ stochastic models or more generally for stochastic differential equations requiring infinite renormalizations. The first topic is a fundamental one as gauge theories provided the first motivation to introduce stochastic quantization. The choice of the other one reflects my subjective inclinations.

Gauge Theories

We consider the Zwanziger[10] scheme with stochastic gauge fixing. This means that the structure of the basic stochastic differential equation is as follows

$$\frac{\partial A_\mu^a}{\partial t} = - \frac{\delta S_{YM}}{\delta A_\mu^a} + K_{GF\mu}^{\ a} + \eta_\mu^a \tag{2.1}$$

where S_{YM} is the usual Yang-Mills action and K_{GF} is the gauge fixing term which we shall take as

$$K_{GF\mu}^{\ a}(x) = - \frac{\delta S_{GF}}{\delta A_\mu^a} + g f^{abc} A_\mu^b (\partial A)^c \tag{2.2}$$

with $S_{GF} = \frac{1}{2} \alpha \int (\partial A)^2 dx$. η_μ^a is the white noise defined by

$$E(\eta_\mu^a(x,t)\eta_\nu^b(x',t')) = \delta_{ab}\delta_{\mu\nu}\delta(x-x')\delta(t-t') \tag{2.3}$$

For the meaning of the above choice and for much of the following discussion we refer to the clear lectures by E.Seiler[11].

Even at the level of a regularized theory eq.(2.1) presents a new basic difficulty if compared with boson theories. In fact (2.1) is not of gradient form due to the second term on the right hand side of eq.(2.2): as a consequence we do not have a formal expression for its equilibrium measure. One has therefore to solve preliminarly the problem of the existence of such a stationary measure and this requires an understanding of the stability properties of (2.1). To study the stabilizing effect of the gauge fixing term K_{GF} we consider first, following/11/, the deterministic dynamical system

$$\dot{A}^a_\mu = K^a_{GF\mu}(A) \tag{2.4}$$

If A^a_μ evolves according to (2.4) one immediately finds that

$$\frac{d}{dt} \| A \|^2 = -2\alpha \int (\partial A)^2 \, dx \tag{2.5}$$

from which it follows that K_{GF} has the character of a restoring force except on the manifold $\partial A = 0$ consisting fixed points of (2.4). However on $\partial A = 0$ there are unbounded field configurations and one has to show that they are not attainable by the stochastically perturbed system.

Zwanziger discovered that on $\partial A = 0$ there is an open convex subset Ω bounded along each ray such that the points in Ω are stable fixed points and the points outside $\bar{\Omega}$ are unstable. The boundary $\partial\Omega$ is the Gribov horizon. In a lattice regularization Ω is bounded in an ordinary sense. To visualize the situation Seiler proposed in/11/ to consider the following two dimensional example which is a modification of a previous suggestion by Zwanziger.

$$\begin{aligned} dx &= -\alpha\, 2xy^2\, dt + dw_1 \\ dy &= -\alpha\,(1-x^2)\, y\,dt + dw_2 \end{aligned} \tag{2.6}$$

where dw_i is a two dimensional Wiener process. The role of the manifold $\partial A = 0$ is played by $y = 0$. The stability of the deterministic part is illustrated in the following figure

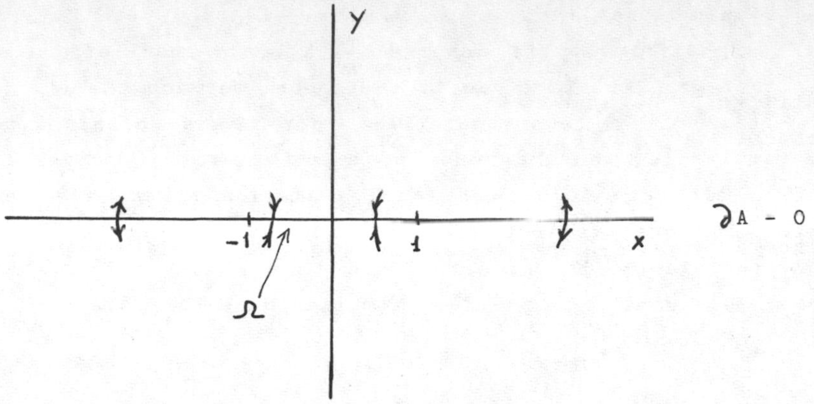

Seiler exhibited the invariant measure of (2.6) for a special value of α and numerical simulations confirmed its existence for other values. The reason why the process does not escape to infinity along $y = 0$ is the fact that even small fluctuations along the y axis will drive the process in a region where the drift is again attractive. This effect of stochastic stabilization can be proved quite generally (that is independently of the value of α) by introducing the notion of stochastic Liapunov function. This may be defined as follows/3/. Given a stochastic differential system $d\underline{y}=\underline{b}(\underline{x})dt+d\underline{w}$ we say that $V(\underline{x})$ is a Liapunov function if it is positive, twice differentiable, $\lim_{|x|\to\infty} V(\underline{x}) = \infty$ and satisfies

$$LV = \frac{1}{2}\Delta V + \underline{b}\,\underline{\nabla} V \leq - C_1 V + C_2 \tag{2.7}$$

where $C_{1,2}$ are positive constants, L is the generator of the Markov process generated by the solutions of the system. The existence of a Liapunov function insures the boundedness of the process in a suitable probabilistic sense.

Going back to equation (2.6), it is easy to check that the expression

$$V(x,y) = x^2 + y^2 + Cx^2e^{-y^2} \tag{2.8}$$

satisfies (2.7).

The previous discussion suggests that a study of the stochastic stability of a regularized version of (2.1) by direct methods may be successfully carried through. Once the stability of a conveniently regularized theory is established and by this the existence of an equilibrium measure, the continuum limit can be approached along more standard lines. In this connection we would like to mention a recent proposal of regularization within the Zwanziger scheme by Bern, Halpern, Sadun and Taubes/12/.

Large Fluctuations

In the previous section we mentioned that in the case $\nu=1$ it is possible to solve eq.(1.4) for each continuous realization of the driving process Z as no renormalization is necessary. This circumstance allowed to develop in/4/ a theory of large fluctuations along lines similar to the case of ordinary stochastic differential equations. In particular assuming a small parameter h in front of the noise, i.e.

$$\frac{\partial \phi}{\partial t} = \Delta \phi - \phi - V'(\phi) + h \frac{\partial W}{\partial t} \tag{2.9}$$

it was proved that if $\phi(t,x)$ is a trajectory of the process solving (2.9) and A a set in the space of continuous functions in t and x equipped with the uniform topology

$$-\lim_{h \to 0} h^2 \ln P(\phi \in A) = I(A) \tag{2.10}$$

where

$$I(A) = \inf_{\phi \in A} \left\| \left(\frac{\partial}{\partial t} - \Delta + 1\right)\phi + V'(\phi) \right\|^2 \tag{2.11}$$

where $\| \ \|$ is the L_2 norm. An estimate like (2.10) tells us that $P(\phi \in A)$ is large if A contains solutions of the deterministic equation obtained setting $h = 0$ and exponentially small otherwise. Since in stochastic quantization h^2 can be identified with $\hbar$, the above estimate describes the semiclassical limit.

The same type of problem arises quite naturally in the case of the ϕ_2^4 stochastic model discussed in the previous section. However the necessity of renormalization introduces new features which make the problem more difficult but richer than in the previous case. First of all it is clear that due to the fact that $\phi(t,\underline{x})$ is now a distribution we can speak of trajectories only for quantities smeared in space like e.g.

$$\phi_g(t,\underline{x}) = \int g(\underline{x}-\underline{x}')\, \phi(t,\underline{x}')\, d^2x' \tag{2.12}$$

where g is an appropriate test function.
Suppose first that the coupling λ in (1.8) or (1.13) satisfies $\lambda \ll 1$. Let us denote by R_0 the diameter of the region over which the field ϕ is smeared by g. That is ϕ_g is a field with an effective cut-off of the order of $\kappa_0 \approx R_0^{-1}$. In this situation we may expect the probability of large fluctuations to be determined by the <u>unrenormalized</u> deterministic part of the equation if

$$\lambda h^2 \ln \kappa_0 \ll 1 \tag{2.13}$$

In other words the typical configurations of the field will have a tendency to be close to solutions of the non renormalized deterministic equation provided we consider their space behaviour over a sufficiently large scale according to (2.13). On the other hand even if we keep the intensity of the noise h fixed and small we must expect renormalization effects to become relevant when we consider the behaviour of the field ϕ at small scales.
In the opposite regime $\lambda \gg 1$, as shown by Glimm, Jaffe and Spencer/13/, the quartic potential $V(\phi)$ is equivalent to a weakly coupled ϕ^4 interaction with a negative quadratic term. In this case therefore we expect also the fluctuations of the field on large scale

to be described by a deterministic equation with a potential different from the original one. That is the effective renormalized potential will be a double well in spite of the fact that the original non renormalized one had only one minimum at $\phi=0$.

It would be interesting to put the above heuristics on firm ground.

Aknowledgments

I would like to express my gratitude to P.K.Mitter for the fruitful collaboration on the subject of this report and to E.Seiler for many interesting discussions.

References

1) G.Parisi, Wu Yong-Shi, Sci.Sin. 24, 483 (1981).

2) For a review see for example B.Sakita, 7th Johns Hopkins Workshop, ed. G.Domokos, S.Kovesi-Domokos (World Scientific, Singapore 1983).

3) See e.g. I.I. Gihman, A.V.Skorohod, "Stochastic Differential Equations", Springer 1972.

4) W.Faris, G.Jona-Lasinio, J.Phys.A, 15, 3025 (1982).

5) R.Benzi, A.Sutera, J.Phys.A, 18, 2239 (1985).

6) M.Cassandro, E.Olivieri, P.Picco, Ann.Inst. H.Poincaré, in Press.

7) E.Nelson, in "Constructive Quantum Field Theory" Lecture Notes in Phys. Vol. 25, Springer 1973;
B.Simon, "The P $(\varphi)_2$ Euclidean (Quantum) Field Theory" Princeton NJ, Princeton University Press 1974;
J.Glimm, A.Jaffe, "Quantum Physics" Springer 1981.

8) S.Cecotti, L.Girardello, Phys.Lett. 110B, 39 (1982);
G.Parisi, N.Sourlas, Nucl.Phys. 206B, 321 (1982);
E.Gozzi, Phys.Lett. 129Bn 432 (1983);
V.de Alfaro, S.Fubini, G.Furlan, G.Veneziano, Phys.Lett. 142B, 399 (1984).

9) G.Jona-Lasinio, P.K.Mitter, Comm.Math.Phys. 101, 409 (1985).

10) D.Zwanziger, Nucl.Phys. B192, 259 (1981), Phys.Lett. 114B, 337 (1982), Nucl.Phys. B209, 336 (1982).

11) E.Seiler, Lectures given at the 23 Internationale Universitatswochen fur Kernphysik, Schladming, Austria 1984.

12) Z.Bern, M.B.Halpern, L.Sadun, C.Taubes, Phys.Lett. 165B, 151 (1985).

13) J.Glimm, A.Jaffe, Th.Spencer, in "Les Méthodes Mathématiques de la Théorie Quantique des Champs", F.Guerra, D.W.Robinson, R.Stora eds. Colloques Internationaux du CNRS n.248, 1976, page 175.

ON MEASURES OF INFORMATION FOR CONTINUOUS STOCHASTIC PROCESSES*,**

Timo Koski
Åbo Akademi
Department of Mathematics
Fänriksgatan 3
SF-20500 Åbo 50

Wilfried Loges
Department of Mathematics
Ruhr-Universität Bochum
D-4630 Bochum

Abstract

The properties of the Kullback-Leibler information for continuous-time stochastic linear filtering dynamical systems are investigated. It is shown that the parameter sensitivity of the filter estimate plays a pre-eminent role in influencing the Kullback-Leibler number. The result is extended to a class of stochastic distributed parameter systems.

1. Introduction

The Kullback-Leibler information number (KL-number) plays an important role in information theory and statistics (see e.g. [1] and the references therein). Furthermore, it has turned out to be intrinsically connected with various properties of continuous time system identification using the method of maximum likelihood (c.f. [2]). With the last mentioned application in mind it would seem to be useful to refer to the pertinent KL-numbers as indirect KL-numbers. In the present case the name has its origin in the fact that the KL-numbers are computed for pairs of measures induced by indirect, noise contaminated linear observations of certain linear,

---

* Research sponsored by the Finnish Academy of Sciences and Research Center Bielefeld-Bochum-Stochastics (Stiftung Volkswagenwerk)

** Talk presented by W. Loges

time-invariant stochastic differential equations under a corresponding pair of values of the parameters determining the system model. By virtue of the standard structure of the stochastic differential system under consideration one may in addition attach another KL-number, which will be called the direct KL-number, to the same pair of parameters. The direct KL-number is in its turn valid for the measures induced by the system process itself i.e. for the measures corresponding to direct, noise-free measurements.

It is a basic intuitive requirement for any reasonable measure of information as well as a general result of Cziszár ([3]) that the indirect KL-number cannot exceed the direct KL-number. The results presented in the sequel offer a more detailed analysis of this circumstance and in some cases a sharper bound for the indirect KL-number in as much as they single out the factors influencing the indirect KL-number. To be more accurate, this paper attempts to clarify the links between the aforementioned KL-numbers and the sensitivity of the filter estimate w.r.t. variations in parameters.

The general definition of a KL-number is given as follows. Suppose that $\{\mu_\theta | \theta \in \Theta\}$ is a family of probability measures on an abstract measurable space $(X, \mathfrak{X})$. Assume also that there exists a fixed probability measure μ which dominates all μ_θ's. Hence there exists a Radon-Nikodym (RN)-density denoted by $f_\theta = d\mu_\theta/d\mu$ uniquely determined up to sets of μ-measure zero. Then the KL-number, $KL(\theta_2;\theta_1)$, is defined as

$$KL(\theta_2;\theta_1) = \int_X \ln\left(\frac{f_{\theta_2}}{f_{\theta_1}}\right) d\mu_{\theta_2} \tag{1}$$

for any couple θ_2, θ_1 in Θ (cf. [4] pp. 3-34). The KL-number can be interpreted as the mean information for discrimination against μ_{θ_1} when the sample is actually taken under μ_{θ_2}. For purposes of heuristic presentation one might talk about $KL(\theta_2;\theta_1)$ as a distance between the measures μ_{θ_2} and μ_{θ_1}, which is however mathematically incorrect, since $KL(\theta_2;\theta_1)$ is, in general, not a metric. It is on the other hand known that

$$2 \cdot \sup_{A \in \mathfrak{X}} |\mu_{\theta_2}(A) - \mu_{\theta_1}(A)| = \int_X |f_{\theta_2} - f_{\theta_1}| d\mu \leq \sqrt{2KL(\theta_2;\theta_1)} \tag{2}$$

(see e.g. [3]), which shows that the KL-number forms an upper bound for a genuine distance measure.

The paper is organized as follows. In section 2 we introduce the formal notations and assumptions governing the stochastic differential system.

In section 3 we derive representations for the indirect and direct KL-numbers and an estimate for the indirect KL-number in terms of the filter sensitivity and the direct KL-number, as explained above. A result showing the applicativity of the same argument for the class of stochastic distributed parameter-state processes studied in [5] is given.

In the paper [6] various information numbers are classified as (1) parametric measures, e.g. Fisher's information, (2) non-parametric measures, e.g. the KL-number, and (3) measures of entropy, e.g. Shannon's entropy. In section 3 we incorporate remarks, based on the work of Duncan [7], establishing some simple connections between these types of measures as applied to the model under consideration.

2. The model and its assumptions

We assume that all the stochastic processes to be considered below are defined on a fixed, common probability space $(\Omega, \mathcal{F}, \mathbb{P})$. We study the following continuous time stochastic linear dynamical system consisting of the system (or state) process

$$dx_t(\theta) = A(\theta)x_t(\theta)dt + Ddw_t \tag{3}$$

and the measurement equation

$$dy_t(\theta) = Cx_t(\theta)dt + Fdv_t \; . \tag{4}$$

Here θ is a generic vector of all the unknown system parameters lying in an abstract parameter space Θ. In the present setting only the $n \times n$-matrix $A(\theta)$ depends on a parameter. Further, D,F and C are $n \times n$, $k \times k$ and $k \times n$-matrices. We assume that D and F are invertible. The processes $w = \{w_t | 0 \leq t \leq T\}$ and $v = \{v_t | 0 \leq t \leq T\}$ are mutually independent $\mathbb{R}^n$ (resp. $\mathbb{R}^k$)-valued Wiener processes with identity covariances. We shall also assume that $x_o(\theta) = 0$.

The direct KL-number, denoted by $KL^D(\theta_2;\theta_1)$, can now be directly defined as the KL-number evaluated for the measures ν_{θ_i}, i=1,2, induced by the processes $x(\theta_i) = \{x_t(\theta_i) \;|0 \leq t \leq T\}$, i=1,2, where θ_1 and θ_2 belong to Θ. The indirect KL-number, denoted by $KL^{IND}(\theta_2;\theta_1)$, is evaluated for the measures μ_{θ_i}, i=1,2, induced by the processes $y(\theta_i) = \{y_t(\theta_i)| \; 0 \leq t \leq T\}$, i=1,2.

Since in computing $KL^{IND}(\theta_2;\theta_1)$ we shall have to exercise some care when dealing with the filtering estimate (see (13) below), we shall now briefly review some relevant facts from the theory of the conditional expectation $E(x_t(\theta)|\mathcal{F}_t^{y(\theta)})$, the well known solution of the linear filtering problem, where $\mathcal{F}_t^{y(\theta)}$ denotes the subsigma-algebra generated by the process $y(\theta)$ up to time t. Omitting the θ-dependence for the moment we may write

$$E(x_t|\mathcal{F}_t^y) = \int_0^t Y(t,s)P(s)(F^{-1}C)^* dy_s \tag{5}$$

where the asterisk * denotes matrix transpose and P(s) is the unique solution of the matrix Riccati-equation

$$\dot{P}(s) = AP(s)+P(s)A^* + DD^* - P(s)C^*(FF^*)^{-1}CP(s) \tag{6}$$

and Y(t,s) denotes the perturbation of the matrix e^{tA} by $-P(t)C^*(FF^*)^{-1}C$ i.e. Y(t,s) satisfies the equation

$$Y(t,s) = e^{A(t-s)} - \int_s^t e^{A(t-u)}P(u)C^*(FF^*)^{-1}CY(u,s)du \tag{7}$$

(see e.g. [8]).

For notational convenience we set

$$K(t,s) = Y(t,s)P(s)(F^{-1}C)^* \tag{8}$$

or $K(t,s;\theta)$ by reverting back to θ-dependence, which is present in Y(t,s) and P(s). The function $K(\cdot,\cdot;\theta)$ will be called the <u>filter kernel</u>.

The process $\hat{\nu}(\theta) = \{\hat{\nu}_t(\theta)|\ 0 \leq t \leq T\}$ constructed for any θ by the rule

$$\hat{\nu}_t(\theta) = y_t(\theta) - \int_0^t CE(x_s|\mathcal{F}_s^{y(\theta)})ds \tag{9}$$

defines the <u>innovation process</u>.

A crucial property of the innovation process is that the equality

$$\mathcal{F}_t^{\hat{\nu}(\theta)} = \mathcal{F}_t^{y(\theta)} \tag{10}$$

holds for any t and θ. Furthermore, $\hat{\nu}(\theta) = \{\hat{\nu}_t(\theta)|\ 0 \leq t \leq T\}$ is a standard Wiener process w.r.t. the stochastic basis $(\Omega, \mathcal{F}, (\mathcal{F}_t^{y(\theta)})_{0 \leq t \leq T}, \mathbb{P})$.

3. Results

In this section we give first exact expressions for the KL-numbers corresponding to direct and indirect, noise perturbed measurement of the underlying stochastic differential systems specified in section 2.

Lemma 1:

(i) $KL^D(\theta_2;\theta_1) = KL_T^D(\theta_2;\theta_1) = \frac{1}{2}\int_0^T E(\| D^{-1}(A(\theta_2)-A(\theta_1))x_t(\theta_2)\|_n^2)dt$ (11)

(ii) $KL^{IND}(\theta_2;\theta_1) = KL_T^{IND}(\theta_2;\theta_1) =$

$$\frac{1}{2}\{\int_0^T E(\|\int_0^t F^{-1}CU_\theta(t,s)F^{-1}Cx_s(\theta_2)ds\|_k^2)dt + \int_0^T\int_0^t \| F^{-1}CU_\theta(t,s)\|^2_{\mathcal{L}(\mathbb{R}^k)} dsdt\} \quad (12)$$

where we denote

$U_\theta(t,s) := U(t,s;\theta_2,\theta_1) := K(t,s;\theta_2)-K(t,s;\theta_1) \in \mathcal{L}(\mathbb{R}^k, \mathbb{R}^n)$.

$U_\theta(t,s)$ is the sensitivity of the filter.

Proof: (i)

The system processes $(x_t(\theta_i))_{0\leq t\leq T}$, i=1,2, induce the measures ν_{θ_i}, i=1,2, on $C([0,T];\mathbb{R}^n)$, the space of continuous functions on [0,T] with values in $\mathbb{R}^n$.

It is well known that the measures ν_θ are equivalent for different $\theta\in\Theta$ and that the Girsanov-formula yields the "likelihood functional"

$$\frac{d\nu_{\theta_2}}{d\nu_{\theta_1}}((x_t(\theta_2))_{0\leq t\leq T}) =$$

$$\exp(-\int_0^T D^{-1}(A(\theta_2)-A(\theta_1))x_t(\theta_2)\cdot dw_t + \frac{1}{2}\int_0^T\| D^{-1}(A(\theta_2)-A(\theta_1))x_t(\theta_2)\|_n^2 dt).$$

By definition (1) we therefore get

$$KL^D(\theta_2;\theta_1) = \int_{C([0,T];\mathbb{R}^n)} \ln\left(\frac{d\nu_{\theta_2}}{d\nu_{\theta_1}}\right) d\nu_{\theta_2} =$$

$$= E(\ln(\frac{d\nu_{\theta_2}}{d\nu_{\theta_1}}(x_t(\theta_2))_{0\leq t\leq T}) =$$

$$= E(-\int_0^T D^{-1}(A(\theta_2)-A(\theta_1))x_t(\theta_2)\cdot dw_t)$$

$$+ \frac{1}{2}E(\int_0^T \|D^{-1}(A(\theta_2)-A(\theta_1))x_t(\theta_2)\|_n^2 dt) =$$

$$\frac{1}{2}\int_0^T E(\| D^{-1}(A(\theta_2)-A(\theta_1))x_t(\theta_2))\|_n^2)dt.$$

(ii): Introducing the processes

$\tilde{y}_t(\theta_i) := F^{-1}y_t(\theta_i) = \int_0^t F^{-1}Cx_s(\theta_i)ds + v_t$, i=1,2, obtained from $(y_t(\theta_i))_{0\leq t\leq T}$ via a bijective transformation it is obvious that the associated KL-numbers remain unchanged.

As in the case of direct observation there is a Girsanov-type result to the effect that (see e.g. [8], Th. 7.15)

$$\frac{d\tilde{\mu}_{\theta_i}}{d\mu_w}\left((\tilde{y}_t(\theta_i))_{0\le t\le T}\right) =$$

$$\exp\Big(\int_0^T (F^{-1}CE(x_t(\theta_i)|\mathcal{F}_t^{\tilde{y}(\theta_i)}))\cdot d\tilde{y}_t(\theta_i) - \frac{1}{2}\int_0^T \|F^{-1}CE(x_t(\theta_i)|\mathcal{F}_t^{\tilde{y}(\theta_i)})\|_k^2 dt\Big)$$

where $\mathcal{F}_t^{\tilde{y}(\theta_i)}$ is the σ-algebra generated by the process $\tilde{y}(\theta_i)$ up to time t, $\tilde{\mu}_{\theta_i}$ is the measure induced by $(\tilde{y}_t(\theta_i))_{0\le t\le T}$ and μ_w is the Wiener measure. Applying the chain rule

$\frac{d\tilde{\mu}_{\theta_2}}{d\tilde{\mu}_{\theta_1}} = \frac{d\tilde{\mu}_{\theta_2}}{d\mu_w} \cdot \left(\frac{d\tilde{\mu}_{\theta_1}}{d\mu_w}\right)^{-1}$ we are able to compute the indirect KL-number:

$$KL^{IND}(\theta_2;\theta_1) = \int_{C([0,T];\mathbb{R}^k)} \ln\left(\frac{d\tilde{\mu}_{\theta_2}}{d\tilde{\mu}_{\theta_1}}\right)d\tilde{\mu}_{\theta_2} = E\left(\ln\left(\frac{d\tilde{\mu}_{\theta_2}}{d\tilde{\mu}_{\theta_1}}\right)\left((\tilde{y}_t(\theta_2))_{0\le t\le T}\right)\right) =$$

$$=E\Big(\int_0^T [F^{-1}C(\int_0^t K(t,s;\theta_2)d\tilde{y}_s(\theta_2))]\cdot d\tilde{y}_t(\theta_2) - \frac{1}{2}\int_0^T \|F^{-1}C(\int_0^t K(t,s;\theta_2)d\tilde{y}_s(\theta_2))\|_k^2 dt$$

$$- \int_0^T [F^{-1}C(\int_0^t K(t,s;\theta_1)d\tilde{y}_s(\theta_2))]\cdot d\tilde{y}_t(\theta_2) + \frac{1}{2}\int_0^T \|F^{-1}C\int_0^t K(t,s;\theta_1)d\tilde{y}_s(\theta_2))\|_k^2 dt\Big)$$

$$= E\Big(\int_0^T F^{-1}C(\hat{x}_t - \hat{\hat{x}}_t)\cdot d\tilde{y}_t(\theta_2) - \frac{1}{2}\int_0^T (\|F^{-1}C\hat{x}_t\|_k^2 - \|F^{-1}C\,\hat{\hat{x}}_t\|_k^2)dt\Big)$$

where we introduced $\hat{x}_t = \int_0^t K(t,s;\theta_2)d\tilde{y}_s(\theta_2) = E(x_t(\theta_2)|\,\mathcal{F}_t^{\tilde{y}(\theta_2)})$ and

$$\hat{\hat{x}}_t = \int_0^t K(t,s;\theta_1)d\tilde{y}_s(\theta_2). \qquad (13)$$

$\hat{\hat{x}}_t$ represents thus the correct observations fed through the wrong filter kernel. Next we employ the innovation process of the underlying dynamical system w.r.t. θ_2 (cf.(9)), i.e.

$$\hat{\nu}_t(\theta_2) = \tilde{y}_t(\theta_2) - \int_0^t E(F^{-1}Cx_s(\theta_2)|\,\mathcal{F}_s^{\tilde{y}(\theta_2)})ds.$$

An elementary algebraic calculation therefore yields by the basic properties of Ito's stochastic integral $KL^{IND}(\theta_2;\theta_1) =$

$$E\Big(\int_0^T F^{-1}C(\hat{x}_t - \hat{\hat{x}}_t)\cdot d\hat{\nu}_t(\theta_2)\Big) + \frac{1}{2}\int_0^T E(\|F^{-1}C(\hat{x}_t - \hat{\hat{x}}_t)\|_k^2)dt$$

$$= \frac{1}{2}\int_0^T E(\|F^{-1}C(\hat{x}_t - \hat{\hat{x}}_t)\|_k^2)dt.$$

With the notion of U_θ as the sensitivity of the filter (see above) we have

$$\hat{x}_t - \hat{\hat{x}}_t = \int_0^t U_\theta d\tilde{y}_s(\theta_2) = \int_0^t U_\theta F^{-1} Cx_s(\theta_2) ds + \int_0^t U_\theta dv_s .$$

Using the independence of the processes $x(\theta_2)$ and v one thus ends up with the final equality. □

As has already been emphasized in the introduction above, the conceptual insight obtained in Lemma 1 lies in the emergence of the sensitivity expression $U_\theta(t,s)$. The topic of sensitivity in systems theory has been discussed e.g. in [9], and [10]. By these accounts we find that the sensitivity of the filter is an indicator of the performance of the state estimator. Bearing in mind the representations found in Lemma 1 we now derive a proposition which clearly shows how sensitivity in our sense also influences the discrimination information in the indirect measurements. To obtain a unified representation of the relation between KL^D and KL^{IND} and to avoid too lengthy calculations we restrict ourselves to the case where the difference of the system matrices, i.e. $A(\theta_2) - A(\theta_1)$ is regular.

Proposition 1: Let $A(\theta_2) - A(\theta_1)$ be regular. Then:

$$KL^{IND}(\theta_2;\theta_1) = KL_T^{IND}(\theta_2;\theta_1) \leq$$

$$\|F^{-1}C\|^2_{\mathcal{L}(\mathbb{R}^n,\mathbb{R}^k)} \cdot \|(A(\theta_2)-A(\theta_1))^{-1}D\|^2_{\mathcal{L}(\mathbb{R}^n)} \cdot [\sup_{t\in[0,T]} \int_0^t \|F^{-1}CU_\theta(t,s)\|_{\mathcal{L}(\mathbb{R}^k)} ds]^2 \cdot KL_T^D(\theta_2;\theta_1)$$

$$+ \frac{1}{2} T \cdot \sup_{t\in[0,T]} \int_0^t \|F^{-1}CU_\theta(t,s)\|^2_{\mathcal{L}(\mathbb{R}^k)} ds \qquad (14)$$

Proof:

First, we obtain the bounds

$$0 \leq E(\|\int_0^t F^{-1}CU_\theta(t,s)F^{-1}Cx_s(\theta_2)ds\|_k^2) \leq$$

$$E([\int_0^t \|F^{-1}CU_\theta(t,s)\|_{\mathcal{L}(\mathbb{R}^k)} \|F^{-1}Cx_s(\theta_2)\|_k ds]^2) =$$

$$\int_0^t\int_0^t \|F^{-1}CU_\theta(t,s)\|_{\mathcal{L}(\mathbb{R}^k)} \cdot \|F^{-1}CU_\theta(t,u)\|_{\mathcal{L}(\mathbb{R}^k)} \cdot E(\|F^{-1}Cx_s(\theta_2)\|_k \cdot \|F^{-1}Cx_u(\theta_2)\|_k) ds du$$

$$\leq [\int_0^t \|F^{-1}CU_\theta(t,s)\|_{\mathcal{L}(\mathbb{R}^k)} \cdot (E(\|F^{-1}Cx_s(\theta_2)\|_k^2))^{1/2} ds]^2$$

by Cauchy-Schwarz inequality.

Elementary linear algebra yields

$$E(\| F^{-1}Cx_s(\theta_2)\|_k^2) = \sum_{j=1}^{k} E(\langle c_j, x_s(\theta_2)\rangle_n^2) \quad \text{for some}$$

c_j, $j=1,\dots,k$, $\in \mathbb{R}^n$, $\langle\cdot,\cdot\rangle_n$ denoting the scalar product in $\mathbb{R}^n$.

Also, the covariance of $x_s(\theta_2)$ is given by

$$\int_0^s e^{A(\theta_2)u} DD^* e^{A(\theta_2)^* u} du,$$

which means that for any $c \in \mathbb{R}^n$

$$E(\langle c, x_s(\theta_2)\rangle_n^2) = \int_0^s \|D^* e^{A(\theta_2)^* u} c\|_n^2 \, du.$$

Obviously the integrand is nonnegative thus $E(\| F^{-1}Cx_s(\theta_2)\|_k^2)$ is monotonically increasing.

Summarizing we have

$$0 \leq E(\| \int_0^t F^{-1}CU_\theta(t,s)F^{-1}Cx_s(\theta_2)ds\|_k^2) \leq$$

$$E(\| F^{-1}Cx_t(\theta_2)\|_k^2) \cdot [\int_0^t \| F^{-1}CU_\theta(t,s)\|_{\mathcal{L}(\mathbb{R}^k)} ds]^2 \tag{15}$$

The stated inequality follows now easily since

$$\| D^{-1}(A(\theta_2) - A(\theta_1))x\|_n \geq \|(A(\theta_2) - A(\theta_1))^{-1}D\|_{\mathcal{L}(\mathbb{R}^n)} \|x\|_n \quad \text{for all } x \in \mathbb{R}^n.$$

□

<u>Remarks:</u>

1) The basic properties of conditional expectation imply that

$$E(\| F^{-1}Cx_t(\theta_2)\|_k^2) = E(\| F^{-1}C(x_t(\theta_2) - \hat{x}_t(\theta_2))\|_k^2) + E(\| F^{-1}C\hat{x}_t(\theta_2)\|_k^2).$$

Inserting this decomposition in the integral

$$\frac{1}{2} \int_0^T E \, \| \int_0^t F^{-1}CU_\theta(t,s)F^{-1}Cx_s(\theta_2)ds\|_k^2 dt$$

leads to the estimate

$$\leq [\frac{1}{2} \int_0^T E(\| F^{-1}C(x_t(\theta_2) - \hat{x}_t(\theta_2))\|_k^2 dt$$

$$+ \frac{1}{2} \int_0^T E(\| F^{-1}C\hat{x}_t(\theta_2)\|_k^2)dt] \cdot [\sup_{0\leq t\leq T} \int_o^t \| F^{-1}CU_\theta(t,s)\|_{\mathcal{L}(\mathbb{R}^k)} ds]^2 \tag{16}$$

as in (15) above. Now, a result by Duncan [7] and several others shows that the term $J_T = \frac{1}{2} \int_0^T E(\| F^{-1}C(x_t(\theta_2) - \hat{x}_t(\theta_2))\|_k^2)dt$

actually represents the <u>mutual information</u> in the process $F^{-1}y(\theta_2)$ about the process $F^{-1}Cx(\theta_2)$, an idea extending Shannon's original concept to continuous time Gaussian processes. Obviously we thus obtain another sort of an upper bound for $KL^{IND}(\theta_2;\theta_1)$ inserting (16) in the appropriate places. Since there is an explicit innovation representation for $\hat{x}_t(\theta_2)$ i.e.

$\hat{x}_t(\theta_2) = \int_o^t e^{\theta_2 A(t-s)} P(s;\theta_2)C^*(FF^*)^{-1}d\hat{\nu}_s(\theta_2)$, the expression

$E(\| F^{-1}Cx_t(\theta_2)\|_k^2)$ is easily evaluated.

2) In the one-dimensional case

$$dx_t(\theta) = \theta x_t dt + dw_t, \; dy_t(\theta) = \rho x_t(\theta)dt + dv_t \tag{17}$$

more explicit expressions concerning the sensitivity terms are easy to derive. In fact, by virtue of the stabilizing effect of the filter we assume for simplicity the stationary filter situation. Then the kernels are given by

$K(t,s;\theta) = \rho\gamma(\theta,\rho)\exp((\theta-\rho^2\gamma(\theta,\rho))(t-s))$ where $\gamma(\theta;\rho) = \rho^{-2}((\theta^2+\rho^2)^{1/2}+\theta)$ is the stationary filter gain.

Since according to the mean value theorem

$U_\theta(t,s) = \frac{\partial}{\partial\theta} K(t,s;\theta)|_{\theta=\xi(t,s;\theta_1,\theta_2)} \cdot (\theta_2-\theta_1)$ we differentiate the kernel w.r.t. θ thus obtaining

$\frac{\partial}{\partial\theta} K(t,s;\theta) = \rho^{-1}((\theta^2+\rho^2)^{-1/2}\theta+1)(1+(s-t)\theta)\exp(-(\theta^2+\rho^2)^{1/2}(t-s))$.

Setting $m = \min(\theta_1,\theta_2)$, $\overline{m} = \min(|\theta_1|,|\theta_2|)$, $M = \max(\theta_1,\theta_2)$, $\overline{M} = \max(|\theta_1|,|\theta_2|)$ one gets

$|U_\theta(t,s)| \leq |\theta_2-\theta_1|\rho^{-1}((M^2+\rho^2)^{-1/2}M+1)(1+(t-s)\overline{M})\exp(-(\overline{m}^2+\rho^2)^{1/2}(t-s))$.

This entails

$$\int_0^t |U_\theta(t,s)|ds \leq |\theta_2-\theta_1|\rho^{-1}((M^2+\rho^2)^{-1/2}M+1)\ (1+(\bar{m}^2+\rho^2)^{-1/2})\cdot(\bar{m}^2+\rho^2)^{-1/2}.$$

Thus the factor in front of $KL_T^D(\theta_2;\theta_1)$ in the equality in Prop. 1, i.e. $\rho^4(\theta_2-\theta_1)^{-2}(\int_0^t |U_\theta(t,s)|ds)^2$, is in many cases easily seen to be considerably smaller than unity.

Furthermore, in the one-dimensional case it is seen that $KL^D(\theta_2;\theta_1) = \frac{1}{2}(\theta_2-\theta_1)^2 \cdot$ FISHER'S INFORMATION at θ_2, which indicates a special case of a more general phenomenon (see [6]).

3) The results of Liese in [11] giving bounds for error probabilities in terms of the Hellinger integral, defined as $\int_X f_{\theta_1}^{1/2} f_{\theta_2}^{1/2}\,d\mu$, (using the notations introduced in section 1) can also be applied to the type of processes considered here. In addition, the well known inequality $e^{-1/2\ KL(\theta_2;\theta_1)} \leq \int_X f_{\theta_1}^{1/2} f_{\theta_2}^{1/2}\,d\mu$ relates the KL-number and the Hellinger integral. The results and objectives of this paper are, however, different from those of Liese's work. □

Finally we present an extension which is concerned with a stochastic distributed parameter system $\{x_t(\theta) \mid 0 \leq t \leq T\}$, i.e. the system process attains values in an infinite-dimensional space. Mathematically this is described as a solution of a stochastic partial differential equation (SPDE) in a separable Hilbert space H where we adopt the formalism developed e.g. in [12]. As solution of the SPDE

$$dx_t(\theta) = A(\theta)x_t(\theta)dt + D\,dw_t,\quad x_o(\theta) = 0 \tag{18}$$

we shall take the stochastic integral

$x_t(\theta) = \int_0^t S_{t-s}(\theta)D\,dw_s$, where $(S_t(\theta))_{t\geq 0}$ denotes the C_o-semigroup (in H) generated by the infinitesimal operator $A(\theta), \theta \in \Theta$; $D \in \mathcal{L}(H)$, D^{-1} exists. $w = \{w_t \mid 0 \leq t \leq T\}$ is an H-valued Wiener process with associated nuclear (and positive-definite) covariance operator W. The observation equation is the same as in the finite-dimensional case where now of course $C \in \mathcal{L}(H, \mathbb{R}^k)$. We can then establish the following

<u>Proposition 2:</u> Let there exist constants $a,b > 0$ such that for all $t \in [0,T]$

$$E(\exp(a \cdot \| W^{-1/2}D^{-1}(A(\theta_2)-A(\theta_1))x_t(\theta_2)\|_H^2) \leq b < \infty\ . \tag{19}$$

Then the processes $\{x_t(\theta_i) \mid 0 \leq t \leq T\}$, i=1,2, induce equivalent measures on C([0,T],H) and

$$\text{(i)}\quad KL_T^D(\theta_2;\theta_1) = \frac{1}{2}\int_0^T E(\| W^{-1/2}D^{-1}(A(\theta_2) - A(\theta_1))x_t(\theta_2)\|_H^2)dt. \tag{20}$$

If furthermore $(A(\theta_2) - A(\theta_1))^{-1}$ exists and $(A(\theta_2) - A(\theta_1))^{-1}DW^{1/2}$ is a bounded operator then

$$\text{(ii)}\quad KL_T^{IND}(\theta_2;\theta_1) \leq$$

$$\| F^{-1}C\|^2_{\mathcal{L}(H,\mathbb{R}^k)} \|(A(\theta_2) - A(\theta_1))^{-1}DW^{1/2}\|^2_{\mathcal{L}(H)} [\sup_{t\in[0,T]} \int_0^t \|F^{-1}CU_\theta(t,s)\|_{\mathcal{L}(\mathbb{R}^k)} ds]^2\, KL_T^D(\theta_2;\theta_1)$$

$$+ \frac{1}{2} T\cdot \sup \cdot \int_0^t \|F^{-1}CU_\theta(t,s)\|^2_{\mathcal{L}(\mathbb{R}^k)} ds \tag{21}$$

Proof: We omit a detailed proof in view of the analogy with that of proposition 1. As far as (i) above is concerned we only mention that one has to exploit a Girsanov-formula for infinite-dimensional state space which was given e.g. in [5]. □

References:

[1] J.C. Cartledge: "Measures of Information for Continuous Observations", IEEE Transactions on Information Theory Vol. IT-29, pp.256-267, 1983

[2] J.K. Tugnait: "Global Identification of Continuous Time Systems with Unknown Noise Covariance", IEEE Transactions on Information THeory Vol. IT-28, pp. 531-536, 1982

[3] J. Csiszár: "Information-type measures of difference of probability distributions and indirect observations", Studia Mathematicarum Hungarica Vol. 2, pp. 299-318, 1967

[4] S. Kullback: "Information Theory and Statistics", New York: Wiley 1959

[5] W. Loges: "Girsanov's theorem in Hilbert space and an application to the statistics of Hilbert space-valued stochastic differential equations", Stochastic Processes and their Applications, Vol. 17, pp. 243-263, 1984

[6] K. Ferentinos and T. Papaioannou: "New Parametric Measures of Information", Information and Control 51, pp. 193-208, 1981

[7] T. Duncan: "On the calculation of mutual information", SIAM Journal of Applied Mathematics Vol. 19, pp. 215-220, 1970

[8] R.S. Liptser and A.N. Shiryayev: "Statistics of Random Processes I", New York: Springer 1977

[9] J.W. Brewer: "Matrix Calculus and the Sensitivity Analysis of Linear Dynamic Systems", IEEE Transactions on Automatic Control Vol. AC-23, pp. 748-751, 1978

[10] J.C. Reid, P.S. Maybeck, R.B. Asher, J.D. Dillow: "An algebraic representation of parameter sensitivity in linear time-invariant systems", J. Franklin Systems Vol. 301, 1972

[11] F. Liese: "Hellinger Integrals of Diffusion Processes", Forschungsberichte der Friedrich-Schiller Universität Jena Nr. 83/39, Jena 1983

[12] R.F. Curtain and A.J. Pritchard: "Infinite Dimensional Linear System Theory", Lecture Notes in Control and Information Sciences, New York: Springer 1978

NONSTANDARD ENERGY FORMS AND
DIFFUSIONS ON MANIFOLDS AND FRACTALS

by

Tom Lindstrøm
Department of Mathematics
University of Trondheim
N-7034 Trondheim-NTH, Norway

1. Introduction.

Consider the bilinear form F_0 defined on the set $C_0^1(\mathbf{R}^d)$ of continuously differentiable functions of compact support by

$$(1.1) \qquad F_0(f,g) = \frac{1}{2}\int_{\mathbf{R}^d} \nabla f\cdot\nabla g \, dx ,$$

and let the <u>Newtonian energy form</u> F be its closure. The selfadjoint operator generating F is $-\frac{1}{2}\Delta$ which also happens to be the infinitesimal generator of Brownian motion. More generally, if we replace F_0 by

$$(1.2) \qquad E_0(f,g) = \frac{1}{2}\int_{\mathbf{R}^d} \nabla f\cdot\nabla g \, dm ,$$

where m is of the form $dm = \varphi^2 dx$ for a function φ with "reasonable" zeros and singularities, it is well known that the closure E of E_0 in $L^2(\mathbf{R}^d, dm)$ generates a diffusion process on $\mathbf{R}^d$ of a special kind often referred to as a "distorted Brownian motion" (see Albeverio, Höegh-Krohn, Streit [2], [3] and Fukushima [6]).

An interesting feature of this relationship between energy forms and processes is that it makes it possible to define a class of diffusions on the space $\mathbf{R}^d$ solely in terms of the natural geometric measure dx on the space. It is easy to think of possible generalizations: If M is a differentiable submanifold of $\mathbf{R}^d$ and m is the volume measure on M, will (1.2) then generate a diffusion on M? Or even more generally, if m is the Hausdorff measure on an irregular (fractal) set M, does (1.2) generate what may be called a diffusion on M?

The obvious answer is that these questions do not make sense! In asking them, we are tacitly assuming that E_0 can be extended to a closed form on $L^2(M,dm)$, which it can not for the obvious reason that E_0 itself is not a form on $L^2(M,dm)$ (since two functions which are identified in $L^2(M,dm)$ may have different gradients on M). For manifolds this problem is easily circumvented; just restrict all functions and gradients to the manifold and consider the form

$$(1.3) \qquad E_0(f,g) = \frac{1}{2}\int_M \langle df,dg\rangle\, dm \quad \text{for} \quad f,g \in C_0^1(M)$$

Now everything makes sense, and the closure of E_0 defines a diffusion on M (even if we replace m by a reasonable measure of the form $\varphi^2 dm$, see Fukushima [6]). However, to pass from (1.2) to (1.3) we need a differentiable structure on M, and hence this approach does not work for fractals and other irregular sets.

The purpose of the present paper is to suggest an alternative approach based on the theory of nonstandard Dirichlet forms developed in Chapter 5 of [1]. As we shall see, this theory leads to a general method for turning non-closable forms into closed forms, which - as a particular example - turns (1.2) into the closure of (1.3) in the differentiable manifold case. The idea is to use the same procedure for fractals; first to turn (1.2) into a closed form, and then to construct a diffusion on the fractal.

Let me say a few words about the organization of the paper. In the next section, I briefly sketch the basic theory for nonstandard Dirichlet forms, and in section 3 I show how they can be turned into closed, standard forms. Section 4 introduces a rescaling trick which is important for fractals, while section 5 explains the technical details hinted at in the discussion above. The last section briefly describes some open problems.

I shall be assuming a basic knowledge of nonstandard analysis; the first ten pages of [8] probably suffice for a fair understanding of what is going on. For more extensive and complete treatments, see [1], [4], [7], [9], [10].

2. Hyperfinite Dirichlet forms.

Consider an internal subset $S = \{s_1, \ldots, s_N\}$ of ${}^*\mathbf{R}^d$, where N is an infinitely large, nonstandard integer. Let $m : S \to {}^*\mathbf{R}_+$ be an internal function; we shall think of m as a measure on S and write

$$(2.1) \qquad m(A) = \sum_{s_i \in A} m(s_i)$$

for all internal $A \subset S$. To simplify notation, let us abbreviate $m(s_i)$ by m_i. Assume that Q is a $N \times N$ transition matrix which is symmetric with respect to m in the sense that

$$(2.2) \qquad m_i q_{ij} = m_j q_{ji}$$

for all i,j. Choose a positive infinitesimal Δt, and let $T = \{0, \Delta t, 2\Delta t, \ldots\}$. We shall be studying the internal Markov chain

$$(2.3) \qquad X : \Omega \times T \to S$$

with initial distribution m and transition matrix Q.

If $l^2(S,m)$ denotes the space of all internal functions $f : S \to {}^*\mathbf{R}$ with the inner product

$$(2.4) \qquad \langle f,g \rangle = \sum_{i=1}^{N} f(i)g(i)m_i \ ,$$

Q defines an operator $Q^{\Delta t}$ on $\ell^2(S,m)$ by

$$(2.5) \qquad Q^{\Delta t}f(i) = \sum_{j=1}^{N} Q_{ij}f(j)m_j .$$

We write $Q^{k\Delta t}$ for the elements $(Q^{\Delta t})^k$ in the semigroup generated by $Q^{\Delta t}$.

The <u>infinitesimal generator</u> of X is the symmetric operator

$$(2.6) \qquad A = \frac{I - Q^{\Delta t}}{\Delta t} \ ,$$

which generates the <u>hyperfinite Dirichlet form</u>

$$(2.7) \qquad \xi(f,g) = \langle Af,g \rangle .$$

Useful approximations to A and ξ are the operators

$$(2.8) \qquad A^{(t)} = \frac{I - Q^t}{t}$$

and the forms

$$(2.9) \qquad \xi^{(t)}(f,g) = \langle A^{(t)}f,g \rangle .$$

The norm $\|A\|$ of the operator A will in general be infinite, and thus there will be elements f and f' in $\ell^2(S,m)$ such that $f \approx f'$ (in the sense that $\|f-f'\| \approx 0$), but $\xi(f,f) \not\approx \xi(f',f')$. Among the different values obtained by applying ξ to infinitely close elements, we shall see that the smallest one is in a certain sense the "right" one. In the following definition, ξ_1 denotes the form

(2.10) $\xi_1(f,g) = \xi(f,g) + \langle f,g \rangle$.

<u>2.1 Definition</u>. An element f in $L^2(S,m)$ belongs to the <u>domain</u> $D[\xi]$ of ξ if $\xi_1(f,f)$ is finite and

(2.11) $^\circ\xi(f,f) \leq {}^\circ\xi(f',f')$

for all $f' \approx f$.

A list of alternative definitions of $D[\xi]$ is provided by

<u>2.2 Lemma</u>. If $^\circ\xi_1(f,f) < \infty$, the following are equivalent:

(i) $f \in D[\xi]$,

(ii) for all $t \approx 0$, $\xi(Q^t f, Q^t f) \approx \xi(f,f)$

(iii) for all $t \approx 0$, $\xi(f - Q^t f, f - Q^t f) \approx 0$

(iv) for all $t \approx 0$, $\xi^{(t)}(f,f) \approx \xi(f,f)$.

This lemma is proved in section 5.1 of [1]. Let me just try to indicate here why it is not very surprising: Think of A as a differential operator; that a function f is not an element of $D[\xi]$ reflects a certain lack of "smoothness" in f. Since Q^t acts as a "smoothing" operator, one would expect this to imply that f and $Q^t f$ are substantially different, and this is exactly what the lemma asserts in three slightly different ways.

The next result is also proved in [1]. It is important because it tells us how to produce elements which are in the domain of ξ.

<u>2.3 Lemma</u>. Assume that $^\circ\xi_1(f,f) < \infty$. Then

(i) $Q^t f \approx f$ for all infinitesimal t,

(ii) for all sufficiently large, infinitesimal t, $Q^t f \in D[\xi]$ and $f \in D[\xi^{(t)}]$.

Let $|\cdot|_1$ be the norm generated by ξ_1, i.e.

(2.12) $\quad |f|_1 = \xi_1(f,f)^{\frac{1}{2}}.$

Note that we always have

(2.13) $\quad |Q^t f|_1 \leq |f|_1;$

this is because

(2.14) $$\begin{aligned}&\xi_1(f,f) - \xi_1(Q^t f, Q^t f)\\ &= \langle (A+I)f,f\rangle - \langle (A+I)Q^t f, Q^t f\rangle\\ &= \langle (A+I)(I-Q^{2t})f,f\rangle \geq 0\end{aligned}$$

since $(A+I)(I-Q^{2\Delta t})$ is positive definite.

A $|\cdot|_1$-Cauchy-sequence is a sequence $\{f_n\}_{n\in\mathbf{N}}$ of elements in $D[\xi]$ such that $^\circ|f_n-f_m| \to 0$ as $n,m\to\infty$. The following proposition is a very simple but also very important observation; it shows that the form ξ is always closed.

2.4 Proposition. Let $\{f_n\}_{n\in\mathbf{N}}$ be a $|\cdot|_1$-Cauchy-sequence of elements in $D[\xi]$. Then there is an $f\in D[\xi]$ such that $^\circ|f-f_n|_1 \to 0$ as $n\to\infty$.

Proof: Let $\{f_n\}_{n\in{}^*\mathbf{N}}$ be an internal extension of $\{f_n\}_{n\in\mathbf{N}}$. Choose an infinitely large element N in ${}^*\mathbf{N}$ such that $^\circ|f_n-f_N| \to 0$ as n goes to infinity in $\mathbf{N}$, and let $f=f_N$. We must show that $f\in D[\xi]$.

Assume not; by lemma 2.2(iii) there exist an infinitesimal t and a positive real number ε such that $|f-Q^t f|_1 > \varepsilon$. Choose $n\in\mathbf{N}$ so large that $|f-f_n|_1 < \frac{\varepsilon}{3}$, and note that by (2.13) this implies $|Q^t f - Q^t f_n| < \frac{\varepsilon}{3}$. But then

$$\varepsilon < |f-Q^t f|_1 \leq$$
$$\leq |f-f_n|_1 + |f_n-Q^t f_n|_1 + |Q^t f_n - Q^t f| \leq$$
$$< \frac{\varepsilon}{3} + \frac{\varepsilon}{3} + \frac{\varepsilon}{3} < \varepsilon,$$

since $f_n \in D[\xi]$ and thus $|f_n-Q^t f_n|_1 \approx 0$.

3. Standard parts of hyperfinite forms.

I shall now briefly explain how hyperfinite forms are turned into standard forms. Let $Fin(\iota^2(S,m))$ be the set of all elements in $\iota^2(S,m)$ with finite norm, and note that the "infinitely close" relation $\approx$ is an equivalence relation on this set. The nonstandard hull of $\iota^2(S,m)$ is the set

$$(3.1)\qquad {}^\circ\iota^2(S,m) = Fin(\iota^2(S,m))/\approx$$

of all equivalent classes given the inner product

$$(3.2)\qquad \langle [f],[g] \rangle = {}^\circ\langle f,g \rangle ,$$

where [f] is the equivalence class of f. It is trivial to check that ${}^\circ\iota^2(S,m)$ is a Hilbert space.

The standard form $\tilde{E}$ induced by ξ is the symmetric bilinear form on ${}^\circ\iota^2(S,m)$ defined by

$$(3.3)\qquad \tilde{E}(v,v) = \inf\{{}^\circ\xi(f,f) \mid f \in v\} ,$$

where we understand $\tilde{E}$ to be undefined if the infimum is infinite. The domain of $\tilde{E}$ is thus the set

$$(3.4)\qquad D[\tilde{E}] = \{v \in {}^\circ\iota^2(S,m) \mid v \cap D[\xi] \neq \emptyset\}.$$

It follows immediately from proposition 2.4 that $\tilde{E}$ is a closed form.

The nonstandard hull is a very large space, and it is often convenient to restrict $\tilde{E}$ to a smaller one of the form $L^2(\mathbf{R}^d,\tilde{m})$. To do this, assume that the internal measure m is reasonably distributed in the sense that

$$(3.5)\qquad {}^\circ m\{s \in S \mid \|s\| < r\} < \infty$$

for all finite r. Let $L(m)$ be the Loeb-measure of m (i.e. the completed measure obtained by applying Caratheodory's extension theorem to the set function $A \to {}^\circ m(A)$ defined for all internal sets $A \subset S$), and define $\tilde{m}$ by

$$(3.6)\qquad \tilde{m}(B) = L(m)(st^{-1}(B)).$$

It is well known that $\tilde{m}$ is a Radon measure on $\mathbf{R}^d$ (see e.g. section 3.4 in [1]).

For all bounded, continuous $f : \mathbf{R}^d \to \mathbf{R}$, define $\tilde{f} \in {}^\circ\ell^2(S,m)$ by

$$(3.7)\qquad \tilde{f} = [{}^*f \restriction S],$$

where ${}^*f\restriction S$ is the restriction of ${}^*f$ to S. The map $f \to \tilde{f}$ is a partial isometry from $L^2(\mathbf{R}^d,\tilde{m})$ to ${}^\circ\ell^2(S,m)$ and extends continuously to all of $L^2(\mathbf{R}^d,\tilde{m})$. An element F of $\tilde{f}$ is called a <u>lifting</u> of f.

The <u>standard part</u> of ξ is the form E defined on $L^2(\mathbf{R}^d,\tilde{m})$ by

$$(3.8)\qquad E(f,f) = \tilde{E}(\tilde{f},\tilde{f}) = \\ = \inf\{{}^\circ\xi(F,F) \mid F \text{ is a lifting of } f\}.$$

It follows immediately from our results above that E is closed. Since ξ is a Markov form, it is easy to check that E has the (sub-)Markov property and hence is a Dirichlet form. This way of producing closed forms as the standard parts of nonstandard forms is at the heart of the paper.

4. Proper scales for transition matrices.

Recall that the Dirichlet form ξ was constructed from the transition matrix Q by defining

$$(4.1) \qquad \xi(f,g) = \frac{1}{\Delta t}\langle (I-Q^{\Delta t})f,g\rangle,$$

where Δt is a positive infinitesimal. Which infinitesimal Δt we choose is obviously important since it determines the timescale of the associated process. It is intuitively clear that if one choice of Δt gives rise to a reasonable process, an infinitely smaller choice will lead to a process which oscillates infinitely fast, while an infinitely larger choice defines a process which hardly moves at all. To make this intuition precise, we must understand how a nonstandard process can be turned into standard one. Let $\overline{\mathbf{R}}^d = \mathbf{R}^d \cup \{\infty\}$ be the one-point compactification of $\mathbf{R}^d$:

4.1 Definition. Let $f: T \to S$ be an internal function and r an element of $\mathbf{R}_+$. The point $a \in \overline{\mathbf{R}}^d$ is the S-right limit of f at r if for all neighborhoods G of a, there is a positive $\delta \in \mathbf{R}$ such that if $r < {}^\circ s < r+\delta$, then $f(s) \in {}^*G$. We shall write

$$(4.2) \qquad a = S - \lim_{s\downarrow r} f(s).$$

The S-left limit $S - \lim_{s\uparrow r} f(s)$ is defined similarly.

An internal process $X: \Omega\times T \to S$ is near-standard if for almost all ω, the path $X(\omega,\cdot)$ has S-right and S-left limits at all $r \in \mathbf{R}_+$. The standard part ${}^\circ X^+$ is defined by

(4.3) $\quad {}^{\circ}X^{+}(\omega,r) = S\text{-}\lim_{s\downarrow r} X(\omega,s).$

Clearly, ${}^{\circ}X^{+}$ is a right-continuous process with left limits. We shall say that X is trivial if almost all the paths of ${}^{\circ}X^{+}$ are constant.

4.2 Definition. An infinitesimal Δt is a proper scale for the transition matrix Q if the associated Markov chain

(4.4) $\quad X:\Omega\times\{0,\Delta t,2\Delta t,\ldots,1\} \to S$

is nearstandard and nontrivial.

If Δt is a proper scale for Q and $\eta/\Delta t$ is finite and non-infinitesimal, then η is also a proper scale for Q, and it is easy to check that all proper scales must be of this form. It is also easy to see that not all transition matrices have proper scales; if, for instance, all elements of S are infinitely close, X is necessarily trivial no matter what Δt is.

Let us take a look at two examples where the proper scales are easy to determine.

4.3 Example. Pick an infinite integer H and let $S = \{0,H^{-1},2H^{-1},\ldots,1\}$. The transition matrix Q is defined by

(4.5) $$q_{ij} = \begin{cases} 0 \text{ if } i \text{ and } j \text{ are not neighbors,} \\ \frac{1}{2} \text{ if } i \text{ and } j \text{ are neighbors and } i \neq 0,1 , \\ 1 \text{ if } i \text{ and } j \text{ are neighbors and } i = 0 \text{ or } 1, \end{cases}$$

and the measure m is given by $m_i = H^{-1}$ if $i \neq 0,1$ and $m_i = \frac{1}{2}H^{-1}$ if $i = 0$ or 1. As everybody has already guessed, a proper scale in this case is $\Delta t = \frac{1}{H^2}$, which makes ${}^{\circ}X^{+}$ a Brownian motion on $[0,1]$ with reflection at the boundary.

The choice of Δt in this example is in accordance with the usual $\Delta x \sim \Delta t^{\frac{1}{2}}$ philosophy for the relationship between the space and time increments of a diffusion. The next example indicates that this philosophy must be modified somewhat when the diffusion is on a fractal.

4.4 Example. The Koch-curve is the fractal with Hausdorff dimension log 4/log 3 obtained by iterating the procedure in Figure 1 infinitely many times. After n steps, the curve consists of 4^n linesegments each of length 3^{-n}.

Figure 1

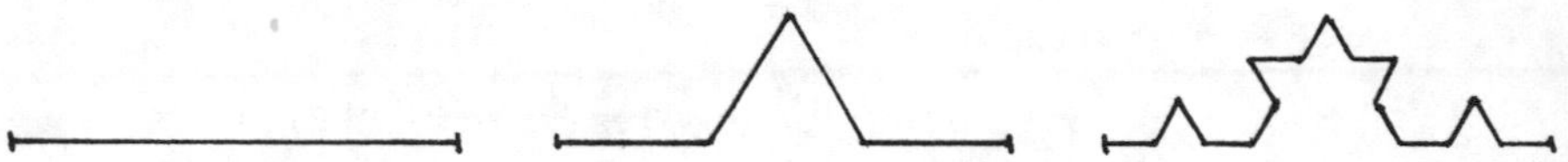

Let us perform the construction in the nonstandard universe and break it off after N steps, where N is an infinitely large integer. The state space S consists of the 4^N+1 vertices of the curve, and we choose the transition matrix Q such that

$$(4.6) \qquad q_{ij} = \begin{cases} 0 \text{ if } i \text{ and } j \text{ are not neighbors,} \\ \frac{1}{2} \text{ if } i \text{ and } j \text{ are neighbors, and } i \text{ isn't an endpoint,} \\ 1 \text{ if } i \text{ and } j \text{ are neighbors, and } i \text{ is an endpoint.} \end{cases}$$

Let $m_i = 4^{-N}$ if i is not an endpoint, and put $m_i = \frac{1}{2}4^{-N}$ if i is an endpoint.

Since the distance between two neighbors in S is 3^{-N}, the $\Delta x \sim \Delta t^{\frac{1}{2}}$ philosophy would lead us to choose $\Delta t = 3^{-2N}$, but it is easy to see that this gives a trivial process. Indeed, using the natural parametrization of S by the set $\{0,4^{-N},2\cdot 4^{-N},\dots,1\}$, we get that the "correct" choice of Δt is 4^{-2N}.

It is often useful to have a criterion which tells us that we have found a proper scale, and which only refers to the form ξ and not to the process X.

4.5 Proposition. Let Q be a hyperfinite transition matrix, Δt a positive infinitesimal, and ξ the associated Dirichlet form. Assume that there is a sequence $\{u_n\}_{n\in\mathbf{N}}$ of internal functions $u_n : S \to {}^*\mathbf{R}$ such that:

(i) $\{u_n\}_{n\in\mathbf{N}}$ separates points in S,

(ii) ${}^\circ\xi_1(u_n,u_n) < \infty$ for all n,

(iii) u_0 is a bounded, quasi-continuous element of $D[\xi]$ and $\xi(u_0,u_0) \neq 0$.

Then Δt is a proper scale for Q.

Let me briefly explain the concepts occuring in this statement. That $\{u_n\}$ separates points in S means that if s and s' are points in S with different standard parts ${}^\circ s$ and ${}^\circ s'$ in $\overline{\mathbf{R}}^d$, then there are neighborhoods G,G' of ${}^\circ s$ and ${}^\circ s'$, respectively, and real numbers $\alpha,\beta,\alpha<\beta$, such that for at least one $i\in\mathbf{N}$, u_i is less than α on one of the neighborhoods and larger than β on the other one. That u_0 is quasi-continuous means that there is an exceptional set $A\subset S$ such that if s and s' are two infinitely close elements in $S-A$, then $u_0(s) \approx u_0(s')$. Finally, a set A is exceptional if there is an infinitesimal $t\in T$ such that for all positive $\varepsilon\in\mathbf{R}$, there exist an internal set $B\supset A$ such that

(4.7) $P\{\omega \mid \text{there is a multiplum } s=kt \text{ of } t \text{ such that } s\leq 1 \text{ and } X(\omega,s)\in B\} \leq \varepsilon.$

Basically, this means that A is never hit by X if we restrict to a sufficiently coarse timeline.

The proof of proposition 4.5 is based on a nonstandard version of Fukushima's decomposition theorem (see [1]) which says that if $u \in D[\xi]$, then

$$(4.8) \qquad u(X) = N_u + M_u,$$

where $N_u : \Omega \times T \to {}^*\mathbf{R}$ is a continuous process with infinitesimal quadratic variation and $M_u : \Omega \times T \to {}^*\mathbf{R}$ is a martingale which is square integrable in the sence that $E(M_u(t)^2)$ is finite for all finite t. Since square integrable martingales have S-right and S-left limits, so has $u(X)$. Moreover, the quadratic variation of $u(X)$ satisfies

$$(4.9) \qquad E([u(X)](t)) = t\xi(u,u), \quad \text{(where } E \text{ denotes expectation)}$$

and since N_u has infinitesimal quadratic variation, this implies that the quadratic variation of M_u satisfies

$$(4.10) \qquad E([M_u](t)) \approx t\xi(u,u).$$

Note that by lemma 2.3, there is an infinitesimal $t \in T$ such that $u_n \in D[\xi]$ for all $n \in \mathbf{N}$, and (replacing ξ by $\xi^{(t)}$ for some sufficiently large infinitesimal t if necessary) it therefore suffices to prove the proposition when all u_n belong to $D[\xi]$, and X hits the set where u_0 fails to be continuous with probability zero.

First, note that since each $u_n(X)$ have S-right and S-left limits, and $\{u_n\}$ separates points, X must be nearstandard. Next, observe that since X doesn't hit the discontinuities of u_0, the nontriviality of X will follow from the nontriviality of $u_0(X)$.

But the latter is an immediate consequence of (4.10) and the assumption that $\xi(u_0,u_0) \neq 0$, and hence proposition 4.5 is proved.

As an illustrative exercise, let us apply proposition 4.5 to our two examples 4.3 and 4.4. In both cases we can let the sequence $\{u_n\}$ consist of a single function u_0. In 4.3, u_0 is simply the identity function $u_0(x) = x$, and in 4.4, $u_0(x_k) = k4^{-N}$ if x_k is the k-th element on the graph counted from the left endpoint.

5. Diffusions on manifolds and fractals.

In this section

$$S = \{(z_1\delta,\ldots,z_d\delta) \in {}^*\mathbf{R}^d \mid z_i \in {}^*\mathbf{Z},\ |z_i| < \delta^{-2} \text{ for all } i\}$$

is a lattice in ${}^*\mathbf{R}^d$ with infinitesimal mesh δ. Let U be the set of all unit vectors in ${}^*\mathbf{R}^d$ of the form $(0,\ldots,\pm 1,\ldots,0)$. Given $s \in S$, $e \in U$ and an internal function $f: S \to {}^*\mathbf{R}$, define

$$(5.1) \qquad D_e f(s) = \frac{f(s+\delta e) - f(s)}{\operatorname{sgn}(e)\delta},$$

where $\operatorname{sgn}(e)$ is the sign of the nonzero component of e. We shall study <u>nonstandard energy forms</u>

$$(5.2) \qquad F(f,g) = \frac{1}{4} \sum_{s\in S} \sum_{e\in U} D_e f(s) D_e f(s) \nu(s),$$

where ν is an internal measure on S - note that since each direction is counted twice, the factor $\frac{1}{2}$ in formula (1.2) has been replaced by $\frac{1}{4}$.

To show that F is a hyperfinite Dirichlet form of the kind we have been studying above, let m be the internal measure on S defined by

$$(5.3) \qquad m(s) = \nu(s) + \frac{1}{4d} \sum_{e \in U} \nu(s+\delta e).$$

Although m and ν are different in general, the measures $\tilde{m} = L(m) \circ st^{-1}$ and $\tilde{\nu} = L(\nu) \circ st^{-1}$ they induce on $\mathbf{R}^d$ are always equal. Define a transition matrix Q over S by

$$(5.4) \qquad q_{s,s'} = \begin{cases} 0 \text{ if } |s-s'| \neq \delta \text{ or } m(s) = 0 \\ \dfrac{\nu(s)+\nu(s')}{4dm(s)} \text{ if } |s-s'| = \delta \text{ and } m(s) \neq 0. \end{cases}$$

If we let

$$(5.5) \qquad \Delta t = \eta \, \frac{\delta^2}{d} ,$$

an easy calculation shows that the Dirichlet form ξ which Q and Δt induce on $\ell^2(S,m)$, satisfies

$$(5.6) \qquad \xi(f,g) = \eta F(f,g).$$

The extra parameter η in (5.5) is very important; it allows us to choose Δt to be a proper scale for Q.

We are now ready to define diffusions x on quite general subsets M of $\mathbf{R}^d$. Assume that M carries a natural, geometric measure $\tilde{m}$, and let ν be an internal measure such that $\tilde{m} = L(\nu) \circ st^{-1}$. Fix a proper scale η for Q; if M is reasonably connected and ν is chosen with a little care, this is usually possible. Let, finally, x be the standard part of the process X generated by ηF. The same construction works if we replace $\tilde{m}$ by a measure of the form $\varphi^2 d\tilde{m}$ where φ and φ^{-1} are bounded.

By construction, x is a right continuous process with left limits taking values in M and having stationary distribution $\varphi^2 d\tilde{m}$.

The justification for referring to it as a diffusion is what happens in the differentiable manifold case. We can then let $\eta = 1$, and the resulting process is (under suitable conditions) the diffusion generated by the form

$$(5.7) \qquad E_0(f,g) = \frac{1}{2} \int_M \langle df, dg \rangle \varphi^2 d\tilde{m}.$$

I shan't prove this rather technical result in the present paper as the following simple example illustrates perfectly what is going on.

5.1 Example. Let $M = \{(x,0) \in \mathbf{R}^2 \mid x \in \mathbf{R}\}$ be the x-axis in $\mathbf{R}^2$, and let $\tilde{m}$ be the one-dimensional Lebesgue measure on M. The natural nonstandard representation of $\tilde{m}$ is the internal measure ν on S given by $\nu(x,0) = \delta$ for all x and $\nu(x,y) = 0$ if $y \neq 0$. Let $\mathcal{F}$ be as in (5.2).

To describe the standard part F of $\mathcal{F}$, pick a continuously differentiable function $f : \mathbf{R}^2 \to \mathbf{R}$ of compact support, and let $\hat{f}$ be defined by $\hat{f}(x,y) = f(x,0)$. Clearly, ${}^*f$ and ${}^*\hat{f}$ are infinitely close in $\mathcal{L}^2(S,m)$, and using lemma 2.2, it is easy to check that ${}^*\hat{f} \in D[\mathcal{F}]$. Hence

$$(5.8) \qquad F(f,f) = {}^\circ\mathcal{F}({}^*\hat{f}, {}^*\hat{f}) = \frac{1}{2} \int \left(\frac{\partial f}{\partial x}\right)^2 d\tilde{m}.$$

What happens is clearly that the infimum in definition (3.3) kills the contribution orthogonal to the manifold.

6. Conclusion.

As the reader has undoubtedly realized, what I have presented above is merely the outline of a theory. There are many questions which remain to be answered, the most urgent, perhaps, concerning the Markovicity of x. In the manifold case, this can be solved fairly easily by using a general method developed in [ ], but for fractals the problem seems much harder. It may come as a surprise to the reader that there should be a problem here at all; after all, ξ generates a standard Dirichlet form E, which in its turn generates an abstract Markov process y on M, and if we can only prove that x and y are equal, we will be done. The problem, of course, is that x and y are not always equal as is easily shown by examples. In fact, we are in the rather ironic situation where we can control the path properties of x and the Markovicity of y, but not vice versa!

Another important question is to relate the scaling factor η in (5.5) to the self-similarity structure of a fractal, and a third (and more ambitious) one is to study the spectrum of the associated Dirichlet form; is there, for instance, a generalization of Weyl's formula for the asymptotic distribution of the eigenvalues of the Laplacian on a manifold?

References

1. S. Albeverio, J.E. Fenstad, R. Høegh-Krohn, T. Lindstrøm: Nonstandard methods in stochastic analysis and mathematical physics, Academic Press, to appear.
2. S. Albeverio, R. Høegh-Krohn, L. Streit: Energy forms, Hamiltonians, and distorted Brownian paths, J. Math. Phys. 18 (1977), 907-917.
3. S. Albeverio, R. Høegh-Krohn, L. Streit: Regularization of Hamiltonians and processes, J. Math. Phys. 21 (1980), 1636-1642.
4. M. Davis: Applied nonstandard analysis, Wiley, 1977.
5. M. Fukushima: Dirichlet forms and Markov processes, North-Holland, 1980.
6. M. Fukushima: Energy forms and diffusion processes, in L. Streit (ed): Mathematics + Physics, Lectures on recent results, World Scientific Publishing Co, 1985, 65-98.
7. A. Hurd, P. Loeb: An introduction to nonstandard real analysis, Academic Press, 1985.

8. T. Lindstrøm: Nonstandard analysis and perturbations of the Laplacian along Brownian paths, to appear in Proceedings of the first BiBoS-symposium, Springer.

9. K. Stroyan, J.M. Bayod: Foundations of infinitesimal stochastic analysis, North-Holland, to appear.

10. K. Stroyan, W.A.J. Luxemburg: Introduction to the theory of infinitesimals, Academic Press, 1976.

SOME RESULTS ON THE EULER AND VLASOV-POISSON FLOWS.

Carlo MARCHIORO, Dipartimento di Matematica,
Università di Trento, 38050 Povo, Trento, Italia

In this lecture we discuss the behaviour for a long time of some systems important in hydrodynamics and in plasma physics. In particular we show some stability conditions for the Euler equations in two dimension and for the Vlasov-Poisson flow when the initial data are non-smooth.

Euler equations.

We consider an ideal incompressible fluid in two dimensions. The Euler equations of motion are:

$$\frac{\partial \omega}{\partial t} + (\underline{u} \cdot \underline{\nabla})\ \omega = 0 \qquad \underline{x} = (x_1, x_2) \in D \subset R^2 \qquad (1)$$

$$\underline{\nabla} \cdot \underline{u} = 0 \quad \text{(Continuity equation)} \qquad (2)$$

$$\underline{n} \cdot \underline{u} = 0 \quad \text{if } \underline{x} \in \partial D \quad \text{or} \quad \underline{u} \underset{|x| \to \infty}{\longrightarrow} 0$$

$$\omega(\underline{x}, 0) = \omega_0$$

where $\omega = \frac{\partial u_2}{\partial x_1} - \frac{\partial u_1}{\partial x_2}$ is the vorticity and $\underline{u} = (u_1, u_2)$ is the velocity.

The nonlinear stability of some stationary states has been investigated by Arnold (1) many years ago. He constructed a Liapunov function by means of energy, vorticity and eventually other conserved quantities and he established sufficient conditions for the stability.

He supposed in an essential way that we deal with smooth quantities and bounded regions. On the other side there are many physical problems of interest in which one or both these conditions are missing. So, we want to generalize the method to non-smooth data.

We write the Euler equations in the weak form

$$\frac{d}{dt}\ \omega_t [\,f\,] = \omega_t [\,\underline{u} \cdot \underline{\nabla}\ f\,] \qquad (3)$$

where f is a smooth test function and

$$\omega_t [\,f\,] = \int d\underline{x}\ f(\underline{x})\ \omega(\underline{x}, t)$$

We don't give here the general statement of the theorems and their proofs, but we only study in some details a particular example.

We consider a vortex patch in R^2. In the stationary state the vorticity is:

$$\bar{\omega}(\underline{x}) = \Lambda_{\Sigma}\rho$$

where $\Lambda_{\Sigma}o$ is the characteristic function of the circle of radious one. Then we perturb $\bar{\omega}$

$$\omega(\underline{x},0) = \Lambda_{\Sigma}$$ where Σ is a bounded region of the same area of the unitary circle but different form. Then we study the time evolution of the vorticity. The new state is very complicated, thin filaments arise and, a priori, they can go to infinity. (There are numerical studies on this subject). However we show that this system is stable in L_1.

Theorem 1. (Wan-Pulvirenti (2)).

For any $\varepsilon>o$, there is $\delta>o$ such that

$$\int_{R^2} |\bar{\omega} - \omega_o|\, d\underline{x} < \delta \tag{4}$$

implies

$$\sup_{t>0} \int_{R^2} |\bar{\omega} - \omega(\underline{x},t)| < o \tag{5}$$

Proof.

The proof is very short. The rotational symmetry implies:

$$I_{\omega} = \int \underline{x}^2\, \omega\, d\underline{x} = \text{constant} \tag{6}$$

We assume it as a Liapunov function.

It is trivial to note

$$I_{\omega_t} - I_{\bar{\omega}} = I_{\omega_o} - I_{\bar{\omega}} \leqslant \text{const.} \int |\bar{\omega} - \omega_o|\, d\underline{x} < \delta\ \text{const.} \tag{7}$$

and we realize that

$$I_{\omega_t} - I_{\bar{\omega}} \geqslant \text{const.} \left(\int |\bar{\omega} - \omega_t|\, d\underline{x} \right)^2 \tag{8}$$

Combining (7) and (8) the theorem is proved.

∎

On the same line we can generalize this result to a stationary state depending only on $|\underline{x}|$ and non increasing.

A similar procedure has been used in the literature to study other cases (3) with convenient symmetries (periodic strip, unbounded strip, rotating sphere)(4).

As a trivial consequence we have the stability of the velocity field. This is called the Eulerian stability. Of course this not exclude that in this system also each particle path can be very unstable (Lagrangian instability).

Vlasov-Poisson Equations.

We use a similar technique to obtain some stability results for non-smooth initial data in an other interesting case.

We consider a continuum of electrons moving in a d-dimensional flat torus

$$T^d = \{ \underline{x} \quad R^d \mid 0 < x_i < 1 \}$$

The electron interact via the Coulomb potential. A spatially symmetric positively charged background is added so that the whole system is neutral. The Vlasov-Poisson equations in the weak form are:

$$\frac{d}{dt} f_t [g] - f_t[\underline{v} \cdot \nabla_{\underline{x}} g] - f_t[\nabla_{\underline{x}} \Phi_t \cdot \nabla_{\underline{v}} g] = 0 \qquad (9)$$

where $g(\underline{x},\underline{v})$ is a smooth test function.

$$\Delta_{\underline{x}} \Phi_t (\underline{x}) = - \rho(\underline{x},t) \qquad (10)$$

$$f_t [g] = \int_{T^d} d\underline{x} \int_{R^d} d\underline{v} \; g(\underline{x},\underline{v}) \, f_t(\underline{x},\underline{v})$$

$$\rho(\underline{x},t) = 1 - \int_{R^d} d\underline{v} \; f_t(\underline{x},\underline{v})$$

Here $f_t(\underline{x},\underline{v})$ is the distribution function.

The physical ideas for the non-linear stability of the stationary states are very old, but only recently a rigorous proof has been given (5). It depends on the regularity of the problem. We want to generalize here for non-smooth data.

We consider stationary states of the form:

$$f_s(\underline{x},\underline{v}) = \overline{f} (|\underline{v}|)$$

Theorem 2. (6)

For any M 0 we define

$$F (f,M) = \{f| \int_{R^d} |f - f_s| \; v^2 \; d\underline{v} \leqslant M \} \qquad (11)$$

Let $\overline{f}$ be a bounded nonincreasing function such that $v^2\,\overline{f}(v) \quad L_1(R^+)$ for d=1,2 and $\overline{f}$ has compact support for d=3 . Then for any $\varepsilon>o$ it exists $\delta>o$ such that for all $f_o \in L_\infty \cap F(f_s,M)$ the condition

$$|f_o - f_s|_{L_1} \tag{12}$$

implies

$$\sup_{t\in R} |f_t - f_s|_{L_1} \tag{13}$$

Proof.

We sketch the proof. We note that it is conserved the total energy of the system:

$$E(f_t) = T(f_t) + U(f_t) \tag{14}$$

where

$$T(f_t) = (1/2) \int_{T^d} d\underline{x} \int_{R^d} d\underline{v} \; v^2 \; f_t \qquad \text{(kinetic energy)} \tag{15}$$

$$U(f_t) = (1/2) \int_{T^d} d\underline{x} \; |\underline{\nabla}_{\underline{x}} \; \Phi_t|^2 \qquad \text{(potential energy)} \tag{16}$$

We use $T(f_t)$ as Liapunov function and we control its growth using the positivity of $U(f_t)$.

In fact

$$\begin{aligned} T(f_t) - T(f_s) &\leq T(f_t) + U(f_t) - T(f_s) = \\ &= T(f_o) + U(f_o) - T(f_s) - U(f_s) \leq g(|f_o - f_s|_{L_1}) \end{aligned} \tag{17}$$

where $g(z)$ is a positive nonincreasing function. It easy to show that

$$\lim_{z\to o} g(z) = o \tag{18}$$

Moreover we control $|f_t - f_s|_{L_1}$ in terms of $T(f_t) - T(f_s)$ as in the Euler equation. (We use here the Liouville theorem to show that the fluid is incompressible in the phase space).

▨

References.

(1) Arnold V.

Dokl. Mat. Nauk, 162 , 773 (1965)

Jour. de Mecanique, 5, 29 (1966)

Ann. Inst. Fourier, 16 (1966)

Am. Math. Soc. Transl., 79, 267 (1969)

"Mathematical Methods of Classical Mechanics" Graduate Texets in Math.

N.60 ,Springer Verlag (1978)

(2) Wan Y.H., Pulvirenti M.,
Commun.Math.Phys.,99 435 (1985)

(3) Benfatto G., Marchioro C., Pulvirenti M., Vortex methods in planar fluid dynamics. Proc. of "Applications af Mathematics in Technology" Roma. Stuttgart: G.B.Teubner 1984

(4) C.Marchioro, Pulvirenti M.,
Commun.Math.Phys. 100, 343 (1985)
Caprino S., Marchioro C.,
"On nonlinear stability of stationary planar Euler flows in an unbounded strip" Nonlinear Anal. (in press)

(5) Holm D.D, Marsden J.E., Ratio T., Weinstein A.,
Nonlinear Stability of Fluid and Plasma Equilibria"
Physics Reports (in press)

(6) Marchioro C., Pulvirenti M.,
A note on the nonlinear stability of a spatially symmetric Vlasov-Poisson flow"
Math.Met.Appl. Sci. (in press).

DIRICHLET FORMS DEFINED BY RIEMANNIAN FLAGS AND APPLICATIONS

by J. Marion (Marseille-Luminy)

Introduction . The original motivation of this work I have done in common with D. Testard was to enlarge the class of the so-called energy representations of the current group $\mathcal{D}(X,G)$ of G - valued and compactly supported smooth mappings on X , where X is a Riemannian manifold and G a compact semisimple Lie group (see [7, 12, 2]).

In particular we had need of nice positive definite inner product of L_2 - type on the space $\mathcal{D}_1(X,\mathbb{R})$ of scalar smooth 1 - forms on X with compact support. Of course, each C^∞ Riemannian structure on X gives rise, in a natural fashion, to such a scalar product, and, equally, to a scalar product on $C_0^\infty(X)$ given by :

$$\varepsilon(f,g) = \sum_{i,j=1}^{\dim(X)} \int_X A_{ij}(x) \frac{\partial f}{\partial x_i} \frac{\partial g}{\partial x_j} dx \quad , \quad \text{where } A = (A_{ij}) \text{ is a}$$

positive definite symmetric $\dim(X) \times \dim(X)$ matrix of C^∞ functions on X and dx is the volume measure on X . In this particular case it is known that, locally, ε is a closable symmetric form (see e.g. [4]) and that two such forms ε and ε' with $\varepsilon \neq \varepsilon'$ give rise to disjoint Gaussian measures on the distribution space $\mathcal{D}'(X)$; these two results play a central role in the study of the irreducibility of the corresponding energy representations, (see e.g. [2, 12]).

The concept of Riemannian flag, which generalizes the classical concept of flag, allows us to get new nice scalar products on $\mathcal{D}_1(X,\mathbb{R})$ and on $C_0^\infty(X)$, having the same properties about closability and disjonction of associated Gaussian measures. So we can apply the method developped in [12] and improved in [2] in order to get new irreducible energy representations of $\mathcal{D}(X,G)$ in the case $\dim(X) \geq 2$.

In order to facilitate the notations, and the clarity of this report we shall always assume that $X = X_n$ is a bounded open domain in $\mathbb{R}^n$, $n \geq 2$.

I. <u>Riemannian flags and associated Euclidean structures.</u>

a) Riemannian flags of X.

Let $X = X_n$ be a bounded open domain in $\mathbb{R}^n$, $n \geq 2$; without loss of generality we shall suppose that 0 belongs to X_n. For each integer s with $1 \leq s \leq n$ we consider the non empty open set X_s in $\mathbb{R}^s$ given by :

(1) $X_s = \{x^s = (x_1,\dots,x_s) \in \mathbb{R}^s \,/\, (x_1,\dots,x_s, 0,\dots,0) \in X_n\}$;

we consider also a C^1 - Riemannian structure on X_s given by a $s \times s$ positive definite symmetric matrix $A^s = (A^s_{i,j})$ of C^1 - functions on X_s, and such that :

(2) $0 < m_s \mathbb{1}_s \leq A^s(x) \leq M_s \mathbb{1}_s$, $\forall\, x \in X_s$,

where $\mathbb{1}_s$ denotes the unit $s \times s$ matrix, $0 < m_s \leq M_s$ are strictly positive real numbers, and $\leq$ denoting the usual order on symmetric operators.

Definition 1. Let k be an integer such that $1 \leq k \leq n$; the family $F = (X_s, A^s)_{k \leq s \leq n}$ will be called a Riemannian flag of $X = X_n$.

Of course two Riemannian flags $F = (X_s, A^s)_{k \leq s \leq n}$ and $F' = (X_s, A'^s)_{k' \leq s \leq n}$ are equal if and only if $k = k'$, $A^s = A'^s$ for all s such that $k \leq s \leq n$.

b) Euclidean structures on $\mathcal{D}_1(X,\mathbb{R})$ and $C_0^\infty(X,\mathbb{R})$ associated with a Riemannian flag.

Let $F = (X_s, A^s)_{k \leq s \leq n}$ be a Riemannian flag of X. For each s such that $k \leq s \leq n$ let us define the positive definite symmetric bilinear form ε_s on $C_0^\infty(X_s,\mathbb{R})$ by :

$$(3) \qquad \varepsilon_s (u,v) = \sum_{i,j=1}^{s} \int_{X_s} A^s_{i,j} (x^s) \frac{\partial u}{\partial x_i} \frac{\partial v}{\partial x_j} dx^s \quad ,$$

where dx^s denotes the Lebesgue measure on X_s , and for all f in $C_0^\infty (X_n , \mathbb{R})$ let $f^{(s)}$ be the element of $C_0^\infty (X_s , \mathbb{R})$ given by :

$$(4) \qquad f^{(s)} (x^s) = f (x_1, \ldots, x_\varepsilon, 0, \ldots, 0)$$

To the Riemannian flag F of X are associated the scalar product E_F on $\mathcal{D}_1 (X, \mathbb{R})$ and ε_F on $C_0^\infty (X, \mathbb{R}) = \mathcal{D} (X, \mathbb{R})$, such that, for all f_1, f_2 in $\mathcal{D} (X, \mathbb{R})$:

$$(5) \qquad E_F (df_1 , df_2) = \varepsilon_F (f_1, f_2) = \sum_{s=k}^{n} \varepsilon_s (f_1^{(s)} , f_2^{(s)}) .$$

We note that, in the case $k = n$, one has $F = (X_n, A^n)$, and ε_F is reduced to the usual scalar product on $\mathcal{D} (X, \mathbb{R})$ coming from the C^1 - Riemannian structure A^n .

We have now :

PROPOSITION 1 : Let F be a Riemannian flag on $X = X_n$, $n \geq 2$; the positive definite symmetric bilinear form ε_F , with domain containing $\mathcal{D} (X, \mathbb{R})$ is closable in $L^2 (X_n, \mathbb{R}, dx^n)$.

Remark 1 : The above result was proved in [6] ; it can be derived also from [4], § 2.1 . In [6] it is also proved that the forms of the type

$$\varepsilon (f_1, f_2) = \sum_{i=1}^{p} \varepsilon_{s_i} (f_1^{(s_i)} , f_2^{(s_i)})$$

with $1 \leq s_1 < s_i < \ldots < s_{i_p} = n$ are generally not closable when $s_{i+1} \neq s_i + 1$.

As a direct consequence of proposition 1 and well-known results about closable positive forms and Dirichlet Laplacians on bounded open sets (See e.g. [4]), one gets :

COROLLARY. Let F be a Riemannian flag of X ; there exists a self-adjoint operator Δ_F on $L^2(X, \mathbb{R}; dx^n)$ with domain containing $\mathcal{D}(X, \mathbb{R})$, and such that for all f_1, f_2 in $\mathcal{D}(X, \mathbb{R})$: $\epsilon_F(f_1, f_2) = (f_1, \Delta_F f_2)$, where $(\ ,\ )_{L^2}$ is the scalar product in $L^2(X, \mathbb{R}; dx^n)$.

Moreover :

a) There exists a strictly positive real number α such that $\Delta_F \geq \alpha \mathbb{1}$,

b) ϵ_F and $\epsilon_F + (\ ,\ )_{L^2}$ define equivalent norms on $\mathcal{D}(X, \mathbb{R})$.

II. Gaussian measures associated to Riemannian flags.

a) Let F be a Riemannian flag of $X = X_n$, $n \geq 2$, and let $\mathcal{D}'(X, \mathbb{R})$ be the dual space of the nuclear space $\mathcal{D}(X, \mathbb{R})$. The function $f \to \exp\{-\frac{1}{2}\epsilon_F(f, f)\}$ is a continuous function of positive type ; from the Bochner - Minloss theorem it follows that there exists a Gaussian measure μ_F on $\mathcal{D}'(X, \mathbb{R})$ whose Fourier transform is given by :

$$(6) \qquad f \to \tilde{\mu}_F(f) = \int_{\mathcal{D}'(X, \mathbb{R})} e^{i<\chi, f>} d\mu_F(\chi) = \exp\{-\tfrac{1}{2}\epsilon_F(f, f)\} .$$

b) An important result about the disjointness of Gaussian measures μ_{F_1}, μ_{F_2} associated to two different Riemannian flags F_1, F_2 is the following, which asserts that μ_{F_1} and μ_{F_2} are not only disjoint, but, in fact, uniformily disjoint with respect to sets of finitely supported distributions of order zero of X ; more precisely one has ([10], lemma II-6), δ_x denoting the Dirac distribution with support $\{x\}$:

PROPOSITION 2 . Let F_1 and F_2 be two different Riemannian flags of $X = X_n$, $n \geq 2$. There exists a Borel subset Q in $\mathcal{D}'(X, \mathbb{R})$ such that :

(i) $\mu_{F_1}(Q) = 1$ and $\mu_{F_2}(Q) = 0$;

(ii) $\mu_{F_1}(Q + \lambda\,\delta_x) = 0$ for all x in X and :

- for all non zero real numbers λ if $n \geq 3$,
- for all real numbers λ such that $|\lambda|$ is sufficiently larg if $n = 2$

(iii) $\mu_{F_2}(Q + \lambda\,\delta_x) = 0$ for all x in X and :

- for all real λ if $n \geq 3$,
- for $\lambda = 0$ and all λ such that $|\lambda|$ is sufficiently larg if $n = 2$.

Sketch of the proof :

a) We first prove that μ_{F_1} and μ_{F_2} are disjoint ; in fact it is proved that if T is a symmetric operator satisfying $\varepsilon_F(Tf, f) = \varepsilon_s(f^{(s)}, f^{(s)})$ for all f in $C_0^\infty(X, \mathbb{R})$, then we can find an infinite dimensional subspace of $C_0^\infty(X, \mathbb{R})$ on which $\alpha\,\mathbb{1} \leq T$ with $\alpha > 0$, from which it follows that T cannot be an Hilbert - Schmidt operator ; then, from the Feldmann-Hajek's theorem (see e.g. [5], theorem 7.3), one concludes that μ_{F_1} and μ_{F_2} are mutually singular, and then disjoint.

b) The method used here is a slightly improvement of that used in [2].
Let $F_i = (X_s^i, A^{i,s})_{k_i \leq s \leq n}$, $i = 1,2$, be two Riemannian flags of X, $F_1 \neq F_2$, let ε_s^i be the symmetric bilinear form associated to $(X_s^i, A^{i,s})$ following (3) , let ε_{F_i} be closable form associated to F_i by (5) , $i = 1,2$ and let Δ_{F_i} the corresponding operator of Laplacian type (defined in the corollary of proposition 1) on X with Dirichlet boundary conditions.
We note that, in the case where F is the trivial Riemannian flag $(X, \mathbb{1})$, then $\Delta_F = \Delta_{\mathbb{1}}$ is the classical Laplacian operator, i.e. :

$$(-\Delta_{\mathbb{1}}\, f_1, f_2) = \int_X \sum_{i=1}^{n} \frac{\partial f_1}{\partial x_i} \frac{\partial f_2}{\partial x_j}\, dx \quad .$$

We denote by G^{F_i} the kernel of the inverse of $\{-\Delta_{F_i}\}$ in the case $n \geq 3$, and the kernel of the inverse of $-\Delta_{F_i}(-\Delta_{F_i} + \mathbb{1})^{-2}$ in the case $n = 2$, $i = 1,2$.

We consider the random field ξ given by $\mathbb{E}(\xi^1(x)\,\xi^1(y)) = G^{F_i}(x, y)$, and we define the random field ξ_k, $k > 0$, such that $\xi^1_k = \xi^1 * \varphi_k$ where φ is a given element in $C_0^\infty(\mathbb{R}^n)$ satisfying $\int_{\mathbb{R}^n} \varphi(x)\,dx = 1$, and φ_k is the dilation : $x \to k^n \varphi(kx)$. To the set of random fields $\xi^1_{2^p}$, p running in the set of positive integers, we associate the functions

$G_p^{F_1}(x, y) = \int \varphi_{2^p}(t) \,.\, \varphi_{2^p}(s)\, G^{F_1}(x - t, y - s)\,dt\,ds$, and

$G_p^{\mathbb{1}}(x, y) = \int \varphi_{2^p}(t) \,.\, \varphi_{2^p}(s)\, G^{\mathbb{1}}(x - t, y - s)\,dt\,ds$ where $G^{\mathbb{1}}$ stands for G^{F_i} in the case where F_i is reduced to $(X, \mathbb{1})$: that is to say $G^{\mathbb{1}}$ is the kernel of the inverse of $-\Delta_{\mathbb{1}}$ or $-\Delta_{\mathbb{1}}(-\Delta_{\mathbb{1}} + \mathbb{1})^{-2}$ (following the case $n \geq 3$ or $n = 2$).

Using the estimate :

$$m\, G_p^{\mathbb{1}}(x, 0) \leq G_p^{F_1}(x, x) \leq M\, G_p^{\mathbb{1}}(x, 0), \quad x \in X ,$$

and the fact that the process :

$$x \to |\xi^1_{2^p}(2^{-p} x)| \,/\, (G_p^{\mathbb{1}}(x, 0))^{1/2}$$

has (by [3]) uniformily bounded covariances, it is then proved that, for sufficiently large real b, the set :

$$Q_b = \liminf_p \{\xi \in \mathcal{D}'(X) / |\xi^1_{2^p}(x)| \leq b\, p^{1/2}\, G_p^{\mathbb{1}}(x, 0)^{1/2},\ \forall x \in X\}$$

satisfies the properties of the set Q.

III. Application to the study of energy representations.

1) Energy representations of the current group $\mathcal{D}(X,G)$.

a) Let X be a bounded open subset in $\mathbb{R}^n$, $n \geq 2$, and let G be a compact semisimple Lie group with Lie algebra $\mathcal{G}$ endowed by the natural scalar product coming from the opposite of its Killing form. The current group $\mathcal{D}(X,G)$ is the gauge group consisting of all the G - valued and compactly supported smooth mappings on X . Such a group appears in gauge fields theories, Yang-Mills equations ([11]) , and from the mathematical point of view, is the relevant generalization of the test-functions space for a non commutative theory of distributions ([8, 12]) . In this spirit, irreducible representations of $\mathcal{D}(X,G)$ with typical properties of localization were attended to convenient multiplicative generalizations of the usual distributions.

b) Let $\mathcal{D}_1(X,\mathcal{G}) = \mathcal{D}_1(X,\mathbb{R}) \otimes \mathcal{G}$ be the nuclear space of $\mathcal{G}$ - valued and compactly supported smooth 1 - forms on X , on which $\mathcal{D}(X,G)$ acts by the pointwise adjoint representation : for ω in $\mathcal{D}_1(X,\mathcal{G})$, g in $\mathcal{D}(X,G)$, $V(g)\,\omega$ is the 1 - form :

(7) $\quad x \to \mathrm{Ad}\, g(x) \circ \omega(x)$,

where Ad denotes the adjoint representation of G in $\mathcal{G}$.

Moreover each Riemannian flag F of X gives rise to a scalar product $<\,,\,>_F$ on $\mathcal{D}_1(X,\mathcal{G})$, with corresponding norm $|\,.\,|_F$, defined as the tensor product of the scalar product $E_F(\,,\,)$ on $\mathcal{D}_1(X,\mathbb{R})$ given in (5) , § I , and the natural scalar product on $\mathcal{G}$.
Owing to the unitarity of the adjoint representation of G in $\mathcal{G}$, it follows from (7) that for all g in $\mathcal{D}(X,G)$, the operators $V(g)$ are unitary with respect to $<\,,\,>_F$.

It follows that V is a unitary representation of $\mathcal{D}(X,G)$ in the prehilbertian space $(\mathcal{D}_1(X,\mathcal{G}), <.,.>_F)$, and it is well-known that the mapping :

$$g \to dg \,.\, g^{-1}$$

is a continuous 1 - cocycle for V, usually called the Maurer-Cartan cocycle ([12]) .

Let $\mathcal{H}_F$ be the complex Hilbert completion of $\mathcal{D}_1(X,\mathcal{G})$ with respect to $<,>_F$, and let $e^{\mathcal{H}_F}$ be the symmetric Fock space constructed with $\mathcal{H}_F$ as the one particle space :

$$(8) \qquad e^{\mathcal{H}_F} = \sum_{q \geq 0}^{\oplus} \mathcal{H}_F^{\otimes q, s}$$

where the sum is taken with orthogonal components, $\mathcal{H}_F^{\otimes q,s}$ denoting the space of symmetric n - tensors on $\mathcal{H}_F$.

As it is well-known ([5]), the set of coherent states :

$$(9) \qquad \{e^{\omega} = \bigoplus_{q \geq 0} (n!)^{-1/2}\, \omega^{\otimes q} \;,\; \omega \in \mathcal{H}_F\}$$

is free and total in $e^{\mathcal{H}_F}$.

2) The energy representation U_F .

Following the procedure described in [5, 12] one gets a unitary representation U_F of $\mathcal{D}(X,G)$ in $e^{\mathcal{H}_F}$ in the following way : for all g in $\mathcal{D}(X,G)$ let $U_F(g)$ be the operator on $e^{\mathcal{H}_F}$ defined on the coherent states by :

$$(10) \quad U_F(g)\, e^{\omega} = \exp\{-\tfrac{1}{2}\, |dg \,.\, g^{-1}|_F^2 - <V(g)\,\omega \,, dg\,.\,g^{-1}>_F\}\, e^{V(g)\omega + dg\,.\,g^{-1}}$$

The representation U_F enters in the class of the so-called energy representations ([1,2,9]).

3) Irreducibility and equivalence of the U_F .

a) Two natural questions come immediately :

(i) For a given Riemannian flag F , what can it be said about the irreducibility of U_F ?

(ii) For two different Riemannian flags F_1, F_2 , what can it be said about the unitary equivalence of U_{F_1} and U_{F_2} ?

These two questions were solved in [12] and, with various improvements in [2,9] in the case where the considered flags are trivial : $F = (X, A)$ where A was the matrix of a C^∞ Riemannian structure on X .

b) In [10] we prove that these results can be extended when we consider general Riemannian flags, by using the crucial proposition 2 above and the method developped in [12,2] . More precisely we get :

PROPOSITION 3 : Let F be a Riemannian flag of X , with $n = \dim(X) \geq 2$.

(i) for $n \geq 3$ the energy representation U_F is irreducible.

(ii) for $n = 2$, if for all roots λ of $\mathcal{G}$ (with respect to some Cartan subalgebra of $\mathcal{G}$), their length $|\lambda|$ satisfy $|\lambda| > K_F$, where K_F is some constant depending only on F , then U_F is irreducible.

PROPOSITION 4 : Let F_1, F_2 be two Riemannian flags of X satisfying the hypothesis of the proposition 3 . Then $F_1 \neq F_2$ implies the unitary inequivalence of U_{F_1} and U_{F_2} .

REFERENCES

[1] S. ALBEVERIO, R. HØEGH-KROHN : The energy representation of Sobolev - Lie groups, Comp. Math., vol. 36 (1978), p. 37-52.

[2] S. ALBEVERIO, R. HØEGH-KROHN, D. TESTARD : Irreducibility and reducibility of the energy representations of the group of mappings of a Riemannian manifold into a compact semisimple Lie group, J. Funct. Anal., vol. 41, n° 3, (1981), p. 378-396.

[3] X. FERNIQUE, J.P. CONZE, J. GANI : Ecole d'été de Probabilités de Saint-Flours n° IV, Lect. Notes in Math., vol. 840, Springer-Verlag (1985).

[4] M. FUKUSHIMA : Dirichlet forms and Markov processes, Amsterdam-Oxford-New-York, North Holland, (1980).

[5] A. GUICHARDET : Symmetric Hilbert spaces and related topics, Lect. Notes in Math., vol. 261, Springer-Verlag (1972).

[6] W. KARWOWSKI, J. MARION : On the closability of some positive definite symmetric differential forms on $C_0^\infty(\Omega)$, preprint 1984, to appear in J. Funct. Anal.

[7] R. ISMAGILOV : On unitary representations of the group $C_0^\infty(X,G)$, $G = SU(2)$, Math. Sb. vol. 100 (2), (1976), p. 117-131 (in Russian).

[8] J. MARION : G - distributions et G - intégrales multiplicatives sur une variété, Annal. Pol. Math., vol. 43 (1983), p. 79-92.

[9] J. MARION : Generalized energy representations for current groups, J. Funct. Anal. vol. 54 (1), (1983), p. 1-17.

.../...

[10] J. MARION, D. TESTARD : Energy representations of gauge groups associated with Riemannian flags, preprint (1985), to appear.

[11] I. SEGAL : The Cauchy problem for the Yang-Mills equations, J. Funct. Anal. vol. 33 (2), (1979), p. 175-194.

[12] A.M. VERSHIK, I.M. GELFAND, M.I. GRAEV : Representations of the group of functions taking values in a compact Lie group, Comp. Math. vol. 35 (1977), p. 299-336.

Jean MARION
Département de Mathématiques
Faculté des Sciences de Luminy
70, Route Léon-Lachamp
F - 13288 MARSEILLE CEDEX 9

A RIGOROUS ANALYSIS OF ANDERSON LOCALIZATION

F. Martinelli
Dipartimento Di Matematica,
Universita "La Sapienza" Roma, Italy

The purpose of this lecture is to describe some recent rigorous results obtained by J. Frohlich, E. Scoppola, T. Spencer and myself in the context of quantum mechanics of disordered systems. [1]

I will be mainly concerned with the Anderson model but later on I will mention other linear systems to which our results apply.

The Anderson Model

This model is used to describe in the one particle approximation the motion of an electron in a crystal when impurities are present. For simplicity the continuum $\mathbf{R}^\nu$ is replaced by the lattice $\mathbf{Z}^\nu$ so that the particle can hop from site to site. The Hamiltonian operator is then given by:

$$H(v) = -\Delta + v \quad \text{on} \quad \ell^2(Z^\nu) \tag{1}$$

where $-\Delta_{xy} = 2\nu$ if $x = y$, -1 if $|x-y| = 1$ and zero otherwise, and the potential $v = \{v(x)\}_{x\in \mathbf{Z}^\nu}$ is a collection of i.i.d random variables with a smooth probability density $g(v)$ given e.g. by:

<u>Gaussian case</u>

$$g(v) = \frac{1}{\sqrt{2\pi\gamma}} e^{-v^2/2\gamma} \tag{2}$$

<u>Uniform case</u>

$$g(v) = \frac{1}{2w} \chi(-w \leq v \leq w) . \tag{3}$$

We shall let

$$\delta = [\sup g(v)]^{-1} \tag{4}$$

be a measure of the strength of the disorder. Thus in our example $\delta = \sqrt{2\pi\gamma}$ or $\delta = 2w$. If δ is large the variables $v(x)$ have fluctuations of order δ and we say that we are in the strong disorder regime. By simple ergodic considerations the spec(Hv) is known to be equal to:

$$[0,4\nu] + \text{supp } g(v) = \text{spec}(-\Delta) + \text{spec}(v) \tag{5}$$

with probability one. The main problem is to study the spectral properties of H(v) and in particular of the time evolution generated by

$$e^{itH(v)} . \tag{6}$$

Let us consider the spread of $\psi_t = e^{-itH}\psi_0$ as measured by:

$$\langle r^2(t,v)\rangle = \langle r^2(t,\psi_o,v)\rangle = \langle \sum_x |x|^2 |\psi_t(x)|^2\rangle . \tag{7}$$

If v were periodic or v = 0 then

$$r^2(t) \sim \text{const } t^2 \quad \text{as} \quad t \uparrow +\infty . \tag{8}$$

In the Anderson model it is believed that:

$$\langle r^2(t)\rangle \sim Dt \quad D = D(\psi_0) < +\infty . \tag{9}$$

If ψ_0 contains only energies in an interval $I = (a,b) \subset \text{spec}(H)$ then we shall refer to $D = D(\psi_0)$ as the diffusion constant associated to I . If the disorder δ is large Anderson argued in his famous paper [2] that:

$$\langle r^2(t)\rangle \leq \text{const } \forall\, t \geq 0 \tag{10}$$

This phenomenon is called localization since the wave packet does not spread. In one dimension localization is known to hold for any $\delta > 0$ [3] and the same it is believed to occur for $\nu = 2$ but no rigorous proof of this conjecture is available.

The main result of [1] concerns a rigorous proof of Anderson conjecture:

Main result i) For large δ the spectrum of $H(v)$ consists of a dense set of eigenvalues with exponentially decaying eigenfunctions

ii)
$$\langle r^2(t)\rangle \leq \text{const} \qquad t \geq 0 .$$

A proof of i) different from ours has been provided recently by Simon-Wolff [4] and Delyon-Levy-Souillard [5]. However, these alternative methods did not provide a control of the time evolution.

Main ideas behind the proof.

As a simple example of an operator having dense pure point spectrum consider:

$$H_0 = v \tag{11}$$

Then $\{v(x)\}$ $x \in Z^\nu$ are the eigenvalues and $\psi_x(y) = \delta(x-y)$ are the normalized eigenvectors. If $\delta >> 1$ then v is typically large compared to $-\Delta$ and it is natural to regard $-\Delta$ as a perturbation of H_0 .

To be more precise let us fix an energy interval:

$$I = [E_0-1, E_0+1] \ , \ E_0 \in \text{spec}(H)$$

and let us consider the set:

$$S_0 = \{x \in Z^\nu ; |v(x) + 2\nu - E_0| \leq \sqrt{\delta}\} .$$

Then it is easy to see that the restriction of H to $Z^\nu | S_0$ has spectrum far away from I and therefore its Green's function decays exponentially:

$$|(H_{Z^\nu|S_0} - E)^{-1}(x,y)| \le e^{-m|x-y|} \qquad E \in I . \tag{12}$$

Thus $Z^\nu \backslash S_0$ behaves like a potential barrier for any $E \in I$. Furthermore it is easy to see that:

$$P(0 \in S_0) \sim \frac{1}{\sqrt{\delta}} \tag{13}$$

and therefore for $\delta >> 1$ so will consists mainly of small clusters well isolated one from the other.

The main idea is to study the quantum tunneling among the components of S_0 and to show that tunneling over long distances is unlikely. This idea first appear in the remarkable paper by Frohlich and Spencer [5] in which they prove by means of a sort of probabilistic K.A.M. scheme that given an energy $E \in I$, then with probability one tunneling at that energy E does not take over too large distances. Technically this is realized by analyzing the decay properties of $(H(v) - E - i\varepsilon)^{-1}(xy)$ for large $|x-y|$. uniformly in ε. Their result implies the vanishing of the diffusion constant $D(I)$ and, as shown by Scoppola and myself [7], the absence of an absolutely continuous spectrum in I. However, it does not imply directly localization since for doing that one has to control the tunneling for all energies $E \in I$ at the same time. This becomes clear if one uses the following eigenfunctions expansion (see [8]):

$$(e^{-itH(v)}P_I(H(v)))(0,x) = \int_I d\rho_v(E)e^{-itE}F(x,0,E;v) \tag{14}$$

where $d\rho_v$ is equivalent to the spectral measure of $H(v)$ and $F(x,0,E;v)$ is given for almost all E with respect to $d\rho_v$ by:

$$F(x,0,E;v) = (1+|x|^2)^{\delta/2} \sum_{j=1}^{N(E)} f_j(x,E)\bar{f}_j(0,E) \tag{15}$$

Here $\delta > \nu/2$ and $\{f_j\}_{j=1}^{N(E)}$ are orthogonal functions in $\ell^2(Z^\nu)$ such that:

$$\varphi_j(x) = (1+|x|^2)^{\delta/2}\, f_j(x;E) \tag{16}$$

are solutions of the Schrodinger equation:

$$(H(v)-E)\varphi_j = 0 \tag{17}$$

The normalization is chosen in such a way that $\sum_{j=1}^{N(E)} \|f_j\|^2 = 1$. Actually for the Anderson model the multiplicity $N(E)$ is equal to one [5] but for continuous systems one has only bounds. The important fact about the above eigenfunctions expansion is that the functions φ_j are polynomially bounded. The energies for which (17) has a polynomially bounded solution are called "generalized eigenvalues". For large disorder δ they strongly depend on the potential configuration v although their closure, that is the spectrum of H , does not. Namely one can prove [6] that given an energy E ,

$$P(E \text{ is a generalized eigenvalue}) = 0 \tag{18}$$

The program of controling the tunneling for all the generalized eigenvalues was carried out for the first time by G.-Jona-Lasinio, E. Scoppola and myself for a hierarchical version of the Anderson model [9]. These models were introduced to study quantum tunneling over a sequence of length scales.

Characterization of the typical configurations of the random potential.

The way the tunneling processes have been controled for large disorder in [1] is through a close analysis of the structure of the typical configurations of the random potential. Let $d_k = \exp(\beta(5/4)^k)$ $\beta > 0$. be a sequence of length scales.

Definition. A set $\Lambda \subset Z^\nu$ is a K-barrier for $E \in I$ iff

$$|(H_\Lambda - E)^{-1}(x,y)| \le e^{-m|x-y|} \quad |x-y] \ge \frac{1}{5} d_k \ .$$

Main Result

For δ large there exists a set Ω_0 of potentials configurations v with $P(\Omega_0) = 1$ such that if $v \in \Omega_0$ and $E(v)$ is a generalized eigenvalue there exists an integer $K(E(v),v)$ i.e., a length scale such that if Λ_K is a box centered at $x = 0$ of side $\sim d_K$: , then the following holds:

1) $\operatorname{dist}(E,\sigma(H_{\Lambda_K})) < e^{-d_k^\alpha}$ $\alpha < 1$ $\forall K > K(E)$

2) $\Lambda_{K+1}\setminus\Lambda_K$ is a K-barrier for E $\forall K > K(E)$

3) if φ is a solution of $(H(v) - E(v))\varphi = 0$ then:

$$|\varphi(x)| \leq e^{-md_{K(E(v))-1}}$$

$$\forall \quad |x| \leq \frac{d_K(E(v))-1}{2}$$

provided $K(E(v)) > K_0(v)$.

Remark. 1) holds only for generalized eigenvalues.

2) shows the absence of tunneling at energy $E(v)$ over scales larger than $d_{K(E(v))}$

3) says that if the localization length $d_{K(E(v))}$ is too large then the eigenfunction φ must be localized far away from the origin. This property is crucial if one also wants to control the time evolution.

Remark. 1) In the case of weak disorder Anderson localization still occur but only near the an edges. The reason for this is that most of the sites in

Z^ν will not be able to support very low energies and again tunneling among the exceptional sites does not take place over large scales.

2) The same kind of ideas apply to continuous systems like the wave equation in stochastic wave guides [10] and to the case of spin-orbit interaction [11].

I would like to conclude with a short discussion on a coarse-grained version of our proof of localization for large disorder which should be useful to study localization near the mobility edge.

For $\nu \geq 3$ it is believed that for weak disorder there is a sharp transition in the spectrum from an exponentially localized regime near the bottom of the spectrum to an extended states regime where the diffusion constant D is positive. However, there is no doubt that the procedure just outlined gives by no means a good estimate on the energy threshold $\equiv$ mobility edge. In order to extend our result to the whole region of the localized states we assumed the following hypothesis:

$$\text{for some} \quad a < 1 \lim_{\ell \to +\infty} P\Big(\sum_{y \in \partial\Lambda_\ell} |G_{\Lambda_\ell}(E,x,y)| < a \;,\; |x| < \frac{\ell}{4}\Big) = 1 .$$

Then around E there is a whole interval of exponentially localized eigenstates. The key idea on which our renormalized scheme is based is to replace the singular or exceptional sites by <u>singular</u> blocks where the event described in the main hypothesis fails and to treat them in perturbation theory.

The expected effect of this renormalization procedure is to drive the system towards a "large-disorder fixed point". Thus a rigorous analysis of the Anderson localization breaks into two step:

1) Verify the hypothesis by means of <u>non-perturbative</u> methods.
2) Once we are in the large-disorder regime apply the perturbation means just described to study the tunneling among the blocks.

This program has been implemented for $\nu = 1$ to show (again) localization for any disorder. The non-perturbative step has been provided by Fucstemberg theorem on the positivity of the Liapunov exponent of infinite product of random matrices.

REFERENCES

[1] J. Fröhlich, F. Martinelli, E. Scoppola, T. Spencer: "Constructive proof of localization in the Anderson tight binding model". Comm. Math. Phys. to appear. See also T. Spencer: "The Schrodinger equation with a random potential-a mathematical reviews" Lectures given at the les Houches summer school on Random Systems '84.

[2] P. Anderson "Absence of diffusion in certain random lattices" Phys. Rev. Lett. 109 (1958).

[3] H. Kunz, B. Souillard: "Sur le spectre des operateurs eux differences finies aleatoires Comm. Math. Phys. 78, 201, (1980).

[4] B. Simon, T. Wolff "Singular continuous spectrum un der cank one perturbations and localization for random Hamiltonian" Preprint Caltech '85.

[5] F. Delyion, Y. Levy, B. Souillard, "Anderson localization for multidimensional systems at large disorder or large energy" Comm. Math. Phys. (to appear).

[6] J. Fröhlich, T. Spencer "Absence of diffusion in the Anderson tight binding model for large disorder or low energy" Comm. Math. Phys. 88 (1983).

[7] F. Martinelli, E. Scoppola: "A remark on the absence of absolutely continuous spectrum in the Anderson model for large disorder or low energy." Comm. Math. Phys. 97 (1985).

[8] B. Simon "Schrodinger semigroups" Bull. Amer. Math. Soc. 7 (1983).

[9] G. Jona-Lasinio, F. Martinelli, E. Scoppola: "Multiple Tunnelings in d-dimension: a quantum particle in a hierarchical potential" Ann. Inst. H. Poincare 42, 73 (1985).

[10] F. Martinelli " The wave equation in random domains: localization of the normal modes in the small frequency region". Ann. Inst. H. Poincare 43 No. 2, (1985).

[11] J. Bellissard, D. R. Grempel, F. Martinelli, E. Scoppola "Localization of electrons with spin-orbit or magnetic interactions in a two dimensional disordered crystal" Phys. Rev. Lett. (to appear)

A FINITE APPROXIMATION TO BOSON FOCK SPACE

by P.A. Meyer

It is well known that boson Fock space is, in some natural sense, isomorphic to the L^2 space associated with Wiener measure. The main theme of this talk consists in using a finite Bernoulli measure instead of Wiener measure, and following the analogy as far as possible. The method turns out to be fruitful, since it suggests some features of continuous Fock space which have been discovered quite recently. On the other hand, it remains a heuristic method : at the meeting itself, the possibility of a rigorous justification via non-standard analysis was suggested, but this seems more unlikely now, in view of the last section.

The author gratefully acknowledges useful conversations with R.L. Hudson, J.L. Journé and K.R. Parthasarathy.

1. Let M be an integer, $\mathcal{P}$ be the set of all subsets of $\{1,\ldots,M\}$. Let Ω be the multiplicative group $\{-1,1\}^M$, with its natural (Haar) probability measure, under which the coordinates x_k $(1\leq k\leq M)$ constitute a sequence of independent, symmetric Bernoulli r.v.. Finally, let $\mathcal{H}$ be the finite (2^M) dimensional Hilbert space $L^2(\Omega)$.

For any $A\in\mathcal{P}$, let $x_A=\prod_{k\in A} x_A$; the r.v. x_A (Walsh polynomials) constitute an orthonormal basis in $\mathcal{H}$. They may also be considered as the characters of the group Ω, and $\mathcal{P}$ is identified with the character group (character multiplication corresponding to the symmetric difference operation in $\mathcal{P}$). We denote by $\mathcal{H}_i$, the i-th Walsh chaos, the linear span of $\{x_A\}_{|A|=i}$.

We now define creation, annihilation, and number operators on $\mathcal{H}$. We set :

(1) $b_k^+(x_A) = x_{A\cup\{k\}}$ if $k\notin A$, 0 otherwise ; $b_k^-(x_A) = x_{A\setminus\{k\}}$ if $k\in A$, 0 otherw.

$$n_k(x_A) = x_A \text{ if } k\in A, \text{ 0 otherwise.}$$

These operators satisfy the following relations

(2) $$b_k^+b_k^+ = b_k^-b_k^- = 0,\quad b_k^+b_k^- = n_k\ ,\ b_k^-b_k^+ = I-n_k$$
$$b_k^+n_k = n_kb_k^- = 0,\quad b_k^-n_k = b_k^-\ ,\ n_kb_k^+ = b_k^+\ ,\quad n_kn_k = n_k\ .$$

b_k^+ and b_k^- are Hilbert space adjoints, from which it follows that n_k is self-adjoint, as well as the << field operators >>

$$q_k = b_k^+ + b_k^-\quad ,\ p_k = i(b_k^+ - b_k^-\ ).$$

The operator q_k is just the multiplication operator by x_k when we consider the elements of $\mathcal{H}$ as random variables. The algebra structure on $\mathcal{H}$ is described by the multiplication table

(3) $$x_A x_B = x_{A\Delta B} \qquad (\text{ group algebra of } \Omega \text{ })$$

When we consider $\mathcal{H}$ as an algebra in this way, we call it the Bernoulli algebra. It is associative, commutative, admits the vacuum vector $1=x_\emptyset$ as its unit element.

The space $\mathcal{H}$ has a rich algebraic structure, another element of which is the Fourier transform $\mathcal{F}$, which acts on the k-th Walsh chaos $\mathcal{H}_k$ by multiplication with coefficient i^k ($\mathcal{F}x_A=i^{|A|}x_A$) ; $\mathcal{F}$ transforms q_k into p_k, p_k into $-q_k$, and preserves n_k .

It is clear that $\mathcal{H}$ looks somewhat like boson Fock space (but may not be a boson Fock space, since it is finite dimensional). If we compute the commutators

$$[b_j^+,b_k^+] = 0 = [b_j^-,b_k^-] \ , \quad [b_j^-,b_k^+] = \delta_{jk}(I-2n_k)$$

the physical meaning of $\mathcal{H}$ becomes clear : we are describing a system of commuting spins. It follows that self-adjoint operators like

(4) $$y_k = q_k+cn_k \ ,$$

which depend on different spins, all commute, and hence can be considered simultaneously as multiplication operators. Since we have $y_k^2=1+cy_k$ instead of $x_k^2=1$, this leads to other interesting algebra structures on $\mathcal{H}$, corresponding in continuous time to the Poisson interpretations of Fock space.

2. We use for the first time the order structure of $\{1,\dots,M\}$ to define $\nu(k,B)$, the number of elements of $B\in\mathcal{P}$ strictly smaller than k , and for $A,B \in \mathcal{P}$, $\nu(A,B) = \Sigma_{k\in A}\, \nu(k,B)$, the number of inversions between A and B . We set

(5) $$f_k^\pm(x_A) = (-1)^{\nu(k,A)} b_k^\pm(x_A)$$

and these operators turn out to satisfy correct anticommutation relations

$$\{f_j^+,f_k^+\} = 0 = \{f_j^-,f_k^-\} \ , \quad \{f_j^-,f_k^+\} = \delta_{jk}I$$

If we remark that the number of elements in the basis (x_A) is the same as for the Grassmann algebra over $\mathbb{C}^M$, we may identify $\mathcal{H}$ with the antisymmetric Fock space, and $f_k^\pm$ with the corresponding fermion creation and annihilation operators. It is well known that $\mathcal{H}$ has a Clifford algebra structure, with multiplication table

(6) $$x_A \cdot x_B = (-1)^{\nu(A,B)} x_{A\Delta B}$$

and that the self adjoint operator $r_k=f_k^+ + f_k^-$ is just the operator of Clifford multiplication by x_k on the left. In this set up, the physical object described by $\mathcal{H}$ is an anticommuting system of spins. The close relationship between commuting and anticommuting spin systems, as well as a large number of interesting algebraic properties of such systems, has been described by Combe, Rodriguez, Sirugue and S.-Collin, Weyl quantization of spin systems, in LN in Phys. 106, Feynman Path Integrals, Marseille 1978. See also their paper in Comm. Math. Phys. 63, 1978, p. 219-235.

3. Now we are going to describe the true boson Fock space over $L^2(\mathbb{R}_+)$, in terms which are as close as possible to the description of the preceding finite model, which we call « toy boson Fock space » . We use the well known identification of true Fock space with $L^2(\Omega)$, where Ω is the canonical space for standard brownian motion (X_t). That is, an element of Fock space $\mathcal{H}$ is given by a Wiener chaos expansion

(7) $$h = f_o + \int f_1(s)dX_s + \int_{s_1<s_2} f(s_1,s_2)dX_{s_1}dX_{s_2} + \dots$$

with norm

(8) $$\|h\|^2 = |f_o|^2 + \int |f(s)|^2 ds + \int_{s_1<s_2} |f(s_1,s_2)|^2 ds_1 ds_2 + \dots$$

(these formulas imply some changes in the usual normalizations, but will spare us a lot of $\sqrt{n!}$ a.e.). The first thing we'll do, to bring these formulas closer to toy Fock space, is to identify an increasing n-uple $(s_1,\dots,s_n)$, $s_1<\dots<s_n$, with a n-element subset A of $\mathbb{R}_+^n$. In this way, the set $\mathcal{P}$ of all finite subsets of $\mathbb{R}_+$ acquires a measurable structure,

$\mathcal{P} = \cup_n \mathcal{P}_n$, $\mathcal{P}_n$ is identified with the increasing octant in $\mathbb{R}_+^n$

($\mathcal{P}_0=\{\emptyset\}$). Il also acquires a measure

$dA = ds_1 \dots ds_n$ on $\mathcal{P}_n$ (on $\mathcal{P}_0$, unit mass at $\emptyset$)

and we use the shorthand notation for (7) and (8)

(9) $$h = \int_{\mathcal{P}} f(A)dX_A \quad , \quad \|h\|^2 = \int_{\mathcal{P}} |f(A)|^2 dA$$

where $f(A)=f(s_1,\dots,s_n)$ if $A=\{s_1<\dots<s_n\}$. In this way, if we forget the meaning of dX_A , Fock space simply becomes the Hilbert space $L^2(\mathcal{P})$. This is Guichardet's first description of Fock space in his lecture notes Symmetric Hilbert spaces, Springer LN in M. 261.

However, we remark that in the representation (8) or (9), the function f is known only through its restriction to the increasing octants. Therefore, our description applies as well to the symmetric and antisymmetric Fock spaces.

Note the difference with sections 1-2 : $\mathcal{P}$ is still a measurable group under symmetric difference, but $\mathcal{P}$ isn't locally compact, and dA isn't a Haar measure. On the other hand, there is a relation between the measure dA and the combinatorial structure of $\mathcal{P}$: assuming $f \geqq 0$ is Borel on $\mathcal{P}\times\mathcal{P}$

(10) $$\int_{\mathcal{P}_{i+j}} dA\,(\Sigma_{\substack{B+C=A\\|B|=i,|C|=j}} f(B,C)) = \int_{\mathcal{P}_i\times\mathcal{P}_j} f(B,C)dBdC$$

where $B+C=A$ means $B\cup C=A$, $B\cap C=\emptyset$.

We give now the dictionary from toy Fock space to true Fock space :

<u>Instead of</u>	<u>Read</u>
x_k	$dX_t/\sqrt{dt}$ (cf. Lévy's heuristic formula $X_t = \int_0^t sgn(dX_s)\sqrt{ds}$)
x_A	$dX_A/\sqrt{dA}$
$b_k^{\pm}$	$db_t^{\pm}/\sqrt{dt}$ (the boson creation and annihilation operators[1])
n_k	dN_t[1] (Hudson and Parthasarathy's « gauge process » Λ_t)
p_k, q_k	$dQ_t/\sqrt{dt}$, $dP_t/\sqrt{dt}$, position and momentum brownian motions on Fock space.

As a first example of translation, let us start from (2) : using the dictionary, and keeping only first order terms, we get

(11) $$db_t^+db_t^+ = 0 = db_t^-db_t^- \ ,\ db_t^+db_t^- = 0 \ ,\ db_t^-db_t^+ = dt \ ,$$
$$db_t^+dN_t = dN_tdb_t^- = 0 \ ,\ db_t^-dN_t = db_t^- \ ,\ dN_tdb_t^+ = db_t^+ \ ,\ dN_tdN_t = dN_t \ .$$

which is the correct multiplication table for the non-commutative stochastic calculus, as given by Hudson-Parthasarathy. We shall discuss later the second order formulas, like $db_t^+db_t^-=dN_tdt$.

As a second example, consider formula (3) for Bernoulli multiplication. Our dictionary translates it into

(12) $$dX_AdX_B = dX_{A\Delta B}\, d(A\cap B)$$

which tells us how to compute $dX_{s_1}\ldots dX_{s_m}dX_{t_1}\ldots dX_{t_n}$ ($s_1<\ldots<s_m$; $t_1<\ldots<t_n$) according to the number of pairs $s_i=t_j$. Assuming φ and ψ are two random variables with finite Wiener chaos expansions (which ensures that their product belongs to L^2)

$$\varphi = \int_{\mathcal{P}} f(A)dX_A \quad , \quad \psi = \int_{\mathcal{P}} g(B)dX_B$$

their product $\varphi\psi$ is given as $\int h(C)dX_C$ with

(13) $$h(C) = \int_{\mathcal{P}} dH\,(\Sigma_{C=K+L}\, f(H\cup K)g(H\cup L))$$

This is a shorthand for the classical multiplication formula for multiple Wiener integrals. The exercise consisting in a <u>direct</u> verification of associativity (formula (10) is the key to the proof) is tedious, but once it

1.For the meaning of these differentials, see Hudson-Parthasarathy, Quantum Ito's formula and stochastic evolutions, Comm. Math. Phys. 93, 1984.

has been done, it isn't really more difficult to follow another suggestion of toy Fock space, namely to check the associativity of the continuous Clifford product, with multiplication table

$$dX_A \cdot dX_B = (-1)^{\nu(A,B)} dX_{A\Delta B}\, d(A\cap B) \tag{14}$$

Formulas (12) and (14) lead to quite concrete computations if necessary. For instance, let us compute the Wiener and the Clifford product of two elements of the first chaos

$$(\int f(s)dX_s)(\int g(t)dX_t) = \int_{s<t} f(s)g(t)dX_s dX_t + \int_{s=t} + \int_{s>t} \quad .$$

The first term is a correctly written element of the Wiener chaos of order two. The middle term is equal to $\int f(s)g(s)ds$. The last term can be written, changing the name of s and t and using the commutation rule $dX_s dX_t = \varepsilon dX_t dX_s$ (ε=+1 for Wiener, -1 for Clifford) $\varepsilon\int_{s<t} g(s)f(t)dX_s dX_t$, which belongs to the second Wiener chaos.

If we let X_t operate on Fock space by Clifford multiplication, we get an operator process called fermion brownian motion, which is non classical in the sense that its values at different times don't commute. In our dictionary, it corresponds to $r_k = f_k^+ + f_k^-$. The fermion creation and annihilation operators themselves can be realized on Fock space, by the following explicit formula, given in the very recent preprint of Hudson-Parthasarathy, Unification of fermion and boson stochastic integrals:

$$df_t^{\pm} = (-1)^{N_t} db_t^{\pm} \tag{15}$$

This is also a translation formula, corresponding to the toy Fock space relation $f_k^{\pm}(x_A) = (-1)^{\nu(k,A)} b_k^{\pm}(x_A)$. This unification considerably simplifies fermion stochastic calculus, which has been studied in an extensive series of papers by Barnett, Streater and Wilde. Apparently, the close relation between bosons and fermions has been noticed also by Sato, Miwa and Jimbo, Proc. Jap. Acad. 53, 1977, p.6,(and somewhere in their immense work of Publ. RIMS Kyoto, 14, 1977 and 15, 1979), but the language is so different that I am unable to decide whether we are talking about the same thing.

4. Let us now discuss the meaning of formulas like

$$db_t^+ db_t^- = dN_t dt \ , \ db_t^- db_t^+ = dt - dN_t dt \tag{16}$$

In integrated form, these relations concern quadratic variation processes like those of classical martingale theory. More precisely, fix an interval of time $[0,t]$, and divide it equally into intervals $[kt/n,(k+1)t/n]$, which we simply denote by $[t_k,t_{k+1}]$. Then the first order statements $db_t^+ db_t^- = 0$, $db_t^- db_t^+ = 0$ can be interpreted as

$$\lim_{n\to\infty} \Sigma_i \, (b^+_{t_{i+1}} - b^+_{t_i})(b^-_{t_{i+1}} - b^-_{t_i}) = 0$$

$$\lim_{n\to\infty} \Sigma_i \{(b^-_{t_{i+1}} - b^-_{t_i})(b^+_{t_{i+1}} - b^+_{t_i}) - (t_{i+1}-t_i)I\} = 0$$

on sufficiently many vectors (as usual with the boson stochastic calculus of Hudson-Parthasarathy, coherent vectors are convenient << test vectors >> Due to the commutation relations, the second formula reduces to the first one. The meaning of formula (16) should be now that, after dividing by $(t_{i+1}-t_i)$ - which doesn't depend on i

$$\lim_{n\to\infty} \Sigma_i \, (b^+_{t_{i+1}} - b^+_{t_i})(b^-_{t_{i+1}} - b^-_{t_i})/(t_{i+1}-t_i) = N_t$$

on coherent vectors. This turns out to be true.

Unfortunately, things go wrong when we look at the other << quadratic variations >> : the toy Fock space relations $b^+_k b^+_k = b^-_k b^-_k = 0$ suggest that

$$\lim_{n\to\infty} \Sigma_i \, (b^\varepsilon_{t_{i+1}} - b^\varepsilon_{t_i})(b^\varepsilon_{t_{i+1}} - b^\varepsilon_{t_i})/(t_{i+1}-t_i) = 0 \quad , \; \varepsilon=\pm1$$

on coherent vectors. Explicit computation for $\varepsilon=-1$ gives a non zero limit, and then one can show that there is no limit for $\varepsilon=+1$ (which shows also that the limit for $\varepsilon=-1$ has no nice adjoint). This isn't particularly disturbing in itself, but suggests that in a non-standard analytic approach, returning to the standard world may be a non trivial problem.

I.R.M.A.
7 rue du Général Zimmer
F-67084 Strasbourg-Cedex.

An Extension of Kotani's Theorem to Random Generalized Sturm-Liouville Operators II

by

Nariyuki Minami

Department of Applied Physics
Tokyo Institute of Technology
O-okayama, Meguro, Tokyo 152, Japan

§1 Introduction

The purpose of this note is to expose the results of [9] under a slightly generalized setting. By a Sturm-Liouville operator, we mean an operator of the following form:

$$(1) \quad (Lu)(x) = (-du^{+}(x) + u(x)Q(dx))/m(dx) ,$$

where $m(dx)$ is a non-negative Radon measure on R, $Q(dx)$ is, in general, a signed Radon measure, which we assume to be non-negative in the following, and $u^{+}(x) = d^{+}u(x)/dx$ is the right-derivative. This L acts in the Hilbert space $H = L^2(R:m(dx))$ and its domain $D(L)$ is defined to be the totality of $u \in H$ which is absolutely continuous and such that the Lebesgue-Stieltjes measure $-du^{+}(x) + u(x)Q(dx)$ has a density with respect to $m(dx)$ which belongs to H. Lu is defined to be this density. In [9], Q is assumed to be $q(x)m(dx)$ with bounded density q.

Let us state several examples: (i) L is a Schrodinger operator if $m(dx) = dx$, typical examples being the case of $Q(dx) = q(x)dx$ and the case in which $Q(dx)$ is a linear combination of Dirac measures. (ii) L is the Hamiltonian of a vibrating string with mass distribution $m(dx)$ if $m(dx)$ is continuous and $Q = 0$. (iii) L is a finite difference operator if m is concentrated on a discrete set and Q is absolutely continuous with respect to $m(dx)$.

In the next section, we will randomize L and investigate the characterization of the essential absolutely continuous spectrum in terms of the Ljapounov indices, but before doing so, let us check that L defines a self-adjoint operator. We assume that $Q \geq 0$ and $m(R_\pm) = \infty$ ($R_- = (-\infty,0]$, $R_+ = (0,\infty)$). In random case, this will be satisfied with probability one. Now let $V(x)$ be the solution of $-du^+(x) + u(x)Q(dx) = 0$, $V(0) = 1$, $V^+(0) = 0$. Let $x(t)$ be the inverse function of

(2) $\quad t(x) = \int_0^x V(s)^{-2} ds$

and set $l_\pm = t(\pm\infty)$. Let $M(dt)$ be the Lebesgue-Stieltjes measure corresponding to the function $M(t)$ on (l_-,l_+) which is defined by

$$(3) \quad M(t) = \int_{0+}^{x(t)+} V(s)^2 m(ds) \quad (t \geq 0),$$

$$= -\int_{x(t)+}^{0+} V(s)^2 m(ds) \quad (t < 0) \quad .$$

Since $M((l_-,0]) = M((0,l_+)) = \infty$, the operator $\tilde{L} = -d/M(dt)d^+/dt$ in $\tilde{H} = L^2((l_-,l_+):M(dt))$ with domain $D(\tilde{L}) = \{u \in \tilde{H}$: u is absolutely continuous, $du^+(x)$ is absolutely continuous with respect to $M(dt)$ and $du^+/dM \in \tilde{H}\}$ is self-adjoint. If we define a unitary transformation T from H onto $\tilde{H}$ by

$$(Tu)(t) = (u/V)(x(t)) ,$$

then $L = T^{-1}\tilde{L}T$, and hence L is self-adjoint.

§2 Kotani's Theorem

Let $(\Omega,\mathbb{F},P)$ be a complete probability space and let $\{T_x : x \in R\}$ be an ergodic flow on it. Let M be the space of non-negative Radon measures on R with the topology of vague convergence. Let (m_ω,Q_ω) be a random variable on $(\Omega,\mathbb{F},P)$ with values in $M \times M$ which satisfies the following conditions:

(i) stationarity: $(m_{T_x\omega}(\cdot),Q_{T_x\omega}(\cdot)) = (m_\omega(\cdot+x),Q_\omega(\cdot+x))$, $x \in R$.

(ii) $0 < E[m_\omega((0,1])] < \infty$, $E[Q_\omega((0,1])] < \infty$.

From (i) and the individual ergodic theorem, we see that $m_\omega(R_\pm) = \infty$ a.s., so that the Sturm-Liouville operator (1) with (m,Q) replaced by (m_ω,Q_ω) is self-adjoint and non-negative in the Hilbert space $H_\omega = L^2(R:m_\omega)$ for P-a.a. $\omega \in \Omega$. For such ω's, the following limits exist for $\lambda \in C-[0,\infty)$:

(4) $$h_\pm(\lambda:\omega) = \mp\lim_{x\to\pm\infty} \phi_1(x,\lambda;\omega)/\phi_2(x,\lambda;\omega) ,$$

where ϕ_j , $j = 1,2$ are the solutions of $L_\omega u = \lambda u$ with initial conditions $\phi_1(0) = \phi_2^+(0) = 1$, $\phi_1^+(0) = \phi_2(0) = 0$. As in [8],[4], and [9], there exists a symmetric and non-negative definite measure matrix $\{\sigma_{ij}(d\lambda;\omega)\}_{i,j=1}^2$ such that the integral kernel $E_\omega(d\lambda;x,y)$ of the resolution of the identity of L_ω is given by

$$E_\omega(B;x,y) = \int_B \sum_{i,j=1}^{2} \phi_i(x,\lambda)\phi_j(y,\lambda)\sigma_{ij}(d\lambda;\omega)$$

for each bounded Borel set $B \subset [0,\infty)$, and that for some $c_\omega \geq 0$,

$$-(h_+(\lambda;\omega)+h_-(\lambda;\omega))^{-1} = c_\omega + \int_{0-}^{\infty} \frac{1}{\lambda-\xi}\,\sigma_{11}(d\lambda;\omega) , \quad \lambda \in C-[0,\infty) .$$

Let Σ^{ac} be the essential support of the spectral measure $\sigma_{11}+\sigma_{22}$ (for the definition, see [1] and [3]). Then there exists a set Σ^{ac} such that for P-a.a. ω, $\Sigma_\omega^{ac} = \Sigma^{ac}$ up to a set of Lebesgue measure zero.

Now for $\lambda \in R$, let $\gamma(\lambda)$ be the Ljapounov index of the equation $L_\omega u = \lambda u$:

$$\gamma(\lambda) = \lim_{x\to\pm\infty} \frac{1}{|x|} \log \|M_\lambda(x,\omega)\| , \text{ P-a.s.},$$

where $$M_\lambda(x,\omega) = \begin{bmatrix} \phi_1(x) & \phi_2(x) \\ \phi_1^+(x) & \phi_2^+(x) \end{bmatrix} .$$

The following theorem is a generalization of the results of [6], [11], and [9].

<u>Theorem 1</u> $\Sigma^{ac}=\{\lambda \in R:\gamma(\lambda) = 0\}$, up to a set of Lebesgue measure zero. Moreover, if $\gamma(\lambda) = 0$ a.e. on an interval $I \subset R$, then with probabili-

ty one, the spectrum of L_ω is purely absolutely continuous on I .

The proof of this theorem is based on the analysis of the function

$$w(\lambda) = \frac{1}{2} E[h_+(\lambda;\omega) + h_-(\lambda;\omega)] \ , \ \lambda \in C-[0,\infty) \ .$$

We will only prove that this expectation is convergent. The rest of the proof is completely parallel to that of [6], [11], and [9]. It suffices to estimate the absolute value of h_+ for $\lambda = -1$, but in this case, we can view $h_+(-1;\omega)$ as the h_+-function of the string $m_\omega(dx) + Q_\omega(dx)$ evaluated at $\lambda = -1$. Using the inequality of I.S. Kac ([7]), we obtain

$$|h_+(-1;\omega)| \leq m_\omega((0,x]) + Q_\omega((0,x]) + 1/x \ , \ x > 0 \ .$$

Hence from the assumption, $E[|h_+|] < \infty$.

§3 A Further Generalization

Let $(\Omega,\mathbb{F},P,\{T_x\})$ and (m_ω,Q_ω) be as in §2, and let $s_\omega(dx)$ be a random Radon measure satisfying the following conditions:

(iii) its distribution function $s_\omega(dx) = s_\omega((0,x]) \ (x \geq 0)$, $= -s_\omega((x,0]) \ (x < 0)$ is continuous and strictly increasing.

(iv) stationarity: $s_{T_x\omega}(\cdot) = s_\omega(\cdot+x)$.

(v) $0 < c \equiv E[s_\omega((0,1])] < \infty$.

Now set

$$\Omega_1 = \{\omega \in \Omega: \lim_{x\to\pm\infty} s_\omega(x)/x = c\} \ .$$

Then from the individual ergodic theorem, we have $P(\Omega_1) = 1$, so that we may restrict our probability space and consider $(\Omega_1,\mathbb{F}\,\Omega_1,P)$ instead of the original one. For each $\omega \in \Omega_1$, let L_ω be the operator in $H_\omega = L^2(R:m_\omega)$ defined by (1) with (m,Q) and $u^+(x)$ replaced by (m_ω,Q_ω) and $D_\omega^+u(x) = d^+u(x)/s_\omega(dx)$ respectively. Ljapounov indices $\gamma(\lambda)$ are defined analogously as in §2. In this section, we will show that this random operator is included in the framework of §2.

For $\omega \in \Omega_1$, $s_\omega(x)$ is a homeomorphism from R to R . Let $x_\omega(t)$

be its inverse function. Let $\hat{m}_\omega(dx)$ and $\hat{Q}_\omega(dx)$ be the Lebesgue-Stieltjes measures corresponding to non-decreasing functions:

$$\hat{m}_\omega(x) = \int_{0+}^{x_\omega(t)+} m_\omega(dy) \ (t \geq 0), \ = -\int_{x_\omega(t)+}^{0+} m_\omega(dy) \ (t < 0) \ ,$$

and

$$\hat{Q}_\omega(x) = \int_{0+}^{x_\omega(t)+} Q_\omega(dy) \ (t \geq 0) \ , \ = -\int_{x_\omega(t)+}^{0+} Q_\omega(dy) \ (t < 0) \ .$$

The transformation S_ω from H_ω onto $\hat{H}_\omega = L^2(R:\hat{m}_\omega)$ defined by

$$(S_\omega u)(t) = u(x_\omega(t)) \ , \ u \in H_\omega$$

is unitary and it is easy to check that $L_\omega = S_\omega^{-1}\hat{L}_\omega S_\omega$, where $\hat{L}_\omega$ is the Sturm-Liouville operator (1) with (m,Q) replaced by $(\hat{m}_\omega,\hat{Q}_\omega)$.

Define a one parameter group of transformations $\{\hat{T}_t : t \in R\}$ on $(\Omega_1, \mathbb{F}\cap\Omega_1)$ by

$$\hat{T}_t\omega = T_{x_\omega(t)}\omega \ , \ t \in R \ .$$

Then it holds that

$$(\hat{m}_{\hat{T}_t\omega}(\cdot), \hat{Q}_{\hat{T}_t\omega}(\cdot)) = (\hat{m}_\omega(\cdot + x), \hat{Q}_\omega(\cdot + x)) \ .$$

According to [10], let $\tilde{P}$ be the Palm measure of the stationary random measure $s_\omega(dx)$, i.e. let $\tilde{P}$ be the measure on Ω_1 which satisfies

(5) $\quad \theta[P(d\omega)s_\omega(dx)] = \tilde{P}(d\omega)dx$,

where $\theta[(\omega,x)] = (T_x\omega,x)$, $(\omega,x) \in \Omega_1 \times R$. From this, we have $\tilde{P}(\Omega_1) = c < \infty$. Let $\hat{P}$ be the normalization of $\tilde{P}$. In general, neither $P << \hat{P}$ nor $\hat{P} << P$ is true, so that the event which occurs P [resp. $\hat{P}$]-a.s. does not necessarily occurs $\hat{P}$ [resp. P]-a.s. However, every event of our interest is shift invariant. In fact it is easy to check that $B \in \mathbb{F}\cap\Omega_1$ is $\{T_x\}$-invariant if and only if it is $\{\hat{T}_t\}$-invariant, and in that case $P(B) = 0$ if and only if $\hat{P}(B) = 0$ in view of (5).

Modifying the argument of [2] Ch.10 §3, it can be proved that $\{\hat{T}_t\}$ preserves the measure $\hat{P}$ and is ergodic. It is also not difficult to show that

$$\int[\hat{m}_\omega((0,1]) + \hat{Q}_\omega((0,1])]\,\hat{P}(d\omega) < \infty .$$

Moreover, the Ljapounov index $\hat{\gamma}(\lambda)$ for $\{\hat{L}_\omega\}$ is related to $\gamma(\lambda)$ by $\hat{\gamma}(\lambda) = \gamma(\lambda)/c$, hence $\{\lambda:\gamma(\lambda) = 0\} = \{\lambda:\hat{\gamma}(\lambda) = 0\}$. Now Theorem 1 holds for the system $(\Omega_1, \mathbb{F}\cap\Omega_1, \hat{P}:\{\hat{T}_t\})$ and $\{\hat{L}_\omega\}$, hence also for $(\Omega,\mathbb{F},P:\{T_x\})$ and $\{L_\omega\}$.

§4 A Criterion for the Absence of the Absolutely Continuous Spectrum

In this section, we again set $s_\omega(dx) = dx$, and consider the one-parameter family of random operators $\{L_\omega(\mu):\mu > 0\}$, where $L_\omega(\mu)$ is the Sturm-Liouville operator (1) with (m,Q) replaced by $(m_\omega,\mu Q_\omega)$. As a weak analogue of Theorem 4.3 of [6] and Theorem 3 of [11], we have the following result, which includes Theorem 3 of [9].

<u>Theorem 2</u> Suppose that the pair of random measures (m_ω,Q_ω) is non-deterministic in the following sense:

$$\mathbb{B} \equiv \sigma[\langle m_\omega,\psi_1\rangle, \langle Q_\omega,\psi_2\rangle:\psi_1,\psi_2 \in C_0(R)]$$

$$\neq \bigcap_t \sigma[\langle m_\omega,\psi_1\rangle, \langle Q_\omega,\psi_2\rangle:\psi_1,\psi_2 \in C_0((-\infty,t])] \equiv \mathbb{B}_{-\infty} .$$

Then the totality of $\mu > 0$ for which $L_\omega(\mu)$ has absolutely continuous spectrum has no accumulation point other than 0 and ∞ .

<u>Sketch of the proof</u> Suppose that there exists a sequence $\{\mu_n\} \subset (0,\infty)$ which has a limit in $(0,\infty)$. Suppose further that for each n , the essential absolutely continuous spectrum A_n of $L_\omega(\mu_n)$ is non-trivial. As in [9], it holds that for P-a.a. ω, m_ω-a.a. x, and each n ,

$$(6) \qquad h_+(\xi+i0;T_x\omega,\mu_n) = -\overline{h_-(\xi+i0;T_x\omega,\mu_n)} \quad \text{a.e. } \xi\in A_n .$$

Now given $(m_\omega,Q_\omega)|_{(-\infty,0]}$, we can recover $h_+(\lambda;T_x\omega,\mu_n)$, $n = 1,2,\ldots$ in view of (6), where $x = \sup[(-\infty,0]\cap \mathrm{Supp}(m_\omega)]$. Let $M(\cdot,\omega,\mu_n)$ and $l_+(\omega,\mu_n)$ be defined by (2) and (3) with (m,Q) replaced by $(m_{T_x\omega}, \mu_n Q_{T_x\omega})$. These will be uniquely determined from the knowledge of $h_+(\lambda;T_x\omega,\mu_n)$ in view of the uniqueness of Krein's inverse problem ([4]). But $l_+(\omega,\mu) = \lim_{x\to\infty} W(t,\omega,\mu)/V(t,\omega,\mu)$, where W is the solution of $dW^+(t) = \mu W(t) Q_{T_x\omega}(dt)$, $W(0) = 0$, $W^+(0) = 1$. This implies that the function $-l_+(\omega,-\mu)$ serves as the h_+-function of the string $Q_{T_x\omega}$. From the analiticity, the values of $l_+(\omega,\mu)$ for $\mu = \mu_n$ determine the whole of $l_+(\omega,\cdot)$. Again from the uniqueness of Krein's inverse problem, this $l_+(\omega,\cdot)$ determines $Q_{T_x\omega}|_{(0,\infty)}$ uniquely. From the knowledge of $Q_{T_x\omega}$ and $M(\cdot,\omega,\mu_n)$, we can determine $m_{T_x\omega}$. Hence we have the determinicity of (m_ω, Q_ω) .

§5 Asymptotics of the Integrated Density of States

In this section, we again set $s_\omega(dx) = dx$. Let I be a finite interval, and let $\lambda_j = \lambda_j(I,\omega)$, $j = 1,2,\ldots$ be the eigenvalues of L_ω considered in I under a fixed boundary condition (e.g. the Dirichlet condition) . Then there exists a continuous non-decreasing function $n(\xi)$ such that with probability one,

$$\lim_{I\uparrow R} \frac{1}{|I|} \#\{\lambda_j \leq \xi\} = n(\xi) \text{ , for all } \xi \in R \text{ ,}$$

and such that the spectrum of L_ω coincides with $\mathrm{Supp}(dn(\xi))$. This $n(\xi)$ is called the integrated density of states. The function $w(\lambda)$ is related to $n(\xi)$ by the following formula: for some $\alpha \in R$,

$$(7) \quad w(\lambda) = \alpha + \int_0^\infty \frac{1+\xi\lambda}{\xi-\lambda} \frac{n(\xi)}{1+\xi^2} d\xi \text{ , } \lambda \in C-[0,\infty) \text{ .}$$

Concerning the asymptotic behaviors of $n(\xi)$, we have the following:

Theorem 3

(i) $n(\xi) \sim (\mu_1/\pi)\xi^{1/2}$, $\xi\to+\infty$, where $\mu_1 = E[\int_0^1 (m'_\omega(x))^{1/2} dx]$, $m'_\omega(x)$ being the density of the absolutely continuous part of m_ω .

(ii) If $Q_\omega \equiv 0$, then

$$n(\xi) \sim (\mu_2/\pi)\xi^{1/2} \text{ , } \xi\to 0+ \text{ , where } \mu_2 = (E[m_\omega((0,1])])^{1/2} \text{ .}$$

Proof

(i) As in Proposition 7.1 of [9], we can prove that

$$w(\lambda) \sim -\mu_1(-\lambda)^{1/2} \text{ , } \lambda \to -\infty \text{ .}$$

On the other hand, we have from (7) that

$$w(\lambda) = \lambda\int_1^\infty \frac{1}{\xi-\lambda}\,\frac{n(\xi)}{\xi}d\xi + O(1) \ , \ \lambda \to -\infty \ .$$

From these two and by the iterated use of the Tauberian theorem ([5], [12]), we see

$$\int_1^\xi \frac{n(t)}{t}\,dt \sim \frac{2}{\pi}\mu_1\xi^{1/2} \ , \ \xi \to +\infty \ .$$

Therefore, integrating by parts, we obtain

$$\int_1^\xi n(t)dt = \int_1^\xi t\frac{n(t)}{t}dt \sim \frac{2}{3}\pi\mu_1\xi^{1/2} \ , \ \xi \to +\infty \ .$$

The desired conclusion follows from the monotonicity of $n(\xi)$.

(ii) From Proposition 7.1 of [9], we have

$$w(\lambda) \sim -\mu_2(-\lambda)^{1/2} \ , \ \lambda \to 0- \ .$$

In particular, $w(0-) = 0$, so that

$$\alpha = -\int_0^\infty \frac{1}{\xi}\,\frac{n(\xi)}{1+\xi^2}\,d\xi \ .$$

Substituting this into (7) and noting that

$$\lambda\int_0^\infty \frac{1}{\xi-\lambda}\,\frac{n(\xi)}{1+\xi^2}\,d\xi = O(|\lambda|) \ , \ \lambda \to 0- \ ,$$

we obtain

$$\lambda\int_0^\infty \frac{1}{\xi-\lambda}\,\frac{n(\xi)}{\xi}\,d\xi \sim -\mu_2(-\lambda)^{1/2} \ , \ \lambda \to 0- \ .$$

From the same argument as (i), we get the desired conclusion.

References

[1] R. Carmona: Random Schrodinger Operators, Ecole d'Eté de Probabilité XIV, Saint Flour, 1984 (to appear)

[2] I.P. Cornfeld, S.V. Fomin, Ya.G. Sinai: Ergodic Theory, Springer Verlag, New York-Berlin-Heidelberg, (1982)

[3] P. Deift, B. Simon: Almost Periodic Schrodinger Operators III. The Absolutely Continuous Spectrum in One Dimension Commun. Math. Phys. 90, 389-411 (1983)

[4] H. Dym, H.P. McKean: Gaussian Processes, Function Theory, and the Inverse Spectral Problems. Academic Press, New York-San Francisco-

London (1976)

[5] W. Feller: An Introduction to Probability Theory and Its Applications, vol. II, second edition. John Wiley & Sons Inc., New York-London-Sydney-Toronto, (1971)

[6] S. Kotani: Ljapounov indices determine absolutely continuous spectra of random one-dimensional Schrodinger operators, Proc. Taniguchi Symp. SA Katata (1982), 225-247

[7] S. Kotani, S. Watanabe: Krein's spectral theory of strings and generalized diffusion processes, Lect. Note in Math. 923, 235-259 Springer, Berlin-Heidelberg-New York (1982)

[8] H.P. McKean: Elementary solutions for certain parabolic partial differential equation, Trans. Amer. Math. Soc. 82, 519-548 (1956)

[9] N.Minami: An Extension of Kotani's Theorem to Random Generalized Sturm-Liouville Operators (to appear)

[10] J. Neveu: Processus Ponctuel, Ecole d'Eté de Probabilités de Saint Flour VI-1976, Lect. Notes in Math. 598, Springer Verlag, Berlin-Heidelberg-New York, (1977)

[11] B. Simon: Kotani Theory for One Dimensional Stochastic Jacobi Matrices, Commun. Math. Phys. 89, 227-234 (1983)

[12] D.W. Widder: The Laplace Transform, Princeton University Press, Princeton (1946)

PATH-WISE CALCULUS OF VARIATIONS IN STOCHASTIC MECHANICS

Laura M. Morato
Dipartimento di Fisica "G.Galilei"
Università di Padova

Abstract: A variational problem that provides a quantization method exploiting a stochastic path-wise calculus of variations with the classical action is illustrated. Possible non conventional solutions and their classical limit are also discussed.

Introduction

It is well known that the laws of motion in classical mechanics can be derived from variational principles.

Denoting by L the Lagrangian of the system, in the most usual version the classical trajectory $q(\cdot)$ of the configuration in the time interval $[t_a,t_b]$ is requested to make stationary the classical action $\int_{t_a}^{t_b} L(q(t)),\dot{q}(t))dt$ with respect to arbitrary variations of $q(\cdot)$ such that the end points of the trajectory, $q(t_a)$ and $q(t_b)$, remain fixed.

The sufficient and necessary condition for the stationarity of the action is then that $q(t)$ satisfies the Euler-Lagrange equation in $[t_a,t_b]$. For the simple Lagrangian $L=\frac{1}{2}m\dot{q}^2-V(q)$, with $q(t)$ taking values in $\mathbf{R}^n$, one gets Newton's equation $\ddot{q}=-\frac{1}{m}\nabla V(q)$.

The classical dynamics can also be described by the Hamilton-Jacobi equation, that can also be derived from a variational principle [1]. In this case a velocity field $v(\cdot,\cdot)$ is introduced, such that $\dot{q}(t)=v(q(t),t)$, and the equations of motion are:

$$v(x,t) = \frac{\nabla S(x,t)}{m}$$
$$\partial_t S + \frac{1}{2m}(\nabla S)^2+V=0 \qquad (1)$$

The structure is not very different in Quantum Mechanics: as it has been illustrated in previous works [1][2][3] it is possible to quantize a system still by means of variational principles with the same action. The critical change is in the kind of motion one assumes in the configurations space.

The assumption is that the sample paths of the configuration are generated by those of a Wiener process, through the stochastic differential equation

$$dq(t)=v_{+}(q(t),t)dt + \left(\frac{\hbar}{m}\right)^{\frac{1}{2}} dw(t) \tag{2}$$

where v_{+}, like v in the classical case, has to be determined by dynamical constraints.

The generalization of the Hamilton-Jacobi scheme, working with a renormalized version of the classical action, directly gives the Hamilton-Jacobi equations with the usual quantum corrections. That is one gets the Madelung fluid equations which, as is well known, are equivalent to the Schrödinger equation.

On the other hand the generalization of the path-wise lagrangian scheme, for the simple Lagrangian quoted above, yields Nelson's dynamical equation of Stochastic Mechanics [3]. Such an equation is nothing but the quantum equivalent of Newton's equation for a classical system [4] [2].

An important difference between the two approaches is that in the first the drift v_{+} is constrained to be irrotational by the principle itself, like the velocity field v in the analogous classical principle (see [1]). But this is no longer true in the path-wise approach.

In this article a short review of the path-wise approach with the classical action is given and the solutions with non irrotational drift-fields are illustrated.

The variational problem and its general solutions.

The structure of the variational problem is the following: denoting by $\{t_i\}_{i=1\ldots N}$ an equipartition of the interval $[t_a,t_b]$, by $\Delta^{+}q(t_i)$ the forward increment $q(t_{i+1}) - q(t_i)$ of the configuration, $\Delta^{-}q(t_i)$ the backward increment $q(t_i) - q(t_{i-1})$ and Δ the time difference $\frac{t_b-t_a}{N}$ one considers the discretized mean classical action

$$A^{N}_{[t_a,t_b]}\ (q(\cdot,\cdot))\equiv E\ \left\{\sum_{1}^{N}{}_{i} \left[\tfrac{1}{2}m\ \frac{\Delta^{+}q(t_i)\cdot\Delta^{+}q(t_i)}{\Delta^{2}} - V(q(t_i))\right]\Delta\right\} \tag{3}$$

Then the class of admissible variations is specified in the most natural way: $\delta q(t)$ is assumed to be an admissible variations of $q(t)$ if $q'(t)=q(t)+\delta q(t)$ is also a diffusion with the same diffusion coefficient $\hbar/m$.

This implies that there must exist a new drift field v'_{+} such that $dq'(t)$ is equal to $v'_{+}(q'(t),t)dt+\left(\frac{\hbar}{m}\right)^{\frac{1}{2}}dw\ (t)$.

Thus, putting $\delta q(t)=\varepsilon h(t)$ and $v'_{+}-v_{+} = \varepsilon f+O(\varepsilon)$ one can see that the sample paths of $\delta q(t)$ can be constructed by means of the solutions of the linear differential equation

$$\dot{h}(t) = \Sigma_j \frac{\partial}{\partial x_j} v_+(q(t),t)h_j(t)+f(q(t),t) \tag{4}$$

Notice that the variations have differentiable sample paths and are measurable with respect to the σ-algebra generated by the past of $q(t)$.

Clearly it is not possible to keep fixed $q(t_a)$ and $q(t_b)$, that would imply $h(t_a)=h(t_b)=0$. As a consequence one has to work with a slightly complicated action, where a boundary term is explicitely added. The action functional then becomes:

$$A^N_{[t_a,t_b]}(q(\cdot,\cdot),\ P_b)= = E\left\{\Sigma_1^N{}_i \left[\tfrac{1}{2}m \frac{\Delta^+q(t_i)\cdot\Delta^+q(t_i)}{\Delta^2} - V(q(t_i))\right] -P_b\cdot q(t_b)\right\} \tag{5}$$

and the variational problem is finding a (smooth) diffusion $q(\cdot,\cdot)$ such that

$$\lim_{N\uparrow\infty} \delta A^N_{[t_a,t_b]}(q(\cdot,\cdot),\ P_b) = o(\varepsilon) \tag{6}$$

for all admissible variations such that $\delta q(t_a)=0$.

To perform the calculus of variations a basic observation is that, by extimating $\Delta^+q(t)$ to the order $\Delta^{3/2}$, the kinetic term can be decomposed as

$$E\left\{\tfrac{1}{2}m \frac{\Delta^+q(t)\cdot\Delta^+q(t)}{\Delta^2}\right\} = E\left\{\tfrac{1}{2}m \frac{\Delta^+q(t)\cdot\Delta^-q(t)}{\Delta^2} + \frac{\hbar n}{2\Delta} + o(\Delta)\right\} \tag{7}$$

Thus the variation of $\frac{\hbar n}{2\Delta}$ is zero and the variation of the first term gives

$$\begin{aligned}\delta E\left\{\frac{\Delta^+q(t)\cdot\Delta^-q(t)}{\Delta^2}\right\} &= \varepsilon\ E\left\{\frac{\Delta^+q(t)\cdot\Delta^-h(t)+\Delta^-q(t)\cdot\Delta h(t)}{\Delta^2}\right\} \\ &= \varepsilon\ E\ \frac{1}{\Delta^2}\left[\dot{v}_+(q(t),t)\Delta+\left(\frac{\hbar}{m}\right)^2\Delta^+w(t)\right]\cdot\Delta^-h(t) + \\ &+ \left[v_-(q(t),t)\ \Delta + \left(\frac{\hbar}{m}\right)^2 \Delta^-w^*(t)\right]\Delta^+h(t) + \\ &+ O(\Delta^2)\Big\} + o(\varepsilon)\end{aligned} \tag{8}$$

where the usual backward representation of $q(t)$ is exploited, namely

$$dq(t)=v_-(q(t),t)dt+\left(\frac{\hbar}{m}\right)^{\frac{1}{2}} dw^*(t) \tag{9}$$

$w^*(t)$ being a reversed version of a standard Wiener process.

The calculus then comes from the properties of the process $h(t)$, in particular from the differentiability of its sample paths, so that $\Delta^{\pm}h(t)$ is of the first order in Δ, and its measurability properties.

The details of the calculation are given in [3].

For the decomposition (7) see for example [2].

One finds

$$\lim_{N\uparrow\infty} \delta A^N_{[t_a,t_b]} (q(\cdot,\cdot),P_{t_b}) =$$

$$= \varepsilon E \left\{ \int_{t_a}^{t_b} \left[-\tfrac{1}{2}m(D_+v_-(q(t),t)+D_-v_+(q(t),t)-\nabla V(q(t)) \right] \cdot h(t)) \right\} +$$

$$+E\left\{ \left[\tfrac{1}{2}m(v_++v_-)(q(t_b),t_b)-P_{t_b}\right] h(t_b)\right\} +o(\varepsilon) + \tag{10}$$

$$+ \lim_{N\uparrow\infty} E \left\{ \sum_{1i}^{N} \tfrac{1}{2}m \left(\frac{\hbar}{m}\right)^{\frac{1}{2}} \sum_{1j}^{n} \left[\dot{h}_j(t_i) - \sum_{1k}^{n} \frac{\partial}{\partial x_j} v_+^k (q(t_i),t_i) \right.\right.$$

$$\left.\left. h_k(t_i)\right] \Delta^- w_*^j(t_i) \right\}$$

where D_+ and D_- denote, as usual in Stochastic Mechanics, the forward and backward conditioned derivatives.

One can see that the first term is the analogue of the classical result and the second is simply a boundary term. The third term, involving $\Delta^- w^*(t)$, comes from the non reversible measurability property of h(t) with respect to q(t). In fact h(t) is measurable with respect to the past of q(t) and so it is independent of $\Delta^+ w(t)$, but it is not independent of the future of q(t) and as a consequence $E\{\Delta^- w^*(t)\cdot\Delta^+ h(t)\}$ is different from zero.

This term disappeardsif v_+ is irrotational, as one can immediatly see by comparing with (4).

Now the first result, corresponding to the orthodox quantization, is the following if q(t) has an irrotational drift field and satisfies Nelson's dynamical equations

$$\tfrac{1}{2}m \left[D_+v_-(q(t),t)+D_-v_+(q(t),t) \right] = -\nabla V(q(t)) \tag{11}$$

with the boundary condition $\frac{1}{2}m(v_++v_-)(q(t_b),t_b)=P_b$, then

$$\lim_{N\uparrow\infty} \delta A^N_{[t_a,t_b]} [q(\cdot,\cdot), P_b] = o(\varepsilon) \tag{12}$$

for every admissible variation such that $\delta q(t_a)=0$. The necessity of the condition can also be proved [3].

Now one can introduce the current velocity $v=\frac{v_++v_-}{2}$ and the osmotic velocity

$u = \frac{v_+ - v_-}{2}$, so that, since for a (smooth) diffusion u is equal to $\frac{\hbar}{2m} \nabla \ell n\, \rho$ and the continuity equation $\partial_t \rho = -\nabla(\rho v)$ holds, the equations of motion can be written as

$$\begin{cases} \partial_t \rho = -\nabla(\rho v) & (13a) \\ \partial_t v + (v\cdot\nabla)v - \left[\frac{\hbar}{2m} \nabla^2 u + (u\cdot\nabla)u\right] = -\frac{1}{m} \nabla V & (13b) \end{cases}$$

and consequently, in terms of a scalar field S such that v is equal to $\frac{1}{m} \nabla S$, and putting $\rho = e^{2R}$, one gets the Madelung fluid equations

$$\begin{cases} \partial_t \rho = -\nabla\left(\rho \frac{\nabla S}{m}\right) & (14a) \\ \partial_t S + \frac{1}{2m} (\nabla S)^2 - \frac{\hbar^2}{2m} \left[(\nabla R)^2 + \nabla^2 R\right] + V = 0 & (14b) \end{cases}$$

The position $\psi = \rho^{\frac{1}{2}}\, e^{\frac{i}{\hbar} S}$ finally gives the Schrödinger equation.

The classical limit of (14) are the well known equations of the Hamilton-Jacobi fluid. The physical interpretation of this fact can be stated as follows: if one considers a statistical ensemble of quantum systems whose initial state is $\psi_o \equiv \rho_o\, e^{\frac{i}{\hbar} S_o}$, corresponding, in the framework of Stochastic Mechanics, to an initial probability density ρ_o and to an initial current velocity field $v_o \equiv \frac{1}{m} \nabla S_o$, then the fluidodynamical state (ρ, S), that evolves according to (14), approaches, at the classical limit, the state of an ideal frictionless fluid whose velocity field v is irrotational for all t.

One can now ask which kind of motions and related classical limits are obtained if the stationarity of the mean classical action is requested without the additional constraint of having an irrotational drift field.

One has to find out a better form for the third term in (10). Here the divergence is only appearent, as one can see replacing $\Delta^- w^*(t)$ by its expression in terms of w(t) [4].

In fact, from (2) and (9) one gets

$$\Delta^- w^*(t) = 2 \left(\frac{m}{\hbar}\right)^{\frac{1}{2}} u(q(t),t)\, \Delta + \Delta^+ w(t-\Delta) + 0(\Delta) \qquad (15)$$

and then substituting in (10) and exploiting (4) and Itô's differentiation rule one has

$$E\left\{\sum_{ij}^{n}\left[\dot h_j(t)-\sum_{1}^{n}{}_k \frac{\partial}{\partial x_j} v_+^k(q(t),t)\, h_k(t)\right]\Delta^- w_A^j(t)\right\} =$$

$$= E\left\{\sum_{1}^{n}{}_j \sum_{1}^{n}{}_k \left[\frac{\partial}{\partial x_k} v_+^j(q(t),t) - \frac{\partial}{\partial x_j} v_+^k(q(t),t\right] h_k(t)\left[2\left(\frac{m}{\hbar}\right)^{\frac{1}{2}} u^j(q(t),t)\Delta+\right.\right.$$

$$\left.\left.+\Delta^+ w_j(t-\Delta)+o(\Delta)\right]\right\} = \qquad (16)$$

$$= E\left\{\sum_{1}^{n}{}_k \left\{\sum_{1}^{n}{}_j \left[\frac{\partial}{\partial x_k} v_+^j(q(t),t)- \frac{\partial}{\partial x_j} v_+^k(q(t),t\right] 2\left(\frac{m}{\hbar}\right)^{\frac{1}{2}} u^j(q(t),t)\,\Delta + \right.\right.$$

$$\left. + \sum_{1}^{n}\left(\frac{\hbar}{m}\right)^{\frac{1}{2}} \frac{\partial}{\partial x_j}\left[\frac{\partial}{\partial x_x} v_+^j(q(t),t) - \frac{\partial}{\partial x_j} v_+^k(q(t),t\right] \Delta+o(\Delta)\right\} h_k(t)$$

As a consequence the dynamical equations (13) become

$$\begin{cases} \partial_t\rho = - \nabla(\rho v) \\ \partial_t v+(v\cdot\nabla)\, v-\left[\frac{\hbar}{2m}\nabla^2 u + (u\cdot\nabla)\, u\right] + \\ \qquad + u\times(\nabla\times v) + \frac{\hbar}{2m}\nabla\times(\nabla\times v) = -\frac{1}{m}\nabla V \end{cases} \qquad (13')$$

The classical limit is the same as in (13) but the classical velocity field is no longer the gradient of some scalar field. Anyway nothing changes in the classical limit if only one system is under consideration, since the equation $\partial_t v+(v\cdot\nabla)\, v=-\frac{1}{m}\nabla V$, for a non irrotational v, works as well as the Hamilton-Jacobi equation, provided $v_o(q_o)= \frac{p_o}{m} = \frac{\nabla S_o(q_o)}{m}$, if (q_o,p_o) is the initial classical state.

But if one considers a statistical ensemble of systems with initial probability density ρ_o and initial current velocity v_o such that $\nabla\times v_o\neq 0$, the classical limit of (13') that is

$$\begin{cases} \partial_t\rho = - \nabla(\rho v) \\ \partial_t v + (v\cdot\nabla)\, v = \frac{1}{m}\nabla V, \qquad (\nabla\times v)\neq 0 \end{cases} \qquad (14)$$

describes a different physical situation, namely the flow of an ideal frictionless fluid with vortices.

Clearly equations (13') can not be reduced to the Schrödinger equation, and their classical limit (14) is not equivalent to the Hamilton-Jacobi fluid equations.

Thus the physical interpretation of (13'), if it exists, has to be considered a matter of future research and discussion.

But it should also be stressed that, if one considers a statistical ensemble of systems, the existence of quantum equations generalizing the physical situation described by (14) looks natural and in this sense the new equations (13') appear as a reasonable completion of the theory.

References

[1] - F. Guerra and L.M. Morato, Phys. Rev. D27, 1774 (1983).

[2] - E. Nelson, "Quantum Fluctuations" (Princeton University, prss, Princeton, N.J. 1984).

[3] - L.M. Morato, Phys. Rev. D31, 1982 (1985).

[4] - The author is grateful to professor E. Nelson for pointing out this fact.

MACROSCOPIC, INTERMEDIATE, MICROSCOPIC and MESONS

by

Masao NAGASAWA
Institut für Angewandte Mathematik
der Universität Zürich
Rämistrasse 74, CH-8001 Zürich

1. Equilibrium distributions of diffusion processes

An arbitrary (given) positive function $g \in C^1(\mathbb{R}^d)$ becomes an invariant (equilibrium) density of a diffusion process $X(t)$ with a differential operator (generator)$^{(*)}$

(1) $$A = \frac{1}{2}\Delta + \mathbb{b}\cdot\nabla ,$$

if the drift coefficient $\mathbb{b}$ is chosen to be

(2) $$\mathbb{b} = \frac{1}{2}\nabla(\log g) .$$

The equality (2), known as Kolmogoroff's relation (1937), connects the drift coefficient and the invariant density of a diffusion process. Therefore, one can claim, for example, the existence of one-to-one correspondence between the ground state ψ_0 of the Schrödinger equation

(3) $$\frac{1}{2}\Delta\psi + (\lambda - V(x))\psi = 0 ,$$

and a diffusion process $X(t)$ which has the generator A in (1) with $\mathbb{b}$ of (2), defining

(4) $$g = |\psi_0|^2 .$$

(*) The transition probability density $p(t,x,y)$ of $X(t)$ is the fundamental solution of the diffusion equation $\partial p/\partial t = \frac{1}{2}\Delta p + \mathbb{b}\cdot\nabla p$, where Δ is the Laplace-Beltrami operator $\frac{1}{\sqrt{a}}\frac{\partial}{\partial x^i}(\sqrt{a}\, a^{ij}\frac{\partial}{\partial x^j})$. In other words, $X(t)$ is a solution of the stochastic differential equation (SDE) $X(t) = X(0) + \int_0^t \mathbb{b}(X(s))ds + \int_0^t \sigma(X(s))\cdot dB(s)$, where $B(s)$ is the d-dimensional Brownian motion and $(\sigma\sigma^T)^{ij} = a^{ij}$.

If one rewrite (2) as

(5) $$g = e^U \ , \quad U = 2\int^x \mathbb{b}\cdot dx \ ,$$

then g is nothing but the Gibbs distribution of U and $\mathbb{b} = \frac{1}{2}\nabla U$. This relation (5) suggests us the existence of a statistical mechanical structure behind the diffusion description of the ground state of Schrödinger equation (3). We shall come back to this point again.

2. Duality and time reversal of diffusion processes

In general, a positive function $g \in C^1(\mathbb{R}^d)$ is an invariant density of two diffusion processes $X(t)$ and $\hat{X}(t)$ with the dual drift coefficients $\mathbb{b}$ and $\hat{\mathbb{b}}$, respectively, determined by the relations

(6) $$\mathbb{b} + \hat{\mathbb{b}} = \nabla(\log g) \ ,$$

(7) $$\nabla\{(\mathbb{b} - \hat{\mathbb{b}})g\} = 0 \ ,$$

(see Nagasawa (1961), Nagasawa-Tanaka (1985)). The probabilistic meaning of the dual processes $X(t)$ and $\hat{X}(t)$ with respect to $g(x)dx$ is given by the relation of time reversal

(8) $$\hat{X}(t) = X(-t)$$

under the condition that $X(t)$ and $\hat{X}(t)$ are distributed according to the given $g \in C^1(\mathbb{R}^d)$, (for time reversal see Schrödinger (1931), Nagasawa (1964), Föllmer-Wakolbinger (1985)).

3. Time inhomogeneous case

For a positive function $g(t,x)$ of time t and position x , $(t,x) \in [0,L]\times\mathbb{R}^d$, where L is a positive constant, let $\mathbb{b}(t,x)$ and $\hat{\mathbb{b}}(t,x)$ satisfy (6). Denote

(9) $$A(t) = \frac{1}{2}\Delta + \mathbb{b}(t,\cdot)\cdot\nabla \ , \quad \hat{A}(t) = \frac{1}{2}\Delta + \hat{\mathbb{b}}(t,\cdot)\cdot\nabla \ ,$$

and let $p(s,x;t,y)$ be the fundamental solution of

(10) $$\frac{\partial p}{\partial t} = A(t)p \ .$$

We impose a condition on $g(t,x)$

(11) $$g(t,y) = \int dx g(0,x)p(0,x;t,y) .$$

Let

(12) $$L(t) = \frac{\partial}{\partial t} + A(t) , \quad \hat{L}(t) = -\frac{\partial}{\partial t} + \hat{A}(t) .$$

Then $L(t)$ and $\hat{L}(t)$ are in duality with respect to $g(t,x)dtdx$, i.e.

(13) $$\int_{[0,L]} dt \int_{\mathbb{R}^d} (uL(t)v)gdx = \int_{[0,L]} dt \int_{\mathbb{R}^d} (v\hat{L}(t)u)gdx ,$$

for any $u \in D$ and $v \in \hat{D}$, where $D = \{u(t,x) : u(0,x) = \int p(0,x;L,y)u(L,y) \times dy\}$ and $\hat{D} = \{v(t,x) : v(L,y)g(L,y) = \int dx v(0,x)g(0,x)p(0,x;L,y)\}$.

One can formulate time reversal of a time inhomogeneous Markov process in terms of the corresponding space-time process, which is a time homogeneous Markov process on an extended space-time state space $[0,L]\times\mathbb{R}^d$.(*) Let $X(t)$ be the time inhomogeneous diffusion process with the transition density $p(s,x;t,y)$. The space-time process $(t,X(t))$ has the transition probability

(14) $$P_{(s,x)}[(t,X(t)) \in d(r,y)] = p(s,x;r,y)dy\delta_{s+t}(dr) ,$$ (**)

In othe words, the transition semi-group $\mathbb{P}_t$ of the space-time process is given by

(15) $$\mathbb{P}_t f(s,x) = \iint_{[0,L]\times\mathbb{R}^d} p(s,x;r,y)\delta_{s+t}(dr)dyf(r,y) ,$$

for $f \in C([0,L]\times\mathbb{R}^d)$. The dual semi-group $\mathbb{P}_t^*$ of $\mathbb{P}_t$ with respect to $g(t,x)dtdx$ is given by

(16) $$\mathbb{P}_t^* f(r,x) = \iint_{[0,L]\times\mathbb{R}^d} p^*(r,x;s,y)dy\delta_{r+t}(ds)f(s,y) ,$$

where

(17) $$p^*(r,x;s,y) = \frac{1}{g(L-r,x)} p(L-s,y;L-r,x)g(L-s,y) .$$

(*) The space-time process is a transient Markov process and any constant time L is an L-time (the last occurrence time) of the space-time process and theorems on time reversal for transient Markov processes can be applied (see Nagasawa (1964)).

(**) $P_{(s,x)}$ denotes conditional probability that $(t,X(t))$ starts at (s,x).

The generator $L^*(t) = \frac{\partial}{\partial t} + (\frac{1}{2}\Delta + \mathbb{b}^*(t,\cdot)\cdot\nabla)$ of $\mathbb{P}_t^*$ is given by

(18) $$L^*(t) = \frac{\partial}{\partial t} + \hat{A}(L-t) \ .$$

That is, the following relation holds between the drift coefficients $\mathbb{b}^*(t,x)$ and $\mathbb{b}(t,x)$

(19) $$\begin{aligned}\mathbb{b}^*(t,x) &= -\mathbb{b}(L-t,x) + \nabla \log g(L-t,x) \\ &= \hat{\mathbb{b}}(L-t,x) \ ,\end{aligned}$$

and by a theorem of time-reversal (Nagasawa (1964)) the dual process $(t,X^*(t))$ is the time reversal of $(t,X(t))$ from L, i.e.,

(20) $$(t,X^*(t)) = (L-t,X(L-t)) \ .$$

4. Stochastic Mechanics

Assume that $\mathbb{b}(t,x)$ and $\hat{\mathbb{b}}(t,x)$ are C^1 in t and C^2 in x. Defining the mean acceleration by

(21) $$\alpha(t,x) = \frac{1}{2}\{-\hat{L}(t)\mathbb{b}(t,x) - L(t)\hat{\mathbb{b}}(t,x)\} \ ,$$

Nelson (1966) proved that the mean Newton's equation

(22) $$\alpha = -\nabla V$$

is equivalent to the Schrödinger equation

(23) $$\frac{1}{i}\frac{\partial\psi}{\partial t} = \frac{1}{2}\Delta\psi - V\psi \ ,$$

where

(24) $$\psi = e^{\alpha+i\beta} \ , \quad g = |\psi|^2$$

(25) $$\mathbb{b} = \frac{1}{2}\nabla(\log g) + \nabla\beta \ , \quad \hat{\mathbb{b}} = \frac{1}{2}\nabla(\log g) - \nabla\beta \ ,$$

when g (therefore ψ) has no zeros. Yasue (1981) formulated this in terms of variational princile. There are many interesting attempts by many authors in this direction, but I will not follow them here, because my intension is different from theirs. References can be found in the articles on this subject in this volume.

5. Singularity

If $g \in C^1(\mathbb{R}^d)$ has zeros (for example, take $g = |\psi|^2$, where ψ is an excited state of (3)), then g can not be, in general, an invariant density of the diffusion process with the drift coefficient $\mathbb{b}$ defined by (2) (for a counterexample see Appendix of Nagasawa-Tanaka (1985)). It is clear that the drift coefficient $\mathbb{b}$ defined by (2) has singularity, if g has zeros. This singularity causes some mathematical difficulties when one discusses the existence of diffusion processes and the duality (time reversal). A sufficient condition for duality is given in Appendix of Nagasawa-Tanaka (1985). For $g = |\psi|^2$, where ψ is a (complex valued) solution of (3), one can overcome the difficulties, because the diffusion process $X(t)$ does not hit the zeros of ψ under some conditions. A sufficient condition is

$$(26) \qquad \frac{2(V(x)-\lambda)+(\nabla(\alpha+\beta))^2}{(\nabla\alpha)^2} \geqq \gamma > 0$$

in a neighbourhood of zeros of $\psi = e^{\alpha+i\beta}$.(*) If $V(x)$ is bounded from below, (26) reduces to

$$(27) \qquad \frac{(\nabla(\alpha+\beta))^2}{(\nabla\alpha)^2} \geqq \gamma > 0 ,$$

and if ψ is real valued (i.e. $\nabla\beta = 0$), then the condition (27) is trivial. According to Zheng-Meyer (1983) the inaccessibility follows, if

$$(28) \qquad \int \|\mathbb{b}\|^2 g dx < \infty , \text{ or}$$

$$(29) \qquad |\psi(x)-\psi(y)| < c|x-y| , \quad \text{where} \quad g = |\psi|^2 .$$

Remark. In $\mathbb{R}^1$ assume that $g(x) = |x|^k$, $k > 0$, in a neighbourhood of $\{0\}$. In this case the integrability condition (28) is equivalent to $k > 1$. According to the Feller's test $\{0\}$ is inaccessible for $k = 1$. This case is not covered by the condition (28), although it looks quite reasonable. The condition (29) is stronger than (28).

(*) In Nagasawa (1980), (6.5) should be read as (26) above, (6.9) as $\frac{1}{2}\frac{1}{|\psi|}\Delta|\psi| = (V-\lambda) + \frac{1}{2}(\nabla\beta)^2$, and (6.12) as $Ag \leqq 0$. Delete (6.10),(6.11).

For singular diffusion processes of this kind see also Carlen(1984), Nelson (1984).

6. A microscopic model

Let $X_i(t)$, $i=1,2,\cdots,N$ satisfy a system of stochastic differential equations (SDE)

$$(30) \qquad X_i(t) = X_i(0) + B_i(t) + \int_0^t \frac{1}{N} \sum_{j=1}^N b(X_i(s),X_j(s))ds ,$$

where $B_i(t)$, $i=1,2,\cdots,N$, are independent d-dimensional Brownian motions and $X_i(0)$ are independent identically distributed random variables which are independent of the Brownian motions. We define

$$(31) \qquad b[x,u] = \int_{\mathbb{R}^d} b(x,y)u(dy)$$

for a probability distribution u on $\mathbb{R}^d$. Then the third term of (30) is $\int_0^t b[X(s),U_N(s)]ds$, where $U_n(s) = \frac{1}{N}\sum_{j=1}^N \delta_{X_j(s)}$. Assuming a Lipshitz continuity for $b(x,y)$, McKean (1967) proved that, as $N\to\infty$, $\{X_i(t)\}$ converges in law to a system of infinitely many independent diffusion processes, each of which satisfies a non-linear SDE(*)

$$(32) \qquad X(t) = X(0) + B(t) + \int_0^t b[X(s),u(s)]ds ,$$

where $u(s)$ denotes the probability distribution of the process $X(s)$ itself (Vlasov-McKean limit of the mean field interaction). For this see also Tanaka (1984), Kusuoka-Tamura (1984), Sznitman (1984), Shiga-Tanaka (1985).

7. Equilibrium distributions

To avoid mathematical (non-trivial) difficulty which arises in higher dimensions, we treat a system of interacting particles on the line. Assume that the process $X(t)$ of (32) is in an equilibrium state, i.e., the probability distribution $u(t)$ of $X(t)$ is independent of t, and a density $g\in C^1(\mathbb{R}^1)$ exists. Then, the Kolmogoroff's

(*) Take the limit $N\to\infty$ formally in (30), assuming $U_N(t)\to u(t)$.

relation (2) claims that the interaction $b(x,y)$ and the equilibrium density $g(x)$ must satisfy the relation

$$\frac{1}{2}\frac{1}{g}\frac{dg}{dx} = \int_{\mathbb{R}^1} b(x,y)g(y)dy \;. \tag{33}$$

Thus the equilibrium density determines the pair interaction between Brownian particles in the system, if the equilibrium distribution is given in advance.

Example. Let $g(x) = ce^{-x^2}$ and $b(x,y) = f(x-y)$. Then, (33) is

$$-x = \int_{\mathbb{R}^1} f(x-y)ce^{-y^2}dy \;, \tag{34}$$

and $f(x) = -x$ is the solution of (34). That is, the Gaussian distribution is the equilibrium distribution of a system of diffusion particles with the linear attractive pair interaction.

Because of this, one can interprete the system of interacting diffusion processes as a microscopic model for the diffusion process with the drift coefficient $\mathbb{b} = \frac{1}{2}\nabla(\log g)$. In other words, this single (non-linear) diffusion process can be thought of a representative of interacting diffusion processes, as $N \to \infty$.

8. Singular interaction between coloured particles

If an equilibrium density g has zeros, there is no solution $f(x)$ of (33), where $b(x,y) = f(x-y)$ is assumed. To construct a microscopic model for such a function g, we must introduce an additional structure. Namely, we consider a system of coloured particles.

As an example, let us consider the case that g is symmetric, positive except at the origin and $g(0) = 0$. We distribute N-blue particles $X_1, \cdots, X_N$ on the negative half line and N-red particles $Y_1, \cdots, Y_N$ on the positive half line. Assume that the particles satisfy the following system of stochastic differential equations with reflecting boundary condition at the origin:

$$(35)\begin{cases} X_i(t) = X_i(0) + B_i^-(t) + \int_0^t ds\{-\frac{1}{N}\sum_{\ell=1}^N f(Y_\ell(s)-X_i(s)) + v(X_i(s))\} - \Phi_i(t) \end{cases}$$

$$(35)\ \left\{ Y_j(t) = Y_j(0) + B_j^+(t) + \int_0^t ds\{+\frac{1}{N}\sum_{\ell=1}^{N} f(Y_j(s)-X_\ell(s))+v(Y_j(s))\} + \Psi_j(t) \right.$$

where $\{B_i^-(t), B_j^+(t)\}$ are independent one-dimensional Brownian motions and $X_i(0)$ (resp. $Y_j(0)$) are independent identically distributed random variables on $(-\infty,0]$ (resp. $[0,\infty)$) which are independent of the Brownian motions. Moreover, assume that $f(x)$ is a nonincreasing continuous function on $(0,\infty)$ which may diverge at the origin, and $v(x)$ is an odd function which is nonincreasing and continuous on $\mathbb{R}^1-\{0\}$. Then $\{X_i(t), Y_j(t), i,j=1,\cdots,N\}$ become, as $N \to \infty$, mutually independent and each pair $(X_i(t), Y_j(t))$ converges in law to $(X(t),Y(t))$ which satisfies the following non-linear SDE with reflecting boundary condition at the origin:

$$(36)\ \begin{cases} X(t) = X(0) + B^-(t) + \int_0^t ds\{-\int_{[0,\infty)} f(y-X(s))u_Y(s,dy)+v(X(s))\} - \Phi(t) \\ Y(t) = Y(0) + B^+(t) + \int_0^t ds\{+\int_{(-\infty,0]} f(Y(s)-x)u_X(s,dx)+v(Y(s))\} + \Psi(t) \end{cases}$$

where u_X (resp. u_Y) denotes the probability distribution of $X(t)$ (resp. $Y(t)$), (see Nagasawa-Tanaka (to appear)).

Example. Let $(X(t),Y(t))$ of (36) be in an equilibrium state distributed according to

$$(37)\qquad g(x) = cx^2 e^{-x^2} .$$

Then, clearly

$$\frac{1}{2}\frac{1}{g}\frac{dg}{dx} = \frac{1}{x} - x .$$

Let us assume that $v(x) = -x$ and

$$(38)\qquad \frac{1}{x} = \int_{(0,\infty)} f(x+y)g(y)dy , \qquad x > 0 .$$

The equation (38) has a unique solution

$$(39)\qquad f(x) = \frac{1}{c}\frac{3}{x^4} + f_0(x)$$

where $f_0(x)$ is positive, completely monotone on $(0,\infty)$ and $O(\frac{1}{x^2})$ as $x \to 0$ (Föllmer-Nagasawa, see Nagasawa-Tanaka (1985)).

Thus we can interprete the distribution $g = cx^2 e^{-x^2}$ $(=|\psi|^2$, ψ is the first sxcited state of the 1-dim. harmonic oscillator) as the equilibrium distribution (as $N \to \infty$) of the system of coloured particles governed by (35). For systems of coloured particles with a random segregating front see Nagasawa-Tanaka (preprint).

For higher excited states, we distribute particles on the line as blues, reds, blues, reds, $\cdots$, separated by zeros of the distributions. In higher dimensions we need more colours depending on the symmetry of distributions (eight colours appear in Nagasawa-Yasue (1982)).

9. An application: Mass-spectrum of Mesons

Our statistical model for interacting particles consists of Microscopic (interacting diffusion processes), Intermediate (a non-linear diffusion process in the mean-field), and Macroscopic (equilibrium distributions, eigenvalue problems) descriptions (Nagasawa (1980)). This statistical model has been applied to analysing the mass-spectrum of Mesons (Nagasawa-Yasue (1982)). In the model a "meson" consists of a pair of quarks (q,q') and an equilibrium distribution (string distribution) $g = |\psi|^2$, where ψ satisfies

$$(40) \quad \frac{1}{2}\{\sigma^2\frac{\partial^2\psi}{\partial x^2} + a(\frac{\partial^2\psi}{\partial y^2} + \frac{\partial^2\psi}{\partial z^2})\} + \{\lambda - k|x| - \varepsilon(y^2 + z^2) + m_a\}\psi = 0 ,$$

where $m_a = \sqrt{2a\varepsilon}$. The mass of a "meson" is, therfore, given by

$$(41) \qquad M_{n,j}(q,q') = \lambda_n + j\cdot m_a + m_q + m_{q'}$$

where m_q denotes the mass of a quark q, λ_n $(n=1,2,\cdots)$ is the eigen values of

$$(42) \qquad \frac{1}{2}\sigma^2\frac{d^2u}{dx^2} + (\lambda - k|x|)u = 0 ,$$

and $j\cdot m_a$ $(j=0,1,2,\cdots)$ is the eigen values of the two-dimensional harmonic oscillator. In (40) σk and $\sigma\varepsilon$ should be determined empirically by the mass of observed mesons. Namely, σk is chosen to be

$$(43) \qquad [\frac{(\sigma k)^2}{2}]^{1/3} = 136.99336 \text{ Mev}$$

by identifying the eigenvalue of the ground state of (42) with the mass of $\pi^{\pm}$-meson. $m_a = \sqrt{2a\varepsilon} \doteq 15$ Mev is chosen to be the difference of the masses of ω- and ρ-mesons. We assume that the mass m_u (m_d) of u- (d-) quark is negligible. $m_s \doteq 50$ Mev is so chosen in comparison of $M_{n,j}$ in (41) to the mass of $K^{\pm}$-meson which is the lightest meson containig one s-quark. $m_c \doteq 700$ Mev is shosen so by comparing $M_{n,j}$ with the mass of $D^{\pm}(D^0)$, which is the lightest meson containing one c-quark. The observed masses of mesons are compared with the computed masses in 68 cases. There were two cases which could not be identified well with computed masses, the case 8 and the case 42. The case 8 possibly indicates, as is remarked, that the mixture of quark states should be considered as the decay mode shows. The case 42 of the charmed strange meson $F^{\pm}$ is different from the case 8. According to the "Data Booklet 1982", the observed mass was 2021 Mev ± 15. On the other hand the mass computed by the rule (25) of Nagasawa-Yasue (1982) is $(c,\phi_{12},s) = 1986$ Mev, which is too light to be identified with 2021 Mev. Therefore, it was not possible to identify $F^{\pm}$ with our composit model of mesons. However, in the "Data Booklet 1984" the mass of $F^{\pm}$ is corrected to be 1971 Mev ±16, which agrees with our predicted value 1986 Mev.

10. Other applications

The statistical model model which is discussed above has been applied to some problems in Biology (Nagasawa (1980),(1981)). See also Albeverio-Blanchard-Høgh-Krohn (1984).

References

Albeverio,S., Blanchard,Ph. & Høgh-Krohn,R.(1984), A stochastic model for the orbits of planets and satelites: An interpretation of Titius-Bode law. Asterisque.

Carlen,E.(1984), Conservative diffusions, Comm.Math.Phys. 94,393-315.

Föllmer,H. & Wakolbinger,A.(preprint), Time reversal of infinite-dimensional diffusions.

Kolmogoroff,A.(1937), Zur Umkehrbarkeit der statistichen Naturgesetze, Math.Ann. 113, 766-772.

Kusuoka,S. & Tamura,Y.(1984), Gibbs measures for mean field potentials, J.Fac. Sci.Univ.Tokyo Sect. 1A Math. 31, 223-245.

McKean,H.P.(1967), Propagation of chaos for a class of non-linear parabolic equations, Lecture series in Diff.Eqs. 41-57, Cath.Univ.

Nagasawa,M.(1961), The adjoint process of a diffusion with reflecting barrier, Kodai Math.Sem.Rep. 13,235-248.

Nagasawa,M.(1964), Time reversions of Markov processes, Nagoya Math.J. 24,177-204.

Nagasawa,M.(1980), Segregation of a population in an environment, Jour. Math.Biology 9,213-235.

Nagasawa,M.(1981), An application of the segregation model for septation of Escherichia coli, J.Theor.Biology 90,445-455.

Nagasawa,M. & Yasue,K.(1982), A statistical model of mesons, Publ. de l'Inst.rech.Math.Avan. (CNRS) 33,1-48, Univ. Strasbourg.

Nagasawa,M. & Tanaka,H.(1985), A diffusion process in a singular mean-drift-field, Z.Wahr.Verw.Geb. 68,247-269.

Nagasawa,M. & Tanaka,H.(to appear), Propagation of chaos for diffusing particles of two types with singular mean field interaction, Z. Wahr.verw.Geb.

Nagasawa,M. & Tanaka,H.(preprint), Diffusion with interactions and collisions between coloured particles and the propagation of chaos.

Nelson,E.(1966), Derivation of Schrödinger equation from Newtonian Mechanics, Phys.Rev. 150,1076-1085.

Nelson,E.(1984), Critical diffusions, Sem. de Probabilités XIX.1-11, Lecture Notes in Math. 1123,Springer.

Schrödinger,F.(1931), Ueber die Umkenrung der Naturgesetze, Berliner Berichte, Sitzung der phy.-math. Klasse, 144-153.

Shiga,H. & Tanaka,H.(1985), Central limit theorem for a system of Markovian particles with mean field interaction, Z.Wahr.verw.Geb. 69,439-459.

Sznitman,A-S.(1984), Non-linear diffusion processes and propagation of chaos, and fluctuations associated, J.Funct.Analy. 56,311-336.

Tanaka,H.(1984), Limit theorems for certain diffusion processes with interaction, Stochastic Analysis (ed.K.Itô) Kinikuniya Co.Ltd. Tokyo,North-Holland Pub.Co. pp.469-488.

Yasue,K.(1981), Stochastic calculus of variations, J.Funct.Anay. 41, 327-340.

Zheng,W. & Meyer,P.A.(1984), Construction de processus de Nelson reversibles, Sem. de ProbabilitésXIX,12-25, Lecture Notes in Math. 1123, Springer.

Field Theory and the Future of Stochastic Mechanics

Edward Nelson
Department of Mathematics
Princeton University

Abstract

Some severe difficulties with stochastic mechanics as a physical theory are pointed out, and it is suggested that these difficulties may be overcome by studying random fields on space-time rather than the diffusion of particle systems in configuration space. A discussion of Bell's theorem leads to the conclusion that it is no obstacle to the description of quantum phenomena by classical random fields. A new quantization method related to stochastic mechanics is developed. The construction of quantum fields from random fields without analytic continuation in time is carried out in the case of the free scalar field. Several open problems concerning random fields are described, in a program relating them to the description of quantum phenomena.

Field Theory and the Future of Stochastic Mechanics

Stochastic mechanics appears to have reached a critical point in its development. In this article I will attempt to describe the direction in which I think it can most fruitfully develop. I have many problems to raise and no solutions to offer. Sections 3, 4, and 5 contain suggestions as to how the viewpoint of stochastic mechanics may be useful in technical problems of constructive quantum field theory. These ideas may be of interest to those mathematical physicists who are not attracted by stochastic mechanics per se. But the article as a whole is informed by a

---

Presented to the International Conference on

Stochastic Processes in Classical and Quantum Systems,
Ascona, June 24-29, 1985.

specific view of what stochastic mechanics is all about: it is an attempt to build a naively realistic picture of physical phenomena, an objective representation of physical processes without reference to any observer. This is undoubtedly its main attraction to many physicists and chemists, and by the same token it is the reason for the strong opposition to it.

It is difficult to express the joy with which I see that so many physicists and mathematicians, especially in Europe, now take stochastic mechanics seriously. This conference is an occasion for celebration, but lest we celebrate unwisely let me begin this article on a cautionary note.

1. The case against stochastic mechanics

It is usual to say that quantum mechanics is nonlocal, but its nonlocal features cannot be used to transmit signals. Despite a proposal made to the U.S. Department of Defense (see [16]), the Einstein-Podolsky-Rosen effect does not yield a practical method for communicating with submarines.

In its most basic form, locality can be discussed without any reference to the nature of space-time, in terms of the separability of two correlated but dynamically uncoupled systems. Suppose that we have two Hamiltonians H_1 and H_2 on the Hilbert spaces $\mathcal{H}_1$ and $\mathcal{H}_2$, and let

$$H = H_1 \otimes 1 + 1 \otimes H_2$$

on $\mathcal{H} = \mathcal{H}_1 \otimes \mathcal{H}_2$. The state vector Ψ may be an arbitrary unit vector in $\mathcal{H}$, not necessarily a tensor product $\Psi_1 \otimes \Psi_2$. But for any observable A_1 of $\mathcal{H}_1$, its time evolution in the Heisenberg picture is given by

$$e^{itH}(A_1 \otimes 1)e^{-itH} = e^{itH_1}A_1e^{-itH_1} \otimes 1 ;$$

it is completely independent of the choice of H_2. This separability is a basic requirement for a physical theory: no matter how two systems may be correlated due to past interactions, there can be no way of telling what forces the second system is being subjected to by examining the first system, unless the two systems are dynamically coupled. Any failure of separability represents an unphysical effect. It is sometimes said that locality is not a feature of a nonrelativistic theory, and that is true, but since $\mathcal{H}_1$ and $\mathcal{H}_2$ may describe two systems with an arbitrarily large spatial separation, any failure of separability would represent an effect that is transmitted instantaneously with no dependence on distance--and that is not a feature of a reasonable physical theory. In the correlated polarization experiments of Aspect, Dalibard, and Roger [1], quantum mechanics does not predict, and observation does not reveal, any dependence of the polarization at one site on the direction of polarization measurement at the other site. This must be said emphatically, because there is a tendency on the part of some to confuse EPR with ESP.

Separability is a well-known feature of quantum mechanics (and of classical mechanics, too). I have discussed it at length because it fails in stochastic mechanics. For example, let $\mathcal{H}_1$ and $\mathcal{H}_2$ be $L^2(\mathbb{R})$, let

(1) $$\Psi = \frac{1}{\sqrt{2\pi}} e^{-\frac{1}{4}\sigma^{-1}(0)x\cdot x}$$

where $x = \binom{x_1}{x_2}$ and $\sigma^{-1}(0) = \begin{pmatrix} 1 & -1 \\ -1 & 2 \end{pmatrix}$, let

$$H_1 = -\frac{d^2}{dx_1^2} \quad , \quad H_2 = -\frac{d^2}{dx_2^2} + \omega^2 x^2 \quad ,$$

and let $\xi = \binom{\xi_1}{\xi_2}$ be the corresponding Markov process given by stochastic mechanics. Then ξ_1 is a Gaussian process of mean 0, so it is completely determined by its autocorrelation function $E\xi_1(t)\xi_1(s)$. Separability requires that this autocorrelation function not depend on ω. In [21] I gave a proof that separability must fail, and since then John Lafferty has made an explicit computation using a symbolic manipulation program. His result is that

$$E\xi_1(t)\xi_1(0) = 2 - \frac{1}{2}t + \frac{1}{4}t - \frac{1}{12}t^3 - \frac{5}{96}t^4 + \left(\frac{13}{192} - \frac{\omega^2}{80}\right)t^5 + O(t^6) .$$

What are we to make of this $-\frac{\omega^2}{80}t^5$? The coordinate x_1 is the distance of the first particle from a certain origin and the coordinate x_2 is the distance of the second particle from its equilibrium position, which may be at an arbitrary distance a from the origin--the parameter a does not enter the problem. I have brought a thousand such particles with me to Ascona and their correlated partners remain with Lafferty in Princeton. I will choose a value of ω and subject my thousand particles to a harmonic restoring force with circular frequency ω. All Lafferty has to do is examine the trajectories of their partners and he will know what value of ω I have chosen. This is a form of communication that does not depend on the separation, so the effect will remain in a relativistic treatment. To an observer flying rapidly over Ascona, Lafferty receives the signal before I apply the force--and what if I change my mind and choose a different value of ω ?

An objection to this discussion is of course that the trajectories cannot be observed because observation of $\xi_1(0)$ affects any later observation of $\xi_1(t)$. An unexceptionable viewpoint towards stochastic mechanics is that it is interesting mathematics and a useful tool for investigating quantum phenomena. But what gives stochastic mechanics its distinctive character is the study of configurations at several times. One cannot coherently maintain that this is physically relevant and simultaneously invoke the uncertainty principle to explain away the failure of separability.

The situation is even worse. In 1967 I argued [18] that the predictions of stochastic mechanics agree with those of quantum mechanics because the results of any experiment can be described in terms of positions of objects at a single time. This argument is correct, but how does stochastic mechanics achieve this agreement?

Again let $\mathcal{H}_1$ and $\mathcal{H}_2$ be $L^2(\mathbb{R})$ and let Ψ be given by (1) but where now $\sigma^{-1}(0)$ is the inverse of

$$\sigma(0) = \begin{pmatrix} 100 & 99 \\ 99 & 100 \end{pmatrix},$$

and let H_1 and H_2 be the harmonic oscillator Hamiltonian with circular frequency ω. We have two dynamically uncoupled but tightly correlated systems; in fact, the correlation coefficient between $\xi_1(0)$ and $\xi_2(0)$ is 99%. Thus a measurement of $\xi_1(0)$ gives a lot of information about $\xi_2(0)$. This could be tested by making many simultaneous measurements at time 0 and compiling statistics. Since the two systems are uncoupled, and could be separated by an arbitrarily large distance, there is no physical reason why a measurement of the first particle at time 0 should interfere with a later measurement of the second particle at time t. In quantum mechanics this is expressed by the fact that the Heisenberg position operators $X_1(0)$ and $X_2(t)$ commute.

But in stochastic mechanics we have the following theorem:

$$\lim_{t\to\infty} E\xi_1(0)\xi_2(t) = 0 .$$

In fact, the matrix $E\xi(0)\xi(t)$ converges exponentially fast to 0. One way to prove this is to perform a rotation of axes so that $\sigma(0)$ becomes diagonal (with entries 1 and 199). Since both oscillators have the same value of ω, they remain uncoupled and we have two uncorrelated and uncoupled one-dimensional harmonic oscillators. Using formula (16.14) of [21] we can compute $E\xi(0)\xi(t)$ and verify its exponential decay to 0.

Now take $t = 2\pi N/\omega$ where N is a large integer. Then $\xi_1(0)$ and $\xi_2(t)$ are practically uncorrelated, so stochastic mechanics predicts practically no correlation between the position of the first particle at time 0 and the position of the second particle time t. But this is false according to quantum mechanics (and it could in principle be tested experimentally). In fact, $X_2(2\pi N/\omega) = X_2(0)$, so we should have a 99% correlation between the two positions.

We can record the position of the first particle at time 0 by means of some device that is uncoupled to the second particle and then read the record at time t and compare this with the observation of the second particle at time t. Now the predictions of stochastic mechanics and quantum mechanics agree--a 99% correlation--because we are making observations at a single time. So, according to stochastic mechanics, no device can make a faithful record!

This example occurred to me after reflecting on some critical remarks about stochastic mechanics that R. Graham made in the course of a stimulating conversation last January, which I gratefully acknowledge.

A component of a Markov process need not itself be a Markov process. In [21] I expressed the hope that by extending the variational principle to a class of non-Markovian diffusions one could recover separability. This appears unlikely now, and in particular the last sentence of Chapter 23 of [21] (to the effect that processes that are absolute minima for the action would satisfy separability) is wrong.

The basic trouble is that the processes of stochastic mechanics live on configuration space (a mathematical object) and the configuration as a whole diffuses. If we are to construct an acceptable naively realistic picture of physical processes, I believe that we must turn our attention to fields. Fields live on physical space-time.

2. Fields and locality

Can nature, including quantum effects, be described in terms of a classical local field interaction?

Let $\mathcal{M} = \mathcal{M}^d$ be d-dimensional Minkowski space, let F be a finite dimensional vector space, and let $\mathcal{F}$ be the set of all C^∞ functions from $\mathcal{M}$ to F with compact support. We assume given a natural action of the restricted Poincaré group $\mathcal{P}$ on $\mathcal{F}$. A stochastic process ϕ indexed by $\mathcal{F}$ such that the mapping $f \mapsto \phi(f)$ is linear is called a <u>random field</u>. We will also be interested in families ϕ of random fields ϕ_p parameterized by p in a parameter set P on which $\mathcal{P}$ acts by permutations. For each T in $\mathcal{P}$ we indicate its action on elements of $\mathcal{F}$ or P simply by juxtaposition. If ϕ is a family of random fields we define the transformed family $T\phi$ by

$$(T\phi)_p(f) = \phi_{T^{-1}p}(T^{-1}f) .$$

We do not require ϕ to transform covariantly under the action of $\mathcal{P}$, but we can always achieve invariance by including elements of $\mathcal{P}$ among the parameters (replacing P by $P \times \mathcal{P}$) and letting

$$\overset{o}{\phi}_{p,T}(f) = (T\phi)_p(f) ;$$

then ϕ^o is invariant under the action of $\mathcal{P}$. Our aim is to study random fields that arise from relativistic interactions, but we do not require that each such field by itself be Poincaré covariant. A solution to a problem with a certain symmetry does not necessarily possess that symmetry, but the solution set does. The passage from ϕ to ϕ^o is simply a way of saying that no preference will be given to any Lorentz frame.

Let J also be a finite dimensional vector space and let $\mathcal{J}$ be the set of all C^∞ functions from $\mathbb{M}$ to J with compact support. We will sometimes let $\mathcal{J}$ be the parameter set. We think of the elements j of $\mathcal{J}$ as <u>currents</u> that can be coupled to the field.

The word "locality" has too many meanings to be used without a modifier. In particular, we will distinguish between a notion of active locality, whose meaning is that whatever an experimenter does in a region A affects the field only in its future cone A^+, and a notion of passive locality, whose meaning is that any correlation between events in two space-like separated regions A and B can arise only from events in the past. Bell has discovered [2] that if we impose the requirements of both active and passive locality on a random field, then it cannot model the results of correlated spin experiments, results which are predicted by quantum theory and confirmed by observation [1]. I will give an exposition of this theme in a somewhat different form, acknowledging with gratitude some very helpful conversations with Bell in June of 1983.

For each open set A in $\mathbb{M}$, let $\mathcal{O}(A)$ be the σ-algebra generated by the $\phi(f)$ with $\operatorname{supp} f \subset A$. If we have a family of random fields ϕ_p, then the ϕ_p are defined on possibly different probability spaces. Let us convene always to use the canonical version [17] of a stochastic process; then for a process indexed by $\mathcal{F}$ the sample space is the set Ω of all functions from $\mathcal{F}$ to the one-point compactification $\dot{\mathbb{R}}$ of the reals (so that Ω is a compact Hausdorff space in the product topology) and the σ-algebra of all measurable sets is the set of all Borel sets (and the probability measurable is required to be regular). Then the σ-algebra

$\mathcal{O}(A)$ is the same for all random fields ϕ_p in the family, since $\phi_p(f)$ is simply the function $\omega \mapsto \omega(f)$ on Ω (but the probability measure on Ω may depend on p).

We also let $\mathcal{O}(A)$ denote the set of all random variables measurable with respect to the σ-algebra $\mathcal{O}(A)$. With another abuse of notation, we let $\phi \restriction A$ be the process $f \mapsto \phi(f)$ restricted to the f with $\operatorname{supp} f \subset A$. Also, we let A^+ and A^- be the forward and backward cones of A. By a <u>slice</u> we mean an open subset of $\mathbb{M}$ bounded by two parallel space-like hyperplanes.

Let ϕ be a family of random fields parameterized by $\mathcal{J}$. We say that it is <u>actively local</u> in case for all open sets A in $\mathbb{M}$ and currents j and k in $\mathcal{J}$ that agree except on A, the processes $\phi_j \restriction \overline{A^{+}}^{c}$ and $\phi_k \restriction \overline{A^{+}}^{c}$ are equivalent stochastic processes (so that their canonical versions are identical). Here $^-$ denotes closure and ^{c} denotes complement.

Let ϕ be a family of random fields. We say that it is <u>passively local</u> in case for all space-like separated bounded open sets A and B in $\mathbb{M}$ there exists a slice X disjoint from $A^+ \cup B^+$ such that $\mathcal{O}(A)$ and $\mathcal{O}(B)$ are conditionally independent given $\mathcal{O}(X)$, for each p in P.

<u>Theorem</u> 1. Let ϕ be a family of random fields parameterized by $\mathcal{J}$ that is both actively and passively local. For $\mu, \nu = 1, 2, 3$ let j_μ and k_ν be in $\mathcal{J}$ with $\operatorname{supp} j_\mu \subset A$ and $\operatorname{supp} k_\nu \subset B$, where A and B are two space-like separated bounded open sets in $\mathbb{M}$. There do not exist random variables α_μ and β_ν (for $\mu, \nu = 1, 2, 3$) with α_μ in $\mathcal{O}(A)$ and β_ν in $\mathcal{O}(B)$ such that each α_μ and β_ν is equal to ±1 and

(2) $$\Pr_{\mu\mu}\{\alpha_\mu \beta_\mu = -1\} = 1 ,$$

(3) $$\Pr_{\mu\nu}\{\alpha_\mu \beta_\nu = -1\} < \frac{1}{2} , \quad \mu \neq \nu ,$$

where $\Pr_{\mu\nu}$ is the probability measure for the process $\phi_{j_\mu + k_\nu}$.

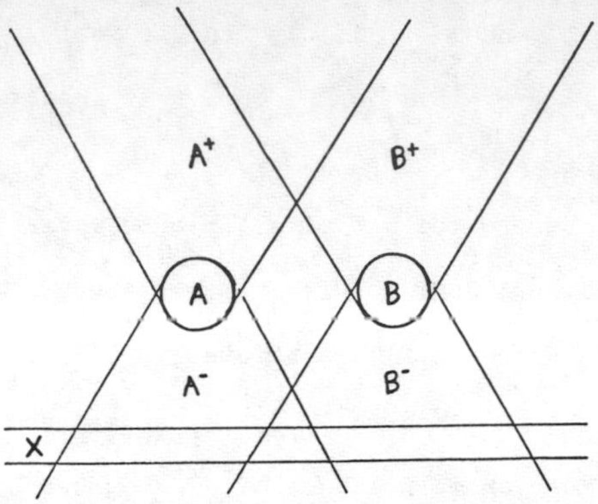

Figure 1

Active locality: an experiment in A affects the field only in A^+. Passive locality: if the field is known in the slice X , then an observation in one of A or B gives no additional information about an observation in the other.

Remarks. The context of this theorem is a correlated spin experiment. Two spin $\frac{1}{2}$ particles are emitted in the singlet state from $X \cap A^- \cap B^-$ and travel to A and B . The experimenter at A chooses one of three coplanar equally spaced directions in which to measure the spin--the choice corresponds to applying the current j_μ--and similarly at B . Then α_μ, under the probability measure $\Pr_{\mu\nu}$ corresponding to measurement in the μ direction at A and in the ν direction at B , is +1 or -1 according as the spin at A is up or down, and similarly for β_ν. Then quantum mechanics predicts that (2) and (3) hold, in fact with $\Pr_{\mu\nu}\{\alpha_\mu\beta_\nu = -1\} = \frac{1}{4}$ for $\mu \neq \nu$, and this prediction is confirmed by experiment [1] for the analogous situation of polarization experiments with photons. The conclusion is that a family of random fields with both active and passive locality cannot describe nature correctly.

In view of Mermin's argument [15], which is also described in [20], it is surprising that this theorem is true with $\frac{1}{2}$ in (3) instead of $\frac{1}{3}$.

Proof. Let the slice X be as in the definition of passive locality, and let ε be +1 or -1 . Then

$$\Pr_{\mu\nu}\{\alpha_\mu = \varepsilon \ \&\ \beta_\nu = -\varepsilon \mid \mathcal{O}(X)\}$$
$$= \Pr_{\mu\nu}\{\alpha_\mu = \varepsilon \mid \mathcal{O}(X)\} \Pr_{\mu\nu}\{\beta_\nu = -\varepsilon \mid \mathcal{O}(X)\}$$

by passive locality. Since α_μ is in $\mathcal{O}(A)$ and $A \cup X \subset \overline{B^{+c}}$,

$$\Pr_{\mu\nu}\{\alpha_\mu = \varepsilon \mid \mathcal{O}(X)\} = \Pr_{\mu\mu}\{\alpha_\mu = \varepsilon \mid \mathcal{O}(X)\}$$

by active locality, and similarly

$$\Pr_{\mu\nu}\{\beta_\nu = -\varepsilon \mid \mathcal{O}(X)\} = \Pr_{\nu\nu}\{\beta_\nu = -\varepsilon \mid \mathcal{O}(X)\} .$$

But by (2) this is equal to $\Pr_{\nu\nu}\{\alpha_\nu = \varepsilon \mid \mathcal{O}(X)\}$, so that

$$\Pr_{\mu\nu}\{\alpha_\mu = \varepsilon \ \& \ \beta_\nu = -\varepsilon \mid \mathcal{O}(X)\}$$
$$= \Pr_{\mu\mu}\{\alpha_\mu = \varepsilon \mid \mathcal{O}(X)\} \Pr_{\nu\nu}\{\alpha_\nu = \varepsilon \mid \mathcal{O}(X)\} .$$

Consequently, writing p_μ for $\Pr_{\mu\mu}\{\alpha_\mu = 1 \mid \mathcal{O}(X)\}$, we have

$$\Pr_{\mu\nu}\{\alpha_\mu \beta_\nu = -1 \mid \mathcal{O}(X)\} = p_\mu p_\nu + (1 - p_\mu)(1 - p_\nu) .$$

Taking the average over $\mu \neq \nu$ we have

$$\frac{1}{6} \sum_{\mu \neq \nu} \Pr_{\mu\nu}\{\alpha_\mu \beta_\nu = -1 \mid \mathcal{O}(X)\} = \frac{1}{6} \sum_{\mu \neq \nu} (p_\mu p_\nu + (1 - p_\mu)(1 - p_\nu)) .$$

But this function takes its minimum where its gradient vanishes, namely at $p_1 = p_2 = p_3 = \frac{1}{2}$, so it is always $\geq \frac{1}{2}$. Therefore

$$\frac{1}{6} \sum_{\mu \neq \nu} \Pr_{\mu\nu}\{\alpha_\mu \beta_\nu = -1\} > \text{or} \geq \frac{1}{2}$$

which contradicts (3). ∎

The theorem remains true, with the same proof, if we replace "passively local" by "locally causal" (in the sense of Bell [2]; see also [21]). For if ϕ is locally causal in the sense of Bell and A and B are space-like separated, then $\mathcal{O}(A)$ and $\mathcal{O}(B)$ are conditionally independent given $\mathcal{O}(A^- \cap B^-)$ (which plays the role of $\mathcal{O}(X)$), and $A^- \cap B^-$ is disjoint from $A^+ \cup B^+$.

One way to construct a family of random fields is the following. Take a classical relativistic field equation

$$\text{(4)} \qquad \Box\phi = G(\phi , \partial^\mu\phi , j)$$

(where ϕ and G take values in F and the current j is in $\mathcal{J}$) whose Cauchy problem admits a unique smooth global solution, such that for all open sets A in $\mathbb{M}$ and currents j and k in $\mathcal{J}$ that agree except on A , if ϕ_j and ϕ_k are respectively solutions of (4) and of (4) with j replaced by k , with the same Cauchy data on some space-like hyperplane disjoint from A^+ , then $\phi_j = \phi_k$ on $\overline{A^{+c}}$. These are familiar properties of the wave equation $\Box\phi = j$, and they hold for some nonlinear equations as well.

Now choose a space-like hyperplane H and an arbitrary probability measure μ_H on the Cauchy data on H . For $j = 0$, construct the random field ϕ_0 simply by weighting the Cauchy data on H by μ_H . We have a unique way of transferring μ_H from the Cauchy data on H to a probability measure μ_K on the Cauchy data on any other space-like hyperplane K . For a general j in $\mathcal{J}$, choose a space-like hyperplane k disjoint from the future cone of the support of j , and construct ϕ_j by weighting its Cauchy data of K by μ_K .

We call this a <u>smooth</u> family of random fields. For a smooth family of random fields, randomness enters only by virtue of our ignorance of the initial conditions. Clearly, a smooth family of random fields is both actively and passively local, so it cannot be a correct description of nature. (But it is not clear that a smooth random field must be locally causal in the sense of Bell.)

Here is another way to construct a family of random fields. Start with a classical relativistic field equation (4), but one for which existence and uniqueness of a smooth global solution to the Cauchy problem fails. Impose a space cutoff L and a momentum cutoff K . That is, fix a Lorentz frame and consider only ϕ that are 0 when one of the spatial coordinates exceeds $\frac{1}{2}L$ in absolute value and whose Fourier series have no momenta exceeding K . Let $G_{LK}(\phi , \partial^\mu\phi , j)$ be the truncated (at K) Fourier series of $G(\phi , \partial^\mu\phi , j)$. Then

$$\Box\phi = G_{LK}(\phi , \partial^\mu\phi , j)$$

is equivalent to a system of ordinary differential equations, which in general will be coupled and nonlinear and will exhibit chaotic behavior. Impose a probability measure μ_{LK} on the initial conditions (at a time anterior to the support of j), obtaining in this way a family of random fields, and let μ be a weak limit of these probability measures as $L , K \longrightarrow \infty$. Call the limit a <u>chaotic</u> family of random fields. For a chaotic family of random fields, randomness is inherent in the development of the fields.

Consider a chaotic family of random fields. Each of the approximating families μ_{LK} will in general fail to be actively local, because coupling the field oscillators to a current in one region instantaneously affects their amplitudes and therefore the global behavior of the field. One would expect this effect to be exponentially small in K and that the limit family μ would be actively local.

Each of the approximating families μ_{LK} is clearly passively local, since the solution of a system of ordinary differential equations is determined by the initial conditions, but this does not imply that the limit family μ will be passively local. The point is that for each L and K, all of the information in $\mathcal{O}(B)$ is stored in $\mathcal{O}(X)$, but in the passage to the limit $\mathcal{O}(B)$ may retain some information that is lost in $\mathcal{O}(X)$. (It is for this reason that a limit of Markov fields may fail to be a Markov field; see [25].)

For a chaotic family of random fields, the approximating families are passively local but not actively local and we may expect precisely the opposite for the limit family. Therefore there is no reason to expect anything like the conclusion of Theorem 1 to be true either for the approximating families or for the limit family.

I want to emphasize that this is not some mathematical pathology, but just what we should expect in a description of microphenomena. Consider a correlated spin experiment as discussed earlier. The development of this system in time is unpredictable, and we do not expect $\mathcal{O}(X)$ to contain enough information to determine the outcome of observations at A and B. But we do expect conservation of angular momentum to hold exactly during the chaotic evolution of the system, and therefore we expect a failure of passive locality: an observation at B should produce relevant information, additional to that available in X, about an observation in A.

Consider a property possessed by some families of random fields. Call the property <u>stable</u> in case whenever ϕ^n is a sequence of families of random fields, all parameterized by the same set P, possessing the property and such that for each p in P the processes ϕ_p^n converge in distribution to ϕ_p, then the family ϕ possesses the property.

Active locality is clearly stable, and passive locality is presumably unstable. Active locality expresses a property of the physical world, a property that is satisfied by quantum theory (see the discussion of separability in the preceding section). Passive locality is a mathematical feature of deterministic systems and of systems in which randomness enters only by virtue of ignorance of the initial conditions. It is not a property of the physical world.

There is no evidence that Bell's inequalities, and their violation in experiments, are an obstacle to the description of nature, including quantum effects, in terms of a classical local field interaction. The determination of whether such a program is indeed possible is in my opinion the most important problem in the study of the relationship between probability and quantum theory.

A third way to construct random fields is to apply the quantization method of stochastic mechanics to fields. This was first done by Guerra and Ruggiero [11] (later work includes [8] [4] [5]) for the ground state of the free scalar field. They choose a Lorentz frame and impose a spatial cutoff L with periodic boundary conditions. Then the field becomes a system of uncoupled harmonic oscillators, and stochastic mechanics is used to construct the ground state process for each oscillator. Since the resulting random field is Gaussian, it is determined by its mean (which is 0) and its autocorrelation, and to take the limit as $L \to \infty$ it is only necessary to compute the limit of the autocorrelation as $L \to \infty$. This turns out to be the autocorrelation of the free Markov field ϕ of Pitt [24], which had been used [19] in the imaginary time approach to constructive quantum field theory. But the Guerra-Ruggiero field lives on Minkowski space.

At first sight this appears unnatural. The procedure yields a random field on Minkowski space that transforms covariantly under the action of the Euclidean group. With respect to the fixed Lorentz frame, let Δ be the d-dimensional Laplacian and let ∇^2 be the (d-1)-dimensional spatial Laplacian. Then $(-\Delta + m^2)\phi = \alpha$ where m is the mass and α is the Gaussian random field of mean 0 and autocorrelation $(-\Delta + m^2)\delta$. But from the viewpoint of stochastic mechanics, as in [11], the equation satisfied by ϕ reads

$$(\frac{1}{2}(DD_* + D_*D) - \nabla^2 + m^2)\phi = 0 .$$

Let us extend thhe Guerra-Ruggiero procedure to construct a family of random fields ϕ_j for scalar currents j with the linear coupling $j(x)\phi(x)$. For $d = 1$ we have a forced harmonic oscillator. Let ξ be the ground state process for the unforced harmonic oscillator with circular frequency ω, so that ξ is the Gaussian process with mean 0 and autocorrelation

$$E\xi(t)\xi(s) = \frac{1}{\omega} e^{-\omega|t-s|} ,$$

which satisfies the stochastic Newton equation

$$\frac{1}{2}(DD_* + D_*D)\xi(t) + \omega^2\xi(t) = 0 .$$

Let μ_j be the solution of the deterministic equation

$$\frac{d^2}{dt^2}\mu_j(t) + \omega^2\mu_j(t) = j(t)$$

(where j is a real C^∞ function with compact support) that is 0 anterior to the support of j, namely

$$\mu_j(t) = \int_{-\infty}^{t} j(s) \sin \omega(t - s)\, ds .$$

Then $\xi_j = \xi + \mu_j$ satisfies

$$\frac{1}{2}(DD_* + D_*D)\xi_j(t) + \omega^2\xi_j(t) = j(t)$$

since for the deterministic function $\mu_j(t)$ we have

$$\frac{1}{2}(DD_* + D_*D)\mu_j(t) = \frac{d^2}{dt^2}\mu_j(t) .$$

Then ξ_j is a Gaussian process of mean $\mu_j(t)$ whose autocorrelation $E(\xi_j(t) - E\xi_j(t))(\xi_j(s) - E\xi_j(s))$ is unchanged.

For $d > 1$, follow [11] with this modification for each oscillator.

The result is that if j is a real C^∞ function with compact support in $\mathbb{M}$ we obtain the random field $\phi_j = \phi + \mu_j$ where μ_j is the solution of

$$(\Box + m^2)\mu_j = j$$

that is 0 anterior to the support of j , i.e. the retarded solution. Then ϕ_j is a Gaussian random field with mean μ_j and the same autocorrelation is .

In this way, following the quantization method prescribed by stochastic mechanics, we have imbedded ϕ in a family of random fields, and the structure of Minkowski space plays a natural role. The family clearly is actively local. The field of Guerra and Ruggiero not only lives in physical space-time, it feels at home there.

Let A , B , and X be as in the definition of passive locality, and suppose that $\operatorname{supp} f \subset A$. Then

$$E\{\phi(f) \mid \mathcal{O}(X \cup B)\} \tag{5}$$

will be of the form $\phi(h)$ where h is in the Sobolev space $H^{-1}(\mathbb{M})$, to which the random field extends by continuity; see [19]. This h is just the balayage, with respect to potential theory for the kernel of $(-\Delta + m^2)^{-1}$, of $(-\Delta + m^2)^{-1}f$ to $X \cup B$; see the proof in [19] that ϕ is a Markov field. It will have support in the upper boundary of X and in the boundary of B , and in general (5) will not lie in $\mathcal{O}(X)$. Thus ϕ is not passively local.

It would be premature to conclude too much from this linear example, but it is encouraging that here we have a family of random fields, with a clear connection to quantum theory, that is actively local but not passively local.

3. Configuration space quantization

In the formalism of quantum mechanics, the Hilbert space, or rather its set of rays, is the state space of a physical system. The analogue of this in classical mechanics is a symplectic manifold. But for most classical systems it is clear what the configuration space M is, and the symplectic manifold of states is the tangent bundle TM . What is the analogue in quantum mechanics of the configuration space?

For simplicity of exposition, let M be the s-dimensional torus $\mathbb{T}^s$. (The general context is a Riemannian manifold, but some secondary problems will be avoided by taking it to be compact and flat.)

Let V be in $C^\infty(M)$, with the dimensions of energy. Then we have classical dynamics on M with the potential V . One approach to this is through Hamilton's variational principle. The Lagrangian is the function L on the tangent bundle $TM = \mathbb{T}^s \times \mathbb{R}^s$ defined by

$$L = \frac{1}{2} v^i v_i - V .$$

(The coordinates on M are taken to have the dimensions of length and the flat metric on M is taken to have the dimensions of mass, so $\frac{1}{2} v^i v_i$ is the kinetic energy of a system of particles of possibly different masses. We will also write v^2 for $v^i v_i$.) For $t_0 < t_1$ the action is

$$I = \int_{t_0}^{t_1} (\frac{1}{2} \dot{\xi}^2 - V(\xi))dt = \int_{t_0}^{t_1} L(\xi , \dot{\xi})dt .$$

A path is critical for L in case I is stationary for variations with fixed endpoints, and these are the trajectories of the dynamical system.

Let $\mathcal{M}$ be the set of all C^∞ strictly positive probability densities ρ on M . We want to study $\mathcal{M}$ as an infinite dimensional pre-Riemannian manifold (here "pre-Riemannian" means that each tangent space is a real pre-Hilbert space).

Let $t \longmapsto \rho(t)$ be a curve in $\mathcal{M}$; we call it <u>smooth</u> in case $\rho(x , t)$ is C^∞ on $M \times \mathbb{R}$. Then we can find a smooth time-dependent vector field v such that under the flow it generates the probability densities follow the given curve, i.e. such that the equation of continuity

(6) $$\frac{\partial \rho}{\partial t} = -\nabla \cdot (v\rho)$$

holds. (For example, we may let $v = -\frac{1}{\rho} \nabla \Delta^{-1} \frac{\partial \rho}{\partial t}$; this is well-defined since $\int_M \frac{\partial \rho}{\partial t} dx = 0$.) Such a vector field is not unique since we can add to it any vector field z such that $\nabla \cdot (z\rho) = 0$. Among all these there will be a unique v such that

$$\int_M \frac{1}{2} v^2 \rho \, dx$$

is a minimum. The condition on this v is that

$$\frac{d}{d\lambda} \int_M \frac{1}{2}(v + \lambda z)^2 \rho \, dx \Big|_{\lambda=0} = 0 ;$$

i.e. $\int_M v \cdot z\rho dx = 0$. Since $\rho > 0$ and the only constraint on z is that $\nabla\cdot(z\rho) = 0$, $z\rho$ is an arbitrary divergence-free vector field. Therefore v is irrotational, and hence v is locally a gradient. We will show that it is globally the gradient of a C^∞ function S on M .

The equation for S is

$$-\nabla\cdot((\nabla S)\rho) = \frac{\partial\rho}{\partial t} , \tag{7}$$

which may be written as $-(\Delta S)\rho - \nabla S \cdot \frac{\nabla\rho}{\rho} \rho = \frac{\partial\rho}{\partial t}$ or

$$-(\frac{1}{2} \Delta + u\cdot\nabla)S = \frac{1}{2\rho}\frac{\partial\rho}{\partial t} = \frac{\partial}{\partial t}(\frac{1}{2}\log \rho) = \frac{\partial R}{\partial t} ,$$

where we have set

$$u = \frac{1}{2} \nabla \log \rho = \frac{1}{2}\frac{\nabla\rho}{\rho} = \nabla R , \tag{8}$$

$$R = \frac{1}{2} \log \rho . \tag{9}$$

Let $H = L^2(\rho \, dx)$ and let H^1 be the Hilbert space of all functions with square-integrable gradient, with the inner product

$$\langle f , g\rangle_1 = \frac{1}{2}\int_M \overline{\nabla f}\cdot\nabla g \, \rho \, dx + \int \bar{f} g \, \rho \, dx .$$

Then H^1 is a dense linear subspace of H and is a Hilbert space in a larger norm, so there is a unique positive self-adjoint operator $-\frac{1}{2}\Delta_\rho$ on H such that H^1 is its quadratic form domain and

$$\langle f , g\rangle_1 = \langle f , -\frac{1}{2}\Delta_\rho g\rangle + \langle f , g\rangle$$

for all f in H^1 and g in $\mathcal{D}(-\frac{1}{2}\Delta_\rho)$. For g in $\mathcal{D}(-\frac{1}{2}\Delta_\rho)$ we have

$$\frac{1}{2}\Delta_\rho g = \frac{1}{2}\Delta g + u\cdot\nabla g .$$

Then $\frac{1}{2}\Delta_\rho g = 0$ if and only if $\frac{1}{2}\int_M \overline{\nabla g}\cdot\nabla g \, \rho \, dx = 0$; that is, if and only if g is a constant. It is an elliptic operator on a compact connected manifold, so it has a bounded inverse $(\frac{1}{2}\Delta_\rho)^{-1}$ mapping the orthogonal complement in H of the constants (i.e. the subspace of all f such that $\int_M f \rho \, dx = 0$) into itself. Now

$$\int \frac{1}{2\rho}\frac{\partial\rho}{\partial t} \rho \, dx = 0 ,$$

so $S = (\frac{1}{2}\Delta_\rho)^{-1}(\frac{1}{2\rho}\frac{\partial\rho}{\partial t})$ exists in H, and is C^∞ by the regularity theorem. Thus (7) has a C^∞ solution, which is unique up to an additive function of t .

Since $\nabla^i S = v^i$, the function S has the dimensions of action. (Recall that v^i is a velocity, and raising an index changes the dimensionality by an inverse mass, so that ∇^i has the dimensions of an inverse mass times an inverse length.)

Now, formally at least, M is an infinite dimensional pre-Riemannian manifled. The tangent space at ρ consists of all smooth gradient vector fields v on M (or, equivalently, of all smooth scalars S modulo additive constants), and the Riemannian metric is the kinetic energy

$$T = \int_M \frac{1}{2} v^2 \rho \, dx \, .$$

Let V be in $C^\infty(M)$, with the dimensions of energy, and define by

$$V(\rho) = \int_M V\rho \, dx \, .$$

Then V is a potential on M .

There is a potential U on M that plays an important role. In (8) we set $u^i = \frac{1}{2} \nabla^i \log \rho$. For this to be a velocity, we must multiply the right hand side by a constant with the dimensions of action. We modify (8) and (9) by setting

$$u = \frac{\hbar}{2} \nabla \log \rho = \frac{\hbar}{2} \frac{\nabla \rho}{\rho} = \nabla R \, ,$$

$$R = \frac{\hbar}{2} \log \rho \, .$$

Then u^i is a velocity, R has the dimensions of action, and

$$(\rho) = \int_M \frac{1}{2} u^2 \rho \, dx = \int_M \frac{1}{2}\left(\frac{\hbar}{2} \nabla \log \rho\right)^2 \rho \, dx$$

is a potential on M (with the dimensions of energy). Having said this, we choose units so that $\hbar = 1$.

Consider the Lagragian

$$L = T - U - V \, ;$$

that is,

$$L(\rho, v) = \int_M \left(\frac{1}{2} v^2 - \frac{1}{2} u^2 - V\right)\rho \, dx \, .$$

The corresponding action is

$$I = \int_{t_0}^{t_1} \int_M \left(\frac{1}{2} v^2 - \frac{1}{2} u^2 - V\right)\rho \, dx \, dt$$

for a curve $t \longmapsto \rho(t)$ from $[t_0 , t_1]$ to M . Notice that v and u are determined by the curve: v is the tanget vector

$$v = \nabla(\frac{1}{2}\Delta_\rho)^{-1}(\frac{1}{2\rho}\frac{\partial\rho}{\partial t})$$

and $u = \frac{1}{2}\nabla \log \rho$.

The introduction of this Lagrangian is motivated by stochastic mechanics--I is the renormalized expected action for the diffusion process with current velocity v and osmotic velocity u ; see [21]. (On a general Riemannian manifold, there is also the Pauli-DeWitt term $-\frac{1}{12}\bar{R}$ where $\bar{R}$ is the scalar curvature, but this can be absorbed into V .)

Now let us apply to this Lagrangian on M exactly the same variational principle as in the finite dimensional case: we say that a curve $t \mapsto \rho(t)$ is critical for L in case I is stationary for variations with fixed endpoints.

More precisely, let ρ_0 and ρ_1 be in M , let $t_0 < t_1$, and let ρ be a smooth curve in M with $\rho(t_0) = \rho_0$ and $\rho(t_1) = \rho_1$. By a <u>variation</u> of ρ we mean a smooth function $\bar{\rho}$ defined on $\mathbb{R} \times M \times [t_0 , t_1]$ with $\bar{\rho}(\alpha,\cdot,t_0) = \rho_0$ and $\bar{\rho}(\alpha,\cdot,t_1) = \rho_1$ for all α, $\bar{\rho}(0 , x , t) = \rho(x , t)$, and with each $\bar{\rho}(\alpha,\cdot,t)$ in M . Notice that in the expression

$$I = \int_{t_0}^{t_1} \int_M (\frac{1}{2}v^2 - \frac{1}{2}u^2 - V)\bar{\rho}\, dx\, dt ,$$

I , v , u , and $\bar{\rho}$ all depend on α . We say that ρ is <u>critical</u> for in case

$$\frac{d}{d\alpha} I \Big|_{\alpha=0} = 0$$

for all variations $\bar{\rho}$ of ρ .

<u>Theorem</u> 2 (Lafferty). The curve ρ is critical for L if and only if

$$\frac{\partial S}{\partial t} + \frac{1}{2}v^2 + V - \frac{1}{2}u^2 - \frac{1}{2}\nabla\cdot u \tag{10}$$

is a function of t alone.

<u>Remark</u>. By choosing the additive function of t in S appropriately we can require (10) to vanish. This is the stochastic Hamilton-Jacobi equation of Guerra and Morato [10].

Proof. We have

$$\frac{d}{d\alpha} I = \frac{d}{d\alpha} \int_{t_0}^{t_1} \int_M \left(\frac{1}{2} v^2 - \frac{1}{2} u^2 - V\right)\bar{\rho}\, dx\, dt$$

$$= \int_{t_0}^{t_1}\int_M v\frac{\partial}{\partial\alpha}(v\bar{\rho})dxdt - \int_{t_0}^{t_1}\int_M u\frac{\partial}{\partial\alpha}(u\bar{\rho})dxdt + \int_{t_0}^{t_1}\int_M\left(-\frac{1}{2}v^2 + \frac{1}{2}u^2 - V\right)\frac{\partial\bar{\rho}}{\partial\alpha}dxdt .$$

The first integral is

$$\int_{t_0}^{t_1}\int_M \nabla S \frac{\partial}{\partial\alpha}(v\bar{\rho})dxdt = - \int_{t_0}^{t_1}\int_M S \frac{\partial}{\partial\alpha} \nabla\cdot(v\bar{\rho})dxdt$$

$$= \int_{t_0}^{t_1}\int_M S \frac{\partial}{\partial\alpha} \frac{\partial\bar{\rho}}{\partial t}dxdt = - \int_{t_0}^{t_1}\int_M \frac{\partial S}{\partial t} \frac{\partial\bar{\rho}}{\partial\alpha}dxdt ,$$

by a spatial integration by parts, the equation of continuity (6), and a temporal integration by parts (notice that $\frac{\partial\bar{\rho}}{\partial\alpha} = 0$ at t_0 and t_1). The second integral (with its minus sign) is

$$-\int_{t_0}^{t_1}\int_M u \frac{\partial}{\partial\alpha} \left(\frac{1}{2} \frac{\nabla\bar{\rho}}{\bar{\rho}} \bar{\rho}\right)dxdt = \int_{t_0}^{t_1}\int_M \frac{1}{2} \nabla\cdot u \frac{\partial\bar{\rho}}{\partial\alpha} dxdt$$

by a spatial integration by parts. Therefore

$$\frac{d}{d\alpha} I = \int_{t_0}^{t_1}\int_M \left(- \frac{\partial S}{\partial t} - \frac{1}{2} v^2 - V + \frac{1}{2} u^2 + \frac{1}{2} \nabla\cdot u\right) \frac{\partial\bar{\rho}}{\partial\alpha} dxdt .$$

The only constraints on $\frac{\partial\bar{\rho}}{\partial\alpha}$ at $\alpha = 0$ are that its spatial integral be 0 and that it vanish at t_0 and t_1, so (10) is a function of t alone if and only if $\frac{d}{d\alpha} I|_{\alpha=0} = 0$. ∎

Rewriting (10) (set equal to 0) and the current equation (6) in terms of R and S, we obtain the system

$$\frac{\partial S}{\partial t} + \frac{1}{2} (\nabla S)^2 + V - \frac{1}{2} (\nabla R)^2 - \frac{1}{2} \Delta R = 0$$

$$\frac{\partial R}{\partial t} + \nabla S\cdot\nabla R + \frac{1}{2} \Delta S = 0 ,$$

which is equivalent by the change of variables $\psi = e^{R+iS}$ to the Schrödinger equation

$$\frac{\partial\psi}{\partial t} = - i\left[- \frac{1}{2} \Delta + V\right] \psi .$$

This is a quantization method that gives quantum mechanics the mathematical structure of classical mechanics by passing to an infinite dimensional manifold. Although it is motivated by stochastic mechanics, it speaks only of matters that can be discussed within quantum theory, such as time-dependent probability densities but not the corresponding diffusion process. Since "stochastic quantization" already has two meanings (the quantization method of stochastic mechanics on the one hand and the method of Marcus [12] [13] [14] and Parisi-Wu [23] on the other), let us call this method configuration space quantization.

This method does not give quantum mechanics the physical structure of classical mechanics. When we make a position measurement in classical mechanics, we observe an element of configuration space M. But when we make a position measurement in quantum mechanics we do not observe an element ρ of M; rather we observe a sample of the probability density ρ. Also, the appropriate configuration space for a combined system is not $M_1 \times M_2$ but the much larger space of probability densities on $M_1 \times M_2$. These two differences are at the heart of the interpretational problems of quantum mechanics. (For these reasons, this quantization method is of technical, rather than interpretive, interest.)

Configuration space quantization raises some interesting mathematical questions of global analysis. With one exception, this article is not a report on work in progress; rather it is meant to stimulate interest in various problems for whoever cares to work on them. The exception is the topic just mentioned. Lafferty is working on it for his thesis, and the topic should remain his for a reasonable period of time.

But here is a topic that I hope will interest someone. A major problem in applying functional integration to quantum field theory is to find a flexible, incisive way to handle Fermi fields, whether in real time as in stochastic mechanics or in imaginary time as in Euclidean field theory. Let me express a personal prejudice. I feel that whenever we admit anything noncommutative into our probability or anything discrete into our treatment of spin, we are turning away from an as yet undiscovered but very natural way of studying Fermi fields. Perhaps configuration space quantization can provide a useful orientation. To apply this method to field theory, one would have to start from a classical configuration space M that is already an infinite dimensional manifold. This of course would cause problems, but the first step is to find the right M.

4. Construction of quantum fields from random fields

Consider quantum mechanics for a potential V on $\mathbb{R}^s$ and use the Heisenberg picture. For an initial wave function ψ let $t \mapsto \xi_\psi(t)$ be the diffusion process of stochastic mechanics--by Carlen's theorem [3] this exists under very mild restrictions on V and ψ --and let $X(t)$ be the Heisenberg position operator at time t. Then the random variable $\xi_\psi(t)$ has the same probability density, namely $|e^{-itH}\psi|^2$, as has the self-adjoint operator $X(t)$ in the state ψ, so that

$$Eh(\xi_\psi(t)) = \langle\psi , h(X(t))\psi\rangle$$

for every bounded Borel-measurable function h. Thus the family of stochastic processes ξ_ψ determines the Heisenberg position operators.

The analogue in quantum field theory of the Heisenberg position operators is the Wightman field Θ. Therefore the same procedure should serve to construct Θ from the stochastic mechanical family of random fields ϕ_Ψ parameterized by the state vector Ψ.

Here we encounter an important technical problem: how do we know that the ϕ_Ψ exist for sufficiently many Ψ? For the free scalar field, if we impose a spatial cutoff L and require Ψ to depend only on the field oscillators with momenta less than some K, and require Ψ to have finite energy, then ϕ_Ψ exists by Carlen's theorem (because we have a finite dimensional Schrödinger equation). Thus with a spatial cutoff L there is a dense set of state vectors Ψ for which ϕ_Ψ is known to exist for the free scalar field. But what is the situation without a spatial cutoff, and in the interacting case? Is there some way of reducing the existence question to the case of finitely many degrees of freedom, or should one try to mimic Carlen's technique for fields?

Here we will consider only the free scalar field and will construct the ϕ_Ψ only for the coherent state vectors Ψ. This is a straightforward extension of a result of Guerra and Loffredo [9] for $d = 1$ (the harmonic oscillator), and it suffices for the construction of the Wightman field Θ.

Let H be a real Hilbert space, ϕ a Gaussian process indexed by H with mean 0 and autocorrelation (covariance) given by the inner product, defined on some probability space $(\Omega , S , \Pr)$ such that the $\phi(u)$ for u in H generate S, and let $\Gamma(H)$ be the Fock space $L^2(\Omega , S , \Pr)$ as in [19]. Then ϕ extends by linearity to the complexification H_c of H. We denote the natural conjugation on H_c by $u \longmapsto \bar{u}$, and set $\mathrm{Re}\, u = (u + \bar{u})/2$.

For u in H_c, let

$$\Gamma(u) = e^{-\|\mathrm{Re}\, u\|^2} e^{\phi(u)} .$$

This is a unit vector, called the <u>coherent</u> <u>state</u> associated to u.

A subset A of a Hilbert space K will be called a <u>determining</u> <u>set</u> in case whenever A and B are in the set $L(K)$ of all bounded operators on K, with $\langle \Psi , A\Psi\rangle = \langle \Psi , B\Psi\rangle$ for all Ψ in A, then $A = B$. For example, the set of all sums of pairs of elements in a set that spans a dense linear subspace is a determining set.

It is known that the set of all coherent states is a determining set in $\Gamma(H)$. To prove this, let A in $L(\Gamma(H))$ be such that $\langle\Gamma(u) , A\Gamma(u)\rangle = 0$ for all u in H_c. We need to show that $A = 0$. By a simple approximation argument, we may assume that H is finite dimensional. Then $\langle e^{\phi(\bar{v})} , Ae^{\phi(u)}\rangle$ is a holomorphic function on $H_c \otimes H_c$ and by assumption it vanishes on the real linear subspace $\bar{v} = u$. But the complex span of this is all of $H_c \otimes H_c$, so the Taylor series is identically 0 and $\langle\Gamma(\bar{v}) , A\Gamma(u)\rangle = 0$ for all u and v in H_c. But the $\Gamma(u)$ span a dense subset of $\Gamma(H)$. For suppose that Ψ is orthogonal to $e^{\phi(u)}$ even just for all purely imaginary u ($\mathrm{Re}\, u = 0$); then the Fourier transform of Ψ times a strictly postive function (the unit Gaussian) is 0, and so $\Psi = 0$. Hence $A = 0$.

Now fix a Lorentz frame on $\mathbb{M}$ and let H be the real Sobolev space $H^{-1}(\mathbb{M})$ with inner product

$$\langle v , u\rangle_{-1} = \langle v , (-\Delta + m^2)^{-1} u\rangle$$

where $m > 0$. Then ϕ is the free Markov field of mass m , as in Section 2 and in [19]. For any subset A of $\mathbb{M}$ we let $\mathcal{O}(A)$ denote the σ-algebra generated by the $\phi(u)$ with u in $\mathcal{H}$ and $\operatorname{supp} u \subseteq A$ (and the set of all random variables measurable with respect to this σ-algebra). Let $\mathbb{M}_t$ be the hyperplane in $\mathbb{M}$ consisting of all points whose time coordinate is t , and let $\mathcal{H}_0$ be the subspace of $\mathcal{H}$ consisting of all u in $\mathcal{H}$ with $\operatorname{supp} u \subseteq \mathbb{M}_0$. Such a u is of the form $f \otimes \delta$ where f is in the real Sobolev space $\mathcal{H}^{-\frac{1}{2}}(\mathbb{M}_0)$; see [19]. Then $\Gamma(\mathcal{H}_0)$ is the space of quantum mechanical state vectors; it is equal to $\mathcal{O}(\mathbb{M}_0) \cap \Gamma(\mathbb{M})$.

Let $\mathcal{E}$ be the set of all real finite-energy solutions μ of the classical Klein-Gordon equation

$$(\Box + m^2)\mu = 0$$

on $\mathbb{M}$. Here "finite-energy" means that the following expression, which is constant in t , is finite:

$$\frac{1}{2}\int_{\mathbb{M}_0} [\mu(x , t)(- \nabla^2 + m^2)\mu(x , t) + (\frac{\partial}{\partial t} \mu(x , t))^2] dx .$$

Let

$$\mu_t = \frac{1}{2} (- \nabla^2 + m^2)\mu(;t) \otimes \delta + i \frac{1}{2} (- \nabla^2 + m^2)^{\frac{1}{2}} \frac{\partial}{\partial t} \mu(;t) \otimes \delta .$$

Then μ_t is in $\mathcal{H}_{0c}$, and every element of $\mathcal{H}_{0c}$ is of this form: there is a one-to-one correspondence between $\mathcal{E}$ and $\mathcal{H}_{0c}$. Letting H_0 be the one-particle Hamiltonian $H_0 = (- \nabla^2 + m^2)^{\frac{1}{2}}$, we have

(10) $$e^{-itH_0} \mu_0 = \mu_t .$$

From the definition in [19] of $\Gamma(e^{-itH_0})$, which governs the time evolution of the free quantum field θ , and the fact (see [27, p. 28]) that

$$: e^{\phi(u)} : = e^{- \frac{1}{2}\|u\|^2_{-1}} e^{\phi(u)} ,$$

it follows from (10) that

(11) $$\Gamma(e^{-itH_0}) \Gamma(\mu_0) = \Gamma(\mu_t) .$$

Now let $\phi_\mu = \phi + \mu$. This is a real Gaussian field of mean μ (that is, for a test function u we have $E\phi_\mu(u) = \mu(u) = \int_{\mathbb{M}} \mu(x)u(x)dx$) and the same autocorrelation as ϕ. We may consider it to be the stochastic mechanical field corresponding to the initial wave function $\Gamma(\mu_0)$. In the present primitive state of the technology of stochastic mechanics for fields, it is difficult to make this statement precise. But if we put a spatial cutoff on the field, so that it becomes a discrete assembly of independent harmonic oscillators, this is simply the result of Guerra and Loffredo [9] for each oscillator. (Notice that the coherent state is just a product of coherent states for each oscillator.) But the construction of the quantum field θ (the free scalar quantum field of mass m) from the family of random fields ϕ_μ can be stated precisely.

<u>Theorem</u> 3. For all real t, all u in H with support in $\mathbb{M}_t$, all bounded Borel-measurable functions h, and all μ in E,

(12) $$Eh(\phi_\mu(u)) = \langle\Gamma(\mu_0),\ h(\theta(u))\ \Gamma(\mu_0)\rangle .$$

The operator $\theta(u)$ is the only self-adjoint operator satisfying (12) for all μ in E.

<u>Proof</u>. The uniqueness holds because the $\Gamma(\mu_0)$ are a determining set. We need only verify (12) for h of the form

$$h(r) = e^{i\lambda r}$$

with λ real. The left hand side of (12) is

$$Ee^{i\lambda\phi(u)+i\lambda\mu(u)} = e^{i\lambda\mu(u)}\, e^{-\frac{1}{2}\lambda^2\|u\|_{-1}^2}.$$

Let $u_0 = T_{-t}u$, where $t \longmapsto T_t$ is time translation. By (11) and the fact (see [19]) that θ and ϕ coincide at time 0, the right hand side of (12) is

$$\langle\Gamma(\mu_t),\ e^{i\lambda\phi(u_0)}\Gamma(\mu_t)\rangle = e^{-2\|\mathrm{Re}\,\mu_t\|_{-1}^2}\, Ee^{\phi(2\,\mathrm{Re}\,\mu_t + i\lambda u_0)}$$

$$= e^{-2\|\mathrm{Re}\,\mu_t\|_{-1}^2}\, e^{\frac{1}{2}[\langle 2\,\mathrm{Re}\,\mu_t,2\,\mathrm{Re}\,\mu_t\rangle_{-1}+2i\lambda\langle 2\,\mathrm{Re}\,\mu_t,u_0\rangle_{-1}-\lambda^2\langle u_0,u_0\rangle_{-1}]}$$

$$= e^{i\lambda\mu(u)}e^{-\frac{1}{2}\lambda^2\|u\|_{-1}^2}. \blacksquare$$

This proof is more a verification than a construction. It would be good to have a general argument analogous to that for the case of finitely many degrees of freedom. It would also be worthwhile to extend this result to other cases, such as those considered in [8], [4], [5], where the stochastic mechanical random field is closely related to, but not identical with, the Euclidean field.

Notice that once again the Guerra-Ruggiero point of view, according to which the random fields live on physical space-time, is seen to be natural. This point of view should prove to be essential if one wants to use the methods of probability theory to construct quantum fields on a space-time that is curved due to an external gravitational field, for then the method of analytic continuation in time is not available. This construction throws a new light on "Euclidean" field theory.

5. Construction of random fields from the action principle

This brief section is merely a suggestion. Euclidean field theory (see [7]) employs the methods of classical statistical mechanics to construct random fields on Euclidean space, which then are related to quantum fields on Minkowski space by means of the Osterwalder-Schrader construction theorem [22]. The exponential of the action is used to weight the various field configurations. But in the interesting cases the action is a very singular object; it needs to be renormalized, and since it occurs in the exponent this leads to great analytical difficulties. The suggestion is to try to construct the random fields directly as stationary fields for the action; this would not entail exponentiating the action.

6. Fields and particles

Perfect crystal neutron interferometry (see [26]) presents puzzles for the interpretation of quantum mechanics, concretely on a macroscopic scale. A beam of neutrons is split at A into two partial beams I and II, which are then deflected and merge again at B, where interference effects can be observed. The beam is of such low intensity that only one neutron at a time goes through; this could be tested by putting counters on the two paths and observing that it always happens that precisely one of them responds. This would destroy any coherence properties at B . But other things can be done to one or both of the partial beams without destroying coherence; perhaps the most spectacular is the effect of flipping the spin in one of the beams by 360°.

The two partial beams are centimeters apart; one can stick one's fist between them. Why cannot one tell which partial beam the neutron is in without destroying later coherence properties? The information desired is very crude, cruder than the track left by a charged particle in a cloud chamber. And what about a negative result experiment: if we look to see whether the neutron is in I, and find that it is not, how can we have affected its motion?

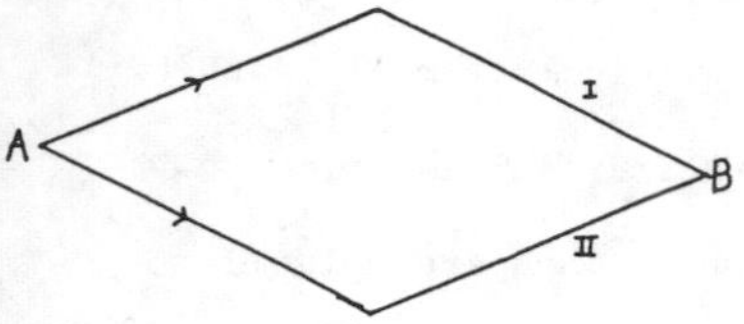

Figure 2
Neutron interferometry

But quantum theory is adamant in maintaining that a localization of the neutron in either partial beam destroys coherence, and there is no experimental evidence to the contrary. Let ϕ_I and ϕ_{II} be states of localization of the neutron in I or II . Then, with an oversimplification due to the neglect of spin, $\phi_I + e^{i\theta}\phi_{II}$ is the state of the neutron, and the relative phase θ can be observed at B . Let ψ_I and ψ_{II} be two orthogonal states of a measuring device, called a pointer, and let

$$\Phi = \frac{1}{\sqrt{2}}(\phi_I \otimes \psi_I + e^{i\theta}\phi_{II} \otimes \psi_{II}) .$$

This Φ is the quantum mechanical description of a state in which we may if we choose determine which partial beam the neutron is in by examining the position of the pointer. We assume that after the state Φ has been prepared there is no further interaction between neutron and pointer. Then if A(t) is an observable of the neutron alone, in the Heisenberg picture, its expected value in the state Φ is

$$\frac{1}{2} <\phi_I , A(t)\phi_I> + \frac{1}{2} <\phi_{II} , A(t)\phi_{II}> .$$

Thus the mere possibility of being able to make the measurement forces the system to behave like a mixture rather than a superposition; all coherence properties and properties depending on the relative phase θ are wiped out. (This is especially puzzling in the case of a radio frequency resonance flipper [26 , §IV]. A coil about II exchanges a photon with the neutron when it passes through, yet coherence is preserved. Rauch argues [26] that this photon transfer cannot in principle be detected, but his reasoning has been challenged by Dewdney, Garuccio, Gueret, Kyprianidis, and Vigier [6]. Their criticism appears persuasive. However, they go on to argue that the photon excange may indeed be detectable, and use this to argue against the Copenhagen interpretation of quantum mechanics. But the familiar analysis given above appears to be independent of any interpretation of the formalism of quantum mechanics and to lead to the conclusion that the exchange is not detectable. The physical reason for this remains obscure to me.)

Thinking of the neutron as a particle creates difficulties of interpretation. (To think of it as something with complementary particle-wave properties is to abandon the attempt to think of <u>it</u> at all, to rest content with a description of our observations.) Perhaps it is better to think of something as moving through both partial beams--something that is not an abstract probability amplitude or a pilot wave living in configuration space, but a disturbance in a random field on space-time that is mainly localized along the two paths. For the correlated spin experiment discussed in Section 2, difficulties were created by thinking of each particle as having definite spin properties; here difficulties are created by thinking of each disturbance as having definite particle localization properties--particle existence or particle non-existence! But the situation may well be analogous. Angular momentum is conserved in the first experiment, particle number in the second. The spin in a certain direction materializes in the process of measurement in the first experiment, particle localization materializes in the process of measurement in the second experiment.

The idea that particle descriptions are only valid in certain circumstances is by no means new. What I want to indicate is that stochastic mechanics gives a specific way to investigate this idea.

In nonrelativistic quantum theory, a description by means of an N-particle Schrödinger equation is equivalent to a descritption by means of a state vector with particle number N in nonrelativistic Fock space, despite the fact that the first is a particle theory and the second is a field theory. But this is very unlikely to be true in stochastic mechanics.

To investigate this question, one should construct the random field ϕ_Ψ where Ψ is a state vector with a definite particle number N, study its nonrelativistic limit (or simply apply the quantization procedure of Guerra and Ruggiero [11] directly with nonrelativistic dynamics), and compare this with the stochastic mechanical diffusion process of N particles with the same quantum state. It is a plausible conjecture that the correspondence between the two is very close in the asymptotic regime $t \longrightarrow \infty$ but that the two pictures are very different for systems that will later produce coherent interference patterns. It would be very interesting to model the observation of particle localization in terms of an external current coupled to the random field.

Let me describe the conjectural mental image that is behind the various suggestions for mathematical investigation that have been made in this article.

Nature is (perhaps) described by a family of random fields on space-time, a chaotic family arising from a classical local relativistic field equation. There is an intrinsic element of randomness in the temporal evolution of the field, a randomness that goes beyond ignorance of initial conditions. Some temporal developments are more probable than others. What determines the weighting is local--stationarity of the expectation of an action that is a local functional of the field. The field does not simply possess properties that can be observed without affecting it. In a region A it may have highly unstable fluctuations among several configurations. An experiment is an intervention in A, coupling the field to a current and thereby producing a different field in the family, that forces the field to assume one of several configurations in A, and the outcome will be random. The intervention leaves the field unaltered outside the future cone of A (active locality) but its outcome may give relevant information about the outcome of another intervention in a space-like separated region B (failure of passive locality). The usual description in quantum theory is a partial description obtained by forming expectation values, thereby constructing noncommuting operators from underlying classical commuting random variables. The random fluctuations of the field are the quantum fluctuations. They are as real as thermal fluctuations and may eventually prove to be observable.

One may question the motivation for studying the problems posed in this article, when we have a quantum theory that gives a perfectly adequate account of microphenomena. For me the motivation is threefold. First, one wants to understand as well as predict. There are problems of interpretation of quantum theory that simply refuse to go away. Understanding in science comes from reduction, and it is important to determine whether or not microphenomena can be explained in classical terms. Second, the problems are mathematically challenging; they seem to involve all three themes of this conference. A model of quantum phenomena by limiting behavior of chaotic systems of ordinary differential equations would be an exciting discovery. Third, it is wise to maintain seed corn. The fact that a physical theory is adequate today does not guarantee that it will be adequate tomorrow, and an alternate theory may turn out to be what is needed to meet future challenges.

References

[1] Alain Aspect, Jean Dalibard, and Gérard Roger, Experimental test of Bell's inequalities using time-varying analyzers, Phys. Rev. Lett. 49, 1982, 1804-1807.

[2] J. S. Bell, The theory of local beables, CERN preprint TH-2053, 1975; reproduced in Epistemological Letters (Association Ferd. Gonseth, CP1081, CH-205, Bienne) 9, 1976, 11.

[3] Eric A. Carlen, Conservative diffusions, Commun. Math. Phys. 94, 1984, 293-315.

[4] Mark Davidson, Stochastic quantization of the linearized gravitational field, J. of Mathematical Physics 23, 1982, 132-137.

[5] Silvio De Siena, Francesco Guerra, and Patrizia Ruggiero, Stochastic quantization of the vector meson field, Phys. Rev. D 27, 1983, 2912-2915.

[6] C. Dewdney, A. Garuccio, Ph. Gueret, A. Kyprianidis, and J. P. Vigier, Time dependent neutron interferometry: Evidence in favour of de Broglie waves, Lett. al Nuovo Cimento 40, 1984, 481-487.

[7] James Glimm and Arthur Jaffe, Quantum Physics--A Functional Integral Point of View, Springer-Verlag, New York, 1981.

[8] Francesco Guerra and Maria I. Loffredo, Stochastic equations for the Maxwell field, Lett. al Nuovo Cimento 27, 1980, 41-45.

[9] ———, Thermal mixtures in stochastic mechanics, Lett. al Nuovo Comento 30, 1981, 81-87.

[10] Francesco Guerra and Laura M. Morato, Quantization of dynamical systems and stochastic control theory, Phys. Rev. D 27, 1983, 1774-1786.

[11] Francesco Guerran and Patrizia Ruggiero, A new interpretation of the Euclidean-Markov field in the framework of physical Minkowski space-time, Phys. Rev. Lett. 31, 1973, 1022-1025.

[12] R. Marcus, Parabolic Itô equations, Trans. Amer. Math. Soc. 198, 1974, 177-190.

[13] ———, Parabolic Itô equations with monotone non-linearities, J. Functional Anal. 29, 1978, 275-286.

[14] ———, Stochastic diffusion on an unbounded domain, Pacific J. Math. 84, 1979, 143-153.

[15] N. D. Mermin, Bringing home the atomic world: quantum mysteries for anybody, Am. J. Phys. 49, 1981, 940-943.

[16] ———, Is the moon there when nobody looks? Reality and the quantum theory, Physics Today 38, No. 4, 1985, 38-47.

[17] Edward Nelson, Regular probability measures on function space, Ann. Math. 69, 1959, 630-643.

[18] ———, Dynamical Theories of Brownian Motion, Princeton University Press, 1967.

[19] ———, The free Markoff field, J. Functinal Anal. 12, 1973, 211-227.

[20] ——, Quantum fluctuations--an introduction, in Mathematical Physics VII, Proc. VIIth Int. Cong. on Math. Phys., Boulder, ed. by W. E. Brittin, K. E. Gustafson, and W. Wyss, North-Holland Physics Publishing, Amsterdam, 1984, 509-519.

[21] ——, Quantum Fluctuations, Princeton University Press, 1985.

[22] K. Osterwalder and R. Schrader, Axioms for Euclidean Green's functions I, II, Commun. Math. Phys. 31, 1973, 83-112; 42, 1975, 281-305.

[23] G. Parisi and Wu Yongshi, Perturbation theory without gauge fixing, Scientia Sinica 24, 1981, 483-496.

[24] L. Pitt, A Markov property for Gaussian processes with a multidimensional parameter, Arch. Rational Mech. Anal. 43, 1971, 367-391.

[25] D. Preiss and R. Kotecký, Markoff property of generalized random fields, Proc. of the 7th Winter School of Abstract Analysis, Strážné, 1979.

[26] H. Rauch, Neutron interferometry and its relation to fundamental physics, J. de Physique, Collogue C3, 45, 1984, C3-197-207.

[27] Barry Simon, Functional Integration and Quantum Physics, Academic Press, New York, 1979.

HAMILTONIAN MODELS FOR THE MADELUNG FLUID AND GENERALIZED LANGEVIN EQUATIONS

T.F. Nonnenmacher
Department of Mathematical Physics
University of Ulm, D-7900 Ulm, Germany

1. Introduction

The Schrödinger equation plays a dominant part in quantum mechanics and many attempts have been made to derive this equation by using different mathematical concepts. The most successful approaches are: Lagrangian or Hamiltonian formulation, canonical quantization procedures, path integration methods, and the stochastic quantization scheme based on the theory of stochastic mechanics, originally formulated by Nelson [1] and successively extended by Guerra [2] and others (see references in [2]). Although the methods listed above do represent different mathematical approaches to the Schrödinger equation, there exist relations between them. So, for instance, it could be shown [3] that it is possible to recast the approach to stochastic quantization in a frame of a stochastic variational principle based on a stochastic action in terms of an appropriate Lagrangian, and a reformulation of the path integral method within the context of stochastic mechanics could also be given [2].

An alternative axiomatic approach to quantum mechanics may be seen in a Hamiltonian formulation in terms of the canonically conjugate Schrödinger field variables $\Psi(\vec{x},t)$ and $\Psi^*(\vec{x},t)$ or its classical fluid mechanics analoga $\rho(\vec{x},t)$ and $S(\vec{x},t)$ and the underlying canonical symplectic structure of the corresponding phase-space. Such a Hamiltonian based formulation of the Schrödinger and Madelung dynamical equations has been given recently [4] and reformulated [5] within the context of stochastic mechanics. The functional bracket formulation discussed in [4] could be extended in order to include electromagnetic field variables [6]. Any (canonical or non-canonical) bracket formulation reveals the geometric structure of the phase-space that is naturally associated with the time evolution equations and is based on the idea that any evolution equation for field variables $u_i(\vec{x},t)$ can be written as $\partial_t u_i = \{u_i,H\}$, where the Lie-Poisson bracket $\{\ ,\ \}$ acts on functionals rather than on functions, satisfies the Jacobi identity, and is antisymmetric. H is the corresponding Hamiltonian functional. In Sect. 2 we shall present a Hamiltonian formulation of some type of an "electromagnetic" Madelung fluid leading to a fluid mechanics interpretation of the Aharonov-Bohm (AB) effect and to a subsidary condition to be required in order to make the correspondence between Schrödinger's quantum mechanics and Madelung's fluid mechanics unique.

In Sect. 3 we shall discuss some problems related with the Brownian oscillator (BO). Our aim is to start out with a Hamiltonian for the composite system (BO plus surrounding heat bath) and to finally arrive at a stochastic differential equation with completely determined statistical properties.

2. A Hamiltonian Model for an Electromagnetic Madelung Fluid and the AB-Effect

The dynamics of a particle with mass m, charge e, which couples to an electromagnetic field

$$\vec{E} = -\nabla A_0 - \frac{1}{c}\vec{A}_t \quad , \quad \vec{B} = \nabla x\vec{A} \tag{2.1}$$

can be described on the basis of the Schrödinger-Maxwell field equations

$$i\hbar\Psi_t = \frac{1}{2m}\left(\frac{\hbar}{i}\nabla - \frac{e}{c}\vec{A}\right)^2\Psi + V\Psi \tag{2.2a}$$

$$-i\hbar\Psi^*_t = \frac{1}{2m}\left(-\frac{\hbar}{i}\nabla - \frac{e}{c}\vec{A}\right)^2\Psi^* + V\Psi^* \tag{2.2b}$$

$$\nabla x\vec{E} = -\frac{1}{c}\vec{B}_t \quad , \quad \nabla x\vec{B} = \frac{1}{c}\vec{E}_t + \frac{4\pi}{c}\vec{J} \tag{2.2c,d}$$

$$\nabla\vec{E} = 4\pi\tilde{\rho} \quad , \quad \nabla\vec{B} = 0 \tag{2.2e,f}$$

$$\vec{J} = \frac{e\hbar}{2im}(\Psi^*\nabla\Psi - \Psi\nabla\Psi^*) - \frac{e^2}{mc}\vec{A}|\Psi|^2 \quad , \quad |\Psi|^2 = \rho \tag{2.2g}$$

where $\tilde{\rho} = e\rho$ is charge density, V is an external potential. We note that Guerra [2] investigated the structure of the stochastic theory for the Maxwell equations in charge free space ($\tilde{\rho} = 0$), and Albeverio [7] discussed the theory of stochastic differential equations for fields in general. Here, we will focus attention to the

Hamiltonian formulation of the coupled system (2) of the Maxwell-Schrödinger equations and its fluid mechanics analogon, which seems not to have been investigated in literature up to now.

It can easily be checked [6] that the Hamiltonian functional

$$H[\Psi,\Psi^*,\vec{P},\vec{A}] = H_S + H_{EM} = \int d^3x\, \mathbf{H} \tag{2.3}$$

with the Hamiltonian density

$$\mathbf{H} = \mathbf{H}_S + \mathbf{H}_{EM}\ , \qquad \text{where} \tag{2.3a}$$

$$\mathbf{H}_S = \frac{1}{2m}\,[(i\hbar\nabla - \frac{e}{c}\vec{A})\Psi^*]\,[(-\,i\hbar\nabla - \frac{e}{c}\vec{A})\Psi] + V\Psi^*\Psi \tag{2.3b}$$

$$\mathbf{H}_{EM} = 2\pi c^2P^2 + \frac{1}{8\pi}\,(\nabla x\vec{A})^2 \quad , \qquad \vec{P} = -\,\frac{1}{4\pi c}\vec{E} \tag{2.3c}$$

together with the canonical Poisson bracket

$$\{F_1,F_2\} = \{F_1,F_2\}(\Psi,\Psi^*) + \{F_1,F_2\}(\vec{A},\vec{P})\ , \qquad \text{where [4,6]} \tag{2.4}$$

$$\{F_1,F_2\}(\Psi,\Psi^*) = \frac{1}{i\hbar}\int d^3x\,\left(\frac{\delta F_1}{\delta\Psi}\frac{\delta F_2}{\delta\Psi^*} - \frac{\delta F_2}{\delta\Psi}\frac{\delta F_1}{\delta\Psi^*}\right) \tag{2.4a}$$

$$\{F_1,F_2\}(\vec{A},\vec{P}) = \sum_i\int d^3x\,\left(\frac{\delta F_1}{\delta A_i}\frac{\delta F_2}{\delta P_i} - \frac{\delta F_2}{\delta A_i}\frac{\delta F_1}{\delta P_i}\right) \tag{2.4b}$$

generates the dynamical equations (2.2a-d). Equation (2.2f) is trivially satisfied by definition of $\vec{B} = \nabla x\vec{A}$, and equation (2.2e) is a side condition which must be added to the Hamiltonian formulation, but it can be derived using the corresponding Lagrange formalism [6]. Note: $P_i = -(1/4\pi c)E_i$ is canonically conjugate to A_i.

Now we are interested in the fluid mechanics analogon of the system of Schrödinger-Maxwell equations (2.2). For this reason we transform both, the Schrödinger-Hamiltonian (2.3b) and the Poisson bracket (2.4a) to real-valued fluid dynamical field variables ρ and S by making use of the following representation of the complex-valued Ψ-functions:

$$\Psi(\vec{x},t) = R\,\exp(\frac{iS}{\hbar}) \quad , \quad \Psi^*(\vec{x},t) = R\,\exp(-\frac{iS}{\hbar}) \tag{2.5}$$

representing a canonical transformation from the field variables $(\Psi,\Psi^*) \rightarrow (\rho,S)$, where $\rho(\vec{x},t) = \Psi^*\Psi = R^2$, and $S = S(\vec{x},t)$ is a phase function. The transformation (2.5) leads to the fluid energy density $\mathbf{H}_F$, [6]

$$\mathbf{H}_S(\Psi,\Psi^*) \to \mathbf{H}_F(\rho,S) = \frac{\rho}{2m}(\nabla S - \frac{e}{c}\vec{A})^2 + \rho V + \frac{\hbar^2(\nabla\rho)^2}{2m\ \rho} \tag{2.6}$$

and to

$$\{F_1,F_2\}(\Psi,\Psi^*) \to \{F_1,F_2\}(\rho,S) = \int d^3x\ (\frac{\delta F_1}{\delta\rho}\frac{\delta F_2}{\delta S} - \frac{\delta F_2}{\delta\rho}\frac{\delta F_1}{\delta S}) \tag{2.7}$$

generating the following system of electromagnetic fluid equations:

$$\rho_t = \{\rho,H\}(\rho,S,\vec{P},\vec{A}) = \frac{\delta H}{\delta S} = -\nabla[(\nabla S - \frac{e}{c}\vec{A})\frac{\rho}{m}] \tag{2.8a}$$

$$S_t = \{S,H\}(\rho,S,\vec{P},\vec{A}) = -\frac{\delta H}{\delta\rho} = -\frac{1}{2m}(\nabla S - \frac{e}{c}\vec{A})^2 - V + \frac{\hbar^2}{2m}\frac{\nabla^2\sqrt{\rho}}{\sqrt{\rho}} \tag{2.8b}$$

$$\vec{A}_t = \{\vec{A},H\}(\rho,S,\vec{P},\vec{A}) = \frac{\delta H}{\delta\vec{P}} = 4\pi c^2\vec{P} - c\nabla A_o \tag{2.8c}$$

$$\vec{P}_t = \{\vec{P},H\}(\rho,S,\vec{P},\vec{A}) = -\frac{\delta H}{\delta\vec{A}} = -\frac{1}{4\pi}\nabla\times\vec{B} + \frac{1}{c}\vec{J}\ ,\quad \vec{J} = \frac{e\rho}{m}(\nabla S - \frac{e}{c}\vec{A}) \tag{2.8d,e}$$

Clearly, (2.8c) and (2.8d) are equivalent to (2.2c) and (2.2d), respectively. We note that $\mathbf{H}$ given in (2.3a) is invariant with respect to the gauge-transformations

$$\vec{A} \to \vec{A} + \nabla\chi \quad , \quad A_o \to A_o - \frac{1}{c}\chi_t \quad , \quad \Psi \to \Psi\exp(\frac{ie}{\hbar c}\chi) \tag{2.9}$$

and $\mathbf{H} = \mathbf{H}_F + \mathbf{H}_{EM}$ is invariant with respect to

$$\vec{A} \to \vec{A} + \nabla\chi \quad , \quad A_o \to A_o - \frac{1}{c}\chi_t \quad , \quad S \to S + \frac{e}{c}\chi \tag{2.10}$$

Introducing the particle current density

$$\vec{j}' = \rho\vec{v} := (\nabla S - \frac{e}{c}\vec{A})\frac{\rho}{m}\ , \text{ (note: charge current density } \vec{J} = e\vec{j}) \tag{2.11}$$

it becomes obvious that (2.8a) is a continuity equation. We mention that between the Schrödinger and Madelung representation, there is no one-to-one correspondence, because the transformation (2.5) is not unique [9]: given Ψ and Ψ^* do not determine R and S uniquely, since $S \to S + nh = \tilde{S}$, or more precisely (note: $h = 2\pi\hbar$)

$$\tilde{S} \equiv \begin{cases} S \bmod(h) \text{ for } R > 0 \\ S \bmod (\frac{h}{2}) \text{ for } R < 0 \end{cases} \tag{2.11a}$$

leads to same Ψ and Ψ^*, where n is an integer for $R > 0$ (and $n = \frac{n'}{2}$ for $R < 0$). Since S is multivalued and remains undetermined at nodal points $R = \sqrt{\rho} = 0$, the circulation Γ around such vortex lines takes the form

$$\Gamma = \int_C dS = \int_C \nabla S \, d\vec{r} = \begin{cases} nh \text{ for } R > 0 \\ \frac{nh}{2} \text{ for } R < 0 \end{cases} \tag{2.12}$$

where integration has to be taken along any closed loop C. When C encloses a nodal line on which $\rho = 0$, then n is generally non-zero. Such vortex lines make the space multiply-connected. The global condition (2.12) represents a topological quantization of the circulation Γ for the canonical momentum field $\vec{p} = \nabla S$, and it must be added as a subsidiary condition to the fluid dynamical Madelung description in order to make the correspondence between Schrödinger's quantum mechanics and Madelung's fluid mechanics unique.

In our case the source responsible for the occurance of vortex lines making the space multiply-connected is the magnetic field $\vec{B} = \nabla x \vec{A}$. Inserting ∇S from (2.11) into (2.12) for R>0 (we are only interested here in this case) one obtains

$$nh = m \oint \vec{v} d\vec{r} + \frac{e}{c} \oint \vec{A} d\vec{r}$$

Using Stoke's integral theorem $\oint \vec{A} d\vec{r} = \oint (\nabla x \vec{A}) d\vec{F} = \oint \vec{B} d\vec{F} = \Phi$ (magnetic flux) one finally gets

$$m \oint \vec{v} d\vec{r} = nh - \frac{e}{c}\Phi \tag{2.13}$$

representing the gauge-independent form of the circulation condition (2.12). Relation (2.13) is closely related to the AB-effect [8-10], since it implies that the magnetic field $\vec{B}$ which only must exist somewhere inside the loop C affects the value of a particle moving along C.

A nice example concerning the AB-effect discussed recently [10] is the following: an electron is moving along a curve C (circle of radius r_0 in the (x,y)-plane) around a cylinder of radius $r_1 < r_0$, enclosing a constant, homogeneous magnetic field $\vec{B} = (0,0,B)$. This is a bound-state problem for a plane-rotator, which in a stationary state $\rho_t = 0$, $\vec{v}_t = 0$, has $v_z = v_r = 0$ and an (angular) ϕ-independent constant v_ϕ. The value of v_ϕ is determined by (2.13), which - in cylindrical coordinates (r,ϕ,z) - leads to the solution

$$v_\phi = \frac{\hbar}{m r_0}\left[n - \frac{e}{hc}\Phi\right] \quad , \hbar = \frac{h}{2\pi}$$

that depends on the magnetic flux $\Phi = \pi r_1^2 B$, i.e. the motion of the electron moving on a circle C of radius r_0 outside the domain (cylinder of radius $r_1 < r_0$) to which $\vec{B}$ is limited, is influenced by Φ, since the very existence of a $\vec{B}$-field somwhere inside C makes the space multiply-connected. This is precisely the AB-effect for a bound-state problem in hydrodynamical formulation.

3. Hamiltonian Models for the Brownian Particle Problem and the Stochastic Langevin Equation

In classical physics, a Brownian oscillator (BO) of mass m_0, frequency ω_0 coupled to a heat bath (m_i and ω_i are masses and frequencies of the bath oscillators) is usually modeled by the Hamiltonian $H = H_O + H_B + H_{OB} + H_1$ with

$$H_O = \frac{p_0^2}{2m} + \frac{1}{2} m_0 \, \omega_0^2 q_0^2 \qquad \text{Oscillator of interest (BO)} \qquad (3.1a)$$

$$H_B = \sum_{i=1}^{n} \left(\frac{p_i^2}{2m_i} + \frac{1}{2} m_i \, \omega_i^2 \, q_i^2\right) \qquad \text{bath oscillators} \qquad (3.1b)$$

$$H_{OB} = \sum_{i=1}^{n} b_i \, q_i \, q_0 \qquad \text{coupling term} \qquad (3.1c)$$

$$H_1 = - q_0 \, f(t) \, , \qquad f(t) = \text{external force} \qquad (3.1d)$$

where b_i are coupling constants. The canonical equations of motion are ($k_\nu = m_\nu \, \omega_\nu^2$, $\nu = 0,1,2,\ldots,n$)

$$\dot{q}_0(t) = \frac{\partial H}{\partial p_0} = \frac{p_0(t)}{m_0} \qquad (3.2a)$$

$$\dot{p}_0(t = -\frac{\partial H}{\partial q_0} = -k_0\, q_0(t) - \sum_{i=1}^{n} b_i\, q_i(t) + f(t) \tag{3.2b}$$

$$\dot{q}_i(t) = \frac{p_i(t)}{m_i}\,, \qquad \dot{p}_i(t) = -k_i\, q_i(t) - b_i\, q_0(t) \tag{3.3a,b}$$

The system (3.3a,b) is equaivalent to

$$\ddot{q}_i(t) + \frac{k_i}{m_i}\, q_i(t) = -\frac{b_i}{m_i}\, q_0(t)\,, \tag{3.4}$$

which can be solved to yield

$$q_i(t) = q_i(0)\cos\omega_i t + \frac{p_i(0)}{m_i\omega_i}\sin\omega_i t - \frac{b_i}{m_i\omega_i}\int_0^t q_0(t')\sin\omega_i(t-t')dt' \tag{3.5}$$

System (3.2a,b) is equivalent to

$$m_0\ddot{q}_0(t) + k_0\, q_0(t) = -\sum_{i=1}^{n} b_i\, q_i(t) + f(t) \tag{3.6}$$

Insertion of (3.5) into (3.6) gives a generalized Langevin-type equation

$$m_0\ddot{q}_0(t) + k\, q_0(t) + \int_0^t \dot{q}_0(t')\, K(t-t')dt' + K(t)q_0(0) = f(t) + \tilde{\Gamma}(t) \tag{3.7}$$

where

$$K(\tau) = \sum_{i=1}^{n} \frac{b_i^2}{m_i\,\omega_i^2}\cos\omega_i\tau\,, \qquad k = k_0 - K(0) \tag{3.7a,b}$$

$$\tilde{\Gamma}(t) = -\sum_{i=1}^{n} b_i\,\left(q_i(0)\cos\omega_i t + \frac{p_i(0)}{m_i\omega_i}\sin\omega_i t\right) \tag{3.7c}$$

In addition we introduce

$$\Gamma(t) = \tilde{\Gamma}(t) - K(t)\, q_0(0) \tag{3.7d}$$

and note that the integro-differential equation (3.7) contains - besides the initial values $q_i(0)$ and $p_i(0)$ of all the bath oscillators - the initial value $q_0(0)$ of the Brownian oscillator coordinate. This term makes trouble in the interpretation of equation (3.7), since it disturbes the identification of $\tilde{\Gamma}(t)$ as a fluctuating (stochastic) force due to the uncertainty in the initial values of the bath oscillators. However, if we interprete $\Gamma(t)$ as a stochastic force one must consider an ensemble of initial states in which the system variables are fixed at the values $q_0(0)$ and the initial bath variables are drawn from an ensemble that is canonical relative to the system. Such a conditional averaging leads to the following fluctuation-dissipation-theorem (FDT)

$$\langle\Gamma(t)\Gamma(t')\rangle = \frac{2}{\beta} K(t-t') , \qquad \langle\Gamma(t)\rangle = 0 \tag{3.8}$$

which relates the fluctuations to the integral kernel $K(t-t')$. Using the Poisson bracket relation

$$\{q_i(0),p_i(0)\} = \delta_{ij} , \qquad \text{one finds also}$$

$$\{\Gamma(t),\Gamma(t')\} = \frac{\partial K}{\partial t} \tag{3.9}$$

Now, if one can make $K(t-t')$ to a δ-function (i.e. $K(t-t') = \gamma_0\delta(t-t')$), then (2.7) approaches the Langevin equation, and (3.8) becomes $\langle\Gamma(t)\Gamma(t')\rangle = (2\gamma_0/\beta)\delta(t-t')$. The approximations to be required in order to make $K(\tau)$ to $\delta(\tau)$ are: (i) continuum limit, i.e. $\sum_i B_i^2 \cos \omega_i\tau \rightarrow \int d\omega\, B^2(\omega)D(\omega)\cos\omega\tau$, where $B_i^2 = b_i^2/m_i\omega_i^2$ and $D(\omega)$ is density of states, (ii) choose $B^2(\omega)D(\omega) = (1/\pi)\gamma^2/(\gamma^2+\omega^2)$ leading to $K(\tau) \sim \gamma\exp(-\gamma\tau)$, and (iii) taking the limit $\gamma \rightarrow \infty$ leading, finally, to $K(\tau) \sim \delta(\tau)$, which means instantaneous dissipation. We note that there is only one time scale $(1/\gamma)$, the memory time of the dissipation, where γ is the bandwidth of the heat bath excitations.

Over the last twenty years many papers [11-14] have appeared investigating the Brownian quantum oscillator in contact with a quantum heat bath. Most attention has been focused to the rotating wave approximation (RWA-oscillator), ignoring rapidly oscillating terms in the oscillator-heat bath interaction. The quantum mechanical Hamiltonian, however, which corresponds to the classical model (3.1) leads to the so-called FC (fully coupled) oscillator as can easily be checked by replacing in (3.1) the canonically conjugate variables q and p by their operators $p \rightarrow \hat{p}$ and $q \rightarrow \hat{q}$ according to

$$\hat{q}_0 = \left(\frac{\hbar}{2m\omega_0}\right)^{1/2} (a^+ + a) , \qquad \hat{p}_0 = i\left(\frac{\hbar m\omega_0}{2}\right)^{1/2} (a^+ - a) \tag{3.10}$$

and the corresponding expressions for $\hat{q}_\nu$ and $\hat{p}_\nu$ replacing in (3.10) $a^+ \rightarrow b_\nu^+$ and $a \rightarrow$

b_ν. The result is the following Hamiltonian operator in terms of creation (a^+, b_ν^+) and annihilation (a, b_ν) operators $(H = H_0 + H_B + H_{OB})$:

$$H_0 = E\, a^+ a \;,\; E = \hbar\omega_0 \qquad \text{Brownian oscillator} \tag{3.11a}$$

$$H_B = \sum_\nu \hbar\omega_\nu b_\nu^+ b_\nu \qquad \text{bath Hamiltonian} \tag{3.11b}$$

$$H_{OB} = \lambda^{1/2} \sum_\nu B_\nu\, (a^+ + a)(b_\nu^+ + b_\nu) \qquad \text{coupling term,} \tag{3.11c}$$

where λ is a parameter that measures the average strength of the interaction. The RWA-oscillator model works with the following coupling term:

$$H_{OB}^{(RWA)} = \lambda^{1/2} \sum_\nu (B_\nu^* a^+ b_\nu + B_\nu a\, b_\nu^+). \tag{3.11d}$$

Recently, Braun [14] analyzed the RWA-oscillator in detail, and Lindenberg and West [13] investigated the FC-oscillator and discussed some aspects of the relation between the weak-coupling limit and the RWA. The equations of motion for the oscillator operators a and a^+, and for the bath oscillators b_ν and b_ν^+ are Heisenberg equations of type $\dot{A} = (1/i\hbar)[A,H]$. In order to derive the quantum mechanical operator Langevin-type equation for the Brownian quantum oscillator one proceeds as in the classical case: 1) one solves the operator equations for the bath oscillators $b_\nu(t)$ and $b_\nu^+(t)$, 2) one substitutes this result into the equations of motion for $a(t)$ and $a^+(t)$ to obtain (taking integration by parts):

$$\dot{a}(t) = -\,i(\omega_0 - \hbar K(0))a(t) + i\hbar K(0)\, a^+(t) - i\,\Gamma(t)$$
$$- i\hbar \int_0^t dt'\; K(t-t')(\dot{a}(t') + \dot{a}^+(t')) \tag{3.12a}$$

$$\dot{a}^+(t) = i(\omega_0 - \hbar K(0))a^+(t) - i\hbar K(0)a(t) + i\,\Gamma^+(t)$$
$$+ i\hbar \int_0^t dt'\; K(t-t')(\dot{a}(t') + \dot{a}^+(t'))\;, \quad \text{where} \tag{3.12b}$$

$$K(\tau) = \frac{2\lambda}{\hbar^2} \sum_\nu \frac{B_\nu^2}{\hbar\omega_\nu} \cos\omega_\nu\tau \tag{3.13}$$

$$\Gamma(t) = \frac{\lambda^{1/2}}{\hbar} \sum_{\nu} B_{\nu} \left(F_{\nu}^{+}(t) + F_{\nu}(t)\right) = \Gamma^{+}(t) \tag{3.14}$$

$$F_{\nu}^{+}(t) = \left\{b_{\nu}^{+}(0) + \frac{\lambda^{1/2} B_{\nu}}{\hbar\omega_{\nu}} \left(a^{+}(0) + a(0)\right)\right\} \exp(i\omega_{\nu} t) \tag{3.15}$$

From (3.12a) and (3.12b) one obtains

$$i(\dot{a}(t) + \dot{a}^{+}(t)) = \omega_{0} \left(a(t) - a^{+}(t)\right) \tag{3.16}$$

which is simply (see (3.10)) the operator version of he Newtonian relation $p = m\,\dot{q}$. We note that the RWA-oscillator violates this momentum-velocity relation [13,14].

Subtracting (3.12a) from (3.12b) we get the operator version of the generalized Langevin equation (3.7)

$$\begin{aligned} i(\dot{a}^{+}(t) - \dot{a}(t)) = &- (\omega_{0} - \hbar K(0))(a^{+} + a) + \hbar K(0)(a^{+} + a) \\ &- (\Gamma(t) + \Gamma^{+}(t)) - \hbar \int_{0}^{t} dt' K(t-t')(\dot{a}^{+}(t') + \dot{a}(t')) \end{aligned} \tag{3.17}$$

The quantum fluctuation-dissipation relation connecting $K(t-t')$ with the symmetrized correlation function

$$C_{\nu}(t-t') = \lambda < \Gamma_{\nu}(t)\, \Gamma_{\nu}(t') + \Gamma_{\nu}(t')\, \Gamma_{\nu}(t) >$$

can now be constructed and is given by [13]

$$\sum_{\nu} C_{\nu}(t-t') \frac{1}{\hbar\omega_{\nu}} \tanh\left(\frac{\beta\hbar\omega_{\nu}}{2}\right) = K(t-t') \tag{3.18}$$

which reduces in the classical limit $\hbar\omega_{\nu} \ll \beta^{-1} = k_{B}T$ to (3.8). Taking the continuum limit one finds

$$K(t-t') = \frac{2\lambda}{\hbar^{2}} \int_{0}^{\infty} d\omega\, D(\omega)\, \frac{B^{2}(\omega)}{\hbar\omega} \cos\omega(t-t') \tag{3.19}$$

and the choice $D(\omega)B^{2}(\omega)/\hbar^{2}\omega = (\gamma^{2}/\pi)/(\gamma^{2}+\omega^{2})$ leads to

$$\sum_{\nu} C_{\nu}(t-t') := C(t-t') = \frac{\lambda\gamma^2}{\pi}\int_0^{\infty} d\omega \frac{\omega}{\gamma^2+\omega^2}\left(2n(\omega)+1\right)\cos\omega(t-t') \tag{3.20}$$

where $n(\omega) = (\exp(\beta\hbar\omega)-1)^{-1}$. As discussed in [13,14] two time scales occur: $\tau_1 = 1/\gamma$ and $\tau_2 = \beta\hbar/2\pi$ and the correlation function $C(t-t')$ relaxes in a time given by $\max(\tau_1,\tau_2)$. A detailed calculation [15] shows that (i) in the classical limit ($\hbar \to 0$ or $T \to \infty$, i.e. $\hbar\omega_0\beta \to 0$) the correlation function (3.20) takes the form $C(t-t') \sim \exp(-|t-t'|/\tau_1)$ and (ii) in the extreme quantum mechanical limit ($\hbar\omega_0\beta \to \infty$) the correlation function approaches the asymptotic expression $C(t-t') \sim 1/(t-t')^2$ for $|t-t'| \gg \tau_1$, i.e. the pure quantum fluctuations decay more slowly than classical-type fluctuations.

References

[1] E.Nelson, Phys. Rev. 150 (1966) 1079, and Physica 124A (1984) 509
[2] F.Guerra, Phys. Reports 77 (1981) 263
[3] F.Guerra and L.Morato, Phys. Rev. D27 (1983) 1774
[4] T.F.Nonnenmacher, G.Dukek and G.Baumann, Lett. Nuovo Cimento 36 (1983) 453
[5] F.Guerra and R.Marra, Phys. Rev. D28 (1983) 1916
[6] T.F.Nonnenmacher, in: Recent developments in non-equilibrium thermodynamics, Lecture Notes in Physics (Eds: J.Casas, D.Jou and J.Rubi), to appear
[7] S.Albeverio and R.Hoegh-Krohn, Phys. Reports 77 (1981) 193
[8] Y.Aharonov and D.Bohm, Phys. Rev. 115 (1959) 485
[9] T.Takabayasi, Progr. Theor. Phys. 69 (1983) 1323
[10] K.Wodkiewicz, Phys. Rev. A 29 (1984) 1527
[11] G.W.Ford, M.Kac and P.Mazur, J. Math. Phys. 6 (1965) 504
[12] J.Meixner, in: Proceedings of the international symposium on statistical mechanics and thermodynamics (Ed: J.Meixner), North Holland Publ. Comp., Amsterdam, 1965
[13] K.Lindenberg and B.West, Phys. Rev. A 30 (1984) 568
[14] E. Braun, Physica 129 A (1985) 262
[15] W. Eckhardt and T.F. Nonnenmacher, to be published

QUANTUM MECHANICS WITH STOCHASTIC TIME DEPENDENT POTENTIALS

Claude-Alain Pillet
Theoretical Physics, ETH-Hönggerberg, CH-8093 Zürich

I. Introduction

Since the development of time dependent perturbation theory in the early days of quantum mechanics few progress has been made in understanding the large time behaviour of the quantum dynamics generated by time dependent forces. Let me mention some results in this sense:

- the *adiabatic theorem* dealing with the limiting case of an infinitely slowly varying force has a long history rooted in classical mechanics, and may be found in most textbooks on quantum theory, (see for example |1| or |2| for the original proof).
- Davies |3| made a rigourous version of time dependent perturbation theory (Dyson expansion) for *weakly coupled* systems, i.e. for Kato-smooth potentials and small coupling.
- Yafaev |4| studied short range *repulsive potentials*, and also some special cases of *slowly varying forces* associated with the breakdown of asymptotic completeness |5|.
- some *time periodic* problems recently received much attention, I refer to the lectures of Bellissard and Casati (this conference).
- *white noise potentials*, i.e. gaussian random fields $V(x,t)$ with covariance $\langle V(x,t)V(y,s)\rangle = C(x,y)\delta(t-s)$, have been studied by Ovchinnikov, Erikhman |6| and Madhukar, Post |7|.

Much in the spirit of the last example, I have been interested in *Markovian potentials*

$$V(x,t) = W(x,\xi(t)) \tag{1}$$

where $W(x,\xi)$ is a deterministic function of $x \in \mathbb{R}^\nu$ (or $\mathbb{Z}^\nu$) and $\xi \in E$; E beeing some set, and $\xi(t)$ a sample path of some Markov process on E. Such potentials are used in solid state physics for example (see |8|), where they discribe the fluctuations of a disordered medium. But they may also be of more fundamental interest since they are in some sense generic, enjoying no special regularity properties. I will consider two types:

a) confining potentials $\lim_{|x|\to\infty} W(x,\xi) = +\infty$,

b) decaying potentials $\lim_{|x|\to\infty} W(x,\xi) = 0$.

In the confining case we may ask for the stability and energy growth of the system and in the decaying case the existence of bound states (in some geometric sense) and the question of asymptotic completeness are of interest. In the following I give some partial answers to this questions, avoiding technicalities and refering to |9|, |10| for a detailed exposition.

II. The semigroup formula

The starting point in the study of the time dependent Schrödinger equation

$$i\partial_t \psi_t = (-\Delta + V(x,t))\psi_t = H(t)\psi_t \tag{2}$$

with a potential given by (1) is a formula for the mean solution of (2), i.e. for the state of the system averaged over all realisations of the potential. Due to the lack of memory characterising Markov processes this mean solution turn out to be given by a semigroup. Let me now describe this.

I will need two copies

$$\mathcal{H}_j = L^2(\mathbb{R}^\nu, dx_j) \qquad j=1,2$$

of the quantum mechanical Hilbert space in which (2) have to be solved. Assuming the Markov Process $\xi(t)$ to have a unique invariant measure μ I also introduce the "disorder space"

$$h = L^2(E, d\mu(\xi)) .$$

Let A be the infinitesimal generator of the process $\xi(t)$, i.e.

$$E(f(\xi(0))|\xi(t)) = (e^{-At}f)(\xi(t)) \qquad f\in h,\ t\geq 0,$$

$E(.|.)$ denoting as usual the conditional expectation (note however the unusual convention in the definition of A). On the space $\mathcal{H}_1 \otimes \mathcal{H}_2 \otimes h$ let

$$L = -\Delta_{x_1} + \Delta_{x_2} + W(x_1,\xi) - W(x_2,\xi) - iA \tag{3}$$

then the semigroup formula for the mean solution is

$$E(\psi_t(x_1)\overline{\phi}_t(x_2)|\xi(t)) = (e^{-iLt}\ \psi_0 \otimes \overline{\phi}_0 \otimes 1)(x_1,x_2,\xi(t)), \qquad (4)$$

ψ_t and ϕ_t beeing two solutions of (2) with initial conditions ψ_0 and ϕ_0. At first sight the generator L defined in (3) looks somewhat nasty: it is neither self adjoint, nor elliptic and has a huge spectrum. However the main feature is its dissipativity resulting from the averaging procedure. The -iA term tends to push down in the complex plane any spectral singularity, possibly leaving the real axis (which is relevant for the large time asymptotic of (4)) free of eigenvalues and resonances. In order for this mechanism to work I have of course to make some assumptions on A and W.

I will assume A to be a positive self adjoint operator with compact resolvent. This is not very restrictive since a lot of processes satisfy this condition: jump processes on finite spaces, diffusions on compact manifolds, $P(\phi)_1$ -processes, etc...

On the other hand I need some non triviality condition on the function $W(x,\xi)$ to be sure there is no state $\psi \varepsilon \mathcal{H}$ which is eigenstate of the Hamiltonian H(t) for all times. This can be avoided, via a unique continuation theorem for Schrödinger operators (and modulo some technical smoothness assumptions I don't want to discuss here), by the condition

$$\mathrm{Var}_\mu(W(x_1,.) - W(x_2,.)) > 0 \qquad \forall (x_1,x_2)\varepsilon \mathcal{O}_1 \times \mathcal{O}_2$$

for some non empty open sets $\mathcal{O}_1, \mathcal{O}_2 \subset \mathbb{R}^\nu$. Here Var_μ is the variance with respect to the probability μ.

III. Results

The first result I obtained is an abstract *RAGE-theorem* for the time evolution of compact observables C. If ψ_t is a solution of (2), then with probability one

$$\lim_{t\to\infty} \frac{1}{t}\int_0^t \|C\psi_s\|^2 ds = 0 \quad \text{uniformly in } \psi_0. \qquad (5)$$

This is proved by applying successively:

i) a pointwise random ergodic theorem to the unitary propagator U(t,s) of the Schrödinger equation (2), which proves the existence of the above limit.

ii) the mean ergodic theorem to the expectation semigroup (4), which together with the absence of zero eigenvalue of L prove the limit is zero.

The most interesting application of this result is for confining potentials

$$W(x,\xi) = U_0(x) + U_1(x,\xi) ,$$

where I assume $H_0 = -\Delta + U_0$ to have compact resolvent, and U_1 to be bounded. Then the RAGE-theorem clearly implies unboundedness of the energy:

$$\limsup_{t\to\infty} (\psi_t, H_0\psi_t) = \infty$$

This is a nice qualitative result and it would be interesting to know the rate of divergence of the energy. There is one case where this can be computed |11|, namely if

$$W(x,\xi) = \lambda x^2 + \beta x\cdot\xi$$

and $\xi(t)$ is the oscillator process. The energy is found to diverges linearly.

The RAGE-theorem can also be applied to decaying potentials, but since I have stronger results in that case I don't want to discuss this here, note however that as a result of (5) all systems (confining or short range) have purely continuous spectrum in the sense Bellissard gaves to this in his lecture.

Let me now describe further results for decaying potentials. Assume the potential is short range in the following sense

$$W(x,\xi) \sim |x|^{-s} \quad \text{as } |x|\to\infty \quad \text{for } s>2,$$

and the dimension satisfy

$$\nu \geqslant 3.$$

Then the wave operators

$$\Omega^{\pm} = \text{s-}\lim_{t\to\mp\infty} U(t,0)^* e^{i\Delta t}$$

exist and are unitary with probability one. In particular the scattering operator

$$S = (\Omega^-)^* \Omega^+$$

is unitary, and any initial state $\psi\varepsilon H$ has asymptotically (as $t\to\pm\infty$) a free evolution and a time bounded energy.

Thus bound states always disappear as a stochastic time dependent perturbation is turned on, no matter how small this perturbation is. Of course they may turn into very long lived resonances, and it would be interesting to have some quantitative information on the lifetime of such resonances.

The proof of this result is "à la Enss" with however one major complication: in the case of time independent potentials very nice estimates on the cutted off free propagator can be used, as a result of energy conservation. Such estimates are useless in the time dependent case since we are unable to controll the infrared behaviour of the wave function. Thus I used estimates on the full free propagator. This is of course not sufficient and has to be supplemented by some estimate of the interacting propagator U(t,0). Here again the semigroup (4) enters the game allowing, via a weighted L^2-estimate of the resolvent $(L - z)^{-1}$, to derive a local decay estimate on U(t,0) and to complete the proof.

Let me conclude by pointing out once again that the above results on stochastic time dependent Schrödinger operators may in some sense be considered as generic. In fact I recently encountered similar behaviour in some time periodic Schrödinger operators |11|, a fact supporting the conjecture that a very large class of time dependent Schrödinger operators has complete scattering (in the very strong sense $\mathcal{H} = \mathrm{Ran}\Omega^{\pm}$). But this also makes more evident the need for a quantitative theory of resonances.

References

|1| W. Thirring: Lehrbuch der Mathematischen Physik III, Springer, Wien, 1979.

|2| T. Kato: J.Phys.Soc.Jpn.,5,435(1950)

|3| E. Davies: Math.Ann.,210,149(1974)

|4| D.R. Yafaev: Fct.An.Appl.,14,325(1980)

|5| D.R. Yafaev: Soviet.Math.Dokl.,19,1517(1978)

|6| A.A. Ovchinnikov,H.S. Erihkman: Sov.Phys. JETP,40,733(1975)

|7| A. Madhukar,W. Post: Phys.Rev.Lett.,39,1424(1977)

|8| D. Paquet, P. Leroux-Hugon: Phys.Rev.B29,593(1984)

|9| C.A. Pillet: to appear in Commun.Math.Phys.

|10| C.A. Pillet: submitted to Commun.Math.Phys.

|11| C.A. Pillet: unpublished

COEXISTENCE OF ATTRACTING AND CONSERVATIVE FEATURES IN REVERSIBLE DYNAMICAL SYSTEMS

A.Politi, G.L. Oppo
Istituto Nazionale di Ottica, Largo E. Fermi 6
50125 Firenze, Italy

and

R. Badii
Physik Institut der Universitat, Schonberggasse 9
8001 Zurich, Switzerland

Physical models are usually divided in two distinct classes: the conservative (hamiltonian), and the dissipative ones. Here we provide the first physical example of a system simultaneously displaying both features. Such a model arises from a suitable approximation for the behavior of a class of externally injected lasers.

Let us first recall the definition of reversible system as given by R.L. Devaney in Ref. 1. The generic flow $\dot{\underline{x}} = \underline{F}(\underline{x})$ in an n-dimensional space is told to be reversible if it is invariant under the composition of time reversal plus the application of a suitable involution (i.e. a transformation such that R^2 = Identity), that is,

$$R \circ F \circ R = - F \qquad 1$$

A chain of interacting particles characterized by the Hamiltonian

$$H(q_1, \ldots, q_n, p_1, \ldots, p_n) = \sum_i p_i^2/2 + V(q_1, \ldots q_n) \qquad 2$$

is, for instance, R-reversible, with R given by the reflection of all the momenta ($p_i \longrightarrow -p_i$).

The reversible property, stating the invariancy under time reversal, apparently implies, as a consequence, the conservativeness of the flow, at least around single trajectories. A further condition has, instead, to be fullfilled, as well: symmmetry of the trajectory under the R-involution. Such a requirement is usually irrelevant in hamiltonian models, being the conservativeness guaranteed by the symplectic structure of the flows. However, in generic reversible systems the failure of such condition can lead to the existence of attractors. In fact, asymmetric trajectories exist in pairs of mutually symmetric solutions, with the only constraint of having inverse stability properties. This is exactly what we have seen in analysing a suitable class of lasers.

Before entering the details of the derivation and discussion of the model, a few more words are needed to discuss the occurrence of reversible models in physics. Often, dissipative systems, driven very far from equilibrium, show very different time scales for the relaxation processes of the variables. The adiabatic elimination of the faster ones leads to simpler models describing the motion on given manifolds of the phase-space. The "fast" motion usually represents a decay towards such a stable manifold. However, this is not the only possible case: excluding the case of unstable motions, a conservative-type behavior remains. Obviously, no first principles exist now which impose symplectic structures, and the fast motion can, in general, be of any possible type.

Lasers can be classified according to the scale of the three damping constants $\gamma_\perp$ $\gamma_\parallel$, k of polarization, population inversion, and field amplitude respectively. In particular, when $\gamma_\perp \gg \gamma_\parallel$,k , the polarization can be adiabatically eliminated and the resulting model is a pair of rate equations. Such equations have been recently shown to be equivalent to a damped Toda oscillator[2], namely

$$\ddot{s} = -\epsilon s (1 + \exp(2s)) + d - \exp(2s) \qquad 3$$

where s = ln E is the logarithm of the field amplitude E, d is the pump parameter (d = 0 corresponds to the laser threshold), and

$$\epsilon = \sqrt{\gamma_\parallel /k} \qquad 4$$

is the ratio between the remaining relaxation rates. If, furthermore, $\gamma_\parallel \ll$ k (see for instance CO_2 and Nd-Yag lasers), eq. 3 corresponds to a quasi-hamiltonian model, and two distinct time scales can be found. A fast one (of order 1) corresponding to the conservative motion, and a slow one (of order $1/\epsilon$ corresponding to the decay of the associated pseudo-energy).

The addition of an extra source to the field equations requires the introduction of the field phase φ as a third variable. Suitably rescaling the variables, the fast motion is ruled by the system

$$\begin{aligned} \dot{\varphi} &= -1 - (f/r)\sin\varphi \\ \dot{r} &= zr + f\cos\varphi \\ \dot{z} &= D - r^2 \end{aligned} \qquad 5$$

where r is the field amplitude, z the population inversion, D the pump rate, and f the amplitude of the external signal. It is easy to recognize the hamiltonian structure of two uncoupled oscillators in the degenerate case f = 0. Indeed, introducing s= ln r , the pair (s,z) yields again the Toda oscillator, while the phase can be interpreted as a free rotator. The presence of an external injection (f $\neq$ 0) not only couples together the oscillators, but changes in a qualitative way the structure of the model, which remains only reversible under the involution

$$R(x,y,z) = (-x,y,-z) \qquad 6$$

where cartesian rather than cylindrical coordinates have been used. For $f > \sqrt{D}$ a pair of fixed points exists: one stable and the other unstable. The main question is hence how and when attracting features arise when f is increased from 0. To this aim we have performed a numerical investigation for different f values (with $0 < f < \sqrt{D}$) and D =4/3. The trajectories have been followed on the surface of section (x,y) determined by the zero crossing of $\dot{r}$.

Let us notice that symmetry of the flow under the involution is automatically translated into symmetry with respect to the y axis for the associated diffeomorphism. In fact, the change of sign of z is assured by the condition for the point to belong to the surface of section: $z = - fx/(x^2 + y^2)$.

Our pictures have been obtained by drawing the first 300 iterates after a transient of 10^4 time-steps (each one 10^{-3} long) for a grid of 400 different initial conditions. The transient has been discarded in order to make the onset of possible dissipative structures clear. The apparent symmetry of trajectories drawn in Fig. 1 indicates the persistence of a globally conservative behavior still at f = 0.2 . A more quantitative analysis based on the evaluation of the time averaged divergence $\langle 2z \rangle$, confirms the previous results. In fact, for integration times up to 10^3, we have observed $\langle 2z \rangle$ values oscillating around zero with maximum absolute values decreasing down to 10^{-4}, 10^{-5}.

It is, furthermore, evident that for f = 0.42 (see Fig. 2) the complement to a still conservative finite region collapses on a period-2 cycle. In order to investigate the transition of a whole finite region to a dissipative behavior, we have also performed a local stability analysis of the center of lower tori in Fig.1. For f=0.392792.., a simple flip bifurcation, corresponding to the first step of a period doubling cascade, occurs. An anomalous bifurcation diagram is, instead, found for $f = f_c = 0.410049..$ where the period-2 cycle becomes hyperbolic and, simultaneously, two asymmetric period-2 solutions appear, one stable and the other unstable. The relevance of this bifurcation lies in its global character; an entire bulk of initial conditions yielding tori for $f < f_c$ (see Fig. 1), instead collapses onto the stable asymmetric period-2 solution for $f > f_c$ (see Fig. 2). This is better clarified in Fig. 3 where for f = 0.42, the stable and unstable manifolds of the symmetric cycle have been drawn. The two points A_1, A_2, of the symmetric solution are connected by a homoclinic cycle (the intersection of their respective stable and unstable manifolds) which acts as a separatrix between the internal conservative region and the external dissipative one. The onset of a dissipative structure has, indeed, to be related to the appearance of such a cycle which, differently from what happens for a generic non reversible flow[3], persists over a finite range of the control parameter values.

The change of behavior of the system close to this bifurcation can be summarized as follows. When approaching the critical point f_c from below, the lower tori of Fig. 1 appear to shrink in the vicinity of the symmetric cycle or, in other words, a volume in the phase space is, at first, strongly contracted and, then, similarly expanded. Such a picture suggests that, through a suitable nonlinear change of coordinates, the flow could be transformed in an everywhere conservative one. For $f = f_c$, a highly degenerate situation occurs since an infinity of tori touches the same cycle, just as an infinity of different initial conditions collapses onto the same attractor. Indeed, for $f > f_c$, the rests of the previous lower tori asymptotically approach the asymmetric, stable period-2 cycle. We can still imagine, in principle, a transformation mapping the flow on a conservative one, but now it should be singular in correspondence of the asymmetric periodic orbits, and the resulting model would be an unbounded one. All of these ideas, even if quite reasonable, are however based on qualitative arguments. A more formal and precise analysis is still under investigation and the results will be presented in the near future.

By further increasing the external field amplitude f to 0.457139 we observe the total disappearance of conservative features through a tangent bifurcation. For the actual f-values the symmetry-breaking contribution to the volume contraction rate is one order of magnitude larger than the one owed to the neglected damping terms, which thus are structurally negligible. The appearance of strongly attracting solutions in the physical model is, hence, related to the above described symmetry-breaking mechanism. We end this survey by noticing that, still increasing f, conservative structures repeatedly appear and disappear through the same bifurcation scheme.

Let us finally discuss the two-dimensional map associated to the flow 5. It has been pointed out that invariancy under the R-transformation is carried over to invariancy under the reflection S ($S(x,y) = (-x,y)$). Hence, calling M our map, the condition for the reversibility is expressed by

$$S \bullet M \bullet S = M^{-1} \qquad 7$$

or, equivalently, $(S \bullet M) \circ (S \bullet M) = Id$. Therefore, defining a new map $G = S \circ M$, we have

$$M = S \bullet G \qquad 8$$

that is, as for any reversible system, M can be written as the product of two involutions . Such a property is, for instance, shared by the Hénon conservative map[4] and by the Standard map[5] , and it can be used to greatly simplify the study of symmetric periodic solutions, following a method introduced by de Vogelaere[6] . The main difference between the above mentioned cases and ours is the non-constancy of the Jacobian which makes possible the onset of attracting sets.

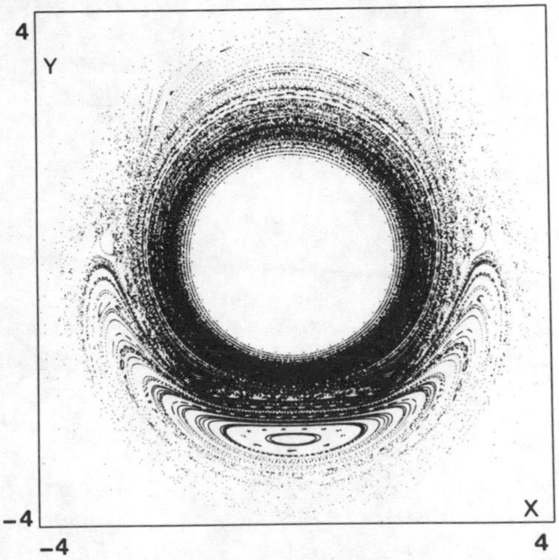

Fig. 1: Poincaré section (r maxima) for D = 4/3 and f = 0.2. Two families of tori are present, separated by a thin chaotic layer. The system appears to be conservative, but no more integrable as for f = 0. The central empty region corresponds to minima of r.

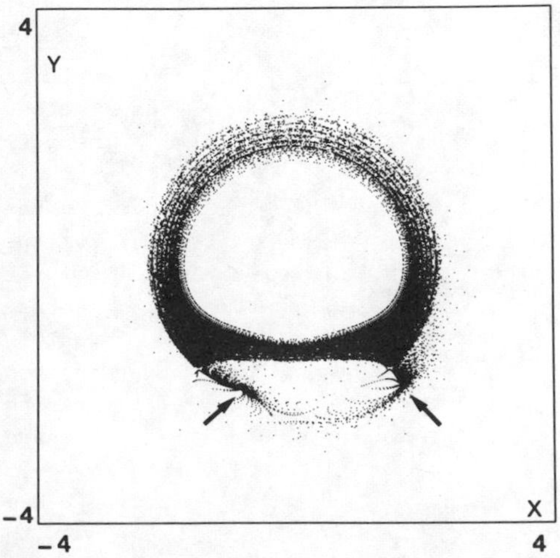

Fig. 2: Same as in Fig. 1 but for f = 0.42. The lower region of tori has disappeared, giving rise to a dissipative structure. All initial conditions outside the upper conservative region asymptotically fall onto the asymmetric period-2 solution shown by the arrows.

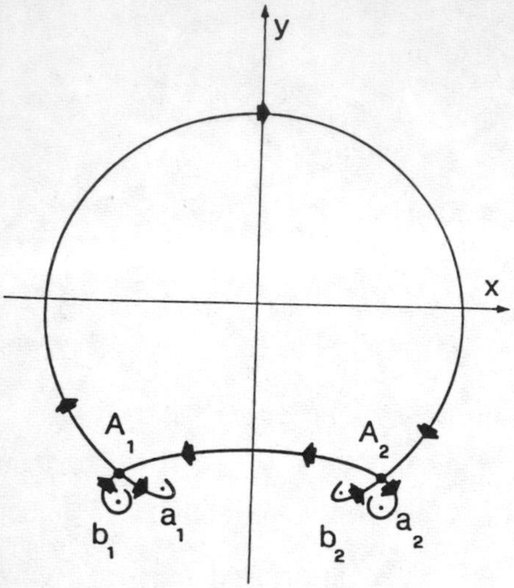

Fig. 3: Stable and unstable manifolds of the hyperbolic orbit (A, A) for f = 0.42. Their intersection corresponds to a homoclinic cycle enclosing the conservative solutions.

References

1)- R.L. Devaney, Trans. Am. Math. Soc. 218, 89 (1976).

2)- G.L. Oppo and A. Politi, Z. Phys. B59, 111 (1985).

3)- J. Guckenheimer and P. Holmes, Nonlinear Oscillations, Dynamical Systems, and Bifurcations of Vector Fields, (Springer,New York 1983)

4) -M. Hénon, Comm. Math. Phys. 50, 69 (1976).

5)- J.M. Greene, J. Math. Phys. 20, 1183 (1979).

6)- R. de Volgelaere, in Contributions to the Theory of Nonlinear Oscillations ed. by S. Lefschetz (Princeton University Press, Princeton, 1958).

Relationship between dynamic, quantum and classical critical phenomena

T. Schneider

IBM Zurich Research Laboratory, 8803 Rüschlikon, Switzerland

Much effort has been devoted to the subjects of dynamic,[1] quantum[2] and classical critical phenomena.[3] These research fields, however, developed rather independently. Recently, remarkable connections have been established.[4-9] This was achieved by using the connection between the time-dependent Ginzburg Landau equation (TDGL) in d-dimensions, describing critical dynamics, and the Fokker-Planck equation. The latter is then reduced to an imaginary-time Schrödinger equation, defining the Hamiltonian of the quantum system, which in turn can be mapped on a static and classical (d+1)-dimensional counterpart.[4,5] Another interesting aspect of these mappings is the simulation of quantum systems in terms of Langevin equations[4,5,10] and the construction of quantum systems with soluble ground-state expectative values.[9] Up to now, and as far as critical phenomena are concerned, these general relationships have been used to derive the following results: (i) Dynamic scaling was traced back to anisotropic scaling in an associated (d+1)-dimensional classical and static model;[5,6] (ii) dynamic critical exponents were calculated with conventional renormalization-group techniques from the (d+1)-dimensional classical and static counterpart;[6] (iii) the equivalence of the real-space renormalization group for critical dynamics and of the real-space renormalization group for quantum systems was established; (iv) the (d+1)-dimensional static and classical model resulting from the TDGL system was shown to exhibit a tricritical Lifshitz point (TLP), belonging to a novel class of TLP's, which result from a relevant, nonlocal quartic field interaction, previously ignored.[8]

In this short review, we sketch the relationship between the TDGL equations, an associated quantum system and its (d+1)-dimensional classical and static counterpart. For this purpose, we consider Langevin processes associated with the Ginzburg-Laundau model

$$W = \frac{1}{2}\sum(r_0 + q^2)\, \phi_q \phi_{-q} + g\sum \phi_{q_1} \phi_{q_2} \phi_{q_3} \phi_{-q_1-q_2-q_3} \,. \tag{1}$$

It is important to emphasize, however, that the approach is not restricted to the above model only, belonging to the Ising universality class. A dynamic system with no conservation laws is defined by the Langevin equations

$$\dot{\phi}_q = -\frac{\partial W}{\partial \phi_{-q}} + \eta_q(t). \tag{2}$$

The Gaussian noise source is assumed to obey

$$\langle \eta_q(t) \rangle = 0, \quad \langle \eta_q(t) \eta_{q'}(t') \rangle = 2\lambda\, \delta_{q,-q'}\, \delta(t-t'). \tag{3}$$

The associated Fokker-Planck equation is

$$\frac{\partial P}{\partial t} = \sum_q \left(\frac{\partial}{\partial \phi_q} \left(\frac{\partial W}{\partial \phi_{-q}} P \right) + \lambda \frac{\partial^2}{\partial \phi_q\, \partial \phi_{-q}} P \right). \tag{4}$$

With the Ansatz

$$P = \sqrt{P_{eq}}\; \psi\{\phi_q, t\} = \exp - \frac{W}{2\lambda}\, \psi\{\phi_q, t\}, \tag{5}$$

we obtain the imaginary-time Schrödinger equation

$$-\frac{\partial \psi}{\partial t} = \mathcal{H} \psi, \tag{6}$$

where

$$\mathcal{H} = \sum_q \frac{|\dot{\phi}_q|^2}{4\lambda} + V\{\phi_q\}, \quad V = \sum_q \left(\frac{1}{4\lambda} \frac{\partial W}{\partial \phi_q} \frac{\partial W}{\partial \phi_{-q}} - \frac{1}{2} \frac{\partial^2 W}{\partial \phi_q\, \partial \phi_{-q}} \right) \tag{7}$$

and

$$\dot{\phi}_q = -2i\lambda \frac{\partial}{\partial \phi_q}. \tag{8}$$

$\mathscr{H}$ is the Hamiltonian of the associated d-dimensional quantum system. This quantum model can now be mapped on its (d+1)-dimensional counterpart with action

$$S = \sum_{q,\,\omega} \left(\frac{\omega^2}{4\lambda} \phi_{q,\,\omega}\, \phi_{-q,-\omega} + \frac{1}{4\lambda} \frac{\partial W}{\partial \phi_{q,\,\omega}} \frac{\partial W}{\partial \phi_{-q,-\omega}} - \frac{1}{2} \frac{\partial^2 W}{\partial \phi_{q,\,\omega}\, \partial \phi_{-q,-\omega}} \right). \tag{9}$$

The Matsubara frequency ω represents the additional dimension. This completes the formal sketch of the mappings of the Langevin process on an associated quantum model and its (d+1)-dimensional classical and static counterpart.

Implications for the critical dynamics are then established as follows. First, we note that the following identity between the zero-frequency susceptibility of the quantum system and the time integral of the correlation function of the associated Langevin model holds:

$$\int_0^\infty S^{W}_{\phi\phi}(q,t)dt = \int_0^\infty dt \,\langle \phi_q(t)\, \phi_{-q}(0) \rangle = \chi^{\mathscr{H}}_{\phi\phi}(q, \omega = 0). \tag{10}$$

This identity is easily established by noting that

$$\begin{aligned} S^{W}_{\phi\phi}(q,t) &= \sum_n |\langle n | \phi_q | 0 \rangle|^2 e^{-\lambda_n t} \\ S^{\mathscr{H}}_{\phi\phi}(q, \omega) &= \sum_n |\langle n | \phi_q | 0 \rangle|^2 \delta(\omega - \lambda_n) \end{aligned} . \tag{11}$$

$|n\rangle$ and λ_n are the eigenvectors and eigenvalues of the Hamiltonian $\mathscr{H}$ with ground-state wave function $|0\rangle = \exp - W/2\lambda$ and eigenvalue $\lambda_0 = 0$. Using the definition of the susceptibility

$$\chi^{\mathscr{H}}_{\phi\phi}(q, \omega = 0) = P \int_{-\infty}^{+\infty} \frac{d\omega}{\omega} S^{\mathscr{H}}_{xx}(q, \omega) \tag{12}$$

and Eq. (11), relation (10) is then easily established. Moreover, there is also equality between the dynamic form factor $S^{w}_{\phi\phi}(q, \omega)$ and the static correlation function $S^{S}_{\phi\phi}(q, \omega)$ of the (d+1)-dimensional model

$$S^{w}_{\phi\phi}(q, \omega) = \int dt\, e^{-i\omega t} S^{w}_{\phi\phi}(q, \omega)\; S^{S}_{\phi\phi}(q, \omega) = \frac{\int \Pi\, d\phi_{q,\omega} | \phi_{q,\omega} |^2 e^{-S}}{\int \Pi\, d\phi_{q,\omega}\, e^{-S}}. \qquad (13)$$

Thus, from Eqs. (10) and (13), we obtain the following identities:

$$\int_0^\infty S^{w}_{\phi\phi}(q,t)\, dt = \chi^{\mathscr{H}}_{\phi\phi}(q, \omega = 0) = S^{S}_{\phi\phi}(q, \omega = 0) \qquad (14)$$

and

$$S^{w}_{\phi\phi}(q, \omega) = S^{S}_{\phi\phi}(q, \omega), \qquad (15)$$

connecting the time integral of the order-parameter correlation function of the W (TDGL) model with the zero-frequency susceptibility of the quantum system and the zero ω wave-vector correlation function of the (d+1)-dimensional system. Moreover, the dynamic form factor of the W-model is equal to the static correlation function of the S-model.

Before turning to the specific implications of these relations, it is useful to recall some critical properties of the W-model [Eq. (1)]. The phase diagram is sketched in Fig. 1. Thus, for fixed λ, the system undergoes a second-order phase transition at $r = r_c$, where r is the renormalized r_0 [Eq. (1)]. At this transition, $S^{w}_{\phi\phi}(q, t = 0)$ behaves as

$$S^{w}_{\phi\phi}(q, t = 0) \sim \begin{cases} q^{-2+\eta_w} & : r = r_c \\ | r - r_c |^{-\gamma_w} & : q = 0 \end{cases}. \qquad (16)$$

The dynamics of the TDGL model [Eq. (2)] will be affected in terms of the slowing down of the time-dependent order-parameter fluctuations, characterized by the frequency

$$\frac{1}{\omega_{\phi\phi}(q)} = \frac{S^{W}_{\phi\phi}(q, \omega = 0)}{S^{W}_{\phi\phi}(q, t = 0)} \sim \begin{cases} q^{-z} & : r = r_c \\ |r - r_c|^{-\nu_W z} & : q = 0 \end{cases} . \tag{17}$$

z is the dynamic critical exponent, and ν_W the correlation-length exponent related to γ_W by $\gamma_W = \nu_W(2 - \eta_W)$ [Eq. (16)]. Recognizing then that both the $\mathscr{H}$ and S-models will also undergo a second-order phase transition at $r = r_c$, implying

$$\chi^{\mathscr{H}}_{\phi\phi}(q, \omega = 0) = S^{S}_{\phi\phi}(q, \omega = 0) \sim |r - r_c|^{-\gamma_{\mathscr{H}}} \sim |r - r_c|^{-\gamma_S}, \tag{18}$$

we obtain by invoking Eqs. (14) and (15) a relation between the dynamic and static critical exponents

$$\nu_W z + \gamma_W = \gamma_{\mathscr{H}} = \gamma_S. \tag{19}$$

Thus, the dynamic critical exponent z can be evaluated in terms of a static one of the associated classical and static S-model.[5,6,8] Moreover, equality (15) immediately implies the equivalence of dynamic and static scaling in (d+1) dimensions.

Stimulating discussions with A. Aharony, R. Badii, P. Sörensen and M. Zanetti are acknowledged.

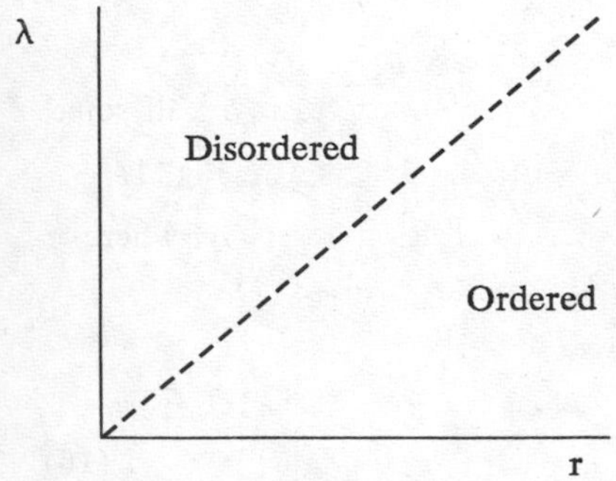

FIG. 1. Schematical phase diagram of the W-model for d ≥ 2. – – is a line of second-order phase transitions separating the ordered and disordered phases.

References

[1]P. C. Hohenberg and B. I. Halperin, Rev. Mod. Phys. **49**, 435 (1977).

[2]R. Morf, T. Schneider and E. Stoll, Phys. Rev. B **16**, 462 (1977).

[3]S. K. Ma, *Modern Theory of Critical Phenomena* (Benjamin, Reading MA, 1976).

[4]T. Schneider, M. Zannetti, R. Badii and H. R. Jauslin, Phys. Rev. Lett. **53**, 2191 (1984).

[5]T. Schneider, M. Zannetti and R. Badii, Phys. Rev. B **31**, 2941 (1985).

[6]T. Schneider and M. Schwartz, Phys. Rev. B. **31**, 7484 (1985).

[7]T. Schneider and M. Zannetti, Phys. Rev. B, in press.

[8]A. Aharony, E. Domany, R. M. Hornreich, T. Schneider and M. Zannetti, Phys. Rev. B **32**, 3358 (1985).

[9]T. Schneider and R. Badii, J. Phys. A **18**, L187 (1985).

[10]T. Schneider, R. Badii and P. Sörensen, to be published.

STABLE DISTRIBUTIONS: FOX FUNCTION REPRESENTATION AND GENERALIZATION

W.R. Schneider
Brown Boveri Research Center
CH-5405 Baden, Switzerland

1. Introduction

Ever since the introduction of the stable distributions by Paul Lévy in 1924 (part of) the scientific community has been intrigued by the missing of a representation in terms of known functions; an illustrious sample is given by [1-3]. Stable distributions play an important role in the theory of sums of random variables [1], [4], [5]; a close connection to the renormalization group idea has been pointed out in [6].

In Section 2 we exhibit the Fox function representation for the stable distributions. Starting from their characterization in terms of Fourier transforms (usually, this is the culmination in their treatment, see e.g. [1]), we obtain their Mellin transforms. Comparison of the inverse Mellin transform with the definition of Fox functions ([7-9] or Section 5 below) yields the desired direct characterization in terms of "known" functions. Note that these functions bear the name of their rediscoverer Fox [7] but they have been known at least since 1888, according to [10]. In addition they have found applications in various branches of mathematics and physics, e.g. in queuing theory [10] or in disordered one-dimensional lattice systems (diffusion or vibration) [11-13]. For special values of the parameters α,β which enter the definition of stable distributions, representations in terms of "simpler" functions are obtained in Section 3. Comparison with results in [14-16] shows that the latter are partly wrong. A subclass of stable distributions called "one-sided" (because their supports are half-lines) allows a generalization which is sketched in Section 4 (an extended version may be found in [17]). Finally, in Section 5 the Fox functions are introduced and some of their properties are exhibited.

2. Fox Function Representation

One possibility to characterize the stable distributions is by means of their Fourier-Stieltjes transforms [1]

$$\int e^{ikx}\, dF_{\alpha,\beta}(x) = \exp \psi_{\alpha,\beta}(k) \tag{2.1}$$

with

$$\psi_{\alpha,\beta}(k) = -k^{\alpha} \exp(i \tfrac{\pi}{2} \beta) \quad , \quad k \geq 0 \tag{2.2}$$

and

$$\psi_{\alpha,\beta}(-k) = \overline{\psi_{\alpha,\beta}(k)} \quad . \tag{2.3}$$

The ranges of the parameters α and β are as follows

$$0 < \alpha < 1 \quad , \quad |\beta| \leq \alpha \tag{2.4}$$

$$1 < \alpha \leq 2 \quad , \quad |\beta| \leq 2-\alpha \quad . \tag{2.5}$$

There exist also stable distributions with $\alpha = 1$ where, however, Eq. (2.2) has to be modified. This case will not be pursued here any further.

For $\beta = \alpha$ $(-\alpha)$ the support of $F_{\alpha,\beta}$ is R_- (R_+) whereas in all other cases the support is R.

From (2.1) - (2.3) it follows [1] that $F_{\alpha,\beta}$ has a density $f_{\alpha,\beta}$ which is obtained by inverse Fourier transformation from (2.1), i.e.

$$f_{\alpha,\beta}(x) = \mathrm{Re}\, \frac{1}{\pi} \int_0^\infty dk\, e^{-ikx} \exp \psi_{\alpha,\beta}(k) \tag{2.6}$$

where (2.3) has been taken into account. Due to (2.2), (2.3) the relation

$$f_{\alpha,\beta}(-x) = f_{\alpha,-\beta}(x) \tag{2.7}$$

holds. Hence, it is sufficient to consider $f_{\alpha,\beta}(x)$ for $x \geq 0$. In particular, $f_{\alpha,\beta}$ is characterized by its Mellin transform

$$\hat{f}_{\alpha,\beta}(s) = \int_0^\infty dx\, x^{s-1} f_{\alpha,\beta}(x) \quad . \tag{2.8}$$

Combining (2.6) and (2.8) yields

$$\hat{f}_{\alpha,\beta}(s) = \varepsilon \frac{\Gamma(s)\Gamma(\varepsilon-\varepsilon s)}{\Gamma(\gamma-\gamma s)\Gamma(1-\gamma+\gamma s)} \quad , \quad \varepsilon = \alpha^{-1} \quad , \quad \gamma = \frac{\alpha-\beta}{2\alpha} \tag{2.9}$$

valid in the strip $0 < \mathrm{Re}\, s < 1$. Details are presented at the end of this Section. The inverse Mellin transform is given by

$$f_{\alpha,\beta}(x) = \frac{1}{2\pi i} \int_{c-i\infty}^{c+i\infty} ds\; x^{-s}\, \hat{f}_{\alpha,\beta}(s) \tag{2.10}$$

where the path of integration is the straight line from $c-i\infty$ to $c+i\infty$ with $0 < c < 1$. Replacing s by -s and inserting (2.9) yields

$$f_{\alpha,\beta}(x) = \frac{\varepsilon}{2\pi i} \int_{-c-i\infty}^{-c+i\infty} ds\; \frac{\Gamma(-s)\Gamma(\varepsilon+\varepsilon s)}{\Gamma(\gamma+\gamma s)\Gamma(1-\gamma-\gamma s)}\, x^{s} \quad . \tag{2.11}$$

The path of integration may be deformed into one running clockwise around $R_{+}-c$. Comparison with (5.1) - (5.9) leads to

$$f_{\alpha,\beta}(x) = \varepsilon\, H^{11}_{22} \left(x \,\middle|\, \begin{matrix} (1-\varepsilon,\varepsilon), & (1-\gamma,\gamma) \\ (0,1) & , (1-\gamma,\gamma) \end{matrix}\right) \quad , \quad \alpha > 1 \quad , \quad \beta > \alpha-2 \quad . \tag{2.12}$$

For $\beta = \alpha-2$ the terms $\Gamma(\varepsilon+\varepsilon s)$ and $\Gamma(\gamma+\gamma s)$ cancel each other, yielding

$$f_{\alpha,\alpha-2}(x) = \varepsilon\, H^{10}_{11} \left(x \,\middle|\, \begin{matrix} (1-\varepsilon,\varepsilon) \\ (0,1) \end{matrix}\right) \quad . \tag{2.13}$$

For $\alpha < 1$ consider

$$x^{-2} f_{\alpha,\beta}(x^{-1}) = \frac{\varepsilon}{2\pi i} \int_{-2+c-i\infty}^{-2+c+i\infty} ds\; \frac{\Gamma(2+s)\Gamma(-\varepsilon-\varepsilon s)}{\Gamma(-\gamma-\gamma s)\Gamma(1+\gamma+\gamma s)}\, x^{s} \quad . \tag{2.14}$$

The path of integration may be deformed into one running clockwise around $R_{+}-2+c$. Comparison with (5.1) - (5.9) leads to

$$x^{-2} f_{\alpha,\beta}(x^{-1}) = \varepsilon\, H^{11}_{22} \left(x \,\middle|\, \begin{matrix} (-1,1)\ ,\ (-\gamma,\gamma) \\ (-\varepsilon,\varepsilon)\ ,\ (-\gamma,\gamma) \end{matrix}\right) \quad , \quad \alpha < 1 \ , \ |\beta| < \alpha \ . \tag{2.15}$$

For $\beta = \alpha$ (2.14) contains $\Gamma(0)$ in the denominator, i.e. $f_{\alpha,\alpha}(x) = 0$, $x > 0$. For $\beta = -\alpha$ nominator and denominator contain $\Gamma(2+s)$ which cancel. This leads to

$$x^{-2} f_{\alpha,-\alpha}(x^{-1}) = \varepsilon\, H^{10}_{11} \left(x \,\middle|\, \begin{matrix} (-1,1) \\ (-\varepsilon,\varepsilon) \end{matrix}\right) \tag{2.16}$$

Because of (2.7) $f_{\alpha,-\alpha}(x) = 0$, $x < 0$, i.e. $f_{\alpha,\alpha}$ and $f_{\alpha,-\alpha}$ have support R_- and R_+, respectively.

From (5.10) we obtain the series expansion of (2.12) and (2.13)

$$f_{\alpha,\beta}(x) = \frac{1}{\pi} \sum_{n=1}^{\infty} \frac{\Gamma(1+n\varepsilon)}{n!} \sin\pi n\gamma\, (-x)^{n-1} \quad , \quad \alpha > 1 \tag{2.17}$$

whereas (5.17) yields the asymptotic behaviour

$$f_{\alpha,\beta}(x) \sim \frac{1}{\pi} \sum_{n=1}^{\infty} \frac{\Gamma(1+n\alpha)}{n!} (-1)^{n-1} \sin\pi n\alpha\gamma\, x^{-1-n\alpha} \quad , \quad \alpha > 1 \ , \ \beta > \alpha-2 \quad , \tag{2.18}$$

for large x. The case $\beta = \alpha-2$ has to be treated separately using (5.19)-(5.24). This leads to

$$f_{\alpha,\alpha-2}(x) \sim A\, x^{\lambda}\, e^{-\mu x^{\delta}} \tag{2.19}$$

for large x where

$$\delta = \frac{\alpha}{\alpha-1} \quad , \quad \mu = (\alpha-1)\alpha^{-\delta} \quad , \quad \lambda = \frac{2-\alpha}{2(\alpha-1)} \quad ,$$

$$A = \{2\pi(\alpha-1)\alpha^{1/(\alpha-1)}\}^{-1/2} \quad . \tag{2.20}$$

An analogous treatment of the case $\alpha < 1$ yields: The series expansion of $f_{\alpha,\beta}$ is given by the r.h.s. of (2.18). For $|\beta| < \alpha$ the small x asymptotic behaviour is given by the r.h.s. of (2.17) whereas (5.19)-(5.24) yield

$$f_{\alpha,-\alpha}(x) \sim B\, x^{-\sigma}\, e^{-\kappa x^{-\tau}} \tag{2.21}$$

for small x where

$$\tau = \frac{\alpha}{1-\alpha} \quad , \quad \kappa = (1-\alpha)\alpha^{\alpha/(1-\alpha)} \quad , \quad \sigma = \frac{2-\alpha}{2(1-\alpha)} \quad ,$$
$$B = \{[2\pi(1-\alpha)]^{-1}\, \alpha^{1/(1-\alpha)}\}^{1/2} \quad . \tag{2.22}$$

The series expansions correspond to those given in [1] whereas the asymptotic expressions are to be compared with those in [18] (taking the different convention in the definition of $\psi_{\alpha,\beta}$ into account).

We conclude this Section with a derivation of (2.9). The subscripts α,β will be dropped from now on. Half-lines occuring as paths in path integrals will be denoted by (ϕ) where

$$(\phi) = R_+\, e^{i\phi} \quad . \tag{2.23}$$

We rewrite (2.6) as

$$f(x) = \mathrm{Re}\; g(x) \quad , \quad x \geq 0 \tag{2.24}$$

where

$$g(x) = \frac{1}{\pi} \int_{(0)} dk\; e^{-ikx}\, \exp(-k^{\alpha}\, e^{i\pi\beta/2}) \quad . \tag{2.25}$$

As $\cos(\pi\beta/2) > 0$, g and all its derivatives are continuous and bounded. The path (0) in (2.25) may be replaced by $(-\delta)$ with $0 < \delta < \pi$ for $\alpha < 1$ and $0 < \delta < \pi(1+\beta)/2\alpha$ for $1 < \alpha \leq 2$. By elementary estimates we see that $|xg(x)|$ is bounded by a constant $C(\alpha,\beta,\delta)$. Hence, the Mellin transform $\hat{g}$ of g exists for $0 < \mathrm{Re}\; s < 1$ and is given by

$$\hat{g}(s) = \int_0^{\infty} dx \int_0^{\infty} dr\; G(x,r;s) \tag{2.26}$$

with

$$\pi G(x,r;s) = x^{s-1} e^{-i\delta} \exp(-irxe^{-i\delta})\exp(-r^{\alpha} e^{i(\pi\beta/2-\alpha\delta)}) \quad . \tag{2.27}$$

For

$$0 < \delta < \delta_o = \min\{\pi, \pi(1+\beta)/2\alpha\} \tag{2.28}$$

we obtain

$$\pi\alpha \int_0^\infty dr \int_0^\infty dx \; |G(x,r;s)| = a^{-s'} \Gamma(s')b^{(s'-1)/\alpha} \Gamma(\frac{1-s'}{\alpha}) \tag{2.29}$$

with $s' = \mathrm{Re}\, s$ and $a = \sin\delta > 0$, $b = \cos(\pi\beta/2-\alpha\delta) > 0$. Hence Fubini's theorem may be applied to (2.26). The x-integration may be rewritten as a path integral along (ε) by setting $z = ix \exp(-i\delta)$ with $\varepsilon = \pi/2-\delta$ $(-\pi/2 < \varepsilon < \pi/2)$. The path (ε) may be replaced by (0) and the integral evaluated in closed form. An analogous statement holds for the remaining r-integration which is rewritten as path integral along (ω), $\omega = \pi\beta/2-\alpha\delta$ $(-\pi/2 < \omega < \pi/2)$ with variable $z = r^{\alpha} \exp i(\pi\beta/2-\alpha\delta)$ and then replacing (ω) by (0). The final result is

$$\pi\alpha\hat{g}(s) = (-i)^s \exp\{-i\pi\beta(1-s)/2\alpha\}\Gamma(s)\Gamma(\frac{1-s}{\alpha}) \quad . \tag{2.30}$$

For s real we have $\hat{f}(s) = \mathrm{Re}\,\hat{g}(s)$. Hence, using $\Gamma(z)\Gamma(1-z)\sin\pi z = \pi$ we obtain (2.9) from (2.30).

Mellin transforms of probability measures have been considered in [20] which also contains a rudimentary derivation of (2.30).

3. Special Cases

For particular values of the parameters α and β there exists a direct representation of the stable density $f_{\alpha,\beta}$ in terms of special functions which are more familiar than the Fox functions used in Section 2 for the general case. The derivation of the following results is mainly based on the series expansion of

$f_{\alpha,\beta}$ in combination with properties of the Γ-function [21]; details may easily be filled in by the reader. Errors in the literature [14-16] are pointed out.

(1) $\alpha = 1/2,\ \beta = -1/2$

This one-sided stable density is given by

$$f(x) = \frac{1}{2\sqrt{\pi}}\, x^{-3/2}\, e^{-1/4x} \quad , \quad x > 0 \quad . \tag{3.1}$$

(2) $\alpha = 2/3,\ \beta = -2/3$

This one-sided stable density is given by

$$f(x) = \sqrt{\frac{3}{\pi}}\, x^{-1}\, e^{-z/2}\, W_{1/2,1/6}\,(z) \quad , \quad x > 0 \tag{3.2}$$

with $z = 4/27x^2$. Hint: Express the series in terms of Kummer's M-functions [21], apply Kummer's transformation [21], rewrite the result with Kummer's U-function [21] which finally is expressed by Whittaker's W-function [21].

The result for $\phi_{2/3}$ in [14] corresponding to (3.2) is wrong. This can also be seen by using the asymptotic behaviour of $W_{-1/2,-1/6}$ occuring there.

(3) $\alpha = 2/3,\ \beta = 0$

This two-sided stable density is given by

$$f(x) = \frac{1}{2\sqrt{3\pi}}\, |x|^{-1}\, e^{z/2}\, W_{-1/2,1/6}\,(z) \tag{3.3}$$

with $z = 4/27x^2$; (2.7) has been taken into account. Hint: As above without Kummer's transformation.

The result for $p(x,2/3,0)$ in [15], reproduced in [16], corresponding to (3.3) is wrong. This can also be seen by evaluating $p(0,2/3,0)$ as limit $x{\downarrow}0$ (with the help of the asymptotic expression for $W_{1/2,1/6}$ occuring in p) and directly (from the inverse Fourier integral representation).

(4) $\alpha = 3/2,\ \beta = 1/2$

This two-sided stable density is given by

$$f(x) = \frac{1}{2\sqrt{3\pi}}\, x^{-1}\, e^{z/2}\, W_{-1/2,1/6}\,(z) \quad , \quad x > 0 \tag{3.4}$$

and by

$$f(x) = -\sqrt{\frac{3}{\pi}}\, x^{-1}\, e^{-z/2}\, W_{1/2,1/6}(z) \quad , \quad x < 0 \tag{3.5}$$

with $z = |4x^3/27|$.

In [15] two expression for p(x,3/2,1), which is related to f by

$$p(x,3/2,1) = \lambda f(\lambda x) \quad , \quad \lambda = 2^{-1/3} \quad , \tag{3.6}$$

are given. They correspond to (3.4) and (3.5), respectively. Erroneously, both are used for $-\infty < x < \infty$. In [16] p(x,3/2,1) is incorrectly treated as one-sided density.

(5) $\underline{\alpha = 1/3,\ \beta = -1/3}$

This one-sided stable density is given by

$$f(x) = \frac{1}{3\pi}\, x^{-3/2}\, K_{1/3}\left(\frac{2}{\sqrt{27x}}\right) \quad , \quad x > 0 \tag{3.7}$$

where K_λ denotes the modified Bessel function of the second kind [21]. Hint: Express K_λ in terms of I_λ and $I_{-\lambda}$ (modified Bessel functions of the first kind [21]).

4. Generalization

The one-sided stable distributions can be generalized in a way indicated below. We introduce the functions $f_\alpha(x;m)$ with m = 1,2,3,... and $0 < \alpha < 1$ by

$$f_\alpha(x;m) = Ax^{-2}\, H^{m0}_{1m}\left((bx)^{-1} \,\middle|\, \begin{matrix} (-1,1) \\ \left(\frac{k-2}{a}, \frac{1}{a}\right)_{k=1,\dots,m} \end{matrix}\right) \tag{4.1}$$

with $x > 0$ and

$$a = m+\alpha-1 \quad , \quad b = \left(\frac{a}{\Gamma(1-\alpha)}\right)^{1/a} \quad , \quad A^{-1} = ab \prod_{k=2}^{m} \Gamma\left(\frac{k-1}{a}\right) \quad . \tag{4.2}$$

They satisfy

$$f_\alpha(x;m) > 0 \quad , \quad x > 0 \tag{4.3}$$

and

$$\int_0^\infty dx\, f_\alpha(x;m) = 1 \quad , \tag{4.4}$$

i.e. they are probability densities on R_+. Comparison with (2.16) yields

$$f_\alpha(x;1) = b\, f_{\alpha,-\alpha}(bx) \quad . \tag{4.5}$$

In view of this fact we call $f_\alpha(x;m)$, $m \geq 2$, generalized one-sided stable densities.

From (5.12) and (5.19) series expansion and asymptotic behaviour are obtainable; details are presented in [17].

The functions $f_\alpha(x;m)$ are solutions of the integral equation [17]

$$f(x) = x^{-m} \int_0^x dy(x-y)^{-\alpha}\, f(y) \tag{4.6}$$

which yields the difference equation

$$\hat{f}(s) = \hat{f}(s+1-m-\alpha)\, \frac{\Gamma(1-\alpha)\Gamma(m+\alpha-s)}{\Gamma(m+1-s)} \tag{4.7}$$

for the Mellin transform of f. A solution of (4.7) is given by

$$\hat{f}_\alpha(s;m) = Ab^{2-s}\, \frac{1}{\Gamma(1-s)} \prod_{k=1}^{m} \Gamma\left(\frac{k-s}{a}\right) \quad . \tag{4.8}$$

Inverse Mellin transformation, deformation of path of integration and (5.1) -(5.9) bring us back to (4.1).

The analyticity properties of $f_\alpha(x;m)$ combined with (4.6) exclude the possibility of positive zeros (by contradiction) which proves (4.3). Taking the limit $s \to 1$ of (4.8) yields the normalization (4.4). Remarkably, also the Laplace transform

$$\phi_\alpha(p;m) = \int_0^\infty dx\, e^{-px}\, f_\alpha(x;m) \tag{4.6}$$

may be expressed in terms of Fox functions [17]

$$\phi_\alpha(p;m) = Ab\, H^{m0}_{0m}\left(\frac{p}{b}\ \Big|\ \begin{matrix} - \\ \left(\frac{k-1}{a}, \frac{1}{a}\right)_{k=1,\dots,m} \end{matrix}\right) . \tag{4.7}$$

5. Fox Functions

The Fox function [7-9]

$$H^{mn}_{pq}(z) = H^{mn}_{pq}\left(z\ \Big|\ \begin{matrix} (a_j,\alpha_j)_{j=1,\dots,p} \\ (b_j,\beta_j)_{j=1,\dots,q} \end{matrix}\right) \tag{5.1}$$

is defined by the contour integral

$$H^{mn}_{pq}(z) = \frac{1}{2\pi i}\int_L K^{mn}_{pq}(s)\, z^s\, ds \tag{5.2}$$

with

$$K^{mn}_{pq}(s) = \frac{A(s)B(s)}{C(s)D(s)} \tag{5.3}$$

where

$$A(s) = \prod_{j=1}^{m} \Gamma(b_j-\beta_j s)$$

$$B(s) = \prod_{j=1}^{n} \Gamma(1-a_j+\alpha_j s)$$

$$C(s) = \prod_{j=m+1}^{q} \Gamma(1-b_j+\beta_j s)$$

$$D(s) = \prod_{j=n+1}^{p} \Gamma(a_j-\alpha_j s) \tag{5.4}$$

Here, m,n,p,q are integers satisfying

$$0 \leq n \leq p \quad , \quad 1 \leq m \leq q \quad . \tag{5.5}$$

In the cases n = 0, m = q, n = p (5.4) has to be interpreted as B(s) = 1, C(s) = 1, D(s) = 1, respectively.
The parameters $a_j(j=1,\ldots,p)$ and $b_j(j=1,\ldots,q)$ are complex whereas $\alpha_j(j=1,\ldots,p)$ and $\beta_j(j=1,\ldots,q)$ are positive. They are restricted by the condition

$$P(A) \cap P(B) = \emptyset \tag{5.6}$$

where

$$\begin{aligned} P(A) &= \{s = (b_j+k)/\beta_j \quad | \quad j = 1,\ldots,m \quad ; \quad k = 0,1,2,\ldots\} \\ P(B) &= \{s = (a_j-1-k)/\alpha_j \quad | \quad j = 1,\ldots,n \quad ; \quad k = 0,1,2,\ldots\} \end{aligned} \tag{5.7}$$

are the sets of the poles of A and B, respectively. The contour L in (5.2) runs from $s = \infty-ic$ to $\infty+ic$ with

$$c > \ |\mathrm{Im}\ b_j|/\beta_j \qquad (j = 1,\ldots,m) \tag{5.8}$$

such that P(A) lies to the left, P(B) to the right of L.

The following additional condition is assumed to hold throughout this Section

$$\mu = \sum_{j=1}^{q} \beta_j - \sum_{j=1}^{p} \alpha_j \ > 0 \tag{5.9}$$

(in [8] also the case $\mu = 0$ is treated). Under these conditions $H_{pq}^{mn}(z)$ is an analytic function for $z \neq 0$, in general multiple-valued (one-valued on the Riemann surface of log z). It is given by

$$H_{pq}^{mn}(z) = - \sum_{s\varepsilon P(A)} \text{res} \left(\frac{A(s)B(s)}{C(s)D(s)} z^s\right) \quad , \tag{5.10}$$

res standing for residuum. If all poles of A are simple, i.e.

$$(b_j + k)/\beta_j \neq (b_{j'} + k')/\beta_{j'} \tag{5.11}$$

for $j \neq j'$ with $j,j' = 1,\ldots, m$ and $k,k' = 0,1,2,\ldots$, then (5.10) yields

$$H_{pq}^{mn}(z) = \sum_{j=1}^{m} \sum_{k=0}^{\infty} c_{j,k} \frac{(-1)^k}{k!\beta_j} z^{(b_j+k)/\beta_j} \tag{5.12}$$

with

$$c_{j,k} = \frac{A_j(s_{j,k})B(s_{j,k})}{C(s_{j,k})D(s_{j,k})} \quad , \qquad s_{j,k} = (b_j+k)/\beta_j \tag{5.13}$$

and A_j defined by

$$A(s) = A_j(s)\, \Gamma(b_j - \beta_j s) \quad . \tag{5.14}$$

Let δ be given by

$$\delta = \left(\sum_{j=1}^{m} \beta_j - \sum_{j=n+1}^{p} \alpha_j\right)\pi \tag{5.15}$$

and assume

$$\delta > \frac{\pi}{2}\mu \quad . \tag{5.16}$$

Then, asymptotically

$$H_{pq}^{mn}(z) \sim \sum_{s\varepsilon P(B)} \text{res} \left(\frac{A(s)B(s)}{C(s)D(s)} z^s\right) \quad , \quad n > 0 \quad , \tag{5.17}$$

as $|z| \to \infty$ uniformly on every closed subsector of

$$|\arg z| < \delta - \frac{\pi}{2}\mu \quad . \tag{5.18}$$

In the case where all poles of B are simple, (5.17) may be written in a form analogous to (5.12).

For the case $n = 0$ exponentially small asymptotic behaviour is derived in [8]. In particular, for $m = q$ (which implies $\delta = \mu\pi$) the asymptotic behaviour for $|z| \to \infty$ is given by

$$H^{q0}_{pq}(z) \sim (2\pi)^{q-p}\, e^{i\pi(\alpha-1/2)}\, E(ze^{i\pi\mu}) \quad , \tag{5.19}$$

uniformly on every closed sector (vertex in 0) contained in $|\arg z| < \mu\pi/2$, where

$$E(z) = \frac{1}{2\pi i\mu} \sum_{k=0}^{\infty} A_k\, (\beta\mu^{\mu}z)^{(1-\alpha-k)/\mu}\, \exp(\beta\mu^{\mu}z)^{1/\mu} \quad . \tag{5.20}$$

The constants α and β are given by

$$\alpha = \sum_{j=1}^{p} a_j - \sum_{j=1}^{q} b_j + (q-p+1)/2 \tag{5.21}$$

and

$$\beta = \prod_{j=1}^{p} \alpha_j^{\alpha_j} \prod_{j=1}^{q} \beta_j^{-\beta_j} \quad , \tag{5.22}$$

respectively. The coefficients $A_k (k = 0,1,2,\ldots)$ are determined by

$$\frac{A(s)B(s)}{C(s)D(s)}\, (\beta\mu^{\mu})^{-s} \sim \sum_{k=0}^{\infty} \frac{A_k}{\Gamma(\mu s+\alpha+k)} \quad . \tag{5.23}$$

In particular

$$A_o = (2\pi)^{(p-q+1)/2} \mu^{\alpha-1/2} \prod_{j=1}^{p} \alpha_j^{1/2-a_j} \prod_{j=1}^{q} \beta_j^{b_j-1/2} \tag{5.24}$$

Fox functions have found applications in other parts of probability theory [10], [22]. Their connection with Lévy distributions however seems to have been unnoticed so far, to the best of the author's knowledge.

References

[1] Feller, W. : An introduction to probability theory and its applications, Vol. II. New York: John Wiley 1971.

[2] Mandelbrot, B.B. : The fractal geometry of nature. New York: W.H. Freeman 1983.

[3] Montroll, E.W., Shlesinger, M.F. : On the wonderfull world of random walks. In: Nonequilibrium phenomena II (Studies in statistical mechanics, Vol. 11). Lebowitz, J.L., Montroll, E.W., (eds.). Amsterdam: North Holland 1984.

[4] Lévy, P. : Théorie de l'addition des variables aléatoires. Paris: Gauthier-Villars 1954.

[5] Gnedenko, B.V., Kolmogorov, A.N. : Limit distributions for sums of independent random variables. Reading: Addison Wesley 1954.

[6] Jona-Lasinio, G. : The renormalization group: A probabilistic view. Nuovo Cimento 26B, 99-119 (1975).

[7] Fox, C. : The G and H Functions as symmetrical Fourier kernels. Trans. Amer. Math. Soc. 98, 395-429 (1961).

[8] Braaksma, B.L.J. : Asymptotic expansions and analytic continuations for a class of Barnes-integrals. Compos. Math. 15, 239-341 (1964).

[9] Gupta, K.G., Jain, U.C. : The H-function-II. Proc. Nat. Acad. Sci. India A36, 594-602 (1966).

[10] Srivastava, H.M., Kashyap, B.R.K. : Special functions in queuing theory and related stochastic processes. New York: Academic Press (1982).

[11] Bernasconi, J., Schneider, W.R., Wyss, W. : Diffusion and hopping conductivity in disordered one-dimensional lattice systems. Z. Physik B37, 175-184 (1980).

[12] Alexander, S., Bernasconi, J., Schneider, W.R., Orbach, R. : Excitation dynamics in rand one-dimensional systems. Rev. Mod. Phys. 53, 175-198 (1981).

[13] Schneider, W.R. : Rigorous scaling laws for Dyson measures. In: Stochastic Processes - Mathematics and Physics. Proceedings of the first BiBoS-Symposium. Albeverio, S., Blanchard, Ph., Streit, L., (eds.). Lecture notes in mathematics. Berlin: Springer (1985).

[14] Pollard, H. : The representation of $\exp(-x^{\lambda})$ as a Laplace integral. Bull. Amer. Math. Soc. 52, 908-910 (1946).

[15] Zolotarev, V.M. : Expression of the density of a stable distribution with exponent α greater than one by means of a frequency with exponent $1/\alpha$. Selected translations in mathematical statistics and probability, Vol. 1, 163-167 (1961). (Original: Dokl. Acad. Nauk. 98, 735-738 (1954).

[16] Montroll, E.W., West, B.J. : On an enriched collection of stochastic processes. In : Fluctuation phenomena (Studies in statistical mechanics Vol. 7). Montroll, E.W., Lebowitz, J.L., (eds.). Amsterdam: North Holland 1979.

[17] Schneider, W.R. : Generalized one-sided stable distributions. Proceedings of the second BiBoS-Symposium. Albeverio, S., Blanchard, Ph., Streit, L., (eds.). Lecture notes in mathematics. Berlin: Springer (1986).

[18] Skorohod, A.V. : Asymptotic formulas for stable distribution laws. Selected translations in mathematical statistics and probability, Vol. 1, 157-161 (1961).

[19] Reed, M., Simon, B. : Methods of modern mathematical physics I: Functional analysis. New York: Academic Press 1972.

[20] Zolotarev, V.M. : Mellin-Stieltjes transforms in probability theory. Theor. Prob. Appl. 2, 433-460 (1957).

[21] Abramowitz, M., Stegun I.A., (eds.): Handbook of mathematical functions. New York: Dover 1965.

[22] Mathai, A.M., Saxena, R.K.: The H-function with applications in statistics and other disciplines. New Delhi: Wiley Eastern Limited 1978.

The geodesic mappings in Riemannian
and pseudo-Riemannian manifolds

Paolo Venzi, Bellinzona

In this survey I mainly discuss the problem of the geodesic (projective)mappings between two Riemannian or pseudo-Riemannian manifolds, that is the problem of the local- diffeomorphisms which take geodesic lines of (M,g) into geodesic lines of $(\bar{M},\bar{g})$, up to reparametrisation. I will not give proofs but will either give references to the original papers.

Let (M,g) be a Riemannian or pseudo-Riemannian manifold and let ∇ be the Levi-Civita connection defined by g. A line u(t) is said to be a geodesic line if $\nabla_X X= .X$ where X:=du/dt. We remind the following interesting result that relates the physical paths of a simple mechanical system and the geodesic lines:

Theorem 1 (Jacobi). The physical paths of a simple mechanical system (M,g,V) -where M is a configuration space and V is the potential energy- of total energy h are precisely the geodesic lines of the Riemannian manifold (M_h,g_h), where $g_h:=(h-V).g$.

The proof of this theorem and other interesting results are given in Ong Chong Ping [4].

We now consider a local diffeomorphism $\Lambda:(M,g)\longrightarrow(\bar{M},\bar{g})$ which takes geodesic lines into geodesic lines. Identifying both manifolds via Λ we can consider the new situation of one manifold M provided with two metrics g and $\bar{g}$, respective Levi-Civita connections ∇ and $\bar{\nabla}$ defining the same geodesic lines.

We have the following relations between the geometric objects corresponding to the geodesically equivalent metrics g and $\bar{g}$, which was first proved by H. Weyl in [10] .

Theorem 2. i)There is a well defined linear form Λ such that for all vectorfiefds X,Y:

$$\bar{\nabla}_X Y - \nabla_X Y = \Lambda(X)Y + \Lambda(Y)X \ .$$

ii) The Riemannian curvature tensors are related by:

$\bar{R}(X,Y)Z=R(X,Y)Z-L(Y,Z)X+L(X,Z)Y$

where $L(X,Y):=(\nabla_X\Lambda)Y-\Lambda(X)\Lambda(Y)$.

iii) The Ricci-tensors are related by:

$\overline{Ric}(X,Y)-Ric(X,Y)=L(X,Y)$,

where $Ric(X,Y):=\frac{1}{n-1}\,Tr\left\{Z\longmapsto R(X,Y)Z\right\}$.

iv) Hence: $W(X,Y)Z=\bar{W}(X,Y)Z$

where $W(X,Y)Z:=R(X,Y)Z-Ric(Y,Z)X+Ric(X,Z)Y$

is the projective Weyl-tensor.

Properties of the projective Weyl-tensor:

i) for $n>2$: $W=0$ if and only if M is a space of constant curvature, i.e. $R(X,Y)Z=R(g(Y,Z)X-g(X,Z)Y)$.

ii) $W(V,Z,X,Y):=g(V,W(X,Y)Z)$ is skew symmetric in V and Z if and only if M is an Einstein space,i.e. $Ric(X,Y)=R.g(X,Y)$.

There are two main directios to study the geodesic mappings: a) The tensor analysis, b) The theorem of Levi-Civita and its applications.

a) The application of the tensor analysis give rise to the following results:

Theorem 3 (Beltrami). There is a geodesc mapping of an (M,g) into a space of constant curvature if and only if (M,g) is a apace of constant curvature.

Theorem 4 (Sinjukov [5]). There is a non-trivial geodesic mapping of (M,g) into a locally symmetric space ($\bar{\nabla}\bar{R}=0$), then both spaces are of constant curvature.

Theorem 5 (Venzi [6]). If there is a geodesic mapping of (M,g) into a semisymmetric space ($\bar{R}(X,Y)\bar{R}=0$), then both spaces are of constant curvature or $L(X,Y)=\Delta.g(X,Y)$ with Δ=const..

Theorem 6 (Mikesh [3]). If there is a non-trivial geodesic mapping of (M,g) into an Einstein space ($\overline{Ric}=\bar{R}.\bar{g}$), then M is an Einstein space ($Ric=R.g$).

b) The theorem of Levi-Civita and its applications:

Let $\Lambda:(M,g)\longrightarrow(\bar{M},\bar{g})$ be a geodesic mapping. We consider the linear function ρ defined by $\bar{g}(X,Y)=g(\rho X,Y)$ and we assume that the eigenvalues of ρ are real -this is the case if $\forall X\neq 0:\bar{g}^2(X,X)+g^2(X,X)\neq 0$- and that their multiplicity is constant -this is the case up to a set of measure zero- .

It is now not difficult to prove that the eigensubspaces are involutive distributions. Consequently we can consider the eigensubspaces as coordinates subspaces. Hence we get:

$$ds^2=\sum_{i=1}^{h} d\sigma_i^{\,2} \quad , \quad d\bar{s}^2=\sum_{i=1}^{h}\varrho_i\cdot d\sigma_1^{\,2} \quad ,$$

where: ϱ_k, $k=1,\ldots,h$ are the different eigenvalues of ρ ,

$\dim d\sigma_i^{\,2}=\nu_i=$multiplicity of ϱ_i, $\nu_i=1$ for $i=1,\ldots,m$.

We call such a geodesic mappings of type $[1,\ldots,1,\nu_{m+1},\ldots,\nu_h]$.
After some computations we infer:

The theorem of Levi-Civita(Levi-Civita[2], Venzi [7]).

There is a geodesic mapping between two Riemannian or pseudo-Riemannian manifolds (M,g) and $(\bar{M},\bar{g})$ such that the eigenvalues of $\bar{g}$ relative to g are real, if and only if there are local coordinates in which the metrics take the form:

$$ds^2=\sum_{k=1}^{m} f_k\,|\Psi'(U_k)|\,.\,(du^k)^2+\sum_{t=m+1}^{h}|\Psi(c_t)|\sum_{r,s\in I_t} g^*_{rs}du^r du^s \quad ,$$

$$d\bar{s}^2=\frac{1}{cU_1\cdots U_m}\left\{\sum_{k=1}^{m}(f_k/U_k)\,|\Psi'(U_k)|\,(du^k)^2+\sum_{t=m+1}^{h}(|\Psi(c_t)|/c_t)\sum_{r,s\in I_t} g^*_{rs}du^r du^s\right\} ,$$

where: $f_k=f_k(u^k)$, $U_k=U_k(u^k)$, $\Psi(x):=\prod_{k=1}^{m}(x-U_k)$, $':=d/dx$,

$c:=\prod_{t=m+1}^{h} c_t^{\nu_t}$, $c_t=$const. , $g^*_{rs}=g^*_{rs}(u^i)$ $i\in I_t:=\{i\,|\,\varrho_i=\varrho_t\}$.

Example: geodesic mapping of type [1,n-1]

$$ds^2 = f(u^1)(du^1)^2 + g(u^1)d\sigma^2 \longrightarrow d\bar{s}^2 = \frac{f}{c^{n-1}(g+c)^2}(du^1)^2 + \frac{g}{c^n(g+c)}\, d\sigma^2 .$$

(cfr. Robertson-Walker metric: $ds^2=-dt^2+S^2(t).d\sigma^2$).

The applications of the theorem of Levi-Civita give rise to the following results:

Theorem 8 (Formella[1]). The classification of the geodesic mappings between two spaces of constant curvature.

Every geodesic mapping of type $[1,..,1,\nu_{m+1},..,\nu_h]$ between two spaces of constant curvature with scalar curvature R, resp. $\bar{R}$, is given by:

$$ds^2 = \sum_{\alpha=1}^{p} \frac{\prod_{\sigma\neq\alpha}^{p}(u^\alpha-u^\sigma)}{h(u^\alpha)}(du^\alpha)^2 + \sum_{i=p+1}^{m} d_i \prod_{\beta=1}^{m}(u^\beta-c_i)(du^i)^2 +$$

$$+\sum_{t=m+1}^{h} \left|\prod_{\beta=1}^{p}(u -\tilde{c}_t)\right|.d\sigma_t^{\,2} ,$$

$$d\bar{s}^2 = \frac{1}{C.u^1..u^p}\left\{\sum_{\alpha=1}^{p} \frac{\prod_{\sigma\neq\alpha}^{p}(u^\alpha-u^\sigma)}{u^\alpha.h(u^\alpha)}(du^\alpha)^2 + \sum_{i=p+1}^{m}\frac{d_i}{c_i}\prod_{\beta=1}^{p}(u^\beta-c_i)(du^i)^2+\right.$$

$$\left.+\sum_{t=m+1}^{h}\frac{1}{\tilde{c}_t}\left|\prod_{\beta=1}^{p}(u^\beta-\tilde{c}_t)\right| d\sigma_t^{\,2}\right\} ,$$

where: $p\geq\frac{m-1}{2}$, $h\leq 2p+1$, d_i,c_i=const.,

$h(x):=\prod_{i=p+1}^{m}(x-c_i).k(x)$ and $k(x):=\sum_{s=0}^{2p-m+1} a_s x^s$

with $a_{2p-m+1}=-4R$ and $a_0=(-1)^m.4\bar{R}.\prod_{i=p+1}^{m} c_i$,

$\tilde{c}_t$=const. such that $k(\tilde{c}_t)=0$, $C:=\prod_{i=m+1}^{h} c_t^{\nu_t}.\prod_{i=p+1}^{m} c_i$,

$d\sigma_t^{\,2}=\nu_t$-dim. metrics of constant curvature with scalar curvature $R^{(t)}=\frac{1}{4}h'(\tilde{c}_t)$ with $':=d/dx$.

The geodesic mappings between two spaces of constant curvature play an important role in the study of the geodesic mappings, indeed we have:

Theorem 9 (Formella[1]). If we sobstitute the ν_t-dim. metrics in the theorem 8 by ν_t-dim. Einsteinian metrics $d\sigma_t^2$ with scalar curvature $R^{(t)}$, we infer the complete classification of the geodesic mappings of an Einstein space of scalar curvature R.

Theorem 10 (Venzi[8] and[9]). If we consider in the theorem 8 the case $a_{2p-m+1}=0$ then, for any choice of the ν_t-dim. metrics $d\sigma_t^2$, we infer the complete classification of the geodesic mappings with $L(X,Y)=\Delta.g(X,Y)$.

Theorem 11 (Venzi[9]). If we consider in the theorem 10 the case $a_0=0$, then we infer the classification of the curvature tensor-preserving geodesic mappings.

References:

[1] Formella S., Geodätische Abbildungen der Riemannschen Mannigfaltigkeiten auf Einsteinschen Mannigfaltigkeiten, Tensor N.S., 37 (1982),137-147.

[2] Levi-Civita T., Sulle trasformazioni delle equazioni dinamiche, Annali di Matematica, 24 (1896),255-300.

[3] Mikesh I., Geodesic mappings of Einstein spaces, Math. Notes of the Academy of Science of the USSR, 28 (1980), 922-924.

[4] Ong Chong Ping, Curvature and Mechanic, Advances in Mathematics, 15 (1975), 269-311.

[5] Sinjukov S., Geodesic mappings onto symmetric spaces, Doklady Akad. Nauk SSSR, 98 (1954), 21-23.

[6] Venzi P., On geodesic mappings in Riemannian and pseudo-Riemannian manifolds, Tensor N.S., 32 (1978), 193-198.

[7]- " -, Geodätische Abbildungen in Riemannschen Mannigfaltigkeiten, Tensor N.S., 33 (1979),313-321.

[8]- " -, Klassifikation der geodätischen Abbildungen mit $\bar{R}ic-Ric=\Delta.g$, Tensor N.S., 37 (1982), 137-147.

[9]- " -, Ruh B., Curvature tensor-preserving diffeomerphisms, (1985), to appear.

Paol Venzi,
Liceo-Bellinzona, 6500 Bellinzona, Switzerland.

(Ascona-Como International Conference, June 24-29, 1985)

VARIATIONAL PROCESSES

J.-Claude Zambrini *

Princeton University

Department of Mathematics

Princeton, NJ 08540

ABSTRACT

A new class of diffusion processes, the "Bernstein processes", is introduced in Theoretical Physics. Their dynamical realization, the "Variational processes" yields a new probabilistic interpretation of the Heat equation, much closer to quantum mechanics than the other known classical analogies, and also a new constructive variational approach to Stochastic Mechanics.

* From October 1985 : Universität Bielefeld, BiBoS, D-4800 Bielefeld 1, Postfach 8640, West-Germany

1. THE VARIATIONAL POINT OF VIEW

The path of a classical system in the configuration space $M = \mathbb{R}^N$, $I = [-\frac{T}{2}, \frac{T}{2}] \underset{t}{\mapsto} X_t \in M$ can be described in terms of differential laws (Newton equations) for a given initial position $X(-\frac{T}{2})$ and initial velocity $V(-\frac{T}{2})$ or via a variational approach (Hamilton's principle) for a given pair of initial and final positions. In contrast to the mathematical equivalence of these approaches, their physical equivalence is somewhat questionable. On the other hand, Stochastic Mechanics is a probabilistic attempt to describe quantum phenomena in the frame of a dynamical structure as close as possible to Classical Mechanics. Due to the irregularities of the quantum "paths", the differential law (stochastic Newton equation) is much more involved [1].

I wish to summarize here the constructive analogue of the variational approach in Stochastic Mechanics. The results are of greater generality than this original motivation. They show, in particular, that the complete realization of a program initiated in 1931 by E. Schrödinger gives the genuine Euclidean version of Stochastic Mechanics.

The Stochastic Calculus of Variations associated to Stochastic Mechanics is due to Yasue (1981) [2]. Let $L_c(x,\dot{x},t) = \frac{1}{2}|\dot{x}|^2 - V(x,t)$ the classical Lagrangian of a "natural" system with unit masses ($|\cdot|$ is the Euclidean norm in $M = \mathbb{R}^N$). The Action functional J is defined by

$$J : X \to \frac{1}{2}E[\int_{-T/2}^{T/2} \{L_c(X(t),DX(t),t) + L_c(X(t),D_*X(t),t)\}dt] \qquad (1.1)$$

for X a smooth diffusion in the Nelson's sense [1]. D_*X is the backward derivative with respect to the future filtration $\mathcal{F}_t$,

$$D_*X(t) = \lim_{\Delta t \downarrow 0} E[\frac{X(t)-X(t-\Delta t)}{\Delta t} | \mathcal{F}_t] \qquad (1.2)$$

and $DX(t)$ the analogue forward concept. X is extremal for J if $J[X+\delta X] - J[X] = 0[\delta X]$ for any smooth vector field δX with compact support in $M \times I$. Yasue's Theorem says that X is extremal for J if and only if the Stochastic Newton equation

$$\frac{1}{2}(DD_*X + D_*DX) = -\nabla V \qquad (1.3)$$

holds. This reduces to Hamilton's principle at the classical limit of smooth trajectories. Our point of view is that such a variational approach is relevant if and only if it is associated to a new probabilistic construction of Stochastic Mechanics. Another derivation of Eq. (1.3) is not sufficient : although it is central in the initial Nelson's interpretation, its probabilistic meaning is still missing.

Therefore, the appealing Yasue's generalization of the classical two fixed end points variational problem suggests some unorthodox questions about the involved processes :

1) How to interpret probabilistically the condition $X_{-T/2}$ and $X_{T/2}$ fixed during the variation ?
2) If the answer to 1) is the data of the two probabilities $\rho(dx,-\frac{T}{2})$ and $\rho(dy,\frac{T}{2})$, how to construct a diffusion process X_t , $t \in I$, from these data ? The point is that $X_{-T/2}$ and $X_{T/2}$ are not two independent random variables, therefore such an hypothesis involves their joint probability $m(dx,dy)$.

Another kind of classical Action, a function of the future configuration of the system, appears in the variational context with transversal conditions. Under some technical assumptions [3], if $\gamma : s \to X(s)$ is a classical extremal between $X_{-T/2}$ and $X(t) = x$, one shows that

$$S_{X_{-T/2}}(x,t) = \int_\gamma L_c(X(t),\dot{X}(s),s)\,ds + S_{-T/2}(X(-\tfrac{T}{2})) \tag{1.4}$$

solves (for the natural L_c) the Hamilton-Jacobi equation

$$\frac{\partial S}{\partial t} + \frac{1}{2}(\nabla S)^2 + V = 0 \quad . \tag{1.5}$$

This is an alternative characterization of the solution of the Newton equation

$$\ddot{X}(s) = -\nabla V(X(s)) \qquad -\tfrac{T}{2} \le s \le t$$

for

$$\dot{X}(-\tfrac{T}{2}) = \nabla S_{-T/2}(X(-\tfrac{T}{2})) \quad \text{and} \quad X(t) = x \quad .$$

Notice that the use of (1.4) requires to know some (actually a "Field" of) classical extremals.

In summary, a constructive variational generalization of Classical Mechanics associated to Yasue's Principle is the following :

a) Construction of the class of processes indexed by I and with two given probabilities $\rho_{-T/2}(dx)$ and $\rho_{T/2}(dy)$.

b) For fixed $\rho_{-T/2}(dx)$ only, construction of an Action depending on the future configuration and of a least Action principle for characterizing the dynamics.

As suggested by a) the admissible processes for such a least Action principle cannot be limited to Markovian processes. (Besides, this is not the case in Yasue's Principle.)

During the realization of this program, the use of all the structural dynamical invariances of Classical Mechanics is, of course, allowed. The proofs are given in [4].

2. BERNSTEIN PROCESSES

The first point of this constructive variational program appeared already once in the physical literature :

i) In 1931, E. Schrödinger proposed a very original description of diffusion phenomena whose motivation was to show that the physical irreversibility of these processes is not intrinsic, but due to a restrictive conception of their dynamics [5].

ii) One year after, the probabilist S. Bernstein proposed the following constructive program for the new class of processes involved in Schrödinger's idea [6] :

Let $Z_t : \Omega = \prod_{t \in I} \dot{M} \to \dot{M}$, $\omega \to \omega(t) = Z(t,\omega)$ be one of these processes defined on the underlying probability space $(\Omega, \mathcal{G}_I, P)$. Let $(\dot{M}, \mathcal{B})$ be its State space ($\dot{M}$ is the compactification of M, a locally compact metric space). If $\mathcal{P}_s$ is the increasing family of sigma-algebras for the past at time s, $\mathcal{F}_u$ the analogue decreasing family for the future at time u,

a) Replace the Markov property, for f bounded, by the "Bernstein property"

$$E[f(Z_t) | \mathcal{P}_s \cup \mathcal{F}_u] = E[f(Z_t) | Z_s, Z_u] \qquad \forall -\frac{T}{2} < s < t < u < \frac{T}{2}$$

b) Replace the (density of) Markovian transition probability by the "Bernstein transition" $h = h(s,x;t,y;u,z)$ such that

b1) $\forall (x,z) \in M \times M$

$\mathcal{B} \ni A \to \int_A h(s,x;t,y;u,z)dy \equiv H(s,x;t,A;u,z)$ is a probability on M.

b2) $h(s,w;t,x;u,y)h(s,w;u,y;v,z) = h(s,w;t,x;v,z)h(t,x;u,y;v,z)$.

c) Replace the data of the Markovian initial probability by the data of the joint probability of $Z_{-T/2}$ and $Z_{T/2}$.

I call "Bernstein processes" the resulting time symmetrical processes. The program of Bernstein has been realized, in a nondynamical context, by Jamison, Beurling and Fortet [7,8,9].

<u>Theorem 1</u> : For $H = H(s,x;t,A;u,z)$ a Bernstein transition, $m = m(dx,dy)$ a probability on $\mathcal{B} \times \mathcal{B}$, there is an unique probability measure P_m such that, with respect to $(\Omega, \mathcal{G}_I, P_m)$, Z_t, $t \in I$ is a Bernstein process and

1) $P_m(Z_{-T/2} \in B_S, Z_{T/2} \in B_F) = \int_{B_S \times B_F} m(dx,dy)$, $B_S, B_F \in \mathcal{B}$

2) $\forall -\frac{T}{2} \leq s < t < u \leq \frac{T}{2}$, $P_m(Z_t \in B | Z_s, Z_u) = H(s,x;t,B;u,y)$

3) $p_m(x_1,t_1;x_2,t_2;\ldots;x_n,t_n) = \int_{B_S \times B_F} m(dx,dy)h(-\frac{T}{2},x;t_1,x_1;\frac{T}{2},y)\ldots$

$\ldots h(t_{n-1},x_{n-1};t_n,x_n;\frac{T}{2},y)$.

In the right hand side, one also may fix the initial position $(-\frac{T}{2},x)$ in all the densities h and change the final ones.

We consider two, apparently independent, ways to construct a

Bernstein transition :

B1) Let $h = h(s,x,t,y)$ the fundamental solution of the Heat equation $-\hbar\frac{\partial\bar{\theta}}{\partial t} = H\bar{\theta}$, for $H = -\frac{\hbar^2}{2}\Delta + V$ essentially self-adjoint, $V = V(x)$ Hölder continuous a.e. on M and bounded below. Then h is strictly positive, continuous in x,y and $(t-s)$, and, for $s<t<u$, $h(s,x;t,y;u,z) \equiv \frac{h(s,x,t,y)h(t,y,u,z)}{h(s,x,u,z)}$ is a Bernstein transition.

B2) Let $\psi(x,t) = e^{(R+iS)(x,t)/\hbar}$ a (classical) solution continuous in $L^2(M)$ of the Schrödinger equation $i\hbar\frac{\partial\psi}{\partial t} = H\psi$, for the same Hamiltonian H as in B1).
For $\nu = (\nabla R)^2 + \hbar\Delta R - V$, let $k = k(s,x,t,y)$ be the fundamental solution of the Heat equation $-\hbar\frac{\partial\bar{\varphi}}{\partial t} = -\frac{\hbar^2}{2}\Delta\bar{\varphi} + \nu\bar{\varphi}$. Under the hypothesis that k is strictly positive,
$k(s,x;t,y;u,z) \equiv \frac{k(s,x,t,y)k(t,y,u,z)}{k(s,x,u,z)}$ is a Bernstein transition.

For any choice of joint probability $m = m(dx,dy)$ the Theorem 1 yields an unique Bernstein process. However, an unique joint probability yields a Markovian Bernstein process. The argument is valid for both kernel B1) or B2). Let us consider B1) :

<u>Theorem 2</u> : Let h be the kernel of B1), and Z_t be the Bernstein process for a given joint probability m. Then Z_t is Markovian iff there are two bounded real functions of same sign on M, $\bar{\theta}_{-T/2}$ and $\theta_{T/2}$ such that

$$\int_{B_S\times B_F} m(dx,dy) = \int_{B_S\times B_F} \bar{\theta}_{-T/2}(x)\,h(-\tfrac{T}{2},x,\tfrac{T}{2},y)\,\theta_{T/2}(y)\,dxdy \quad . \qquad (2.1)$$

The proof shows that this Markovian Bernstein process is characterized by the forward (density of) transition probability

$$q(s,x,t,y) = h(s,x,t,y)\frac{\theta(y,t)}{\theta(x,s)} \tag{2.2}$$

where $\theta(x,s)$ is defined by

$$\theta(x,s) = \int_M h(s,x,\tfrac{T}{2},y)\,\theta_{T/2}(y)\,dy \tag{2.3}$$

or equivalently by the backward (density of) transition probability

$$\bar{q}(s,x,t,y) = \frac{\bar{\theta}(x,s)}{\bar{\theta}(y,t)}h(s,x,t,y) \tag{2.4}$$

where $\bar{\theta}(y,t) = \int_M \bar{\theta}_{-T/2}(x)\,h(-\tfrac{T}{2},x,t,y)\,dx$.

It follows easily that Z_t , $t\in I$, is a diffusion process with forward and backward drifts respectively given by

$$B(x,t) = \hbar\,\frac{\nabla\theta}{\theta}\,(x,t) \tag{2.5}$$

$$B_*(y,t) = -\,\hbar\,\frac{\nabla\bar{\theta}}{\bar{\theta}}\,(y,t) \tag{2.6}$$

and diffusion matrix

$$C = C_* = \hbar\mathbb{1} \tag{2.7}$$

where $\mathbb{1}$ is the $N\times N$ identity matrix and $\hbar$ the Planck constant. Its density of probability on I (after normalization) is

$$p(x,t) = \bar{\theta}(x,t)\,\theta(x,t) \quad . \tag{2.8}$$

Now, by hypothesis, the boundary probabilities $p(dx,-\frac{T}{2})$ and $p(dy,\frac{T}{2})$

are given, but not the pair $\bar{\theta}_{-T/2}$ and $\theta_{T/2}$. Nevertheless, by definition of the Markovian joint density, we have the constraints

$$\begin{cases} \bar{\theta}_{-T/2}(x)\int_M h(x,-\frac{T}{2},y,\frac{T}{2})\,\theta_{T/2}(y)\,dy = p(x,-\frac{T}{2}) \\ \\ \theta_{T/2}(y)\int_M \bar{\theta}_{-T/2}(x)\,h(x,-\frac{T}{2},y,\frac{T}{2})\,dx = p(y,\frac{T}{2}) \quad . \end{cases} \tag{2.9}$$

I call this the Schrödinger's system (1931) for $\bar{\theta}_{-T/2}$ and $\theta_{T/2}$. Bernstein, Fortet, Beurling and Jamison contributed to the following result :

<u>Theorem 3</u> : Let $p_{-T/2}(dx)$ and $p_{T/2}(dy)$ be two strictly positive probability measures on $\mathcal{B}$. Let h be the continuous and strictly positive kernel of B1). Then we have existence and uniqueness of the solution $\bar{\theta}_{-T/2}$ and $\theta_{T/2}$ (with same sign on M) of the Schrödinger's system.

3. VARIATIONAL PROCESSES

To realize the point b) of our program (§1) we will characterize variationaly the unique Markovian Bernstein process Z_τ in a class of non Markovian diffusions $\hat{Z}_\tau$ with a fixed future position. $\hat{B}_*$ is an admissible drift if it is adapted to a decreasing filtration $\mathcal{F}_\tau$ and if there is an $\mathcal{F}_\tau$-martingale $\hat{W}_*$ such that $\hat{Z}(t) = z$ and

$$d\hat{Z}(\tau) = \hat{B}_*(\tau)dt + \mathbb{1}\hbar^{1/2}d\hat{W}_*(\tau) \qquad -\frac{T}{2} \le \tau < t < \frac{T}{2} \tag{3.1}$$

and

$$\int_{-T/2}^{t} |\hat{B}_*(\tau)|\,d\tau < \infty \quad \text{a.s.}$$

Let $\bar{\theta}(x,t)$ the unique positive solution of the Heat equation $-\hbar\frac{\partial\bar{\theta}}{\partial t} = H\bar{\theta}$ for a solution $\bar{\theta}_{-T/2}(x) \equiv e^{(\bar{R}_{-T/2}-\bar{S}_{-T/2})(x)/\hbar}$ of the Schrödinger system. The stochastic Action for any admissible process is defined by the conditional expectation given $\hat{Z}(t) = z$,

$$\bar{I}_{\hbar,\hat{B}_*}(z,t) = E_{z,t}\int_{-T/2}^{t}\{\frac{1}{2}|D_*\hat{Z}(\tau)|^2 + V(\hat{Z}(\tau))\}d\tau +$$

$$+ E_{z,t}(\bar{S}_{-T/2} - \bar{R}_{-T/2})(\hat{Z}(-\frac{T}{2})) \qquad (3.2)$$

where $D_*\hat{Z}(\tau) = \hat{B}_*(\tau)$. Let us define $\bar{A}_h(z,t) = -\hbar\log\bar{\theta}(z,t)$. Then the following stochastic least Action principle holds :

<u>Theorem 4</u> : For any admissible process $\hat{Z}(\tau)$, $\bar{I}_{\hbar,\hat{B}_*}(z,t) \geq \bar{A}_{\hbar}(z,t)$ (*). Moreover, the Markovian Bernstein process Z_τ is admissible, and its drift $\hat{B}_*(\tau) = B_*(z(\tau),\tau) = \nabla\bar{A}_{\hbar}(Z(\tau),\tau)$ reduces (*) to an equality. Finally, Z_τ satisfies the Newton equation in imaginary time

$$\frac{1}{2}(DDZ + D_*D_*Z)(\tau) = +\nabla V \quad , \quad -\frac{T}{2} \leq \tau < t \qquad (3.3)$$

with $D_*Z(-\frac{T}{2}) = (\nabla\bar{S}_{-T/2} - \nabla\bar{R}_{-T/2})(Z(-\frac{T}{2}))$ and $Z(t) = z$.

<u>Remarks</u> :

1) This is a reversible dynamics associated to B1) and then a new probabilistic interpretation of the Heat equation. I call it (Schrödinger's) Stochastic Variational Dynamics. Actually, the "Bernstein property" a) is closely connected to the one dimensional version of Markov random Field and the resulting theory contains the Euclidean version of Stochastic Mechanics [10].

2) According to Theorem 4, there is no dynamically relevant non

Markovian diffusion process in the theory.

3) At the classical limit $\hbar = 0$, the Action $\bar{I}_{\hbar,\hat{B}_*}$ reduces to the classical one and the equation of motion to the (imaginary time) Newton equation.

The structure of the construction starting from B2) is identical. The analogue results are

$$p(s,x,t,y) = k(s,x,t,y)\frac{\varphi(y,t)}{\varphi(x,s)} \tag{2.2'}$$

$$\bar{p}(s,x,t,y) = \frac{\bar{\varphi}(x,s)}{\bar{\varphi}(y,t)}k(s,x,t,y) \tag{2.4'}$$

where $\bar{\varphi}(y,t)$ is the forward evolution of $\bar{\varphi}_{-T/2}$ by k, $\varphi(x,s)$ the backward one of $\varphi_{T/2}$, and $\bar{\varphi}_{-T/2}$, $\varphi_{T/2}$ are the solutions of a Schrödinger system. Moreover,

$$I_{\hbar,\hat{B}_*}(x,t) = E_{x,t}\int_{-T/2}^{t}\left\{\frac{1}{2}|D_*\hat{X}(\tau)|^2 + \nu(\hat{X}(\tau),\tau)\right\}d\tau +$$

$$+ E_{x,t}(S_{-T/2} - R_{-T/2})(\hat{X}(-\tfrac{T}{2})) \tag{3.2'}$$

$$\frac{1}{2}(DD_*X + D_*DX)(\tau) = -\nabla V \qquad -\frac{T}{2} \leq \tau < t \tag{3.3'}$$

with $D_*X(-\frac{T}{2}) = (\nabla S_{-T/2} - \nabla R_{-T/2})(X(-\frac{T}{2}))$ and $X(t) = x$.

Remarks :

1) This is a new construction of Nelson's Stochastic Mechanics. Actually it is not independent of the one starting from B1) : one shows that Stochastic Mechanics is a particular realization of (Schrödinger's) Stochastic Variational Dynamics [10].

2) The analogue of the abovementioned Remark 2) is the negative answer to Nelson's conjecture [1,§23] about physically relevant non Markovian processes in his theory.

3) The main interest of this second construction is to clarify the origin of the yet unsolved problem to find a probabilistic interpretation of Nelson's stochastic acceleration. For a given potential V the basic kernel k is far to be unique in a dynamical context; therefore, the resulting processes have few common probabilistic properties. This difficulty is absent from Stochastic Variational Dynamics [11].

4) The Absolute expectation of the Action (3.2') (without boundary conditions) for $t = T/2$ is, in the notations of Stochastic Mechanics, namely if u denotes the osmotic velocity,

$$E[\int_{-T/2}^{T/2}\{\frac{1}{2}|D_*X|^2 - V - u^2\}d\tau] \quad .$$

It does not involve the Guerra-Morato Lagrangian [12] but under weaker hypothesis (Non Markovian Admissible processes) it provides stronger conclusion (Minimum of the Action) for the same dynamical content (the Newton equation (3.3')).

5) In any stationary situation, this approach gives explicit closed formulas out of reach in the usual construction, and shed some light on what is known about quantum stationary states [11,13,14,15,16,17].

6) In conclusion, it is worth mentioning that this new constructive approach to Stochastic Mechanics also suggests new physical interpretations of Quantum phenomena [11].

BIBLIOGRAPHY

[1] Nelson E., "Quantum Fluctuations", Princeton University Press (1985).

[2] Yasue K., J. Funct. Anal. 41, 327 (1981).

[3] Arnold V., "Méthodes mathématiques de la mécanique classique", Ed. de Moscou (1976).

[4] Zambrini J.-C., "Variational Processes and Stochastic Versions of Mechanics", to appear in J. of Math. Physics (1986)

[5] Schrödinger E., Ann. Inst. Henri Poincaré 2, 269 (1932).

[6] Bernstein S., "Sur les liaisons entre les grandeurs aléatoires", Verh. des Intern. Mathematikerkongr., Zürich, Band 1 (1932).

[7] Jamison B., Z. Wahrscheinlich. ver Gebiete 30, 65 (1974).

[8] Beurling A., Annals of Mathematics 72, 1, 189 (1960).

[9] Fortet R., J. Math. Pures et Appl. IX, 83 (1940).

[10] Zambrini J.-C., K. Yasue, in preparation.

[11] Zambrini J.-C., "Stochastic Mechanics according to E. Schrödinger", Phys. Rev. A, Vol. 33, No 3, 1532 (1986)

[12] Guerra F., Morato L., Phys. Rev. D, 1774 (1983).

[13] Albeverio S., Hoegh-Krohn R., J. Math. Phys. 15, 10, 1745 (1974).

[14] Carmona R., "Processus de diffusion gouverné par la forme de Dirichlet de l'opérateur de Schrödinger", Sémin. Prob. XIII, LN721 (1979).

[15] Carlen E., Commun. Math. Phys. 94, 293 (1984).

[16] P.A. Meyer, W.A. Zheng,"Construction de processus de Nelson réversibles", Sémin. Prob. XIX, LN1123 (1985).

[17] Blanchard P., Zheng W.A., in this conference.

SPECIAL LECTURES

LEVELS OF STRUCTURE AND FUNCTION IN NEUROBIOLOGY

K. Hepp, Physics Dept., E.T.H. CH 8093 Zürich

The central problem of brain research (or neurobiology) is to understand on various levels the functions of brains, and, hopefully, of our mind, in terms of structural properties of nervous systems. The precise meaning of this program becomes clearer, if one compares the notions of "structure", "function" and "level" in mathematics, physics, computer engineering and in neurobiology.

Mathematics deals with immaterial logical objects, like the rational numbers with one of their "natural" topologies. Sets, whose elements have certain axiomatic properties, define a "structure" in the sense of Bourbaki [1] , and every proposition, which is a consequence of these axioms, belongs to the theory of this structure. By adjoining compatible axioms to a structure, one obtains a "richer" structure. It is important to know whether two structures are isomorphic and whether a proposition valid in a structure (e.g. the existence of the Haar measure in Lie groups) is valid in a poorer structure (e.g. in a locally compact separable metrizable topological group). Mathematics is democratic in the sense that all deep theorems are equally interesting, and it is not customary to distinguish different "levels". The notion of a "function" as a 1-valued relation between two sets is fundamental. A mathematical function has no utilitarian aspects.

In physics the "real world" objects under study have observable regularities which one calls their "structure". The more subtle regularities are only observed, if one uses a theoretical model of the objects under consideration. These models predict "functional" relations between observable quantities in the mathematical sense which can be experimentally verified. Structures in physics are often observed only in a certain range of lengths, times or energies. Similarly theories contain quantities like Planck's constant h or the velocity of light c, such that in certain limits, like $h \to 0$ or $c \to \infty$ a simpler theory for the structures in the corresponding ranges holds. A grouping of structures and functions according to this principle introduces "levels" in physics, like the classical level or the nonrelativistic level. It is believed and partially established that one fundamental theory describes all structures in physics and that all descriptions at the different levels can be obtained by mathematical limits. The use of levels in physics is extremely useful, because many approximatively valid functional relations become exact at a certain level and allow a simplified description of observable regularities.

Computers as material objects have structures which can be described in the framework of physics. However the levels of physics, microscopic quantum mechanics, classical mechanics and electrodynamics, are too general for a detailed description of a computer. Computer engineering has introduced a number of additional levels, which can be obtained from the physical levels by limiting processes. The levels of structure and function in modern computers has been admirably discussed by Tanenbaum [2]. There is a level of analog "devices" with objects like transistors and capacities which are idealizations in electrical engineering. At the next level of "digital logic" the idealized descriptors are gates, which transform inputs into outputs according to the laws of Boolean algebra, and latches, which remember previous input values. For describing the input-memory-output relations in a complex computation the hardware levels are much too detailed. They are overlayed by a number of software levels, as the microprogramming, the machine language, the operating system and the higher language level. These levels become increasingly implementation independent, but for every computer high-level commands are functionally related to operations on the digital logic level. These relations are all functions in the sense of mathematics. The word "function", however, acquires in technology and biology a second meaning with the implication of "purpose". The LINK and UNLK instructions in the assembly language of the Motorola MC 68000 processor are useful for passing the control to and from procedures in Pascal, and this is their function at the higher language level, which contributes in the Darwinian struggle for the "survival of the fittest" computer.

In biology, functions are also primarily mathematical functions and structures physical structures. However, the teleological meaning, which one can give to some functions (like the relation between oxygen pressure and binding in haemoglobin is all important: one can establish infinitely many different functional relations between physical quantities in a living organism, but one is mostly interested in those functions which enter in an important manner as subroutines at a higher level. Similar to computer engineering neurobiology has a physico-chemical level (P-level), and to the device level corresponds the cellular level (C-level) with neurons, muscle fibers and receptor cells as new descriptors. For simple brains of molluscs the C-level is sufficient, but even there it has been useful to induce a higher modular level (M-level), in which new descriptors like "central pattern generators" and "memories" occur. In molluscs many neurons are large and identifiable in intact preparations, and one could try to give a sharp structural definition of a module. One finds, however, that a subset of neurons which is a candidate for an "oscillator" has also aspects of a "memory", since the synaptic coupling strengths is plastic. This is a general problem in the brain: unlike in computers structural and functional modules do not always coincide, a structural module can generate a number of different functions and one function is generated by neurons from many different anatomical structures. However, it is hoped that even in the mammalian brain, where a modular level is indispensible for describing the operation of billions of neurons, one can find a subdivision into neuronal populations, in which several subroutines are generated either somehow independently from one another (like a rapidly changing pattern and a memory on a much larger time scale) or by multiplexing using a switching according to "sets" [3]. On the modular level one can analyse entire mammalian brains or, when one restricts oneself to one species, certain subsystems of the brain, like the eye movement (or oculomotor) system, which in certain situations can be studied as an independent structure.

The P-, C- and M-level of neurobiology are hardware levels, and here theory can be closely related to experiment. Marr [4] has strongly argued for an algorithmic and a computational level for computer vision and robotics. Neurobiology, however, is a natural science and differs from engineering in that not all technical constructions are interesting but only real brains, and most importantly the human brain. In this context the investigation of abstract algorithms is a useful tool like the study of other mathematical structures (e.g. dynamical systems), but it is not a higher level of neurobiology.

In the second part of this lecture I shall present some typical investigations of the structure-function problem at the P-, C- and M-level. At every level the theory will employ the descriptional primitives of its and lower levels and establish functional relations between structure at this level and possibly emergent properties of higher levels.

(1) Muscle-brain interface (P-level). Skeletal muscle is a phantastically effective generator of rapid and slow length changes and of powerful or finely graded force under the continuous control of the

brain. Under static conditions the force F generated by a muscle fiber is a function of its length L and its innervation I from a motoneuron. The molecular structure of a muscle fiber consists of repeated assemblies of myosin and actin filaments. The contraction occurs as filaments slide past each other, and this is effected by ATP hydrolysis at the myosin heads, stimulated by actin and controlled by calcium ions, whose influx is a function of the firing rate of the motoneuron [5]. The motoneurons are the final common pathway for the action of the brain on the outside world. For motor control it would be highly desirable to derive the equations of motion of a limb with the innervation as control parameters. For the eye, which is in good approximation a center-fixed rigid sphere with 3 muscle pairs to activate all 3 degress of freedom, Robinson [6] has calculated for every fixed position the innervations I_i of all six eye muscles from their geometry, the laws of static equilibrium and from the measured functions $F_i(\cdot,\cdot)$. It would be desirable to calculate these functions from the microscopic structure of the muscle, and also its time-dependence. A first step has been achieved by Huxley (see e.g. [7]), who has determined the decrease of muscle force with contraction velocity. A theoretical understanding of muscle physiology is necessary, because it is impossible to measure all mechanical and physiological parameters in an active multi-joint movement of a free-moving animal. For the motoneurons of the eye, the length L in the pulling direction of the muscle is in first approximation a linear function of the firing rate R, which is the solution of the differential equation $R = a(L-L_0) + b\dot{L} + c\ddot{L}$ with constants a,b,c and L_0 [8]. Since the activity patterns of motoneurons are easily accessible, one can for the purpose of neurophysiology circumvent the difficulties in understanding the muscle and skeletal dynamics and define the "movement from within" by these output parameters, provided one can establish and solve the equations of motion of the body.

(2) Morphology and function of neurons (P-level). The electrodynamics of neurons is a beautiful biophysical problem which has culminated in the Nobel prize for Hodgkin and Huxley for the elucidation of the action potential generation at nerve membranes. Linear passive conduction of the postsynaptic potentials to the soma often determinates the "integration" of incoming signals in the all-or-nothing action potential at the axon hillock. These boundary value problems have been extensively studied by Rall [9] and others. There is the ambitious program to predict from morphology and electrodynamics the functional significance of the dendritic tree. Since the synaptic conductivity is in the theory of Hodgkin and Huxley a function of transmembrane voltage, the simple linear-addition-plus-threshold model of a neuron is not always true, and in the non-linear range the output can be e.g. the product of the inputs. Koch, Poggio and Torre [10] have used a convergent iterative solution to predict the "device properties" of identified neurons in the retina. The application of electrodynamics can be carried on to simple neuronal networks for describing the firing patterns of slices of tissue of the hippocampus [11].

(3) Motor learning in the cerebellum (N-level). The cerebellar cortex (see e.g. [12]) is a laminated structure of billions of neurons (in man) whose basic circuitry is everywhere similar and organized geometrically so that the output neurons, the Purkinje cells, receive on the average inputs from about 100 000 parallel fibers. This input from everywhere in the nervous system generates a modulated discharge pattern of high frequency of "simple spikes". By another multiple synaptic connection every Purkinje cell receives input from one climbing fiber, where every action potential generates a powerful "complex spike". Since the classical account of Cajal [13] neurophysiologists

have tried to find the functional explanation of this neuronal network which is incorporated with little evolutionary changes in the brains of all mammals. Marr [14] and Albus [15] have proposed that the cerebellum operates as a perceptron and is used as a motor memory, which can learn motor patterns by changing the synaptic strength of all parallel fiber synapses on a Purkinje cell which are active at the time of a complex spike. Ito [12] has applied this idea to the regulation of the gain of the vestibulo-ocular reflex (VOR). The VOR is a rapid open loop reflex by which the eyes are stabilized in space when the head is turning, in order to provide unblurred vision. The gain of the VOR can be modified adaptively (see e.g. [16]) and this plasticity is lost after the lesion of the flocculus, which is a region in the cerebellum where visual, vestibular and oculomotor signals converge. Mathematically the action of the flocculus in this situation can be modelled as an adaptive linear filter [17]. However, despite of hundreds of truely remarkable experiments which have been inspired by the perceptron hypothesis, the correctness of this theory is still in doubt. It is probable that gain changes of the VOR are effected also by plastic synapses outside of the flocculus, which on the other hand contributes in many other oculomotor functions (see e.g. Waespe and Henn in [16]).

(4) Associative recall (N-level). One of the amazing properties of human memory is its associative and distributive character which is rather insensitive against cell degeneration and where the stored information can be rapidly recalled despite the slow action of neurons in the millisecond range. Hopfield [18] has introduced an associative memory where the "learned" pattern (which is encoded in the synaptic strenghts in the network) is recalled as the firing pattern of an attractor which is reached by giving as address a neighboring pattern in the basin of the attractor. The dynamics is a rapid asynchronous paral-

lel relaxation of the "energy", which has the structure of a spin-glass Hamiltonian, and it resembles an integration and thresholding process of neurons. In one learning algorithm by Kinzel (see e.g. [19]) "frustrated" bonds are suppressed with a storage capacity of $O(\ell nN)$ for N neurons, which is not optimal. The Hopfield model shows that "holographic" action patterns of the brain can be generated by quasirealistic neurons, but nothing is known about the implementation of this algorithm. The strongest competitor, for which there is some experimental evidence, is a memory organization in terms of feature detectors [20].

(5) Oculomotor system (M-level). Some of the most beautiful M-level models have been devised by Robinson [8], [21] for the generation of eye movements under visual and vestibular stimulation. Along the path of discovery one first identifies a number of purposeful functions generated by this system and neuronal populations with a task-related activity pattern whose inactivation leads to typical dysfunctions. Furthermore the anatomical excitatory and inhibitory connections of these neuronal populations have to be established. By knowing that the human eye has a fovea of maximal visual acuity of about 1 degree diameter and that this acuity is lost if the target moves over the retina at a few degrees per second, one can predict the existence of two purposeful oculomotor subroutines: a voluntary "foveation" process, which rapidly brings the image of an excentric target into the fovea by "saccades" and keeps moving targets in the fovea by "pursuit", and a "compensatory" subroutine during head movements, in which the VOR takes part as well as an "optokinetic" reflex (OKR), which is induced by visual flow patterns. The models of these brain functions are (often piece-wise linear) dynamical systems and introduce the activity in (at least some) task-related neuronal populations as state variables. The motor output is gen-

erated by central "decisions" and by visual and vestibular input. The models are modular and contain pattern generators like the "saccadic burst generator" and short term memories like the "head velocity storage" and the "eye position integrator". Such models have predicted a number of nontrivial aspects of visuo-vestibular interaction [21] and of the spatio-temporal transformations in the generation of saccades (see e.g. [22]). A closer inspection of the experimental data shows again the difficulties of the modular approach. For instance, in the "simple" VOR process the "velocity storage" and the "position integrator" comprise many common neurons with very complex firing patterns [23]. By what mathematical structures can one quantify such "distributed functions"?

(6) Early vision (M-level). The algorithms by which the brain arrives at its amazing perceptual competence are widely unknown. Marr [4] and his group have postulated that the early stages of vision are elaborated by modules like stereo-, color- and movement vision, which operate automatically on the retinal images without an understanding of their content. In the case of stereovision the existence of an automatic matching process has been established by Julesz [24], and an algorithm by Marr and Poggio [25] has shown in a computer implementation by Grimson [26] a rather satisfactory performance. The proposed modular nature of early vision has found considerable interest among neurophysiologists who find neuronal populations in the visual cortical and subcortical areas which seem to be "predominantly" dedicated to one or the other subroutine. More difficulties arise at the next stage, where Marr proposes a visual representation in terms of a view-centered "2 1/2 dimensional sketch", which is transformed into a viewpoint-independent "3 dimensional representation" for the purpose of recognition. Most difficult problems with the M-level de-

scription of perception are related to the use of this information in a brain in which no "homunculus" is allowed. Fortunately most of our visual operations do not deal with perception per se, but are used for the guidance of movement. In the alert monkey the transformations from the vision of a target to the signals which drive the saccade or smooth pursuit system have been carefully studied by Goldberg, Mountcastle and Wurtz and collaborators (see e.g.[27]).If one examines how a cell population responds not only when the sensory stimulus is present or when an automatic motor command is generated but also when the stimulus is used in the course of the behavior, one arrives at the important notion of "selective attention", which distinguishes different cortical areas. Even very close to the motor output the modulation of neurons can be very complex: in the superior colliculus one finds a 2-dimensional organization of neurons in a retinocentric and saccade vector map, where purely visual, saccade-enhanced visual, vision-enhanced saccadic and purely saccadic neurons are close together [28].

It is time to conclude this review of my ignorance. There is no hope for a concise world formula (like $i\hbar\dot{\psi} = H\psi$) which coupled to a powerful computer solves all mysteries of the brain with arbitrary precision. However, there is also no a priori reason why a multidisciplinary effort of generations of experimenters and theorists together should not clarify many neurobiological problems of the mind and body.

References

[1] N Bourbaki "Theory of Sets", Hermann, Paris (1968)

[2] AS Tanenbaum "Structured Computer Organization", Prentice/Hall, Englewood Cliffs (1984)

[3] EV Evarts, Y Shinoda, SP Wise "Neurophysiological Approaches to Higher Brain Function", Wiley, NY (1984)

[4] D Marr "Vision", Freeman, San Francisco (1982)

[5] B Alberts et al. "Molecular Biology of the Cell", Garland, NY (1983)

[6] DA Robinson, Invest. Ophthalmol. 14, 801 (1975)

[7] TA McMahon"Muscles, Reflexes, and Locomotion", Princeton U. Press, Princeton (1984)

[8] DA Robinson "Control of Eye Movements" in "Handbook of Physiology - The Nervous System II" (JM Brookhart, VB Mountcastle, eds.), Amer. Physiological Soc., Bethesda (1981)

[9] W Rall "Core Conductor Theory and Cable Properties of Neurons" in "Handbook of Physiology-The Nervous System I", Amer. Physiological Soc., Bethesda (1978)

[10] C Koch, T Poggio, V Torre, Phil.Trans.R.Soc. London B 298, 227 (1982)

[11] RD Traub, RKS Wong, Science 216, 745 (1982)

[12] M Ito "The Cerebellum and Neural Control", Raven, NY (1984)

[13] S Ramón y Cajal "Histologie du système nerveux de l'homme et des vertébrés", Maloine, Paris (1911)

[14] D Marr, J. Physiol. 202, 437 (1969)

[15] J Albus, Math. Biosci. 10, 25 (1971)

[16] A Berthoz, G Melvill Jones,"Adaptive Mechanisms in Gaze Control: Facts and Theories", Elsevier, Amsterdam (1984)

[17] M Fujita, Biol. Cybernetics 45, 195, 207 (1982)

[18] JJ Hopfield, Proc.Nat.Acad.Sci. (USA) 79, 2554 (1982)

[19] W Kinzel, in "Complex Systems-Operational Approaches" (H. Haken ed.), Springer, Berlin (1985)

[20] DI Perret, ET Rolls, W Caan, Exp. Brain Res. 47 329 (1982)

[21] DA Robinson, Ann. Rev. Neurosci. 4, 463 (1981)

[22] K Hepp and V Henn in "Synergetics of the Brain" (E Başar, H Flohr, H Haken, AJ Mandell eds.), Springer, Berlin (1983)

[23] RD Tomlinson, DA Robinson, J. Neurophysiol. 51, 1121 (1984)

[24] B Julesz "Foundations of Cyclopean Perception", U. Chicago P., Chicago (1971)

[25] D Marr, T Poggio, Proc.R.Soc. London B204, 301 (1979)

[26] WEL Grimson "From Images to Surfaces", MIT Press, Cambridge (1981)

[27] GM Edelman, WE Gall, WM Cowan "Dynamic Aspects of Neocortical Function", Wiley, NY (1984)

[28] LE Mays, DL Sparks, J. Neurophysiol. 43, 207 (1980)

Forma matematica e realtà fisica*

Edward Nelson

(Dipartimento di Matematica, Università di Princeton)

Voglio ringraziare gli organizzatori di questo congresso per l'invito a fare questa conferenza di natura generale. Ma è veramente un peccato che il nostro amico Francesco Guerra non abbia potuto essere qui.[#]

Mi sarebbe piaciuto sentire quello che ha da dire sulla stocasticità in matematica, in fisica, in linguistica, ...

Ho deciso di parlare in italiano per due motivi. Il primo è a causa del carattere ticinese di questo congresso; è un tentativo di esprimere da parte dei partecipanti la nostra riconoscenza per la gentilissima ospitalità che ci è stata mostrata qui ad Ascona. Il secondo motivo è il fatto che uno dei temi di questo discorso è l'abisso che separa il linguaggio umano dalla realtà. Se faccio degli errori che non farebbe un ragazzo di sei anni, spero che questo possa servire a rammentarci che il linguaggio è una conquista recente della specie umana, e che noi tutti abbiamo dovuto fare questa conquista da bambini. E perciò i modi di pensare infantili costituiscono sempre una parte profonda del nostro uso del linguaggio.

Quando mia figlia era piccola, facevo spesso una passeggiata con lei. Una volta quando ci siamo avvicinati ad un bosco, lei non voleva entrare nel bosco. Mi disse che aveva paura dei mostri. Le ho detto, calmamente, che i mostri non esistono. Dopo un po' mi ha preso per la mano e mi ha detto: << Hai ragione, babbo. Non ci sono i mostri - in questo bosco qui. >> Alcuni anni più tardi mia nipote, la figlia di mia figlia, mi disse che aveva paura del boogyman. Non è necessario tradurre questa parola, appunto perchè non significa niente. Le ho detto, calmamente, che il boogyman non esiste. Dopo un po' mi ha preso per la mano e mi ha detto, << Hai ragione, nonno. Non c'è il boogyman - solo uno piccolo piccolo. >>

Questo è lo stadio infantile, oppure platonico dell'uso del linguaggio: si immagina che i concetti astratti, le parole (per esempio: mostri, boogyman, principio della complementarità, insieme di tutti i numeri naturali,...), abbiano una realtà superiore alla realtà dei fatti del mondo attuale. Tornerò su questo tema.

Ho promesso ai professori Albeverio e Merlini di fare un discorso di natura non tecnica, ma non ho promesso di fare un discorso facile. Al contrario, indendo parlare dei

---

* A similar paper in English has appeared in Sankhyá. (The Indian Journal of Statistics) Ser. A, Vol. 47, pt 1, 1-5 (1985)

F. Guerra was invited to the conference and in the special session he was expected to give a talk on "Processi stocastici in matematica, fisica, linguistica,..." Unfortunately,because of a sudden illness of his mother,he was not able to attend [Note of the Edts.].

problemi più difficili della fisica e della matematica.

Nella prima metà di questo secolo un fisico e un matematico dell'Europa settentrionale hanno cercato di far cambiare ai colleghi il loro modo di percepire il mondo, ed in maniere molto simili. Secondo il danese Niels Bohr, lo stato di un sistema fisico non è una descrizione obbiettiva di questo sistema, è una descrizione della nostra conoscenza di questo sistema. Non ha senso dire che una particella ha una posizione q e una velocità v perchè ogni tentativo di osservare l'una cambia l'altra. Secondo l'olandese Brouwer, un'asserzione matematica non è una descrizione obiettiva di fatti matematici, è una descrizione della nostra conoscenza di un calcolo. Non ha senso dire che << A o non-A >> sia sempre vero, perchè per un intuizionista come Brouwer questo significa "so A oppure so come dedurre una contraddizione da A".

Bohr è riuscito e Brouwer ha fallito. I fisici erano pronti ad abbandonare il concetto di un mondo obiettivo esterno; i matematici invece hanno rifiutato di fare questo. Quando si pensa alla materia delle due discipline, questo fatto storico diventa veramente straordinario.

Facciamo più concreta la discussione, e parliamo della interferometria dei neutroni - lavoro di Rauch e collaboratori a Vienna. Si ha un raggio di neutroni che incontra un cristallo al punto A e che si spacca in due raggi parziali I e II, che poi si ricombinano al punto B, dove si manifestano fenomeni di interferenza coerente. Voglio insistere sul fatto che non si tratta qui del moto al livello microscopico: la separazione fra i due raggi parziali è di qualche centimentro. L'intensità del raggio è molto bassa: i neutroni passano uno alla volta. Questo si potrebbe dimostrare per mezzo di due strumenti sui due cammini, constatando che capita sempre che precisamente uno degli strumenti risponde al passaggio di un neutrone. Questo invervento sperimentale distruggerebbe gli effetti di coerenza al punto B. Dunque, che cos' è il neutrone: una particella discreta che passa per un cammino o l'altro, oppure un'onda che passa per tutt'e due e che poi dopo manifesta fenomeni d'interferenza?

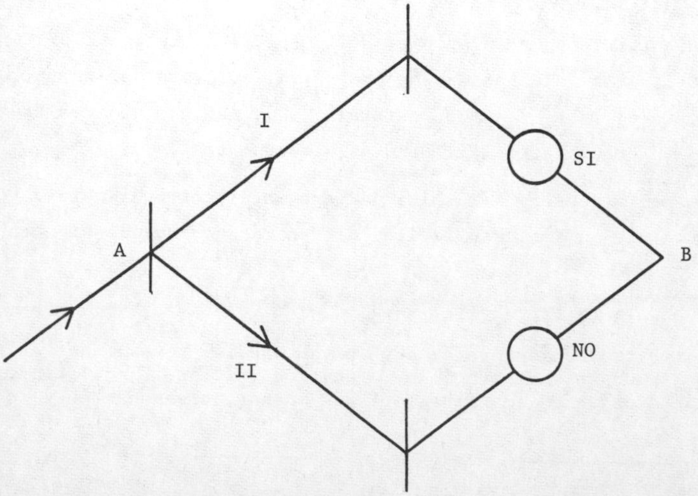

Secondo il concetto della complementaritò di Bohr, bisogna concepire il neutrone o come una particella o come un'onda secondo l'esperimento che si fa. Ma a mio parere questo concetto della complementarità è un abuso di linguaggio; non significa niente. È semplicemente una rinuncia al tentativo di capire il mondo, accontentandosi di prevedere i risultati sperimentali.

(A proposito, conveniamo che tutto quello che dico stasera sia preceduto dalle parole "nella mia opinione"). La meccanica stocastica, che è uno dei temi di questo congresso, è un tentativo appunto di capire, di costruire una descrizione obiettiva dei fenomeni. È un tentativo che finora non è riuscito in modo soddisfacente, ma credo che sia sulla buona strada.

Secondo la maggioranza dei fisici, il teorema di Bell e gli esperimenti di Aspect e dei suoi collaboratori costituiscono una barriera insuperabile ad ogni tentativo di costruire un modello obiettivo dei fatti sperimentali. Voglio spiegare queste cose per mezzo di un'analogia, di un giuoco.

Ci sono due giocatori A e B, in due stanze diverse. Ciascuno ha un cartello con tre rettangoli I, II, e III, coperti da una sostanza oscura. Ciascuno sceglie, a caso, un rettangolo, e rimuove la sostanza oscura - poi vede o rosso o verde. Poi ripetono il giuoco molte volte, con altre paia di cartelli.

Bene, si osserva che ogni volta che i due giocatori scelgono lo stesso rettangolo, vedono colori opposti. Quando sçelgono rettangoli differenti, vedono colori opposti solo un quarto delle volte. L'indovinello è questo: come sono preparati i cartelli?

Supponiamo che siano preparati prima del giuoco. Allora, non si può sapere quali rettangoli saranno scelti; forse A e B sceglieranno lo stesso rettangolo, dunque i colori devono essere opposti in tutti i rettangoli I, II, e III. Ci sono due casi: o i cartelli hanno un solo colore ciascuno, oppure no. Nel primo caso, i colori trovati da A e B sono sempre opposti. Nel secondo caso, ci sono sei modi di scegliere rettangoli differenti, due dei quali conducono a colori opposti. Dunque, quando A e B scelgono rettangoli differenti, devono vedere colori opposti almeno un terzo

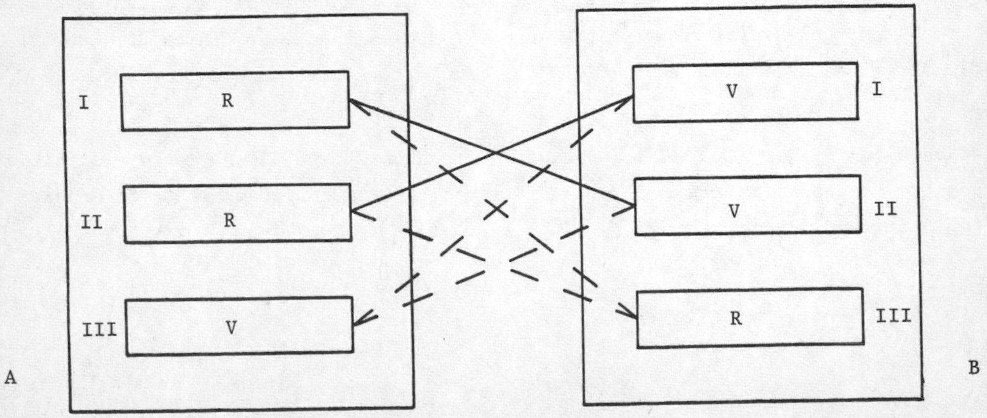

delle volte - ma abbiamo detto che questo accade solo un quarto delle volte. Nell'esperimento di Aspect, i cartelli sono due fotoni, i rettangoli sone tre direzioni per misurare la polarizzazione, e i colori sono polarizzazioni o a destra o a sinistra. I cartelli non possono essere preparati prima del giuoco. Dunque l'indeterminismo non è più una speculazione filosofica, è un fatto stabilito dalla fisica.

Ma Bell trae delle conseguenze ancora più serie: secondo il suo argomento, questi fatti distruggono la possibilità di costruire un modello obiettivo, anche stocastico, della natura. Ma un'analisi delle ipotesi del suo argomento rivela che sono esclusi solo i modelli in cui la stocasticità è dovuta all'ignoranza delle condizioni iniziali - ci rimane la possibilità molto attraente di un modello stocastico nel quale la stocasticità sia intrinsica allo sviluppo temporale del sistema. Sono venuto in Europa per dire questo, e dunque lo ripeto: non c'è niente nella teoria o nella pratica attuali che esclude la possibilità di un modello della natura per mezzo di un campo stocastico per il quale il caso fa parte intrinsica dello sviluppo temporale.

Forse i fisici hanno scelto male sessant'anni fà quando hanno abbandonato precipitevolissimevolmente il concetto di un mondo obiettivo esterno.

Adesso parliamo del concetto della realtà dei matematici. Prendiamo come punto di partenza il teorema più elementare della matematica: il principio dell'induzione. Per <<numero>> si intende <<numero naturale>>: 0,1,2,3,... . Il difficile è sempre capire il significato di questi tre puntini. Ma solitanente si parte da un concetto platonico del sistema di tutti i numeri, come un dato di un mondo concettuale astratto. Allora, se 0 ha una certa proprietà, e se ogni volta che un numero n ha la proprietà accade che anche n+1 ha la proprietà, allora si conclude che ogni numero ha la proprietà. Questo è il principio dell'induzione, e il sistema matematico basato se questo principio si chiama l'aritmetica di Peano, designata con P.

Hilbert ha posto il problema di dimostrare per mezzi elementari la consistenza della matematica, a cominciare dall'aritmetica di Peano. Il suo punto di vista era quello del formalismo: un'asserzione matematica è una formula, una serie finita di simboli; una dimostrazione matematica è una lista di formule costruita secondo certe regole formali.

Il programma di Hilbert ha fallito, a causa del teorema di Gödel. Ho detto all'inizio che questa sarebbe stata una conferenza difficile. Bene, ecco l'argomento di Gödel. Nell'aritmetica di Peano P si

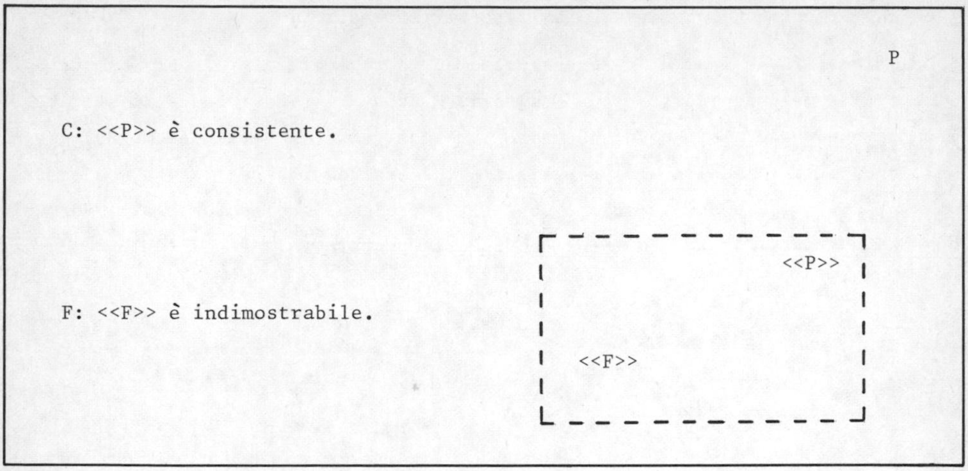

può parlare dell'aritmetica di Peano stessa <<P>>, comprese le regole di deduzione. La <<P>> fra virgolette è il sistema P aritmetizzato. Per ogni formula F di P si ha una formula aritmetizzata corrispondente <<F>> di <<P>>. Si può costruire una certa formula F di P con l'interpretazione:<<F>> è indimostrabile (cioè io stessa sono indimostrabile).

Supponiamo che sia data una dimostrazione per mezzi elementari della consistenza dell'aritmetica di Peano P. Siccome questa dimostrazione è per mezzi elementari, abbiamo una dimostrazione in P di una formula C con l'interpretazione: <<P>> è consistente. Supponiamo anche di avere una dimostrazione in P di F.

Possiamo ripetere questa dimostrazione in <<P>>, e dimostrare <<F>> in <<P>>. Ma secondo l'interpretazione di F, questo conduce immediatamente ad una contraddizione in <<P>>, quello che è impossibile secondo l'ipotesi C. Dunque F è indimostrabile. Ma quello che abbiamo appena detto è una dimostrazione di F! Dunque, se si potesse dimostrare per mezzi elementari la consistenza dell'aritmetica di Peano, allora l'aritmetica di Peano sarebbe inconsistente.

Di solito si conclude da questo che i mezzi elementari di Hilbert sono troppo ristretti. Ma il teorema die Gödel può anche condurci ad una conclusione più radicale: forse l'aritmetica di Peano è inconsistente. Forse l'idea platonica del sistema di tutti i numeri naturali non corrisponde a niente nel mondo attuale. Cercare una contraddizione esplicita nella matematica, anche nell'aritmetica, non mi sembra un'attività irrazionale.

In modo un po' più conservativo, si può cercare di costruire una matematica radicalmente elementare e dimostrabilmente consistente, una matematica non basata sulle idee platonishe della teoria cantoriana degli insiemi, e neppure sul principio dell'induzione. Questo programma è già stato realizzato fino al punto di costruire una teoria radicalmente elementare dei processi stocastici.

In conclusione, la scelta dello scienziato o della scienziata mi sembra questa: di seguire o Platone o don Chisciotte. Chi segue Platone reifica i concetti astratti, cioè le parole umane. Chi segue don Chisciotte costruisce modelli del mondo, pur sapendo che tutti i modelli sono sbagliati e che bisogna interagire col mondo attuale. È ovvio quale scelta voglio consigliare: siamo donchisciotteschi! Forse il boogyman non esiste affatto, nemmeno uno piccolo piccolo.

PARTICIPANTS

S.	Albeverio	(Bochum/Bielefeld)
R.	Badii	(Zürich)
A.	Barchielli	(Milano)
J.	Bellissard	(Marseille)
G.	Benettin	(Padova)
F.	Benvenuto	(Milano)
M.	Berry	(Bristol)
M.	Bianda	(Locarno)
Ph.	Blanchard	(Bielefeld)
O.	Bohigas	(Orsay)
J.	Brasche	(Bielefeld)
G.	Broggi	(Zürich)
E.	Carlen	(Boston)
C.	Carvalho	(Bielefeld)
C.	Casanova	(Bellinzona)
G.	Casati	(Milano/Como)
D.	Castrigiano	(München)
O.	Cattaneo	(Locarno)
W.	Cegla	(Wrocław)
M.	Celio	(Zürich)
S.D.	Chatterji	(Lausanne)
Ph.	Combe	(Marseille)
F.	D'Ambrogio	(Lausanne)
F.	De Angelis	(Salerno)
D.	De Falco	(Salerno)
J.D.	Deuschel	(Zürich)
D.	Dohrn	(Roma)
D.	Dürr	(Bielefeld)
G.O.S.	Ekhaguere	(Ibadan/Bielefeld)
R.	Esposito	(Roma)
G.	Felder	(Zürich)
H.	Föllmer	(Zürich)
G.	Fonte	(Catania)
J.	Fröhlich	(Zürich)
L.	Galgani	(Milano)
G.	Gallavotti	(Roma)
S.	Golin	(Bielefeld)
V.	Gorini	(Milano)
Ch.	Gruber	(Lausanne)
Z.	Haba	(Bielefeld/Wrocław)
K.	Hepp	(Zürich)
A.	Hilbert	(Bielefeld)
H.	Holden	(Oslo)
R.	Jancel	(Paris)
J.	Jedrzejewski	(Wrocław)
Ph.	Jetzen	(Zürich)
S.	Johannesen	(Oslo)
G.	Jona-Lasinio	(Roma)
F.	Koukiou	(Lausanne)
T.	Lindstrøm	(Trondheim)
J.J.	Loeffel	(Lausanne)
M.I.	Loffredo	(Siena)
W.	Loges	(Bochum)
C.	Marchioro	(Trento)
J.	Marion	(Marseille)
R.	Marra	(Roma)
F.	Martinelli	(Roma)
D.	Merlini	(Bellinzona/Milano)
P.A.	Meyer	(Strasbourg)
N.	Minami	(Tokyo)
A.	Monge	(Pavia)
L.	Morato	(Padova)
M.	Nagasawa	(Zürich)
G.	Nappo	(Roma)
E.	Nelson	(Princeton)
H.	Nencka-Ficek	(Poznan/Bielefeld)
Th.	Nonnenmacher	(Ulm)
C.	Ogney	(Lausanne)
S.	Olla	(Roma)
E.	Omerti	(Trento)
L.	Perotti	(Milano)
D.	Petritis	(Paris)
C.A.	Pillet	(Zürich)
A.	Politi	(Firenze)
G.	Schlichting	(München)
T.	Schneider	(Zürich)
W.	Schneider	(Baden)
M.	Sirugue-Collin	(Marseille)
U.	Spönemann	(Bielefeld)
C.	Tupini	(Locarno)
P.	Venzi	(Bellinzona)
P.	von Vintscher	(Zürich)
C.	Wayne	(University Park)
J.C.	Zambrini	(Princeton)
N.	Zanghi	(Bielefeld)
W.	Zheng	(Shanghai/Bielefeld)
A.	Zinoun	(Lille/Villeneuve)